CW00347442

18th Edition
WRECKS & RELICS
Ken Ellis

MIDLAND PUBLISHING

CONTENTS

Preface			3
	Acknowledgements	4 &	5
	Further Reading	5 &	6
	How to Use *Wrecks & Relics*	7 &	8
Part One	England	9 –	96
	Photograph Section	97 –	128
Part One	England, continued	129 –	224
	Photograph Section	225 –	256
Part One	England, continued	257 –	273
Part Two	Channel Islands		273
Part Three	Scotland	274 –	285
Part Four	Wales	286 –	295
Part Five	Northern Ireland and Ireland	296 –	304
Part Six	RAF Overseas		304
Appendix A	Auctions	305 –	306
Appendix B	Exports	306 –	307
Appendix C	Lost! and Found!		307
Appendix D	Abbreviations	308 –	311
Index I	Types	312 –	317
Index II	Locations	318 –	320

Front Cover:
Nestled in the 'Superhangar' amid other impressive hardware, the Imperial War Museum's SR-71A 64-17962 in May 2001. This was after the 'unveiling' but before the hand-over. It is due to enter the American Air Museum during 2002. *Roger Richards*

Rear Cover:
Caught in the crisp light of January 2001, HS.748-2B G-BORM serves Exeter's fire crash rescue crews. *Hugh Trevor*

Never ceasing to raise sighs from passing motorists, Lightning F.2A XN728 continues to rot at Balderton. *Jonathan Longbottom*

Title Page:
Keeping to the 'trend' for title plates (with apologies to Phil Whalley!), another with a 'JCB' theme. Two Phantom FGR.2s were smashed to pieces at Leeming in July 2001 as part of a renewed 'cull' of the 'phleet' *RAF Leeming*

Copyright 2002 © Ken Ellis

This eighteenth edition published by Midland Publishing
(An imprint of Ian Allan Publishing Ltd)
4 Watling Drive, Sketchley Lane Industrial Estate,
Hinckley, Leics, LE10 3EY.

ISBN 1 85780 133 4

Printed in the UK by Ian Allan Printing Ltd, Riverdene Business
Park, Molesey Road, Hersham, Surrey KT12 4RG

PREFACE

I could lament at length about the continued contraction of the British armed forces and their increasing 'greyness' and the impact that is having on the nation's aviation heritage; or on the ever-diminishing chances of anyone other than the 'nationals' getting their hands on recently-retired hardware like Tornados (remember them?), or the effect of the lottery in pump-priming museum projects of horrendous scale instead of a more egalitarian or even regional approach.

But no, I will indulge in the folklore of the title of this very book...

A note from Mike Bursell (he of the first edition of *European Wrecks & Relics* and more recently a student of Greek mythology) sets the mind stirring... Mike has found what he thinks is the earliest use of the phrase 'wrecks and relics'. It was in *Registration News Sheet* No.8 of February 1952 edited by no less a luminary than the late Arthur Pearcy. A news snippet supplied by L T Chamberlain went like this:

"Wrecks and Relics – LTC. Aeronca 100 G-AEVE is still lying in the open at Hi-Low Garage on the Lytham-Preston road near Warton airfield. It is in a very bad state of repair."

Mr Bursell, hails 'appen from close t' River Humber while I was born – a year after *RNS* No.8 appeared by the way – in what was then Lancashire. Mike concludes: "It is debatable if the words 'a very bad state of repair' refer to the Lytham-Preston road, Warton aerodrome, or Lancashire in general. Some have even suggested it refers to the Aeronca. So, once again, a Yorkshire invention passed off in later years as of Lancastrian origin." Doh!

This edition comes to you courtesy of a time-challenged organic input device at one end of the mouse and yet another computer – which I note should be called *Deeply Fraught V* – at the other. I remain contactable via the 'wire' with the usual two provisos. I accept material by e-mail and give a mention in the 'Acknowledgements' section *only* if a 'terrestrial' address is supplied. I do not accept 'forums' or similar or even 'cut and pastes' from them – I'm looking for original thinkers only!

Several readers have asked if I can take jpegs, tiffs, pdfs and other alphabetic gymnastics by way of illustrations. The answer currently is no. But it *may* be the case next time. I suggest you contact me before committing pixels to the airwaves... I have long since discovered that in terms of 'IT' and all the gizmos that are part and parcel of it all, I am not in the techno-joy category, nor do I fall into the techno-fear one. I sit comfortably in the realms of techno-notice!

Sadly, my buddy and moggie, **Fleas**, did not get to see the birth of this edition, but her marks can be found subtly within! As ever, this book – and the many avenues it takes me down – would not be possible without **Pam**'s understanding and patience.

Deadline for the next edition is 31st January 2004 for illustrations and 1st March 2004 for information and comments.

Ken Ellis
April 2002

Myddle Cottage, Welland Terrace, off Mill Lane, Barrowden,
Oakham, Rutland, LE15 8EH

wrecksandrelics@compuserve.com

Acknowledgements

This book relies on the inputs of a huge spectrum of contributors, each making their mark on the contents in different ways. My many thanks to them all.

Overseeing the draft, adding and refining it were **Alan Allen, Dave Allport, David J Burke, John Coghill** and **Nigel Price**. A special note here about Dave Allport ('DJ' to the chosen few!) who first 'turns up' in *W&R7* (1980) and has been a stalwart behind-the-scenes researcher ever since. Civil, military, the more obscure the better, he is seldom found wanting! Major photographic input came from **Tim R Badham, Roger Cook–Pynelea Photo Bureau, Ian Haskell, Alf Jenks, Tony McCarthy, Duncan Parnell, Roger Richards, Brian Roffee, Phil Whalley** and **Andy Wood**. Photos help considerably in terms of problem-solving and substantiation as well as – well – illustrating the book! Many thanks to everyone else who contributed photographs, they are credited with their work.

The following subject and area specialists made vital inputs: **Phil Ansell**, Sussex; **Peter R Arnold**, Spitfire restorer and historian; **Mike Cain**, Southend; **David S Johnstone**, Scotland; **Tony** and **Brenda McCarthy** for their detailed notes from their many travels; **Chris Michell**, Isle of Wight and 'warbirds'; **Alistair Ness**, Central Scotland Aviation Group for Scotland; **John Phillips**, rotorcraft; **Mike Phipp**, Bournemouth and area; **Geoffrey Pool**, Bruntingthorpe; **Col Pope**, East Anglia and 'warbirds'; **Stephen C Reglar**, Coventry; **Lloyd P Robinson** for detailed notes from his extensive travels; **Peter Spooner**, for notes on his travels; **Mervyn Thomas**, St Athan and South Wales; **David E Thompson**, northern England; **Hugh Trevor**, Lightnings and others; **Andy Wood**, Humberside, Lincolnshire and Yorkshire. Also to the following at Key Publishing, in addition to Dave (*AIR International* and many other 'hats') and Nigel (*FlyPast*) mentioned above: **Jarrod Cotter** – *FlyPast*; **Mark Nicholls** – on the 'Specials' desk and **Dave Willis** – *AirForces Monthly*. Big thanks to **Steve Donovan** of the Flight-Test Department for skilful mouth-to-mouth on *Deeply Fraught V* in its hour of need! All of this mob are gluttons for punishment in their 'spare' time!

A mail-shot is made to the wide array of organisations working within the heritage movement. Thanks to the following for taking the time to update items and for their constant help and support: **Gary Adams**, Ulster Aviation Society; **Cliff Aldred**, Blyth Valley Aviation Collection; **Andrew Allen**, EI-BAG and EI-BGB; **Peter Amos**, Miles Aircraft Collection; **Deborah Andrews**, National Museum of Wales; **Martin Baggott**, Buckinghamshire Aircraft Recovery Group; **Philip Baldock**, Robertsbridge Aviation Society; **Frank Beckley**, Brenzett Aeronautical Museum; **Bournemouth Aviation Museum**; **Alan Beattie**, Yorkshire Helicopter Preservation Group; **Phil Bedford**, South East Aviation Enthusiasts; **Blessingbourne Carriage Museum**; **Bletchley Park Museum**; **Andy Bostock**, The Aeroplane Collection; **Mick Boulanger**, JP T.5 XW315 / Wolverhampton Aviation Group; **Kevin Bowen**, Trident Preservation Society; **Alan Bower**, Tangmere Military Aviation Museum; **Alec Brew**, Black Country Aircraft Collection; **Ben Brown**, Sywell Aviation Museum; **Raymond Burrows**, Ulster Aviation Society; **D Butt**, Tank Museum; **Caernarfon airparc**; **Glenn Cattermole**, Buccaneer XT284; **Martin Chiappini**, Bomber County Aviation Museum; **City Museum and Art Gallery, Bristol**; **Ron Clarke**, Harrington, Aviation Museum Society; **Richard Clarkson**, Vulcan Restoration Trust; **Doug Cockle**, RAF Manston History Museum; **David Collins**, Hornet Project; **Cranwell Aviation Heritage Centre**; **Clare Davies**, RAF Museum, Cosford; **Lewis Deal MBE**, Hurricane and Spitfire Memorial Building / Medway Aircraft Preservation Society; **Derby Industrial Museum**; **Doncaster Museum and Art Gallery**; **Bob Dunn**, Wolverhampton Aviation Group; **David Dunstall**, Shoreham Airport Visitor Centre and Archive; **Colin Durrant**, 390th BG Memorial Air Museum; **Tony Dyer**, Air Defence Collection / Boscombe Down Project; **Mark Evans**, Midland Warplane Museum; **Eden Camp Modern History Theme Museum**; **Huby Fairhead**, Norfolk and Suffolk Aviation Museum; **Ken Fern**, for notes on his own projects; **Flambards Village Theme Park**; **Nick Forder**, Museum of Science and Industry in Manchester; **Ken** and **Jean Fostekew**, Museum of Berkshire Aviation; **Glasgow Museum of Transport**; **Nigel** and **Kerry Goodall**, Buccaneer Supporters Club; **Hack Green Secret Nuclear Bunker**; **Henry Hall**, RAF Museum, Hendon; **Ian Hancock**, Norfolk and Suffolk Aviation Museum; **Paul Hartley** XH558 Club and Vulcan XA903; **R F Hartley**, Leicestershire County Council Museums, Arts and Records Service; **Howard Heeley**, Newark Air Museum; **Maureen Hind**, Stondon Transport Museum; **Historic Warship Preservation Trust**; **Mike Hodgson**, Thorpe Camp Visitor Centre; **Nigel Hodgson**, RAF Manston History Museum; **Stewart Holder**, Jet Aviation Preservation Group; **John Hunter**, Dundonald Aviation Centre; **Sam Hurry**, 100th BG Memorial Museum; **Imperial War Museum, Duxford**; **Roy** and **Sue Jerman**, Military Aircraft Cockpit Collection; **Alan Jones**, Southampton Hall of Aviation; **Keith Jones**, WAR Group Aviation Museum; **Mark Jones**, Meteor Flight; **Mark A Jones**, Phantom Preservation Group; **Tim Jones**, 'JP' T.5 XS231; **Mark Kennedy**, Ulster Folk and Transport Museum; **Bob Kent**, Balloon Preservation Group (and for notes on Sussex); **Mike Killaspy**, East Anglian Aviation Society; **Andy King**, Bristol Industrial Museum; **Eileen Kinghan**, FirePower; **David Kirkpatrick**, Solway Aviation Museum; **Land's End**; **Eric Littledike**, Pilcher BAPC.57; **Roger Marley**, WAR Group Aviation Museum; **Diana Matthews**, Windermere Steamboat Centre; **Trevor Matthews**, Lashenden Air Warfare Museum; **Chris May**, Bristol Aero Collection; **Graham McIntosh**, RFC/RAF Montrose Museum; **Midland Air Museum**; **Dave Morris**, Fleet Air Arm Museum; **Naylan Moore**, AeroVenture; **Jurgen Morton-Hall**, Brimpex Metal Treatments; **Museum of Army Transport**; **Museum of D-Day Aviation**; **Grant Newman**, Museum of Flight; **John Nixon**, RAF Millom Museum; **North East Aircraft Museum**; Colonel **John Nowers**, Royal Engineers Museum; **Dick Nutt**, Douglas Boston-Havoc UK Preservation Trust; **Margaret O'Shaughnessy**, Foynes Flying-Boat Museum; **Chris Page**, Northern Aeroplane Workshops; **Harold Panton**, Lincolnshire Aviation Heritage Centre; **Parachute Regiment and Airborne Forces Museum**; **Alan Partington**, Catford Independent Air Force; **Alan Partington**, Catford Independent Air Force; **Peter Pavey**, Rolls-Royce Heritage Trust, Bristol Branch; **Robin Phipps**, Buccaneer XX899 / Sea Vixen XN647; **Cyril**

Plimmer, Boulton Paul Association; **Nigel Ponsford** and **Anne Lindsay**, Real Aeroplane Museum and their own collection; **Potteries Museum and Art Gallery**; **Derek Powell**, Wellesbourne Wartime Museum and Vulcan XM655; **Mike Pratt**, Chatham Historic Dockyard Trust; **RAF Manston History Museum**; **Elfan ap Rees**, The Helicopter Museum; **David Reid**, Dumfries and Galloway Aviation Museum; **Ridgewell Airfield Commemorative Museum**; **Frank Sherman**, Horham Airfield Heritage Association; **Andy Simpson**, RAF Museum Hendon; **Peter Smith** for details of his own collection; **Tom Smith**, Rolls-Royce Heritage Trust, Coventry Branch; **Mike Sparrow**, Second World War Aircraft Preservation Society; **Stanford Hall**; **John Stride**, de Havilland Aircraft Heritage Centre; **Dave Stubley**, Lincolnshire Aircraft Recovery Group; **Christine Swettenham**, Muckleburgh Collection; **Suzanne Tagg**, Science Museum; **Bill Taylor**, Aerial Application Collection / de Havilland Support Ltd; **Bernard Tebbutt**, 'Carpetbagger' Aviation Museum; **Julian Temple**, Brooklands Museum; **Mark Templeman**, Hunter cockpit 'WB188'; **Steve Thompson**, Cotswold Aircraft Restoration Group; **Bob Turner**, Fleet Air Arm Museum; **Jim Turner** Station 146 Control Tower Museum; **Tim Turner**, British Balloon Museum and Library; **Gerry Tyack**, Wellington Aviation Museum; **Graham Vale**, East Midlands Airport Volunteers Association; **Peter Vallance**, Gatwick Aviation Museum; **Margaret White**, Croydon Airport Society; **John Wilkins**, Yorkshire Air Museum; **Karen Wilsher**, Shuttleworth Collection; **Keith Williams**, Bristol Scout 'A1742'; **Colin Wingrave**, Thameside Aviation Museum; **Pete Winning**, Fenland and West Norfolk Aviation Museum

And to the many readers who take the time and trouble to send in reports of sightings, snippets and reports – large and small. Without their help this book would not be as topical or authoritative. Also listed here, as ever, are people who have supplied other services vital to the production of W&R! Thanks to each and every one of you!

Barry H Abraham, David Allen, Gerry Allen, Andrew Appleton, Dave Arkell, Paul Atkin, Greg Baddeley, Nigel Bailey-Underwood, Alan G L Barclay, Steve Barker, Allan Barley, Andrew Paul Barley, Len Bachelor, Allan Barley, M S 'Dicky' Bird, Nick Blacow, Roy Bonser, Des Brennan, Peter Budden, Simon Bullimore, Damien Burke, Mike Causer, Mike Clarke, Paul Carr, Russell Carter, Nancy Cartwright, Richard Cawsey, Mike Clarke, John D Coleman, Martin Condon, Glyn Coney, Martyn Cooke, Tim Crowe, Alan and Colers Curry, Howard J Curtis, Andy Day, Nick Deakin, Bo Diddly-Squat, Mike Drake, Dr Bruce A Duguid BDS, John Dyer, Dylan Eklund, Bryn Elliott, Chris Farmer, Bill Fisher, Mike Freshney, Paul Fry, Steve Gardner, Dave Gilmour, Gilmar Green, J D Green, Trevor Green, Stuart Greer, Alan Hardcastle, Arthur Harris, Thomas Harris, Bill Harrison, Ben Hartmann, Ian Haskell, Mark Hazell, Phil Hewitt, Michael Hill, Jason Howe, Paul Hughes, Tony Hyatt, Bill Hyslop, Shane Illsley, the late David James, Mark Jackson, Tony Jarvis, Jim Jobe, David Jowett, Dave King, Simon King, Otger van der Kooij, Andrew Lee, Steve Locke, Dave Long, Jonathan Longbottom; Andy Marden, Bernard Martin, Nick Mason, Kirsty McColl, David McNally, Seamus Mooney, Simon Murdoch, Steve Osfield, Michael O'Sullivan, Bob Parnell, Duncan Parnell, Dave Peel, Darren Pitcher, David Potter, Martin Powell, Keith Preen, Doug Pritchard, Simon Pulford, Norman Roberson, Mark Roberts–Aerobilia, Es Robinson, Stephen Robson, Mark Russell, Graham Salt, Chris Salter, Rob Sawyer, Paul Scrivens, Harry Seddon, Tim Senior, Jim Simpson, Paul Singleton, Nick Skinner, Noel Smith, Roger Smith, Tony Smith, Paul Snelling, Allen Stacey, Brian Stafford, Mike Stannard, Clarice Starling, Graham Tanner, Peter Taylor, David M Thomas, Jurgen van Toor, Rich Tregear, Tim and Dominic Trethewey, David Trott, Chris Wagstaff, Roger Waters, Eric Watts, Johnnie Walker, Mike Westwood, Phil Whalley, Jon Wickenden, Dave Whitaker, Mark Whitnall, Michael Wilcock, Nick Wilson, Tony Wood, Dave Woods, John Worth, Jonathon Woss, Richard Wright

Further Reading

Many references are made while assembling W&R, although the over-riding quest is for first-hand information and comment. The following enthusiast-published magazines have proved to be particularly conscientious in their coverage, sticking as much as possible to first-hand reportage and not the ever-increasing recirculation and 'massaging' of other journals, or acknowledging other sources when brought in. The first four offer specific 'leanings' for the W&R reader, the second offer regional coverage. I've noted how I find each particularly helpful, as a guide. All offer a variety of other features and articles. Addresses are given for further information.

Air-Britain News, monthly journal of Air-Britain (Historians) Ltd. Good coverage of the civil scene via the *Around and About* section. ✉ Barry Collman, 1 Rose Cottages, 179 Penn Road, Hazlemere, Bucks, HP15 7NE **web** www.air-britain.co.uk

Hawkeye, monthly journal of the Gatwick Aviation Society. Excellent, mostly primary, coverage of the UK civil scene plus Gatwick movements, world travels and much more. ✉ Mike Green, 144 The Crescent, Horley, RH6 7PA. **fax** 08453 349266 **e-mail** gas.membership@btinternet.com

Military Aviation Review, monthly journal published by Military Aircraft Photographs. In-depth UK military and an excellent 'Out of Service' section. ✉ Brian Pickering, MAP, Westfield Lodge, Aslackby, near Sleaford, Lincs, NG34 0HG ☎ 01778 440760 **fax** 01778 440060 **e-mail** brianmap@btinternet.com

Osprey monthly journal of the Solent Aviation Society. Comprehensive coverage of civilian airfields, particularly the south of England, using almost exclusively first-hand information. ✉ Paul Chandler, 20 Goring Field, Teg Down, Winchester, Hants, SO22 5NH. **e-mail** paulchand@compuserve.com **web** www.solent-aviation-society.co.uk

Air North, monthly journal of the North-East Branch of Air-Britain. Detailed civil and military for the north-east of England, and Carlisle. ✉ Graeme Carrott, 47 Park Avenue, Grange Park, Gosforth, Newcastle-upon-Tyne, NE3 2HL. e-mail graeme@airnorth1.demon.co.uk **web** www.airnorth.demon.co.uk

Humberside Air Review monthly journal of the Humberside Aviation Society. Civil and military, from Yorkshire to the Wash. Also published is an excellent additional *Residents Review* annually. ✉ Pete Wild, 4 Bleach Yard, New Walk, Beverley, HU17 7HG **web** http://members.netscapeonline.co.uk/pgwild/has.tm

Irish Air Letter monthly journal published by Paul Cunniffe, Karl Hayes and Eamon Power. Detailed coverage, civil and military, current and historic. ✉ 20 Kempton Way, Navan Road, Dublin 7, Ireland. **fax** 00 353 1 838 0629

Scottish Air News, monthly journal of the Central Scotland Aviation Group. In-depth coverage of Scotland, civil and military, plus Cumbrian aviation. Also publishes an occasional comprehensive residents run-down, *The Scottish Register*, in the form of a supplement. ✉ Steve Martin, 3 Pittrichie View, Hattoncrook, Aberdeen, AB21 0UX. **e-mail** scotairnews@btinternet.com **web** www.scottishairnews.co.uk

SWAG-Mag, monthly journal of the South West Aviation Group. With Mike Screech at the helm, the magazine made a very welcome come-back in 2001. Detailed reporting of military happenings in the south-west and on other military concerns further afield. Welcome back! ✉ Mike Screech, 4 West Meadow Road, Braunton, EX33 1EB. **e-mail** michael.screech@virgin.net

Ulster Air Mail, monthly journal of the Ulster Aviation Society, civil and military, modern and historic for Northern Ireland. ✉ Kevin Johnston, 16 Ravelston Avenue, Newtownabbey, BT36 6PF. **web** www.ulsteraviationsociety.co.uk

Winged Words monthly journal of The Aviation Society. Increasingly good coverage of residents and happenings in the north-west of England. A sad note to record the passing of TAS stalwart for the last 20 years, Evan Higson, who died on 7th December 2001. ✉ TAS, Airport Tour Centre, Manchester Airport, M90 1QX. ☎ 0161 489 2443 **fax** 0161 436 3030 **e-mail** admin@tasmanchester.com **web** www.tasmanchester.com/home.html

In late 2001 the Midlands Branch of Air-Britain was wound-up and its place taken by the West Midland Branch, organising meetings and visits for members. With this move the magazine *Air-Strip* also died. In its day it was an icon of in-depth regional reporting, in recent times but a very pale shadow of its former self.

◆

Plus the following:
Propliner, superb, fully-illustrated quarterly published by Tony Eastwood and devoted to world coverage of piston- and turbo-powered airliners past and present. ✉ 'New Roots', Sutton Green Road, Sutton Green, Guildford, GU4 7QD

And of course (!):
FlyPast , monthly magazine published by Key Publishing Ltd. ✉ PO Box 300, Stamford, Lincs, PE9 1NA. ☎ 01780 480404 **fax** 01780 757812 **e-mail** subs@keypublishing.com **web** www.flypast.com

◆

A huge array of books have been dipped into, far too many to list completely. The following have been on and off the shelf with great speed and are regarded as trusted friends:
American Air Museum Duxford – A Tribute to American Air Power, Roger A Freeman, Midland Publishing, 2001
Aviation Museums of Britain, Ken Ellis, Midland Publishing, 1998
British Civil Aircraft Register 1919-1999, Michael Austin, Air-Britain, 1999
British Military Aircraft Directory, Bob Dunn and Mick Boulanger, Wolverhampton Aviation Group, 2002
British Military Aircraft Serials 1878-1987, Bruce Robertson, Midland Counties Publications, 1987
Jet Airliner Production List, Tony Eastwood and John Roach, The Aviation Hobby Shop, Volume One, Boeing 1997, Volume Two, the rest, 1995
Military Airfields of the British Isles 1939-1945 (Omnibus Edition), Steve Willis and Barry Holliss, self-published, 1987
Piston Airliner Production List, Tony Eastwood and John Roach, The Aviation Hobby Shop, 1996
Royal Air Force Aircraft XA100 to XZ999, Jim Halley, Air-Britain, 2001 – and others in the series
Royal Air Force Flying Training and Support Units, Ray Sturtivant, John Hamlin and James J Halley, Air-Britain, 1997
Royal Navy Instructional Airframes, Ray Sturtivant and Rod Burden, British Aviation Research Group/Air-Britain, 1997
Squadrons of the Fleet Air Arm, Ray Sturtivant, Air-Britain, 1984
Squadrons of the Royal Air Force 1918-1988, Jim Halley, Air-Britain, 1988
Turbo-Prop Airliner Production List, Tony Eastwood and John Roach, The Aviation Hobby Shop, 2001
United Kingdom and Eire Civil Registers, Barry Womersley, Air-Britain, 2001
70 Years of the Irish Civil Register, Peter J Hornfeck, Britten-Norman Historians, 1999.

How To Use Wrecks & Relics

Scope: *Wrecks & Relics* serves to outline, in as much detail as possible, the status and whereabouts of all known PRESERVED (ie in museum or other collections, under restoration etc); INSTRUCTIONAL (ie static airframes in use for training); and DERELICT (ie out of use for a long period of time, fire dump aircraft, scrapped or damaged etc) aircraft in the United Kingdom and Ireland and HM Forces aircraft based on Crown Territory. Where information permits, all aircraft that fall into these categories are included, with the following exceptions:–
*   Airworthy aircraft not part of a specific collection.
*   Aircraft that fall into any of the above categories for only a short period of time.
*   Aircraft without provision for a human pilot, below the size of the GAF Jindivik or Fieseler Fi 103.
*   In general, aircraft will only be considered if they are at least a cockpit/nose section.

Locations: Are listed by county/province and then alphabetically. County Boundaries are as given by the Ordnance Survey and as defined by the Local Government Act and include the changes confirmed up to April 1999. At the beginning of each county heading, notes on unitary authorities within those country boundaries are given.
    The entries for both Scotland and Wales are purely an alphabetic listing, primarily to help the English! From 1st April 1996 all of Scotland and all of Wales were wholly divided into 'Single Tier' Unitary Authorities, with their previously-held 'Counties' now having little meaning.
    Directions are given after each place name. Readers should note that these are to the town or village mentioned and not necessarily to the actual site of the aircraft in question. Directions are *not* given in the following instances:
*   Where the location is a large city or town.
*   Where specific directions to the site are not fully known.
*   At the request of several aircraft owners, who have every right to preserve their peace and quiet as well as their aircraft, some locations have been 'generalised'.
A form of notation relating to the status of an 'aerodrome' is given. Bearing in mind that in the Air Navigation Order *all* places where flying is conducted are known as aerodromes, a wider interpretation has been employed: 'Aerodrome' signifies a civilian flying ground used by aircraft up to King Air, 'biz-jet' etc size. 'Airfield' is used to signify a flying ground used by the forces, test establishments or manufacturers. 'Airport' is used to denote a flying ground that takes 'serious' sized airliners on a regular basis. For privacy and security purposes, private strips etc are frequently not denoted as such.

Access: Unless otherwise stated, all locations in this work are PRIVATE and access to them is strictly by prior permission, *if at all*. Museum opening times etc are given as a *guide only* and readers are advised to contact the museum in question *before* setting out on a journey. A couple of symbols have been adopted:
◆   Used to define locations that are happy with public access, details beyond this explain times of admission or who to apply to if prior permission is needed. Occasionally used to draw attention to locations that particularly *do not* allow access or where prior permission is required.
✉   Contact details, starting with the postal address for enquiries, a stamped addressed envelope would be most helpful. Then, if applicable, come: ☎ Daytime telephone number for enquiries. This section also includes such new-fangled gizmos as **faxes**, recorded information lines, **e-mail** addresses and even **web-sites**, where applicable. Note that with web-sites, these are given for information only, no recommendation of content is meant, or to be implied.

Entries and Aircraft Listings: Generally, entries are all dealt with in a standard manner. As *W&R* covers a two year period, in this case 2000 to 2002, beyond the location header there is a narrative explaining the current status of the entry and outlining any airframes that have moved since the last edition. Airframes moving on are given underlined forwarding references, including the county, or province, that reference can be found in. This allows the reader to follow the more energetic examples around the book!
    'Ownership' or 'custodianship' of airframes within this work is not to be inferred as definitive.
    Any aircraft which fall out of any of the four categories above, or are exported, will not have forwarding references and their entry should be considered closed. The LOST! section acts as a 'safety net' for aircraft that have no determined fate. Where notes are made to further explain the listed entries, footnotes (①) are used – see the HS.125 reference in the mock-up example given overleaf.
    A few random entries from the main text may help to familiarise readers with the data presented:

Col 1	Col 2	Column 3	Column 4	Column 5	Col 6
❏ G-AFIR*		Luton Minor	ex Cobham, Rearsby. CoA 30-7-71.		1-01
❏ DNB		Grunau Baby IIb	BGA.2238, ex Bicester, RAFGSA380, D-8039.		12-99
❏ 5N-AWD		HS.125-1	ex G-ASSI. Fire crews.	①	10-97
❏ XV140	'K'	Scout AH.1 ✈	G-KAXL, ex Fleetlands.	®	7-01
❏ XV748	'3D'	Harrier GR.3	ex Bedford, 233 OCU, 1, 233 OCU, 1. Sectioned.		4-96
❏ *		Typhoon I	ex Chippenham. Forward fuselage.		2-99
❏ *	TAD.001	Gazelle CIM	ex Middle Wallop. First noted 5-96.		2-98
❏ 153008		F-4N-MC	ex VF-154 - USS *Coral Sea*. ABDR.		11-01
❏	BAPC.237	Fi 103 (V-1)	ex St Athan.		2-02

Columns 1 and 2: Aircraft are listed alpha-numerically, using the following rubric. British civil first (except in Ireland where EI- comes first), followed by British Gliding Association (BGA) and 'B Condition' (or 'trade plate') markings, then overseas civil registrations in alpha-numeric order. British military serials follow (with reversal again in Ireland) followed by overseas military listed by country – ie France before Netherlands before USA. Finally, come British Aviation Preservation Council (BAPC) identities as these can take in both civil or military airframes. Anonymous airframes are inserted where it is thought most logical! Incorrect or fictitious registrations and serials are marked in quotes, eg 'VZ999' or 'G-BKEN'. Codes worn by aircraft are given in column two, eg 'AF-V' or '825'. Entries new to a heading in this edition are marked *. A dash (—) is used to denote an airframe that is confirmed as not wearing an identity.

Registrations or serials, where applicable, are given a two-column treatment. Column 1 gives the *primary* identifier (if applicable). The primary identifier is most often the one *worn* on the airframe. The *secondary* identifier is a way of helping further identification of the airframe, most likely a code letter or number, or another form of identity that will help the reader 'place' the entry. Where space, permits, identities known not to be worn are given in Column 2, frequently leaving Column 1 empty. Note that other identities, present or previous, appear in Column 4.

Column 3: Aircraft type/designation, frequently abbreviated. To acquaint readers with the nature of some of the types listed, some abbreviations are used:
+   Believed airworthy, at time of going to press.
CIM   Purpose-built instructional airframe, not intended for flight – Classroom Instruction Model, or even Module.
EMU   Purpose-built test and evaluation airframe, not intended for flight, in most cases using prototype or production jigs and tooling – Engineering Mock-up.
FSM   Full-scale model. Faithful external reproduction of an aircraft, but using construction techniques completely unrelated to the original – frequently fibreglass.
PAX   Cockpit section used for crew emergency egress training, mostly (now retired) Chipmunk T.10s – Passenger (= PAX) Trainer.
REP   Reproduction, ie a faithful, or near-faithful copy or a facsimile of an aircraft type. Occasionally built to a different scale, but using construction techniques and proportions in keeping with the original. In the past, the author has used the word 'replica' but in strict usage the only people who can make a replica is the design company involved and in the aviation world, very few such instances exist. (The Yak-3UAs coming out of Orenburg, Russia, from the direct lineage of the Yakovlev OKB, are examples of 'true' replicas.)

Column 4: Where possible, brief historical details of the aircraft listed are given, in a necessarily abbreviated form. In each case, units, operators, previous identities etc are listed in *reverse* order, ie the last user (or identity) is given first. Readers should have little trouble with these potted histories, especially with continued reference to the 'Abbreviations' section. Also given here are other registrations, or maintenance serials applicable to the airframe. Note that Royal Navy maintenance serials, 'A' numbers were reallocated, creating a somewhat confusing vista. Second, third or even fourth allocations are known and are noted in square brackets after the 'A' serial [3]. Readers should refer to the masterful BARG/Air-Britain *Royal Navy Instructional Airframes* for the 'Full Monty'. Where a date is given prefixed 'CoA' (Certificate of Airworthiness), this is the date at which it lapsed and is given as an *indication* of how long the airframe has been flightless. The term 'CoA' is used for all levels of certification, eg Permit to Fly, Ferry Permit etc.

Column 5: Used to denote an aircraft known to be undergoing a restoration or conservation programme at time of going to press, with the symbol ®. Also used as footnotes (eg ③) to refer readers back up to the narrative section for specific details on that airframe.

Column 6: 'Last noted' dates are given primarily to help historians to trace the history (or demise) of an airframe and perhaps to alert readers intending to visit the airframe involved as to the 'currency' of the information given. The listing of these dates, it is hoped, will persuade some readers and some of the less enlightened enthusiast and professional magazines to actually note the dates of sightings/reports in future jottings – the *date* of an observation can be a crucial form of evidence in many cases. Physical, first-hand reports – instead of assumptions and handed-on information – are vital for the monitoring of our aviation heritage.

ENGLAND

Bedfordshire 10 - 15
Berkshire 15 - 19
Buckinghamshire 20 - 22
Cambridgeshire 23 - 35
Cheshire 35 - 37
Cornwall 37 - 40
Cumbria 41 - 43
Derbyshire 43 - 44
Devon 44 - 47
Dorset 47 - 51
Durham & Cleveland 52
Essex 52 - 61
Gloucestershire 61 - 68
Hampshire 68 - 80
Hereford & Worcester 80 - 81
Hertfordshire 82 - 85

Isle of Man 85
Isle of Wight 86 - 87
Kent 87 - 93
Lancashire 93 - 96
Leicestershire 96; 129 - 135
Lincolnshire 135 - 146
Greater London 146 - 154
Greater Manchester 154 - 157
Merseyside 158 - 159
West Midlands 159 - 161
Norfolk 161 - 167
Northamptonshire 167 - 169
Northumberland &
   Tyneside 169 - 172
Nottinghamshire 172 - 176
Oxfordshire 176 - 178

Shropshire 179 - 188
Somerset 188 - 197
Staffordshire 197 - 199
Suffolk 199 - 205
Surrey 205 - 210
East Sussex 210 - 212
West Sussex 213 - 218
Warwickshire 218 - 224
Wiltshire 224; 257 - 261
East Yorkshire 261 - 264
North Yorkshire 264 - 268
South Yorkshire 269 - 272
West Yorkshire 272 - 273

Maps by Mary Denton

BEDFORDSHIRE

☞ Within the administrative county boundaries can be found the unitary authority of Luton.

BEDFORD
Bedford College: Located adjacent to Cauldwell Street. The content is thought to be unchanged.

❏ G-AVCC	Cessna F.172H	damaged 31-12-87. Inst airframe.	6-99
❏ (XM473)	Jet Provost T.3A	ex Norwich Airport 'G-TINY', Halton 8974M, 7 FTS, 1 FTS, 7 FTS, 1 FTS, CFS, 3 FTS, 1 FTS.	6-99

Others: Richard Farrer has three Austers in the area. G-AJDY is a candidate for Lycoming conversion. It is thought to have used the fuselage frame of J/1N Alpha G-ASEE ①. Chipmunk T.20 1366 was crated and exported to the USA during August 2000.

❏ G-AGTT	J/1 Autocrat	CoA 11-2-93. Stored.		12-97
❏ G-AJDY	J/1 Autocrat	ex Cranfield, Northampton, Spanhoe, Cossall, Sherburn. CoA 9-7-71.	® ①	12-97
❏ G-AJUD	J/1 Autocrat	ex Camberley, Tongham. CoA 18-5-74.		12-97
❏ 1360	Chipmunk T.20	G-BYYU, ex Spanhoe, CS-DAP ntu, Cascais, Port AF. Stored.		12-97
❏ 1367	Chipmunk T.20	G-BYYW, ex Spanhoe, Viseu, Port AF. Stored.		12-97

BEDFORD AIRFIELD (or Thurleigh) north of Bedford, east of the A6
Defence Science and Technology Laboratory (DS&TL): *W&R15* paid its respects to the 'end' of this great airfield. What is best described as a DS&TL 'enclave' here took on a Tornado nose in 2000.

❏ ZD936*	'AO' Tornado F.2	ex St Athan, 229 OCU. Nose. Arrived 11-00.	11-00

CARDINGTON AIRFIELD south of the A603, south-east of Bedford
Cardington Laboratory: The *original* gondola of the damaged military Skyship 600 was offered up for tender in January 1998. Last noted in March 1998, it has floated off into LOST!

CLAPHAM on the A6 north of Bedford
Skeeter AOP.12 XL765 left on 5th August 2000 for storage in Northamptonshire, before settling upon Melksham, Wilts, on 22nd July 2001.

COLMWORTH west of the A1 and Eaton Socon
Luscombe Silvaire G-AKUP is known to have moved on — but where?

CRANFIELD AERODROME east of Newport Pagnell
Cranfield Institute of Technology (CIT) / **College of Aeronautics** / **Cranfield Aerospace Ltd**: The HS.125 on the dump – which is on a low-loader chassis so it can move around – has had its registration doctored to read G-DHEA. One possible 'translation' of this could be De Havilland Executive Aircraft! ① The Jetstream 200 has been out of the air for some time. The Spirit microlight has not been noted since March 1996 and is best deleted. Harrier GR.3 XV748 moved to Elvington, N Yorks, on 21st October 2000.

❏ G-AWBT	Twin Com' 160B	ex N8508Y. Damaged 10-3-88. Inst airframe.		7-00
❏ G-AZXG	Aztec 250D	ex Little Snoring, N6963Y. Crashed 25-10-91. Inst.		7-00
❏ G-OHEA	HS.125-3B/RA	ex Hatfield, G-AVRG, G-5-12. Dump.	①	2-02
❏ G-RAVL*	Jetstream 200	ex G-AWVK, N1035S, G-AWVK. CoA 26-2-94. Stored. First noted 7-00.		7-00

Kennet Aviation: The Seafire project represents a major restoration task. *W&R17* spoke of Provost T.1 WW453 (G-TMKI) moving to the 'West Country', this was so true. For a more precise location, see Clevedon, Somerset. On 2nd November 2001 another Kennet Provost T.1 was on the move, this time XF603 (G-KAPW) by air to Old Warden, Beds. Meteor F.8 VZ467 (G-METE) flew in from Kemble, Glos, on 18th June 2000 and delighted all who saw *Winston* on the show circuit. On 18th May 2001 it flew to Southampton, Hants, were it was freighted to the Temora Aviation Museum in Australia.

Other departures: Safir G-SAFR to Thatcham, Berks, -01; Chipmunk T.10 WK511 (G-BVBT) sold, late 2001, flying in Cambs; Wasp HAS.1 XT781 (G-KAWW) sold in 2000, flying from Swansea; Venom FB.50 J-1632 to London Colney, Herts, 2-02.

☐ SX336*		Seafire XVII	G-BRMG, ex Twyford, Newark, Warrington, Stretton A2055, Bramcote. Arrived by 6-01.	® 3-02
☐ 'WK436'		Venom FB.50 ✈	G-VENM, ex J-1614, East Dereham, G-BLIE, Ipswich, Glasgow, Swiss AF. 11 Sqn colours. First flown 23-11-01.	3-02
☐ 'XD693'	'Z-Q'	Jet Provost T.2 ✈	G-AOBU, ex Winchester, Thatcham, Old Warden, Loughborough, Luton, XM129, G-42-1. 2 FTS c/s.	3-02
☐ XF515	'R'	Hunter F.6A ✈	G-KAXF, ex Binbrook, Scampton 8830M, Kemble, 1 TWU, 229 OCU, 43, 247. 43 Sqn colours.	3-02
☐ XF690		Provost T.1 ✈	G-MOOS, ex Thatcham, G-BGKA, 8041M, XF690, CATCS, CNCS, 64 GCF, Queens UAS.	3-02
☐ 'XM693'		Gnat T.1 ✈	G-TIMM, ex Leavesden, Halton 8618M, XP504, 4 FTS, CFS, 4 FTS.	3-02
☐ 'XR993'		Gnat T.1 ✈	G-BVPP, ex XP534, Halton 8620M, 4 FTS, CFS, 4 FTS, CFS, 4 FTS. Red Arrows colours.	3-02
☐ XV140	'K'	Scout AH.1 ✈	G-KAXL, ex Fleetlands.	3-02
☐ XW289	'73'	Jet Provost T.5A ✈	G-JPVA, ex G-BVXT, Binbrook, Shawbury, 1 FTS, RAFC, CFS.	3-02
☐ NZ3905*		Wasp HAS.1	G-KAXT ex W-s-Mare, RNZN, XT787. Arr 23-5-00.	3-02
☐ NZ3909		Wasp HAS.1	ex RNZN, XT782. Composite, for spares.	3-02

Others: Jet Provost T.3A G-TORE moved to Ipswich, Suffolk, on 8th December 2000. By August 2001 (probably much earlier) J/1N Alpha G-AJIW had moved to Nottingham, Notts.

☐ G-BAEW	Cessna F.172M	ex N12798. Crashed 12-11-93. Fuselage.	3-96
☐ G-BALI	Robin DR.4002+2	ex Meppershall. CoA 3-9-88.	® 3-96
☐ G-BAUJ	Aztec 250E	ex N14390. CoA 25-7-94. Stored.	7-97
☐ G-BDUX	Motor Cadet	CoA 23-2-84. Stored in trailer.	7-90
☐ G-BMSG	SAAB Lansen	ex VAT area, Swedish AF, Malmslatt, Fv32028. Stored.	3-02
☐ G-FRCE	Gnat T.1	ex North Weald, Halton 8604M, XS104, 4 FTS, CFS, 4 FTS. CoA 17-4-95. Stored.	3-02
☐	BXR	L 13 Blanik	BGA.1321, ex G-ATPX. Stored, on trailer.	7-97
☐	CYR	L 13 Blanik	BGA.1917, crashed 8-7-90. Original fuselage.	7-97
☐ XS101	'1'	Gnat T.1 ✈	G-GNAT, ex Cranwell 8638M, Red Arrows, CFS.	3-02
☐ XS458	'T'	Lightning T.5	ex Binbrook, LTF, 11, LTF, 5-11 pool, LTF, 5, 226 OCU. 226 OCU c/s port, 111 Sqn, stb. Taxiable.	3-02

DUNSTABLE AERODROME on the B489 south-east of Dunstable

☐ G-BLGS*	Rallye 180T	ex Lasham. CoA 21-5-99. Stripped out. F/n 6-00.	6-01
☐ PH-MSB*	Rallye Club	G-OIAN. Canx 2-9-91. First noted 1-01. off-site	5-01
☐ WJ731	Canberra B.2T	ex Willington, Wyton, Wyton SF, 231 OCU, 7, 231 OCU, 50, 90. Nose, trailer-mounted.	7-01

EATON BRAY west of Dunstable
Peter Underwood:

☐ ACH	'F'	T.6 Kite I	BGA.400, ex Brooklands, VD165, BGA.400. Stored.	1-00
☐ ALZ		Dagling	BGA.493 / BAPC.81, Dunstable, Duxford, Warton. ®	1-00
☐ BCF		T.21B	BGA.856, ex Haddenham. Damaged 1980. Stored.	1-00
☐ DNB		Grunau Baby IIb	BGA.2238, ex Bicester, RAFGSA380, D-8039.	1-00

Others: Two Evans types are stored at a strip.

❏ G-BEKM	Evans VP-1	CoA 23-3-95. Stored.	7-98
❏ G-BFFB	Evans VP-2	Unflown. Stored.	7-98

HATCH off the B658, south-west of Sandy
Skysport Engineering: By the summer of 2001 the RAF Museum's Miles Mohawk had arrived for restoration ①. A major oversight here is the Gemini, owned jointly by Skysport's Tim Moore and Vintec's Mike Vaisey, the pair trading under the glorious name Gemini Wanderers! Restoration is on 'as and when time permits' priority ②. After four years of restoration work, Hawker Fury rep 'K1930' (G-BKBB) made its first flight from here on 17th January 2001, ending up at Old Warden, Beds, where flight tests continued. A DH.2 REP is in the early stages of construction.
Notes: The Humming Bird project uses the wings of the Martin Monoplane G-AEYY – see under Hitchin, Herts ①. Tiger G-ACDA and N6720 are being worked on for Bryn Hughes ③. The DH.9 is a major find and is being worked on for Aero Vintage – see under St Leonards-on-Sea, East Sussex ④. The Demon is for Demon Displays Ltd. It is reported to be a composite with the front end of a former Irish Air Corps Hector. This would almost certainly be the one that was at Cloughjordan, Ireland ⑤.
◆ Access *strictly* by prior permission only.

❏ G-EBQP*	Humming Bird	ex Audley End, Bishop's Stortford.	③	6-01
❏ G-ACDA	Tiger Moth	ex Chilbolton, BB724, G-ACDA. Cr 27-6-79.	④	10-99
❏ G-AEKW*	Mohawk	ex Wyton, USA, Tablada, Spain, HM503, MCCS, Turnhouse SF, G-AEKW. Arr by 6-01.	®①	8-01
❏ G-AKEK*	Gemini 3A	ex Blackpool. CoA 22-9-72.	®②	6-00
❏ G-AXRP	SNCAN SV-4A	ex G-BLOL, G-AXRP, F-BDCZ. Dam 19-10-74.		2-01
❏ G-DINT	Beaufighter I	ex Halton, 3858M, X7688, 29, 153.	®	8-00
❏ F-BGNR	Viscount 708	ex Perth, Air Inter. Stored.	off-site	7-01
❏ N5595T	C-47A-85-DL	ex Thruxton, Blackbushe, G-BGCG, Spanish AF T3-27, N49V, N50322, 43-15536. Stored.		8-00
❏ D5649*	Airco DH.9	ex Bikaner, India, Imperial Gift 1920, RAF/RFC. Major components, long-term project.	⑤	1-01
❏ K8203	Demon I	G-BTVE, ex Cardington, 2292M, 9 BGS, 9 AOS, 64.	®⑥	2-01
❏ N6720	Tiger Moth	G-BYTN, ex Levenshulme, 'G-ABEE' Kings Heath, West Bromwich, 7014M, 9 AFTS, 2 GS, Lon UAS, Queens UAS, 11 RFS, 11 EFTS, 4 CPF, 206.	®③	8-00
❏	Wallace repro	Stored.		7-01
❏	Stampe SV-4	ex Spanhoe Lodge, Les Mureaux. Forward fuselage.		11-97

HENLOW AIRFIELD on the A6007 south-west of Biggleswade
RAF Henlow: The Hunter still guards the station.

❏ WT612	Hunter F.1	ex Halton, Credenhill 7496M, Hawker, A&AEE. Gate.		8-01

Others: Dick Horsfield and Rod Robinson, trading as HCR and Sons, are rebuilding a Vampire.
◆ Visits not possible, but check progress on **web** www.project-vampire.org.uk

❏ XE856	Vampire T.11	G-DUSK, ex Catfoss, Long Marston, Lasham, Welwyn GC, Woodford, Chester, St Athan, 219, North Weald SF, 226 OCU.	®	8-01

LOWER STONDON west of the A600/Henlow aerodrome, north of Hitchin
Stondon Transport Museum: A superb collection of 400-plus motor vehicles and other transport artefacts, including a full-scale replica of HMS *Endeavour* and a coffee shop and gift shop.
◆ Open daily, 10am to 5pm. ✉ Station Road, Lower Stondon, Henlow, SG16 6JN ☎ 01462 850339
   e-mail info@transportmuseum.co.uk **web** www.transportmuseum.co.uk

❏ 'G-ADRG'	HM.14 'Flea'	BAPC.77, ex Cheltenham, Long Marston, Innsworth, Ross-on-Wye, Staverton.	3-02

❏ G-AXOM	Penn-Smith gyro	wfu 11-10-74.	3-02
❏ XN341	Skeeter AOP.12	8002M, ex Luton, St Athan, 4 SoTT, 3 RTR, 651.	3-02

LUTON
Philip Leaver: This entry is more appropriately listed under Hitchin, Herts.

LUTON AIRPORT off the A505 east of Luton
W&R17 (p13) talked of HS.125 5N-AWD leaving by lorry in 1998. Not so, it was being moved around, but did not leave the confines of the airport! It still serves on the dump, in an inverted pose.

❏ G-AOVS	Britannia 312	ex Redcoat, 'G-BRAC', Lloyd, BOAC.	
		CoA 31-7-79. Fuselage. Fire crews.	5-01
❏ 5N-AWD*	HS.125-1	ex G-ASSI. Fire crews.	10-00

OLD WARDEN AERODROME west of Biggleswade, signposted from the A1
Shuttleworth Collection: A busy day for the collection on 29th September 2000 with no less than *three* first flights on the lovely aerodrome. The Chipmunk had its first 'outing' in the hands of the collection. The latest Northern Aeroplane Workshops masterpiece, the Bristol M.1C took to the air. Crowning them all was the first flight of the oldest of all Miles types, the Southern Martlet again got the air under its wings. As *W&R* closed for press, the DH.88 was engine running and ready for its turn.
The arrival of the Provost T.1 in November 2001 saw another of the 'trainer' theme completed. *W&R9* recorded the sale of XF836 (G-AWRY) in 1982 as part of a change of policy – thankfully things have changed since. The markings are those of a Provost on delivery to the Sultan of Oman's Air Force ①. Both the Belgian-owned Fury REP ② and the Aero Vintage Bristol F.2b ③ have arrived for continued flight test and in readiness for flight, respectively.
W&R14 'wrote out' the Dixon Ornithopter as having been reduced to small parts only. Not, so, in 1999 an SVAS team started restoration of the totally uncovered airframe, much of which showed elements of damage. Completed in late 2000, it can be found 'flying' within the rafters of Hangar No.6. Welcome back! ④
Notes: EE Wren G-EBNV is mostly the unregistered No.4 with parts from G-EBNV ⑤. As a reminder that the LVG is an Air Historical Branch aircraft, it was allocated an 'M' number in 1997 ⑥. It will ultimately be grounded and join the RAF Museum. The Me 163B Komet full-scale model includes an original Walter rocket motor ⑦. Several aircraft based at Old Warden are on loan to the Shuttleworth Collection. With the new hangar space available – Hangar No.8 – the number of 'loaned-in' aircraft has increased somewhat: Dove G-EAGA Andrew Wood; Moth G-EBLV BAE Systems (Operations); Active II G-ABVE and Mew Gull G-AEXF with Desmond Penrose; Messenger G-AKBO Bravo-Oscar Syndicate; Cygnet repro G-CAMM Don Cashmore and Falcon Major G-AEEG and Hawk Trainer V1075 with Peter Holloway. All are marked ‡. Some Shuttleworth aircraft can be found elsewhere: Archaeopteryx G-ABXL at Radcliffe on Trent, Notts and Northern Aeroplane Workshops – see under Batley, W Yorks.
Departures: In a move that was hardly surprising, the collection sold unfinished Blake Bluetit G-BXIY during mid-2000. The SVAS (see below) had been working on the restoration of this one-off for many years. It moved to North Weald, Essex. Granger Archaeopteryx G-ABXL moved to Radcliffe on Trent, Notts, on 13th December 2000 for restoration by Don Cashmore. BA Swallow II G-AFCL was sold by its owner and moved out in late 2000. The combined Airship Heritage Trust and British Balloon Museum and Library display has been removed and by October 2002 the organisation will have left Old Warden. See under Newbury, Berks.

◆ Open daily throughout the year, but is closed for up to 14 days covering Xmas Eve, and up to and including New Year's Day. Open April to October 10am to 5pm, November to March 10am to 4pm, the hangar displays are closed one hour after the last admission time. Supporting the Collection in many ways is the **Shuttleworth Veteran Aeroplane Society** (SVAS) which has an extensive series of activities during the year, a regular journal – the excellent *Prop-Swing* – and welcomes new members. Address as below. ✉ Old Warden Aerodrome, Biggleswade, SG18 9EP ☎ 01767 627288 fax 01767 626229 hot-line 090 68 323310 e-mail collection@shuttleworth.com web www.shuttleworth.org

❏ G-EAGA	Sopwith Dove ✈	ex Hatch, G-BLOO ntu, Australia, G-EAGA, K-157.	‡	3-02
❏ G-EBHX	Humming Bird ✈	ex Lympne No 8. *L'Oiseau Mouche.*		3-02
❏ G-EBIR	DH.51 ✈	ex VP-KAA, G-KAA, G-EBIR. *Miss Kenya.*		3-02
❏ G-EBJO	ANEC II	ex Radcliffe on Trent, Old Warden, Lympne No 7. CoA 30-11-35.	®	3-02
❏ G-EBLV	DH.60 Moth ✈	ex Hatfield.	‡	3-02
❏ [G-EBNV]	EE Wren	No.4, BAPC.11. CoA 23-6-87.	⑤	3-02
❏ G-EBWD	DH.60X Moth ✈	Bought by Richard Shuttleworth in 1932.		3-02
❏ G-AAIN	Parnall Elf II ✈	ex Southend, Fairoaks, Badminton.		3-02
❏ G-AANG	Blériot XI ✈	No.14, BAPC.3, ex Ampthill, Hendon.		3-02
❏ G-AANH	Deperdussin ✈	No.43, BAPC.4, ex Ampthill. CoA 14-5-83.		3-02
❏ G-AANI	Blackburn Mon ✈	No.9, BAPC.5, ex Wittering.		3-02
❏ G-AAPZ	Desoutter I ✈	ex Higher Blagdon, Old Warden.		3-02
❏ G-AAYX	Southern Martlet ✈	ex Woodford. First flown 29-9-00.		3-02
❏ G-ABAG	DH.60 Moth ✈	ex Perth.		3-02
❏ G-ABVE	Active II ✈	ex Tiger Club.	‡	3-02
❏ G-ACSS '34'	DH.88 Comet	ex Hatfield, Farnborough, Old Warden, Leavesden, K5084, G-ACSS. *Grosvenor House.*		3-02
❏ G-ACTF	Comper Swift ✈	ex Rhos, VT-ADO. *The Scarlet Angel.* CoA 6-10-90.		3-02
❏ G-AEBB	HM.14 'Flea'	ex Southampton. CoA 31-5-39. Taxies.		3-02
❏ G-AEEG*	Falcon Major ✈	ex Turweston, SE-AFN, RSwAF Fv913, SE-AFN, G-AEEG, U-20.	‡	3-02
❏ G-AEXF	Mew Gull ✈	ex Sudbury, Old Warden, ZS-AHM.	‡	3-02
❏ G-AKBO*	Messenger 2A ✈	arrived 5-01.	‡	3-02
❏ [G-ARSG]	Triplane REP ✈	BAPC.1, ex *Those Magnificent Men...* Hants A/C built.		3-02
❏ [G-ASPP]	Boxkite REP ✈	BAPC.2, ex *Those Magnificent Men...* Miles-built.		3-02
❏ G-CAMM	Cygnet REP ✈	ex Hucknall, G-ERDB ntu.	‡	3-02
❏ 'C4918'	Bristol M.1C REP ✈	G-BWJM. 72 Sqn c/s. First flown 29-9-00.		3-02
❏ 'D7889'*	Bristol F.2b	G-AANM / BAPC.166, ex St Leonards-on-Sea, Sandown, St Leonards-on-Sea, Old Warden, Weston-on-the-Green. Arrived 3-01. Pending flight test.	③	3-02
❏ D8096	Bristol F.2b ✈	G-AEPH, ex Filton, Watford, D8096, 208.		3-02
❏ F904 'H'	SE.5A✈	G-EBIA, ex 'D7000', Farnborough, Whitley, G-EBIA, F904 84 Sqn. 56 Sqn colours.		3-02
❏ H5199	Avro 504K ✈	G-ADEV, ex G-ACNB, 'E3404' and Avro 504N.		3-02
❏ 'K1930'	Hawker Fury ✈	G-BKBB, ex Hatch, Belgium OO-HFU, OO-XFU, G-BKBB, Wycombe Air Park. 43 Sqn colours. Arrived 17-1-01. For flight tests.	②	3-02
❏ K1786	Hawker Tomtit ✈	G-AFTA, ex 5 GCF, 23 GCF, 3 FTS.		3-02
❏ K3215	Avro Tutor ✈	G-AHSA, ex HSA, RAFC.		3-02
❏ 'K5414'	Hind (Afghan) ✈	G-AENP, BAPC.78. ex 'K5457', Kabul.		3-02
❏ 'N6181'	Sopwith Pup ✈	G-EBKY, ex N5180. *Happy.* 3 (Naval) Sqn c/s.		3-02
❏ 'N6290'	Sopwith Tri' ✈	G-BOCK, ex Dewsbury. 8 Sqn RNAS c/s, *Dixie II.*		3-02
❏ P6382	Magister I ✈	G-AJRS, ex 'G-AJDR', P6382, 3 EFTS, 16 EFTS.		3-02
❏ T6818	Tiger Moth II ✈	G-ANKT, ex Aston Down, 21 EFTS.		3-02
❏ V1075*	Magister ✈	G-AKPF, ex Shoreham, Sandown, Shoreham, V1075, 16 EFTS. First noted 9-01.		3-02
❏ 'V9367' 'MA-B'	Lysander III ✈	G-AZWT, ex 'V9441', Duxford, Strathallan, RCAF 2355. 161 Squadron colours.		3-02
❏ W9385 'YG-L' '3'	Hornet Moth ✈	G-ADND, ex Chester, W9385, St Athan SF, 3 CPF, G-ADND. 502 Sqn colours.		3-02
❏ Z7015 '7-L'	Sea Hurricane I ✈	G-BKTH, ex Duxford, Staverton, Old Warden, Loughborough, Yeovilton, 759, 880. 880 Sqn c/s.		3-02
❏ AR501 'NN-A'	Spitfire V ✈	G-AWII, ex Duxford, Henlow, Loughborough, CGS, 61 OTU, 1 TEU, 58 OTU, 422, 312, 504, 310. 310 colours.		3-02

❑ VS610* 'K-L'	Prentice T.1	G-AOKL, ex Bassingbourn, VS610, 1 FTS, 22 FTS, RAFC, 22 FTS. CoA 20-9-96.	⑧	3-02
❑ XA241	G'hopper TX.1	ex Cambridge.		3-02
❑ XF603*	Provost T.1 ✈	G-KAPW, ex Cranfield, Filton, Bristol, 27 MU, CAW, RAFC. RAF grey / green camo. Arr 2-11-01.	①	3-02
❑ '18671'	Chipmunk 22 ✈	G-BNZC, ex G-ROYS, 7438M, WP905 CFS, 664, RAFC. RCAF colours. First flown 29-9-00.		3-02
❑ 7198/18	LVG C.VI✈	9239M, G-AANJ, ex Stanmore, Colerne, Fulbeck.	⑥	3-02
❑ '191454'	Me 163B FSM	BAPC.271. Wingless.	⑦	3-02
❑ '423' and '427'	Gladiator I✈	G-AMRK, ex L8032, 'N2308', L8032, 'K8032', Gloster, Hamble, 8 MU, 61 OTU, 1624F, 2 AACU. Norwegian AF c/s. '423' port, '427' stb.		3-02
❑ —*	BAPC.8 Dixon Orni'	restored 1999-2000.	④	3-02

SANDY on the A1 north of Biggleswade.

❑ G-AXNZ	Pitts S-1S	ex Little Gransden. CoA 30-8-91. Stored.	12-97

BERKSHIRE

☛ Within the administrative county boundaries can be found the unitary authorities of Bracknell Forest, Newbury, Reading, Slough, Windsor and Maidenhead and Wokingham.

ARBORFIELD on the A327 south of Reading
Princess Marina College / School of Electrical and Aeronautical Engineering (SEAE) within Hazebrouck Barracks: SEAE maintain a detachment at Middle Wallop, Hants, which see. A trimming down of the instructional fleet has occurred. Over many years, the AAC have developed their own method of numbering instructional airframes, with some receiving 'TAD' prefixes mostly followed by three numbers. TAD stands for Technical Aid and Demonstrator – but there are other interpretations! Purpose-built instructional airframes and teaching aids are generally known as 'CIMs' – Classroom Instructional Models.
   Departures: Gazelle **AH.1** ZB668 (TAD.015) to Middle Wallop, Hants, 1-7-99, but returned – see below. Scout **AH.1**s XP888 to Ipswich, Suffolk, 6-01; XP905 to Ipswich, Suffolk, 6-01; XP953, last noted 2-98, moved to Bramley, Hants; XR635 to Ipswich, Suffolk, 6-01; XT623 gone by 2-01; XT640 to Ipswich, Suffolk, 6-01;

❑ XP848	Scout AH.1	ex Middle Wallop, Wroughton, 659, 669. Gate	7-01
❑ XP855	Scout AH.1	ex Wroughton, 652, 651, 655.	2-01
❑ XP884	Scout AH.1	ex Middle Wallop. ARWS.	2-98
❑ XP899	Scout AH.1	ex Middle Wallop, ARWF. Crashed 1-11-79.	2-01
❑ XR601	Scout AH.1	ex BATUS, 657, 665, 666. Damaged 26-8-79.	2-01
❑ XT633	Scout AH.1	ex Wroughton, 659, 653, 661, 660, Wroughton.	2-01
❑ XV124 'W'	Scout AH.1	ex Middle Wallop, Arborfield, Middle Wallop, Wroughton, 656, 653, 654.	2-01
❑ XV141	Scout AH.1	ex Wroughton, 657, 659, 654, 661. REME museum.	2-01
❑ [XW838]	Lynx 1-03	TAD.009, ex Middle Wallop, Yeovil.	2-01
❑ XW860	Gazelle HT.2	TAD.021, ex Middle Wallop, Fleetlands, Wroughton, 705. ABDR	2-01
❑ XW863	Gazelle HT.2	TAD.022, ex Middle Wallop, Wroughton, 705.	2-01
❑ XW888	Gazelle AH.1	TAD.017, ex Middle Wallop, ARWF, GCF.	2-01
❑ XW889	Gazelle AH.1	TAD.018, ex Middle Wallop, ARWF, GCF.	2-01
❑ XW900*	Gazelle AH.1	TAD.900, ex Middle Wallop SEAE, 660. Crashed 25-5-76. First noted 3-00.	2-01

☐ XW912	Gazelle AH.1	TAD.019, ex Fleetlands, 655, 3 CBAS, 656, 655, 3 CBAS.	2-01
☐ XX387	Gazelle AH.1	TAD.014, ex Fleetlands, 651, 661, 657, 16/5 Lancers. Crashed 15-12-95. Avionics and Systems trainer.	2-01
☐ XX454*	Gazelle AH.1	TAD.023, ex Waddington, Middle Wallop, 663, 1 Rgt, 662, 656, 657, 4 Rgt, 3 Rgt, 4 Rgt, 659, 669, 664, 654, 4 Rgt, 669, 659. Arr 1-2-01.	2-01
☐ XZ188	Lynx AH.7	ex Fleetlands, 4 Rgt, 654, 662, 655, 665, 655, LCF, 651.	2-01
☐ XZ305	Gazelle AH.1	TAD.020, ex 3 Regt, 665, 662, 654, GCF.	7-00
☐ XZ325 'T'	Gazelle AH.1	ex Middle Wallop, 670, 655, 3 Regt.	2-01
☐ XZ332	Gazelle AH.1	ex Middle Wallop, 670, ARWF, 656, 664.	2-01
☐ XZ333	Gazelle AH.1	ex Middle Wallop, 670, ARWF.	2-01
☐ XZ613 'F'	Lynx AH.1	ex Fleetlands, 695, 665, 655, NI Regt, 657, 654.	2-01
☐ XZ666	Lynx AH.7	ex 669, 655, 665, 655, LCF, 651.	2-01
☐ ZA769 'K'	Gazelle AH.1	ex Middle Wallop, 670, ARWF.	2-01
☐ ZB668*	Gazelle AH.1	TAD.015, ex Middle Wallop, Arborfield, Fleetlands, UNFICYP. Crashed 30-11-92. First noted 9-00.	2-01
☐ ZB678	Gazelle AH.1	ex 16 Flt.	2-01
☐ QP30	Lynx HC.28	TAD.013, ex Fleetlands, Almondbank, Wroughton, Qatar Police, G-BFDV.	2-01
☐	TAD.001 Gazelle CIM	ex Middle Wallop.	2-01
☐	TAD.002 Gazelle CIM	ex Middle Wallop.	8-99
☐	TAD.007 Lynx CIM	ex Middle Wallop. Fuselage number TO.42.	2-01
☐	TAD.008 Gazelle CIM	ex Middle Wallop. 'Engine/Control Systems' sim.	2-01
☐	TAD.010 Lynx CIM	Cockpit. 'Engine/Control Systems' sim.	2-01
☐	TAD.011 Lynx CIM	ex Middle Wallop.	2-01
☐	TAD.012 Lynx CIM	ex Middle Wallop.	2-01

Rowcroft Barracks: By February 2001, and likely much earlier (it was last noted here in October 1996) Scout AH.1 XR597 moved to Wattisham, Suffolk.

BARKHAM south of the B3349, south-west of Wokingham
Barkham Antiques: Have the former Stamford, Lincs, Robinson as an attraction-cum-stock item.

☐ G-KENN*	Robinson R-22B	ex Stamford, Sandtoft. Damaged 31-10-94. F/n 4-01.	7-01

BINFIELD north of the B3034, north-west of Bracknell
Amen Corner: The Brantly had been joined by a locally-built Hollman Sportster and a Cessna.

☐ G-ASXF	Brantly 305	ex Thruxton, Biggin Hill, CoA 16-2-79.	11-01
☐ G-BJOD*	HA-2M Sportster	ex Bracknell. Unflown? First noted 4-01.	7-01
☐ G-BPCJ*	Cessna 150J	ex Solihull, Tattershall Thorpe, N61096. Damaged 25-1-90. *Charlie*.	11-01

HUNGERFORD on the A4 east of Marlborough
Newbury Aeroplane Company: Jan Cooper and team continue the standards of excellence that NAC is famed for. The Tiger Moth is being restored to static condition for the Brooklands Museum ①.

☐ G-AAUP	Klemm L.25	*Clementine*. CoA 21-11-84. Stored.		2-98
☐ G-ADWT*	Hawk Trainer	ex CF-NXT, G-ADWT, NF750, 26 OTU, G-ADWT. First noted 3-00.	®	1-01
☐ G-AFGH	Chilton DW.1	ex Billingshurst. CoA 7-7-83.	®	2-98
☐ F-BGEQ*	Tiger Moth	ex Brooklands, Chessington, Brooklands, Le Mans, French mil, NL846. F/n 9-00.	® ①	3-02

Others: A former Spanish Bf 109E is *believed* under restoration in the area.
❑ C4E-88   Bf 109E   ex Tangmere, Stubbington, Spain, SpanAF '6-88'.   ® 12-93

LAMBOURN on the B4000 north of Hungerford
Work is being carried out in the general area on the Gannet to get it to ground-running status.
❑ XA459   Gannet AS.4   ex Cirencester, Cardiff, Culdrose
                                   SAH-7/A2608, Lee-on-Solent, 831.   10-01

MEMBURY close to the Membury services, east of Swindon on the M4
Southern Sailplanes: The fuselage of Super Cub G-APZJ is the original one ①.

❑ G-AHAG	Dragon Rapide	ex Blandford, Ford, Whitney, RL944. CoA 15-7-73.		1-00
❑ G-APZJ	Super Cub 150	crashed 12-6-83. Original fuselage frame, stored.	①	9-89
❑ G-AWHX	Beta B.2	ex G-ATEE ntu. *Vertigo*. CoA 14-6-87.	®	1-00
❑ G-BAMT	DR.400 Knight	crashed 8-1-78. Wreck.		9-89
❑ G-BAVA	Super Cub 150	ex D-EFKC, ALAT 18-5391. Cr 20-11-77. Frame.		1-92
❑ G-BAZC	DR.400 Knight	crashed 21-5-88. Fuselage.		7-98
❑ G-BEHS	Pawnee 260C	ex Lancing, OE-AFX, N8755L. CoA 25-6-93.		2-95
❑ G-RBIN	DR.400 2+2	crashed 21-5-93. Wreck.		7-98
❑ 'Z7258'	Dragon Rapide	G-AHGD, ex Old Warden, NR786.		
		Women of the Empire. Crashed 30-6-91. Wreck.		8-97

NEWBURY on the A34 west of Reading
British Balloon Museum and Library (BBM&L): Envelopes are to be seen during events such as
the Icicle Meet and the occasional inflation day. BBM&L maintains strong links with The Airship
Heritage Trust (see below) and looks after the display in the West Berkshire Museum, also see below.
Colt Coffee Jar G-BVBJ returned to Lancing, East Sussex, W Sussex.
✉ Tim Turner, 3 Chancel Road, Locks Heath, Southampton, SO31 6IF. e-mail tjthafb@aol.com
☞ From this edition, a two-column layout has been adopted. This means that some of the details
   previously given have been omitted, but for those with a specific interest in balloons and airships,
   this will be readily available elsewhere. Letters are used to denote the 'extent' of the artefact: **-B**
   Basket; **-C** complete (including burner), **-E** Envelope; **-G** Gondola and combinations thereof.

❑ G-ATGN	Thorn Coal Gas -C	3-02		❑ G-BBLL	Cameron O-84 -E	3-02
❑ G-ATXR	Abingdon Gas -B	3-02		❑ G-BBOD	Cameron O-5 -E / B	3-02
❑ G-AVTL	HAG Free -E	3-02		❑ G-BBOX	Thunder Ax7-77 -C	3-02
❑ G-AWCR	Piccard Ax6 -E	3-02		❑ G-BBYU	Cameron O-65 -E	3-02
❑ G-AWOK	Sussex Free Gas -E	3-02		❑ G-BCAR	Thunder Ax7-77 -E	3-02
❑ G-AXVU	Omega 84 -E	3-02		❑ G-BCFD	West -E	3-02
❑ G-AXXP	Bradshaw Free -E / B	3-02		❑ G-BCFE*	Portslade School -E	3-02
❑ G-AYAJ	Cameron O-84 -C	3-02		❑ G-BCGP	Gazebo Ax-65 -E	3-02
❑ G-AYAL	Omega 56 -C	3-02		❑ G-BDVG*	Thunder Ax6-56A -E	3-02
❑ G-AZBH	Cameron O-84 -C	3-02		❑ G-BEEE	Thunder Ax6-56A -E	3-02
❑ G-AZER*	Cameron O-42 -E	3-02		❑ G-BEPO	Cameron N-77 -E / B	3-02
❑ G-AZJI	Western O-65 -E	3-02		❑ G-BEPZ	Cameron D-96 -G	3-02
❑ G-AZOO	Western O-65 -E	3-02		❑ G-BETF	Cameron SS -E	3-02
❑ G-AZSP	Cameron O-84 -E	3-02		❑ G-BETH	Thunder Ax6-56 -E	3-02
❑ G-AZUV	Cameron O-56 -E	3-02		❑ G-BEVI	Thunder Ax7-77A -E	3-02
❑ G-AZYL*	Portslade School -E	3-02		❑ G-BFAB	Cameron N-56 -E	3-02
❑ G-BAMK	Cameron D-96 -E / G	3-02		❑ G-BGAS	Colt 105A -B	3-02
❑ G-BAVU	Cameron A-105 -E	3-02		❑ G-BGHS	Cameron N-31 -E	3-02
❑ G-BAXF	Cameron O-77 -E	3-02		❑ G-BGOO	Colt 56 -E	3-02
❑ G-BAXK*	Thunder Ax7-77 -E	3-02		❑ G-BGPF	Thunder Ax6-56Z -E	3-02
❑ G-BBFS	Van Bemden Gas -E	3-02		❑ G-BHKN	Colt 14A -E	3-02
❑ G-BBGZ	Cambridge -B	¶ 3-02		❑ G-BHKR	Colt 14A -C	¶ 3-02

❏	G-BHUR	Thunder Ax3 17.5 -E	3-02	❏ G-HOUS	Colt 31A -E	3-02
❏	G-BIAZ	Cameron AT-165 -E	3-02	❏ G-ICES	Thunder Ax6-56 -E	3-02
❏	G-BIDV	Colt 17A -E	3-02	❏ G-LCIO	Colt 240A -E / C	3-02
❏	G-BIGT	Colt 77A -E	3-02	❏ G-LOAG	Cameron N-77 -E	3-02
❏	G-BIUL	Cameron 60 -E	3-02	❏ G-NUTS	Cameron 35SS -E	3-02
❏	G-BKES	Cameron SS 57 -E	3-02	❏ G-OBUD	Colt 69A -E	3-02
❏	G-BKMR	Thunder Ax3 -C	3-02	❏ G-OFIZ	Colt 80SS -E	3-02
❏	G-BKRZ	Dragon 77 -E	3-02	❏ G-PARR	Colt 90SS -E	3-02
❏	G-BLIO	Cameron R-42 -E	3-02	❏ G-PERR	Cameron SS 60 -E	3-02
❏	G-BLKU	Colt 56 -E	3-02	❏ G-PLUG	Colt 105A -E	3-02
❏	G-BMEZ	Cameron DP-50 -E	3-02	❏ G-PUBS	Colt SS -B	3-02
❏	G-BMYA	Colt 56A -E	3-02	❏ G-ZUMP	Cameron N-77 -E	3-02
❏	G-BNHN	Colt SS -E	3-02	❏ EI-BAY	Cameron O-84 -E	3-02
❏	G-BOGR	Colt 180A -E	3-02	❏ F-WGGM	T & Colt AS-261 -E	3-02
❏	G-BOTL	Colt 42R -E	3-02	❏ HB-BOU	Brighton HAB -B	3-02
❏	G-BPKN	Colt AS-80 -E	3-02	❏ N4990T	Thunder Ax7-65B -C	3-02
❏	G-BRZC	Cameron N-90 -E	3-02	❏ N12006	Raven S.50 -E	3-02
❏	G-BUBL	Thunder Ax8-105- E	3-02	❏ OY-BOB	Omega 80 -C	3-02
❏	G-BUUU	Cameron 77SS -E	3-02	❏ OY-BOW	Colting 77A -E	3-02
❏	G-BVBX	Cameron N-90M -E / B	3-02	❏ 5Y-SIL	Cameron A-140 -E	3-02
❏	G-CHUB	Colt N-51 SS -E	3-02	❏ —	Gas balloon -B	3-02
❏	G-ERMS	Thunder AS-33 -C	3-02	❏ —	Cam' DG28 Gas -G	3-02
❏	G-FTFT	Colt 90SS -E	3-02	❏ —	Military Gas -B	3-02
❏	G-FZZZ	Colt 56A -E	3-02	❏ — BAPC.258	GQ 5,000ft³ -E	3-02
❏	G-HOME	Colt 77A -E	3-02			

West Berkshire Museum : BBM&L artefacts on show are marked ¶ above.
◆ At The Wharf in Newbury. Note, *closed* every Wed – except school holidays Open Apr to Sep 10am to 5pm Mon to Sat and 1pm to 5pm Sun and Bank Hos. Oct to March 10am to 4pm Mon to Sat and closed Sun and Bank Hols ✉ The Wharf, Newbury, RG14 5AS ☎ 01635 30511 **fax** 01635 519562

The Airship Heritage Trust (AHT): The hoped-for Airship and Balloon Museum at Old Warden, Beds, failed to materialise. With its considerable connections with the BBM&L (see above), it has been decided to append the AHT entry here for at least the time being.
◆ Not available for viewing at present. ✉ G/C Peter A Garth, 5 Orchard Lane, Brampton, Huntingdon, PE1 8TF. Research and general enquires to: ☎ 01767 627195, am only.

❏	G-BECE	AD-500 Skyship	ex Old Warden, Cardington, Kirkbymoorside. Gondola, damaged 9-3-79. Stored.	3-02
❏	G-BIHN	Skyship 500	ex Old Warden, Cardington. Wrecked 27-4-87. Gondola, stored.	3-02
❏	–*	K88 Airship	ex St Athan, Pensacola, USN. Gondola.	3-02

READING
Ben Borsberry: No news on the biplanes believed held in the area.

❏	G-AGNJ	Tiger Moth	ex VP-YOJ, ZS-BGF, SAAF 2366.	® 6-95
❏	G-AZGC	SNCAN SV-4C	ex Hungerford, Booker, F-BCGE, French mil No.120. Damaged 28-5-90. Stored.	6-95
❏	G-BRHW	Tiger Moth	ex 7Q-YMY, VP-YMY, ZS-DLB, SAAF 4606, DE671.	® 6-95

Kelvin Petty: Kelvin also had the cockpit of Lightning F.53 ZF587, but this moved to Lashenden, Kent, on 17th May 2001 after sale to another collector. Kelvin acquired the MiG-21MF at Boscombe Down, Wilts, in the summer of 2001 and presented it to the museum project there – *qv*.

❏	ZF582*	Lightning F.53	ex Llantrisant, Luton, Desborough, Portsmouth, Stretton, Warton, RSAF 207, 53-676, G-27-46. Nose. Arrived 12-8-00.	12-01

Others: The spares-ship Provost was offered for sale in mid-2000.

❑ WW447	Provost T.1	ex Exeter, CATCS, CNCS, RAFC. Stored.		6-00

THATCHAM or Brimpton, north of the A4, west of Newbury
Sylmar Aviation / Provost Team: Alan House and team operate from a strip in the area. *W&R16*
(p21) 'wrote off' the two Provost 'spares ships' WV486 and 181. Not so, they are stored, off-site ①.

❑ G-HRLK	SAAB Safir ✈	ex G-BRZY, PH-RLK.	off-site	1-02
❑ G-SAFR*	SAAB Safir 91D	ex Cranfield, Coventry, Rugby, Bruntingthorpe, PH-RLR RLS.	®	1-02
❑ N16403*	C34 Airmaster ✈	—		1-02
❑ WV486	'N-D' Provost T.1	ex Reading, Halton 7694M, 6 FTS. Spares.	①	1-02
❑ XF545	'O-K' Provost T.1	ex Linton-on-Ouse, Swinderby, Finningley 7957M, Shawbury, 6 FTS, 2 FTS. Fuselage, stored.		1-02
❑ XF597	'AH' Provost T.1 ✈	G-BKFW, ex CAW, RAFC.		1-02
❑ XF836	Provost T.1	G-AWRY, ex Popham, Old Warden, 8043M, 27 MU, CATCS, CNCS, RAFC, Man UAS. Damaged 28-7-87.	off-site	1-02
❑ 181	Provost T.51	ex Casement, IAAC. Spares.	①	1-02

WHITE WALTHAM AERODROME south of the A4 south-west of Maidenhead

❑ G-AFLW*	Miles Monarch	CoA 30-7-98. Stored.	6-01
❑ G-BBNY	Cessna FRA.150L	ex Lasham, Blackbushe. Crashed 8-6-86. Wreck.	9-96

WOODLEY east of Reading
Museum of Berkshire Aviation (MBA): Work continues on the major reconstruction of the
Martinet – bringing an otherwise 'extinct' type back to the public gaze.
  Co-operating within the site are several other bodies: the **Royal Berkshire Aviation Society**,
The Herald Society undertaking the restoration of *Whisky-Alpha* (contact for both K Freeman, 269
Wykeham Road, Reading, Berkshire RG6 1PL) and the **Miles Aircraft Collection**. Items are on
show at MBA from MAC include the Bristol Mercury and propeller from the second prototype M.37
JN668 and a 'slice' of upper fuselage of Marathon G-AMEW. As the bulk of the MAC collection is
widely dispersed, their main 'reference' is now to be found under Pulborough, West Sussex.
◆ Sat, Sun and Bank Holidays Mar to Oct, 10.30am to 5pm. During May, Jun and Jul also open Wed
  11.30am to 4pm. Sun only 12 noon to 4pm Oct to Mar. ✉ Mohawk Way (off Bader Way),
  Woodley, near Reading, Berkshire RG5 4UF ☎ 01734 340712 **Hot-line** 0118 9448089

❑ G-APLK	Miles Student 2	ex North Weald, Bruntingthorpe, G-APLK, Cranfield, G-MIOO, Duxford, G-APLK, Glasgow, Shoreham, XS941, G-35-4. Crashed 24-8-85.	®	3-02
❑ G-APWA	Herald 100	ex Southend, BAF, PP-SDM, PP-ASV, G-APWA. CoA 6-4-82.		3-02
❑ TF-SHC	Martinet TT.1	ex Reykjavik, Akureyri, MS902, Reykjavik SF, 251. Crashed 18-7-51. Major reconstruction.	®	3-02
❑ 'L6906'	Magister I	BAPC.44, ex Brooklands, Woodley, Wroughton, Frenchay, G-AKKY, T9841, 11 EFTS, 16 EFTS.		3-02
❑ XG883	'773' Gannet T.5	ex Cardiff, Yeovilton, 849. FAAM loan.		3-02
❑ XJ389	Jet Gyrodyne	ex Cosford, Southampton, G-AJJP, XD759, makers.		3-02
❑ —	BAPC.233 Wanderlust	ex Farnborough.		3-02
❑ —	BAPC.248 McBroom h-g	built 1974.		3-02

BUCKINGHAMSHIRE

AYLESBURY
No.1365 Squadron Air Cadets: Keep their Hunter nose at the TAVR Centre at the corner of
Gatehouse Road and the A41, with the 'Hen and Chickens' pub opposite.
- ❏ XF522   Hunter F.6   ex Bucks Ambulance Service, Aylesbury, Aylesbury
     Fire Service, Halton, 92, 66, 92. Nose.   ℗   2-98

Others: Stored in the area is a Luton Minor. During late 2000 **Stewart Thornley** acquired the cockpit
section of a Chipmunk and is turning it into a full-blown motion simulator.
- ❏ G-AFIR   Luton Minor   ex Cobham, Rearsby. CoA 30-7-71.   1-96
- ❏ WB626*   Chipmunk T.10   ex South Molton, Fownhope, Firbeck,
            PAX   Houghton-on-the-Hill, Southampton, Swanton
     Morley, Bicester, Kemble, Hendon SF, 5 FTS,
     18 RFS. Acquired late-2000.   6-01

BLETCHLEY PARK south of the A5, near Milton Keynes
Bletchley Park Museum: The mansion and its surroundings are embedded in military history as the
home of the 'code breakers' and as well as many other exhibits, there is a fascinating Cryptology
Museum among many other 'themes'.
- ◆ Off the B4034. Open weekends 10.30am to 5pm (last admission 3.30pm). ✉ The Mansion,
Bletchley Park, MK3 6EB ☎ 01908 640404 web www.bletchleypark.org.uk

Buckinghamshire Aircraft Recovery Group (c/o The Mansion as above, web www.bargbp.com)
have a large collection of aviation memorabilia on display. BARG's collection includes uniforms, flying
equipment, engines and other items from 'digs'. Sea Vixen FAW.2 cockpit XN651 moved to Lavendon,
Bucks, and Jet Provost T.4 cockpit XS181 to North Weald, Essex, in September 2001.

HALTON AIRFIELD on the A4011, north of Wendover
RAF Halton: 'JP' XS215 is used by the Airman's Command School and is fitted with the wings of
XS218 ①. The Bulldog is with **2409 Squadron ATC** (Herts and Bucks Wing ATC) ②.
- ❏ ETE*   Fauvel AV.36C   BGA.2932, ex RAFGSA.53, D-5353, D-8259.
     CoA 6-98. Stored.   1-02
- ❏ XF527   Hunter F.6   8680M, ex 1 SoTT, Laarbruch SF, 4 FTS, CFE,
     19, Church Fenton SF, Linton SF. Gate.   3-02
- ❏ XR672   '50' Jet Provost T.4   8495M, ex SoRF, 6 FTS, CAW, CATCS,
     3 FTS, 1 FTS. Fuselage in use as horse jump.   3-02
- ❏ [XS215]   '17' Jet Provost T.4   8507M, ex CAW. Fuselage. GIA.   ①   3-02
- ❏ XV408   'Z' Phantom FGR.2   9165M, ex Cranwell, Wattisham, 92, 29, 23,
     228 OCU. In main camp, displayed.   2-02
- ❏ XX665*   Bulldog T.1   9289M, ex Newton, E Lowlands UAS, Abn UAS,
     E Lowlands UAS. Cr 20-9-97. Fuselage. F/n 11-00.   ②   6-01

HIGH WYCOMBE or Walter's Ash, north-west of Naphill, north of the town
Spitfire V EF545 has moved on to a private owner in 'Sussex'. The two Mk.XIVs remain.
- ❏ RM694   Spitfire XIV   ex USA, Bitteswell, Southend, Henlow, Charnock
     Richard, Hoylake, Dishforth, Bicester, Hornchurch,
     Locking 6640M, CFE, 402, 91. Stored.   1-02
- ❏ RM927   Spitfire XIV   ex USA, Southend, Charnock Richard, Ostend,
     Belg AF SG-25, RAF, 29 MU, 403. Stored.   1-02

IVER HEATH on the A412 west of Uxbridge
Pinewood Studios: Various second-hand reports are to hand as to airframe 'props' in use on the film
set. Sightings in late 2000 included a Cessna 172, Hawker Hunter, a badly hacked about JetRanger and
the rear end (at least) of a Lancaster. This is almost certainly the tail section of KB976 (G-BCOH) last

known to have been in the grounds of a house at Crowland, Lincs. A visit during the summer of 2001 found only a JetRanger on scaffolding poles, but nothing else. (See also Leavesden, Herts.)

Much more substantial – in every way – was the arrival on 18th December 2001 of Mil Mi-9 *Hip-G* 93+97 (407) from Cottbus, Germany. For use in the 'pre-titles' sequence in the latest 'James Bond' spectacular – the 20th no less. (Does that count the spoof one with David Niven in the lead role?) It was painted in 'North Korean' colours and then blown up as part of the filming during January 2002 and was moved out by a scrappy from the Bicester/Aylesbury area the following month.

On 13th March 2002 the forward fuselage of a TriStar arrived 'on set', also for the 'Bond' epic. Given the 'utility' of such 'props', it may well have a live after the film, so is listed formally.

❏ TF-ABP*	TriStar	ex Bruntingthorpe, Air Atlanta Icelandic, VR-HOG Cathay Pacific, LTU, Eastern N323EA. Forward fuselage, arrived 13-3-02.	3-02

LAVENDON on the A428 west of Bedford
Tony and **Nick Collins**: The collection continues to flourish!

❏ WT319*	Canberra B(I).6	ex Castle Carey, ?, Filton, Samlesbury, 213, Laarbruch SF, 213. Nose.	3-02
❏ WT684*	Hunter F.1	ex Doncaster, Firbeck, Long Marston, Brize Norton, Halton 7422M, 229 OCU, DFLS. Nose.	3-02
❏ XN651*	Sea Vixen FAW.2	ex Bletchley Park, Bristol, Culdrose A2616, SAH, 766, FAW.1, 893. Nose.	8-01
❏ XP642*	Jet Provost T.4	ex Luton, Bruntingthorpe, Nottingham, Finchampstead Ridges, Lasham, Shawbury, 2 FTS, CFS. Nose.	3-02
❏ XS898	'BD' Lightning F.6	ex Bruntingthorpe, Cranfield, Binbrook, 11, 5. Nose.	3-02

NEWPORT PAGNELL on the B526 north of Milton Keynes
Peter R Arnold: Continues to work on his Seafire and Spitfire projects.

❏ EN224	Spitfire XII	G-FXII, ex Cranfield, 595, 41.	®	3-02
❏ LA564	Seafire F.46	ex Redbourn, Newark, Southend, Charnock Richard, Carlisle, Anthorn, 738, 767, A&AEE.	®	3-02

TWYFORD east of Bicester
Peter Wood: Seafire XVII SX336 moved by mid-2001 to Cranfield, Beds.The forward cockpit section of Chipmunk T.10 WZ876 moved to Yateley, Hants.

❏ AD540	Spitfire V	ex Dumfries, Carsphairn, 242, 122. *Blue Peter*. Crashed 23-5-42. Stored.		3-02
❏ WB763	Chipmunk T.10	G-BBMR, ex Camberley, Feltham, Southall, 2 FTS, 4 FTS, AOTS, 1 ITS, 1 AEF, Bri UAS, 3 AEF, AAC, 652, Odiham SF, 24 RFS, 14 RFS.	®	6-01
❏ WK620	'T' Chipmunk T.10	ex Tattershall Thorpe, Middle Wallop, BFWF, Hull UAS, Mcr UAS, QUAS, Bri UAS, 22 RFS. Damaged 19-5-93. Stored.		6-01

WOBURN SANDS on the A5130 east of Milton Keynes
David Underwood: Still has the oldest surviving Slingsby, Kite I AAF.

❏	AAF T.6 Kite I	ex Dunstable, G-ALUD, BGA.236, BGA.222. Stored.	6-01

WYCOMBE AIR PARK or Booker, on the B482 south-west of High Wycombe
Personal Plane Services (PPS) / **Antique Aero Engines**: Several airframes are being restored or stored for US collector Kermit Weeks (KW). Spitfire IX PL344 (G-IXCC) made its first flight on 17th October 2000 and exported to the USA in June 2001 as N644TB. Sheringham Aviation's Spitfire Ia AR213 has begun a full restoration by PPS ①. The Travelair 2000 is bedecked as a Fokker D.VIII ②. Fiat G.46-3B G-BBII flew again during 2001 and settled upon Sandown, IoW, on 11th May 2001.
◆ Visits possible *only* via prior arrangement.

❏ G-AWXZ	SNCAN SV-4C ✈	ex F-BHMZ, Fr mil No 360, F-BCOI. Dismantled.		11-01
❏ G-AZTR	SNCAN SV-4C	ex F-BDEQ. CoA 15-7-94. Dismantled.		6-01
❏ [G-BAAF]	MF.1 REP ✈	Manning-Flanders monoplane, Blériot-like, PPS-built.		6-01
❏ [G-BPVE]	Blériot XI REP	ex N1197.		6-01
❏ [G-BTZE]	Yak C-11	ex Egypt (?), OK-JIK. Last flown 12-6-76. Stored.		6-01
❏ 'B2458' 'R'	Camel REP ✈	G-BPOB, ex N8997, Tallmantz Av.		11-01
❏ AR213 'PR-D'	Spitfire Ia ✈	G-AIST, ex Patrick Lindsay, Old Warden, *Battle of Britain*, 8 MU, 53 OTU, 57 OTU. 609 Sqn c/s. CoA 6-9-00.	①	3-02
❏ EJ693	Tempest V	N7027E, ex Norfolk (?), USA, Chichester, Henlow, Delft, 486. Crashed 1-10-44.	KW ®	6-01
❏ 'MS824'	MS 'N' REP ✈	G-AWBU, built by PPS.		6-01
❏ MV262	Spitfire XIV	G-CCVV, ex Winchester, Bitteswell, Blackbushe, Calcutta, Ind AF, ACSEA, 9 MU.	KW	3-02
❏ TE517	Spitfire IX	G-CCIX, ex Winchester, Nailsworth, G-BIXP ntu, Duxford, Israel, Israel DF/AF 2046, Czech AF, RAF TE517, 313. Stored.	KW	3-02
❏ '422/15'	Fokker E.III REP ✈	G-AVJO, built by PPS.		6-01
❏ '626/8'	Travel Air 2000	N6268, ex USA, NC6268. Crash scene.	②	7-96
❏ —	Pilatus P.2	fuselage. Film mock-up. Luftwaffe colours.		3-96
❏	Yak C-11	ex La Ferté Alais, Egypt AF. c/n 172623.	off-site	3-96
❏ — BAPC.103	Hulton hang-glider	built 1969.		3-96
❏ — BAPC.238	Ornithopter	built by PPS for *Young Sherlock Holmes*.		7-96

Parkhouse Aviation: The whole Lightning is in store pending display at Farnborough, Hants. During early 2001 it was briefly moved out to grace Jeremy Clarkson's garden for a series the man was doing on speed or some such similar wheeze. While the programme wasn't much to write home about, the lease fee fattened the appeal fund to have XM172 preserved ①.

❏ 'XF314'* 'N'	Hunter F.51	ex Sandown, Tangmere, Dunsfold, G-9-439, Danish AF E-412, Esk.724. 43 Sqn c/s. Arr by 6-00.		3-02
❏ XM144*	Lightning F.1A	ex Eaglescott, Burntwood, Leuchars 8417M, Leuchars TFF, 23 Leuchars TFF, 226 OCU, 74. Nose. 74 Sqn c/s. Arrived by 6-00.		3-02
❏ XM172 'B'	Lightning F.1A	ex Coltishall 8427M, 226 OCU, 56. Stored.	①	3-02
❏ 764*	MiG-21SPS	ex Bonn-Hangelar, East GermAF. Cockpit.		2-02

Others: The trailer-mounted Tomahawk fuselage is the *original* one, the aircraft still flies from here in 'transplanted' form ①.

❏ G-AWFZ*	Musketeer	ex N2811B. CoA 12-5-<u>94</u>. Stored.		5-01
❏ G-BSVF*	Warrior II	ex C-GVSJ, N9575N. Wreck. Stored.		2-01
❏ G-DYOU	Tomahawk 112	fuselage. Crashed 23-7-92.		11-01
❏ G-EORG	Tomahawk 112	fuselage, trailer-mounted.	①	9-96
❏ G-KUTU	Quickie Q.2	damaged 18-5-85. Stored.		11-01
❏ [G-RPEZ]	Rutan LongEz	incomplete, stored up hangar wall. F/n 3-00.		8-00
❏ T7230*	Tiger Moth	G-AFVE, ex 2 GU, 24 EFTS, 3 EFTS. Stored.		2-01
❏ T7404* '04'	Tiger Moth	G-ANMV, ex F-BHAZ, G-ANMV, T7404, 22 RFS, 2 RFS, 8 RFS, 8 EFTS, 10 FIS, 26 EFTS. Stored.		6-01

CAMBRIDGESHIRE

☞ Within the administrative county boundaries can be found the unitary authority of Peterborough.

ALCONBURY AIRFIELD north-west of Huntingdon at the A1/A604 junction
USAF Alconbury: A USAF enclave is still here. F-4N 153008 in use for ABDR is 'long gone'.

❏ '01532'	F-5E Tiger II	mock up, on 'outer' gate, 527 TFTAS c/s.	5-99
❏ 80-0219	GA-10A	ex 509th TFS, Bentwaters. Accident 4-4-89.	
	Thunderbolt II	'Inner' gate. 10th TFW, 509th TFS-511th TFS colours. *Phoenix.*	9-94

BASSINGBOURN on the A1198 north of Royston
Tower Museum and 91st Bomb Group (H) Museum: Run and maintained by the **East Anglian Aviation Society** (EAAS) the original tower is the basis for the long-established, but recently upgraded, museum dedicated to the history of the once resident 91st BG(H), 11 OTU, 231 OCU, the Army and others. Exhibits include parts and relics from aircraft that served here, plus a vast array of other artefacts, photographs and documents. EAAS share joint maintenance of the static 'Army' Canberra preserved within the camp – see below.
◆ Visits by prior appointment *only*, contact Steve Pena on ☎ / **fax** 01359 221151 **e-mail** AN6530 @aol.com, or Peter Roberts ☎ 01223 356314 **e-mail** prtnmga@aol.com or Ray Jude ☎ / **fax** 01799 527932 e-mail margaretjude@hotmail.com ✉ (Society details) Mike Killaspy, 3 Sainfoin Close, Sawston, Cambs, CB2 4JY

Army Training Regiment, Bassingbourn: WJ821 is kept inside the camp, EAAS (see above) help maintain it. **No.2484 Squadron Air Cadets** have a Canberra nose. 'Parent' is Wyton, Cambs.

❏ WJ821	Canberra PR.7	8668M, ex RAE Bedford, 13, 58, 82. Displayed.	3-02
❏ WK127	'FO' Canberra TT.18	8985M, ex Wyton, 100, 7, 10. Dam 13-12-88. Nose.	2-00

BOURN AERODROME on the A45 west of Cambridge
At Rotortech the 'spare' Bö 105 pod (c/n 915) was last noted December 1997 and is best deleted.

❏ G-AZLO	Cessna F.337F	ex Land's End. CoA 22-4-82. Poor state.	2-02
❏ G-BEKN	Cessna FRA.150M	ex Peterborough Sport. CoA 8-10-89. Stored.	2-02
❏ G-BEZS	Cessna FR.172J	ex Cranfield, Stapleford, I-CCAJ. Cr 15-6-79. Stored.	2-02
❏ G-BCJH	Mooney M.20F	ex N9549M. CoA 30-6-91. Engineless.	2-02

BRAMPTON on the A14/A141 south-west of Huntingdon
RAF Brampton / Defence Logistics Organisation: Is 'guarded' by a pristine Phantom.

❏ XT914	'Z' Phantom FGR.2	ex Leeming, 74, 56, 228 OCU, 92, 228 OCU, 56, 228 OCU, 14. 74 Sqn c/s. Gate.	7-01

CAMBRIDGE
Arbury College / Cambridge Regional College: In King Heges Road. It is thought that the instructional airframes at the college are unchanged. Gnat XP540 is on loan from Phoenix Aviation at Bruntingthorpe, Leics ①.

❏ G-XITD	Cessna 310G	ex Tattershall Thorpe, Leavesden, Denham, G-ASYV, HB-LBY, N8948Z. Accident 14-7-88.		2-97
❏ XN582	'95' Jet Provost T.3A	ex Cambridge Airport, Cosford 8957M, 7 FTS, 1 FTS, 3 FTS, RAFC.		3-97
❏ XP540	'62' Gnat T.1	ex Bruntingthorpe, Halton 8608M, 4 FTS.	①	1-02

Others: Volunteers from the Cambridge Strut of the PFA are working on a 'Flea' in the area.

❏ G-ADXS	HM.14 'Flea'	ex East Tilbury, Andrewsfield, Southend, Staverton, Southend. CoA 1-12-36.	®	7-96

CAMBRIDGE AIRPORT or Teversham, on the A1303 east of Cambridge
Former Air Gabon L.100-30 TR-LBV finally got rolling here – it had been parked on the airfield since
1996 – as G-52-53 on 26th October 2001, destined for the UAE Air Force as 1215.

❑ [N913PM]	TriStar 200	ex A40-TT Gulf Air. Arrived 15-5-98. Spares.	4-01
❑ WJ863	Canberra T.4	ex 231 OCU, 360, Akrotiri SF, 231 OCU,	
		Honington SF, Cottesmore SF. Nose.	12-99
❑ XV201	Hercules C.1K	ex 1312F, LTW. Stored.	2-02
❑ XV296	Hercules C.1K	ex 1312F, LTW. Stored.	2-02

COMBERTON on the B1046 west of J12 of the M11
No news on the Moth, it may be heading for LOST!

❑ G-AANO	DH.60GMW	ex Southampton, N590N, NC590N.	® 11-91

DUXFORD AERODROME south of Cambridge, Junction 10 M11
Imperial War Museum (IWM): The permanent Battle of Britain exhibition opened officially on 16th
June 2000. Centre-piece, in 'crashed' pose, is the former Bournemouth Bf 109, with the fully-restored
Hurricane and the Avro Rota flanking it. When operational conditions permit, the ARCo Blenheim and
the HAC's Spitfire V are also parked nearby. During mid-2000 IWM acquired the former OFMC CASA
2-111, filling a major 'hole' in its collecting policy. The fuselage has been at Duxford since March 1998,
the wings and engines arrived during October 2000.
  In September 2001 the IWM announced that it had been successful in getting another Heritage
Lottery Fund grant of £9 million to dramatically enlarge the 'Superhangar' and turn it into a gallery that
will tell the story of the UK aerospace industry. This will come under the quaint name of 'Air-Space'.
The entire project will cost £19.3 million and BAE Systems will be supporting it to the tune of £5
million. Within the new complex will be a conservation area. Completion is due in 2005.
  Notes: The 'Superhangar' is home to the 'British Aircraft Collection' – see above; while Hangar 4
contains the 'Air Defence Collection' of fighter types; Hangar 5 is the main restoration hangar; Hangars 2
and 3 continue their traditional role of housing the 'flyers' – see below. Because the aircraft inside the
American Air Museum are there on a long-term basis, they are listed separately from this edition –
see below. From the summer of 2001 and February 2002, Hurricane FSM 'R4115' and Cadet TX.3
XN239 were on loan to the museum at Cardiff, Wales – *qv* – ±.
  Departures: Firefly TT.1 Z2033 moved to Yeovilton, Somerset, on 25th July 2000. Restoration of
Bf 109G-2 10639 *Black-6* was completed and it moved to Hendon, Gtr Lon, on 10th March 2002. The
stripped airframe of Bolingbroke IVT 9893 is being incorporated in the static rebuild for the IWM by
ARCO and has been moved to their 'site' below.
◆ Open daily 10am to 6pm Apr to Oct and 10am to 4pm the remainder of the year. Last admission 45
  minutes before closing. Closed New Year's Day and Dec 24-26. On days other than special events
  two of the civil airliners are open to inspection free of charge, one of which is normally Concorde. A
  large SAE will bring a leaflet on special events, airshows etc. ✉ Imperial War Museum, Duxford
  Airfield, Cambs, CB2 4QR ☎ 01223 835000 fax 01223 837267 web www.iwm.org.uk

❑ [G-AFBS]	Magister I	ex Staverton, G-AKKU ntu, BB661,	
		G-AFBS. CoA 25-2-63.	® 2-00
❑ G-USUK	Colt 2500A	gondola. *Virgin Atlantic Flyer*.	4-01
❑ – G-9-185	Hunter F.6	ex Wroughton, South Kensington,	
		Kingston, Dutch AF N-250. Nose.	3-02
❑ E2581 '13'	Bristol F.2b	ex South Lambeth, 2 GCF, 30 TS,	
		HQ Flt SE Area, 1 CS	3-02
❑ F3556	RAF RE.8	ex Lambeth. *[A Paddy Bird from Ceylon]*	3-02
❑ N4877	Anson I	G-AMDA, ex Staverton, Derby AW, Watchfield	
		SF, 3 FP, ATA, 3 FPP. CoA 14-12-62.	® 3-02
❑ 'R4115'*	Hurricane FSM	BAPC.267, ex South Lambeth. Arrived by 10-00.	
'LE-X'		242 Sqn colours. For the 'gate'.	± 10-00
❑ V3388	Oxford I	G-AHTW, ex Staverton, BP, V3388. CoA 15-12-60.	3-02
❑ 'V9673''MA-J'	Lysander III	G-LIZY, ex RCAF 1558, V9300. 161 Sqn c/s.	3-02
❑ 'Z2315' 'JU-E'	Hurricane IIb	ex TFC, Russia. 111 Sqn colours.	3-02

☐	HM580		Cierva C.30A	G-ACUU, ex Staverton, HM580, 529,		
				1448 Flt, G-ACUU. CoA 30-4-60.		3-02
☐	KB889	'NA-I'	Lancaster X	G-LANC, ex Bitteswell, Blackbushe, RCAF		
				107 MRU, 428. 428 Sqn colours.		3-02
☐	LZ766		Proctor III	G-ALCK, ex Staverton, Tamworth,		
				HQBC, 21 EFTS. CoA 19-6-63.		3-02
☐	ML796		Sunderland	ex La Baule, Maisden-le-Riviere, Aéronavale,		
			MR.5	27F, 7FE, RAF 230, 4 OTU, 228.		3-02
☐	NF370		Swordfish III	ex South Lambeth, Stretton, RAF.	®	3-02
☐	TA719		Mosquito TT.35	ex Staverton, G-ASKC, Shawbury, 3/4 CAACU,		
				4 CAACU, Shawbury. Crashed 27-7-64.		3-02
☐	TG528		Hastings C.1A	ex Staverton, 24, 24-36, 242 OCU,		
				53-99 pool, 47. 24 Sqn colours.		3-02
☐	VN485		Spitfire F.24	ex Kai Tak 7326M, RHK Aux AF, 80.		3-02
☐	WH725		Canberra B.2	ex Wroughton, 50, 44. 50 Sqn colours.		3-02
☐	WJ945	'21'	Varsity T.1	G-BEDV, ex CFS, 5 FTS, AE&AEOS,		
				CFS, 115, 116, 527. CoA 15-10-87.		3-02
☐	WK991		Meteor F.8	ex Kemble, 7825M, 56, 46, 13 GCF, NSF.		3-02
☐	WM969	'10'	Sea Hawk FB.5	ex Culdrose, A2530, FRU, 806, 811, 898.		3-02
☐	WZ590	'19'	Vampire T.11	ex Woodford, Chester, St Athan,		
				8 FTS, 5 FTS, 228 OCU.		3-02
☐	XE627	'T'	Hunter F.6A	ex Brawdy, 1 TWU, TWU, 229 OCU, 1,		
				229 OCU, 54, 1, 54, Horsham St Faith SF,		
				54, 229 OCU, 92, 65. 65 colours.		3-02
☐	XF708	'C'	Shack' MR.3/3	ex Kemble, 203, 120, 201. 203 Sqn colours.		3-02
☐	XG613		Sea Ven FAW.21	ex Old Warden, RAE, A&AEE, RAE.		3-02
☐	XG797	'277'	Gannet ECM.6	ex Arbroath, 831, 700, 810. 849 Sqn c/s. 'Flook' logo.		3-02
☐	XH648		Victor B.1A(K2P)	ex 57, 55, Honington Wing, 15, 57. 57 Sqn c/s.		3-02
☐	XH897		Javelin FAW.9	ex A&AEE, 5, 33, 25.		3-02
☐	XJ824		Vulcan B.2	ex 101, 9-35, 9, 230 OCU, 27.		3-02
☐	XK936	'62'	W'wind HAS.7	ex Wroughton, 705, 847, 848, 701, 820, 845.		3-02
☐	XM135	'B'	Lightning F.1	ex Leconfield, Leuchars TFF, 226 OCU,		
				74, AFDS. 74 Squadron colours.		3-02
☐	XN239	'G'	Cadet TX.3	ex CGS 8889M.	±	2-00
☐	XP281		Auster AOP.9	ex AFWF, Middle Wallop. MoAF loan. Stored.		3-02
☐	XR222		TSR-2 XO-4	ex Cranfield, Weybridge. Unflown.		3-02
☐	XS567	'434'	Wasp HAS.1	ex Lee-o-S, 829 *Endurance* Flt.		3-02
☐	XS576	'125'	Sea Vixen FAW.2	ex Sydenham, 899, Brawdy. 899 Sqn colours.		3-02
☐	XS863	'304'	Wessex HAS.1	ex A&AEE. Royal Navy colours.		3-02
☐	XV865		Buccaneer S.2B	ex Coningsby 9226M, Lossiemouth, 208, 12,		
				237 OCU, 208, 12, 208, 237 OCU, FAA, 809, 736.		3-02
☐	XZ133	'10'	Harrier GR.3	ex South Lambeth, St Athan, 4, 1, 1417F, 233 OCU.		3-02
☐	ZA465*	'FF'	Tornado GR.1B	ex Lossiemouth, 12, 617, 17, 16. Arrived 25-10-01.		3-02
☐	*		Hunter	cockpit, kids' play area. Likely ex-procedure trainer.		7-01
☐			Typhoon	ex South Lambeth. Cockpit.		3-02
☐	A-549		FMA Pucará	ex ZD487 ntu, ex Boscombe Down,		
				Yeovilton, Stanley, FAA.		3-02
☐	18393		CF-100 Mk IVB	G-BCYK, ex Cranfield, RCAF, 440, 419, 409.		3-02
☐	3794		MiG-15 (S-102)	ex Czech AF. Stored.		7-97
☐	57	'8-MT'	Mystère I VA	ex Sculthorpe, FAF 8 Esc, 321 GI, 5 Esc.		3-02
☐	1190		Bf 109E-3	ex Bournemouth, Buckfastleigh, Canada, USA,		
				Canada, *White-4* of II/JG.26. Crashed 30-9-40.		3-02
☐	100143		Fa 330A-1	ex Farnborough.		11-97
☐	191660	'3'	Me 163B-1	ex South Lambeth, Cranwell, 6 MU,		
				RAE, AM.214. Stored.		3-02
☐	—	'CF+HF'	MS.502	EI-AUY, ex USA, F-BCDG, ALAT.		3-02
☐	—	'4V+GH'	Amiot AAC.1	ex Port AF 6316. Luftwaffe c/s.		3-02

❑	– BAPC.93	Fi 103 (V-1)	ex Cosford. Inside.	3-02
❑	96+21	Mi-24D *Hind*	ex Basepohl, WGAF HFS-80, LSK KHG-5 406.	3-02
❑	501	MiG-21PF	ex St Athan, Farnborough, Hungarian AF.	3-02
❑	3685	A6M3 Model 22	ex Boise, USA, Taroa, Marshall Islands.	
	'Y2-176'	*Zeke*	Stored.	3-02
❑	B2I̱-27*	CASA 2-111	ex OFMC, Seville, Spanish AF. Stored.	3-02
❑	1133	Strikemaster 80	ex Warton, RSaudiAF, G-BESY, G-27-299.	3-02
❑	Fv 35075 '40'	J35A Draken	ex RSwAF F16.	3-02

American Air Museum: As noted above, because of the long-term nature of the exhibits in the award-winning building, it has been decided to list them separately. The AAM received three new airframes during 2001, the SR-71, F-105 and F-15. The SR-71 is destined to be installed within the building by mid-2002 with the F-105 and F-15 due to act as 'guardians'. Work continues on the B-24, also destined to be squeezed in! (All four marked ➡) In the period March to mid-August 2002 the AAM will be in a considerable state of flux as aircraft exhibits are relocated within and the new inmates installed.

❑	'S4513'	SPAD XIII REP	G-BFYO, ex 'S3398', Yeovilton, Land's End,	
	'1'		Chertsey, D-EOWM. CoA 21-6-82.	3-02
❑	14286	T-33A-1-LO	ex Sculthorpe, FAF CIFAS 328. USAF c/s.	3-02
❑	31171	B-25J-30-NC	N7614C, ex Shoreham, Dublin, Prestwick,	
		Mitchell	Luton, 44-31171. USMC PBJ-1J colours.	3-02
❑	42165	'VM' F-100D-11-NA	ex Sculthorpe, FAF *Esc* 2/11, *Esc* 1/3,	
		Super Sabre	USAF. 352nd TFS, 35th TFW colours.	3-02
❑	'46214'	'X-3' TBM-3E	ex CF-KCG, RCN 326, USN 69327.	
		Avenger	'Lt George Bush' titling. *Ginny.*	3-02
❑	60689	B-52D-40-BW	ex 7 BW Carswell and others, USAF.	3-02
❑	66692	U-2CT-LO	ex Alconbury, 5 SRTS/9 SRW, Beale.	3-02
❑	155529	'114' F-4J(UK)	ZE359, ex Wattisham, 74, USN 155529.	
		Phantom II	USN VF-74, *America* colours.	3-02
❑	'217786'	'25' PT-17 Kaydet	ex Swanton Morley, Duxford, CF-EQS,	
			Evergreen, New Brunswick, Canada, 41-8169.	3-02
❑	'226413'	P-47D-30-RA	N47DD, ex USA, Peru AF FAP 119,	
	'UN-Z'	Thunderbolt	USAAF 45-49192. 56th FG colours,	
			Zemke's a/c. *Oregon's Britannia.*	3-02
❑	'231983'	B-17G-95-DL	ex IGN F-BDRS, N68269, 44-83735.	
	'IY-G'	Flying Fortress	401st BG colours. *Mary Alice.*	3-02
❑	251457	B-24D-5-FO	ex NASM. *Fightin' Sam.* Nose section.	3-02
❑	252983	Schweizer TG-3A	ex N66630.	3-02
❑	315509	C-47A-85-DL	G-BHUB, ex Aces High G-BHUB, *Airline* :	
	'W7-S'	Skytrain	'G-AGIV', 'FD988' and 'KG418', Spanish AF	
			T3-29, N51V, N9985F, SAS SE-BBH, 43-15509.	3-02
❑	'450493'*	B-24M-25-FO	44-51228, ex Lackland, EZB-24M.	
		Liberator	*Dugan.* ® ➡	3-02
❑	461748	'Y' TB-29A-45-BN	G-BHDK, ex China Lake, 307th BG, Okinawa.	
		Superfortress	*It's Hawg Wild* (stb). 307th BG colours.	3-02
❑	'463209'	'WZ-S' P-51D FSM	BAPC.255, ex OFMC, London. 78th FG colours.	3-02
❑	–	Harvard IIB	ex North Weald, Amsterdam, Dutch AF B-168,	
			FE984, RCAF, 2 FIS, 42-12471.	3-02
❑	48-0242	'242' F-86A-5-NA	N196B, ex Chino, 48-0242.	3-02
❑	59-1822*	F-105D-6-RE	ex AMARC Davis-Monthan, Virg ANG	
			192nd TFG, 23rd, 355th, 388th, 18th, 23rd,	
			355th,TFWs, 4520 CCTW. Arr 4-01. ® ➡	3-02
❑	64-17962*	SR-71A	ex Palmdale, 9th SRW. Arrived 5-4-01.	
			Unveiled 11-4-01 and handed-over 14-6-01. ➡	3-02
❑	67-0120	F-111E-CF	ex Upper Heyford, 20th TFW. *The Chief.*	3-02
❑	72-1447	F-111F-CF	escape module.	3-02
❑	72-21605	UH-1H 'Huey'	ex Coleman Barracks, ATCOM.	3-02

❑ 76-0020*	F-15A-15-MC	ex AMARC Davis-Monthan, Mass ANG 102nd FIW,5th FIS, 33rd TFW, 36th TFW. Arrived 4-01, unveiled 22-1-02.	➠	3-02
❑ 77-0259 'AR'	A-10A Thunderbolt II	ex Alconbury, 10th TFW, 11th TASG, 128th TFW.		3-02

Duxford Aviation Society (DAS) / **Friends of Duxford**: DAS were awarded a Heritage Lottery Fund grant of £314,500 in late 2000 to restore five of the airliners in its care (the Ambassador, York, Concorde, Comet and Hermes), to allow for more displays and better access for those of restricted mobility. The airliner collection is their most 'high profile' presence, but without the many, many efforts put in by DAS crews on restoration projects, special events, vehicle displays, airshow days etc, the entire Duxford site would not function.
✉ Duxford Airfield, Duxford, Cambridge, CB2 4QR ☏ 01223 835594

❑ G-AGTO	J/1 Autocrat ✈	on loan.		3-02
❑ G-ALDG	Hermes 4	ex Gatwick, Silver City, Britavia, Airwork, BOAC. CoA 9-1-63. BOAC c/s, *Horsa*. Fuselage.		3-02
❑ G-ALFU	Dove 6	ex CAFU Stansted. CoA 4-6-71.		3-02
❑ G-ALWF	Viscount 701	ex Liverpool, Cambrian, BEIA, Channel, BEA. CoA 16-4-72. BEA colours, *Sir John Franklin*.		3-02
❑ G-ALZO	Ambassador 2	ex Lasham, Dan-Air, Handley Page, Jordan AF 108, BEA. CoA 14-5-72. *Christopher Marlowe*.	®	3-02
❑ G-ANTK	York C.1	ex Lasham, Dan-Air, MW232, Fairey, 511, 242. CoA 29-10-64. Dan-Air colours.	®	3-02
❑ G-AOVT	Britannia 312	ex Monarch, BEIA, BOAC. CoA 11-3-75. Monarch colours.		3-02
❑ G-APDB	Comet 4	ex Dan-Air, MSA 9M-AOB, BOAC G-APDB. CoA7-10-74. Dan-Air colours.		3-02
❑ G-APWJ	Herald 201	ex Norwich, Air UK, BIA, BUIA. CoA 21-12-85. Air UK colours.		3-02
❑ G-ASGC	Super VC-10	ex BA, BOAC. CoA 20-4-80. BOAC-Cunard c/s.		3-02
❑ G-AVFB	Trident 2E	ex BA, Cyprus 5B-DAC, BEA. CoA 30-9-82. BEA colours.		3-02
❑ G-AVMU	BAC 111-510ED	ex Bournemouth, BA, BEA. CoA 8-1-95. BA colours. County *of Dorset*.		3-02
❑ G-AXDN	Concorde 101	ex BAC/SNIAS. CoA 30-9-77.		3-02
❑ G-OPAS	Viscount 806	ex Southend, Parcelforce/BWA, BAF, BA, BEA G-AOYN. CoA 26-3-97. Nose.		3-00
❑ XB261	Beverley C.1	ex Southend, HAM, A&AEE. Cockpit.		3-02

Aircraft Restoration Company (ARCo) / **British Aerial Museum** (BAM) / **PropShop Ltd** (PSL): By April 2001 ARCo had moved into a new purpose-built restoration facility at the 'M11 end' of the aerodrome. This is shared in a co-operative arrangement with Historic Flying Ltd (HFL – see below). ARCo aircraft will continue to be listed under this heading, but long term restoration projects are now located in the new facility. Please note that the new building is *not* open to public inspection. PropShop have the contract to maintain the BBMF Chipmunks.

Vought FG-1D 92399 (G-CCMV) flew into Duxford on 21st November 2001 for operation by ARCo on behalf of the family of Paul Morgan (PM). Paul – half of the highly successful Northamptonshire-based Ilmor Engineering who make ultra-high performance engines for the motor racing industry – died when his Sea Fury FB.11 WH588 (G-EEMV) tipped over on landing at Northampton on 12th May 2001. Paul had developed a 'stable' of warbirds and is sadly missed in both the 'warbird' and motor racing worlds. The Corsair will be operated for at least the 2002 season and it may be that P-51D 4727773 (G-SUSY) will be similarly operated.

Notes: The recently reflown Tiger Moth includes the wings of G-ANFW ①. (The remainder of this aircraft went via Sudbury, Suffolk, to Malta.) The nose of Bolingbroke 9893 and other parts are being used in the static 'Blenheim' being built by ARCO for the IWM. Accordingly, 9893 has been moved from a listing with the IWM above to under this heading and the rebuild will take its identity for the purposes of this book ②. The MS.505 was re-engined with an Argus in-line by February 2001 for static scenes in the superb TV drama *Conspiracy* ③. As well as the Corsair mentioned above, ARCo maintains and operates a series of aircraft on behalf of their owners: Golden Apple Trust (GA); Historic Aircraft Collection of Jersey (HAC); Real Aviation (RA); Radial Revelations (RR — ie Martin Willing); and Transair UK (TR). Nord 1002 'KG+EM' (G-ETME) was flying again by mid-2000 and moved on to its new base at Wycombe Air Park, Bucks. (See under Sudbury, Suffok, for HAC's Yak-1 project and under St Leonards-on-Sea, East Sussex, for details of HAC's closely-related Aero Vintage.) The hulk of Spitfire Tr.IX PV202 which fatally crashed at Goodwood in April 2000 was acquired by ARCo and is now with HFL for restoration. It will be used in the 'warbird' training scheme pioneered by ARCo and HFL. Spares-ship Harvard IIB KF487 is thought to have been 'consumed' in various rebuild projects and has been deleted. ARCo's T-6G Texan 51-14526 (G-BRWB) was involved in a take-off accident at Duxford on 5th July 2001. It left for Shoreham, Sussex, on 21st September 2001.

❑ G-ASTG	Nord 1002	ex Sutton Bridge, F-BGKI, FAF No.183.		
		CoA 26-10-73. Stored.		3-02
❑ G-BZGK*	OV-10B ✈	ex Luftwaffe 99+32, D-9561, 158308. Arr 16-10-01.	RA	3-02
❑ G-BZGL*	OV-10B ✈	ex Luftwaffe 99+26, D-9555, 158302. Arr 13-9-01.	RA	3-02
❑ 'D8781'	Avro 504K REP✈	G-ECKE. Arrived by 4-00.		3-02
❑ 'R3821' 'UX-N'	Bolingbroke IVT ✈	G-BPIV, ex 'L8841', 'Z5722', Strathallan, Canada, RCAF 10201. *Spirit of Britain First.* 82 Squadron colours.		3-02
❑ R5136	Tiger Moth ✈	G-APAP, ex R5136, Sealand SF, 7 FTS, CFS, 16 EFTS, 54 OTU. First flew 8-4-01.	①	3-02
❑ 'V6028' 'GB-D'	Bolingbroke IVT	G-MKIV, ex G-BLHM ntu, RCAF 10038. Crashed 21-6-87. Spares for rebuild of 9893.		1-02
❑ 'Z7381'* XR-T '	Hurricane XII ✈	G-HURI, ex TFC, Coningsby, Coventry, Canada. 71 *Eagle* Sqn colours.	HAC	3-02
❑ BM597 'JH-C'	Spitfire Vb ✈	G-MKVB, ex Audley End, Fulbourne, Church Fenton, Linton-on-Ouse, Church Fenton, St Athan, 5713M, 58 OTU, 317.	HAC	3-02
❑ 'DE998' 'RCU-T'	Tiger Moth	ex Stamford, Hooton, Warmingham, 'K2572', Hereford, Lutterworth, Holme-on-Spalding Moor. Static restoration for IWM. Cam UAS c/s.	®	1-02
❑ WP929 'F'	Chipmunk T.10 ✈	G-BXCV, ex Shawbury, 8 AEF, Lpl UAS, Cam UAS, Wittering SF, RAFTTC, Coningsby SF, 61 GCF, 661.	PSL	3-02
❑ WV740*	Pembroke C.1 ✈	G-BNPH, ex 60, 21, WCS, MCCS, MC FU, BCCS, MCS, Eastleigh SF, Khormaksar SF, 84, APSF.	RR	3-02
❑ WZ879*	'73' Chipmunk T.10	G-BWUT, ex Newton, CFS, RAFC, CFS, 3 FTS, RAFC, CFS, 2 FTS, Benson SF, PFTS, AOTS, Wales UAS, AOTS, PFS, AOTS, 1 ITS, Leeds UAS, Nott UAS, RAFC, Marham Sf, BCCF, Marham SF, BCCF.	HAC	11-00
❑ XP772	Beaver AL.1	G-BUCJ, ex Middle Wallop, Beverley, Leconfield, Middle Wallop, 15 Flt, 667, 132 Flt, AFWF. Stored.		3-02
❑ XX543	Bulldog T.1	G-CBAB, ex Shawbury, York UAS, 6 FTS, York UAS, RNEFTS, CFS. *Donna.* Arrived 25-7-01.	PSL	1-02
❑ OJ4	Z-2 Strikemaster Mk.87 ✈	G-UNNY, ex G-AYHR, Botswana AF OJ4, Kenya AF 601, G-27-191, G-AYHR, G-27-191.	TR	3-02
❑ 3349	NA-64 Yale	G-BYNF, N55904, ex N55904, Canada, RCAF.	®	1-02
❑ 9893	Bolingbroke IVT	ex Canada. RCAF 'TT' stripes.	②	3-02
❑ '42161'	Silver Star Mk.3 ✈	G-TBRD, ex N33VC, Switzerland, G-JETT, G-OAHB, CF-IHB, CAF 133261, RCAF 21261. 'Official' first flight post restoration 4-4-01.	GA	3-02
❑ 119	T-28B Fennec ✈	N14113, ex USA, Haiti AF 1236, N14113, FAF (No.119), USAF 51-7545. *Little Rascal.*	RR	3-02

❑ –	'C' MS.505 ✈	G-BPHZ, ex F-BJQC, French mil. Luftwaffe c/s.	③ 3-02
❑ 1747	Harvard IV ✈	G-BGPB, ex '20385' North Weald, Port AF 1747, WGAF BF+050, AA+050, 53-4619. PortAF colours. *Taz.*	3-02
❑ 1108*	Strikemaster Mk.80	ex Humberside, RSaudiAF, G-27-27. Arrived 15-6-01.	TR ® 3-02
❑ A-125*	Pilatus P.2-05	G-BLKZ, ex Swiss AF U-125, A-125. Based since 1998. Reflown 3-1-02.	3-02
❑ 8178 'FU-178'	F-86A-5-NA ✈ Sabre	G-SABR, ex Bournemouth, N178, N68388, 48-0178. 4th FW colours.	GA 3-02
❑ '1164'	Beech 18 3TM ✈	G-BKGL, ex Prestwick, CF-QPD, RCAF 5193, RCAF 1564. USAAC colours.	3-02
❑ 92399*	'17' Vought FG-1D ✈	G-CCMV, ex USA, N448AG, N4717C, USN 92399. Arrived 21-11-01.	PM 3-02
❑ 474008* 'VF-R'	P-51D-25-NA ✈	G-SIRR, ex North Weald, N51RR, N151MC ntu, N76AF, N8676E, RCAF 9274, 44-74008. 4th FG colours. Arrived 6-7-01. Stored.	1-02

B-17 Preservation Ltd / B-17 Charitable Trust: *Sally B* took to the air again on 25th May 2000, the first time since her return from Guernsey. The 'first' flight was used to mark the launch of the B-17 Charitable Trust. On that day the IWM presented a cheque for £20,000 to get the ball rolling. *Sally B's* future flight programme will be essentially restricted to Duxford displays, plus memorial flypasts and selected airshow participation. The B-17 has permanent space indoors in the northern 'T2' hangar via the IWM's commitment to the Charitable Trust. From July 2001 *FlyPast* magazine was proud to support the operation of *Sally B* and its logos are carried subtly on the nose. On 19th October 2001 Boeing issued Airworthiness Directive 2001-22-06 which grounded the world's B-17 fleet for inspection of the wing spar chords. This was a major blow to the team but – with the help of an inspection procedure agreed with the CAA – work started in January and was completed on 7th March 2002. It is thought that *Sally B* beat the US-based B-17s in getting back into the air! ✉ PO Box 92, Bury St Edmunds, Suffolk ☎ 01638 721304 **fax** 01638 720506 **e-mail** sallyb@B-17preservation.demon.co.uk **web** www.deltaweb.co.uk/sallyb Lifeblood of the operation is the *Sally B* **Supporters' Club** – membership details from the contacts above. The club holds a variety of exclusive events and publishes the excellent *Sally B News.*

| ❑ '124485' 'DF-A' | B-17G-105-VE ✈ Flying Fortress | G-BEDF, ex N17TE, IGN F-BGSR, 44-85784. *Sally B* (port), *Memphis Belle* (stb). | 3-02 |

The Fighter Collection (TFC): A double tragedy occurred at the Biggin Hill airshow on 2nd/3rd June 2001. On the 2nd, DHA's Vampire T.55 crashed while displaying, killing two (see under Bournemouth, Dorset, for details). On the following day, former 'Red Arrows' pilot Guy Bancroft-Wilson died when P-63A 269097 (G-BTWR) crashed while displaying. (In France on the 4th, Martin Sergeant perished in Spitfire PR.XI PL983 (G-PRXI) while attempting a forced-landing following engine problems during a display.) A poignant 'missing man' formation was flown at Duxford in salute to all of these flyers in July.
As outlined in *W&R17*, Hurricane XII 'Z7381' (G-HURI) was exchanged for the HAC Nimrod I at the end of the 2000 'season'. G-HURI is now based with ARCo, see above. During mid-2000 TFC announced that it was disposing of several aircraft not central to its collecting policy.
Notes: TFC's composite 'P-51B' is an interesting shape to see on the show circuit. A heavily-modified former Israeli AF/DF P-51D fuselage, it is fitted with the wings of a P-51B, also found in Israel. This aircraft returned to the USA in late 1998 for remedial work to be carried out on the airframe. It returned from the USA on 7th January 2000, ready for flight testing ①. During 2001 several aircraft were announced as available for sale, these are marked ➪.
Departures: Spitfire IX ML417 (G-BJSG) was exported to the USA during October 2001, becoming N2TF.
◆ Hangar open to the public during normal museum hours. TFC stages the annual 'Flying Legends' airshow and operate **Friends of the Fighter Collection** as a support group. ✉ c/o IWM, Duxford Airfield, Duxford, Cambs, CB2 4QR

| ❑ G-AKAZ '57-H' | L-4A-PI ✈ | ex F-BFYL, ALAT, 42-36375. USAAF c/s. | 3-02 |
| ❑ G-AWAH | Baron D55 ✈ | 'hack'. | 3-02 |

❑ G-AYGE		SNCAN SV-4C	ex F-BCGM. CoA 8-5-97. Stored.	3-02
❑ —	'F'	FM-2 Wildcat ✈	G-RUMW, ex USA N4845V, 86711. FAA colours.	3-02
❑ N88972		B-25D-30-ND	G-BYDR, N88972, ex CF-OGQ, KL161 5 OTU	
	'VO-B' ✈		(RCAF), 43-3318. *Grumpy* (port). 98 Sqn c/s.	⇨ 3-02
❑ 'D8084'	'S'	Bristol F.2b ✈	G-ACAA, ex Hatch, Weston-on-the-Green.	
			139 Sqn colours.	3-02
❑ N5903		Gladiator II	G-GLAD, ex Yeovilton, 'N2276',	
			'N5226', Old Warden, 61 OTU.	® 3-02
❑ S1581*	'573'	Nimrod I ✈	G-BWWK, ex St Leonards-on-Sea, St Just,	
			Henlow, ?, 802. First flown 11-7-00. Arr 7-00.	3-02
❑ EP120		Spitfire V ✈	G-LFVB, ex Audley End, Duxford, St Athan	
	'AE-A'		8070M, Wattisham, Boulmer, Wilmslow,	
			St Athan, 5377M, 53 OTU, 402, 501.	
			City of Winnipeg (pt), 402 Sqn c/s.	3-02
❑ FE695	'94'	Harvard IIB ✈	G-BTXI, ex Vasteras, RSwAF Fv16105,	
			RCAF, 6 SFTS, RAF FE695, 42-892.	® 3-02
❑ 'KD345'		FG-1D Corsair	G-FGID, ex N8297, N9154Z, USN 88297.	
	'A-130' ✈		1850 Sqn, SEAC colours.	3-02
❑ KZ321		Hurricane IV	G-HURY, ex Biggin Hill, Bitteswell,	
			Blackbushe, Israel, Yugoslav AF, RAF.	off-site ® 1-02
❑ 'MV268'		Spitfire XIV ✈	G-SPIT, ex Sleaford, Blackbushe, G-BGHB ntu,	
	'JE-J'		Bangalore, Indian inst T20, Indian AF, MV293	
			ACSEA. 'Johnnie' Johnson colours by 4-01.	3-02
❑ PK624		Spitfire F.22	ex St Athan, Abingdon 8072M, Northolt,	
			Uxbridge, North Weald, 'WP916', 9 MU, 614.	® 3-02
❑ TV959		Mosquito T.3	ex Hounslow, Lambeth, Bicester, 3 CAACU,	
	'AF-V'		HCEU, 228 OCU, 13 OTU. Stored.	off-site 1-02
❑ VX653		Sea Fury FB.11	G-BUCM, ex Hendon, Yeovilton, Lee-on-Solent,	
			Lossiemouth, FRU, 811, 738, 736.	® 3-02
❑ 'A19-144'		Beaufighter Mk.21	ex Melbourne, Sydney, RAAF A8-324.	® 3-02
❑ —	'LG+01'	Bü 133C ✈	G-AYSJ, ex D-EHVP, G-AYSJ, HB-MIW,	
			Swiss AF U-91. Luftwaffe colours.	⇨ 3-02
❑		Ki-43 Hyabusa	ex Australia. Stored.	1-02
❑ '20'		Lavochkin La-11	ex Monino, CIS, USSR. Stored	1-02
❑ '69'		Yak-50 ✈	G-BTZB, ex USSR.	11-99
❑ —		Spitfire IX ✈	ex CIS, USSR, RK858 no RAF service. Stored.	1-02
❑ —*		P-40	ex USSR. Substantial remains. Stored.	1-02
❑ —		Yak-3U	G-BTHD, ex Russia, Duxford, LET-built C-11	
			La Ferté Alais, Egyptian AF 533.	3-02
❑ '40467'	'19'	F6F-5K Hellcat	G-BTCC, ex N10CN ntu, N100TF, Yankee Air	
	✈		Corps, N80142, USMC Museum, 80141.	3-02
❑ 80425		F7F-3P Tigercat	G-RUMT, N7235C, ex Chino, Butler,	
	'WT-4' ✈		USN 80425. VMP-254 colours.	3-02
❑ 21714	'201'	F8F-2P Bearcat	G-RUMM, ex NX700HL, N1YY, N4995V, 121714.	
	✈		VF-20 c/s, Lt/Cdr 'Whiff' Caldwell's a/c.	3-02
❑ 126922		AD-4NA	G-RAID, ex F-AZED, La Ferté Alais, Gabon AF,	
	'AK-402'	Skyraider ✈	FAF No.42, USN 126922. VA-176, *Intrepid* c/s.	⇨ 3-02
❑ 219993		P-39Q-5-BE	N139DP, ex Santa Monica, Australia, New Zealand,	
			New Guinea, 82nd TRS '71st TRG. *Brooklyn Bum*.	3-02
❑ '226671'		P-47D/N ✈	G-THUN, ex NX47DD, 45-49192. 'MX-X',	
	'MX-X'		*No Guts, No Glory*. 78th FG c/s.	
❑ '2106449'		P-51C	G-PSIC, ex N51PR, Chino. Composite.	
			Princess Elizabeth, 352nd FG c/s.	① 3-02
❑ —	'49'	P-40M-10-CU ✈	G-KITT, ex 'P8196', F-AZPJ, Duxford	
			N1009N, 'FR870', N1233N, RCAF 840,	
			43-5802. 343rd FG colours.	3-02

Historic Flying Ltd (HFL): During mid-April HFL started relocating to Duxford into a purpose-built workshop/hangar at the M11 end of the complex. This is shared with ARCo (see above). Only aircraft operated, or being restored by, HFL are given here. Tr.IX PV202 is being restored for ARCo. As *W&R* closed for press, the first flight of Mk.XIV RN201 was imminent. Painted in the same colours as Mk.XVI TD248, there are plans to operate the two on the airshow circuit as the 'Silver Duo'. Mk.XVI TD248, the Harvard and Chipmunk WB569 are the personal mounts of HFL's owner, Karel Bos. (See also under Flixton, Suffolk for 'another' TD248.)
◆ *Not* available to public inspection.

❑ FE992	'K-T'	Harvard IIB ✈	G-BDAM, ex North Weald, LN-MAA, Fv16047, FE992, 42-12479. 5 PAFU colours.		3-02
❑ MK912*	'SH-L'	Spitfire IX ✈	G-BRRA, ex Audley End, Paddock Wood, Ludham, Saffraanberg, Belgian AF SM-29, RNeth AF H-59, H-119, RAF MK912, 84 GSU, 312. Arrived 8-9-00.		3-02
❑ PV202*		Spitfire Tr.IX	G-TRIX, ex Goodwood, G-BHGH ntu, IAAC 161, G-15-174, PV202, 412, 33. Crashed 8-4-00. Arrived 28-2-01.	®	3-02
❑ RN201*		Spitfire XIV	G-BSKP, ex Audley End, Sandown, Audley End, Duxford, Paddock Wood, Audley End, Ludham, Beauvechain 'SG-3', Belg AF SG-31, RAF, 350, 83 GSU, RN201. F/n 4-01.41 Sqn 'racing' colours.		3-02
❑ TD248*	'D'	Spitfire XVI ✈	G-OXVI, ex Audley End, Braintree, Earls Colne, Sealand, Hooton Park 7246M, 610, 2 CAACU, 695. 41 Sqn 'racing' colours.		3-02
❑ SM845*		Spitfire XVIII ✈	G-BUOS, ex Audley End, Witney, USA, Ind AF HS687, SM845. Arrived 7-7-00.		3-02
❑ WB569*		Chipmunk T.10 ✈	G-BYSJ, ex SE-BON, WB569, 1 AEF, Camb UAS, Ox UAS, South Cerney SF, RAFTC CF, 4 SoTT, 22 GCF, 2 SoTT, 22 RFS, Cam UAS, 22 RFS.		
❑ WK522*		Chipmunk T.10	G-BCOU, ex Audley End, Abn AUS, Lpl UAS, Man UAS, Gla UAS, Stn UAS, Bri UAS, 3 RFS, 5 BFTS. Thunderbird 5. CoA 30-3-95. Arrived 30-5-01. Stored.		5-01

Old Flying Machine Company (OFMC) / **Classic Aviation** (CA): At the end of 2001 it was announced that sponsorship for the excellent Breitling Fighters Team would continue, the team appearing in new colours for 2002. Aircraft in BFT colours are marked ß below. In mid-2000 it was announced that OFMC had elected Pioneer Aero Restorations of New Zealand to restore Lavochkin La-9 G-BWUD. It is hoped to have it flying in New Zealand by mid-2002. To this end it was cancelled from the UK civil register on 11th August 2000 and as such appears as an 'export' in Appendix B. It left Duxford on 11th August. Hunter T.8C G-BWGL wears the markings of the prototype Hunter T.7, XJ615 ①. Note that OFMC have a store of jets at Scampton, Lincs – *qv*.
   Departures: Hunter T.7 XL587 (G-HPUX) to Scampton, Lincs, 13-12-00; Dewoitine D.26 '290' (F-AZJD) returned to France 8-01; MiG-21SPS 959 to Coventry, Warks, on 25-6-01; SBLim-2A 6247 (G-OMIG) was sold in Brazil and was freighted out via Tilbury Docks, Essex, 20-11-00; SBLim-5 (MiG-17) 1211 (G-BWUF) moved to Bournemouth, Dorset, 20-2-02; Hunter F.58 J-4090 (G-SIAL) to Scampton, Lincs, 13-12-00. During mid-2000 CASA 2-111 B2I-27 was acquired by the IWM and is now listed under their heading.
◆ Aircraft on show to the public during normal museum hours. OFMC run **The Tiger Squadron**, a support group for their activities which includes the production of a bi-annual newsletter *Tiger Tales*. ✉ The Tiger Squadron, The Old Flying Machine Co, Duxford Airfield, Duxford, Cambs, CB2 4QR web www.ofmc.co.uk

❑ G-BTGA*	PT-17 Kaydet ✈	ex N65501, 41-25625. Arrived 4-01.	4-01
❑ G-BWFM	Yak-50 ✈	ex NX5224R, DDR-WQX, DM-WQX.	11-99
❑ LN-AMY	AT-6D Texan ✈	ex Norway, LN-LCS ntu, LN-LCN ntu, N10595, 42-85068. RAF SEAC c/s. *Amy*.	ß 3-02

❏ MH434		Spitfire IX ✈	G-ASJV, ex Booker, COGEA Nouvelle OO-ARA, Belgian AF SM-41, Fokker B-13, Netherlands H-68, H-105 322, MH434, 349, 84 GSU, 222, 350, 222.	ß	3-02
❏ XF375	'05'	Hunter F.6A	G-BUEZ, ex Cranwell, 8736M, ETPS, Warton, AWA, C(A). Stored.		3-02
❏ 'XJ615'*		Hunter T.8C ✈	G-BWGL, ex Exeter, XF357, Shawbury, Yeovilton, FRADU, 130. Arrived 29-5-00.	①	3-02
❏ XV474	'T'	Phantom FGR.2	ex Wattisham, 74, 56, 23, 56, 23, 19, 2, 31, 17. 74 Sqn colours.		3-02
❏ 517692		T-28A Fennec	G-TROY, ex F-AZFR, AdA Fennec No.142, 51-7692. EALA 09/72 c/s.		3-02
❏ 316	'315-SN'	Broussard	F-GGKR.		11-99
❏		A6M *Zeke*	ex Russia (?), USA, Pacific. Stored.		7-98
❏ NZ3009		P-40E-CU ✈ Kittyhawk	ZK-RMH, ex MoTaT Auckland, RNZAF NZ3009, RAF ET482, no service.	ß	3-02
❏ NZ5648		FG-1D Corsair ✈	G-BXUL, ex NX55JP, TFC. Bournemouth, Biggin Hill, USA, Canada, MoTaT Auckland, NZ, RNZAF NZ5648, Bu88391. RNZAF c/s.	ß	3-02
❏	G-BWOE	Yak-3U	ex Russia, G-BUXZ ntu, Duxford, LET-built C-11 N11SN, La Ferté Alais, Egyptian AF.	®	4-01
❏ '111'		L39ZO Albatros ✈	G-OTAF, ex '2802' Breighton, North Weald, N40VC, N159JC, N4312X ntu, Chad, Libyan AF 3227. Soviet colours.	ß	3-02
❏ E3B-153		CASA 1-131E ✈	G-BPTS, ex Spanish AF.		2-98
❏ '463221' 'E2-Z'		P-51D-25-NA ✈	G-BTCD, ex TFC, N51JJ, N6340T, RCAF 9568, USAAF 44-73149. 361st FG c/s.	ß	4-01

Others: A series of aircraft are also resident. Owner/operator decodes are follows: Carolyn Grace (CG); Classic Wings (CW); James Maskell and friends (JM); Mark Miller and friends (MM); Gary Numan (GN). Chipmunk T.10 WK624 (G-BWHI) flew off to Chester, Wales, during early 2000. PBY-5A N423RS was delivered to Lee-on-Solent, Hants, on 10th November 2001. Harvard IIB FE992 (G-BDAM) was acquired by HFL and has moved 'up' the list accordingly.

❏ G-ACMN*	Leopard Moth ✈	ex X9381, 9GCF, Netheravon SF, 297, 7 AACU, 6 AACU, 24, G-ACMN.	CG	3-02
❏ G-AGJG	Dragon Rapide	ex X7344, 1 Cam Flt. CoA 15-5-74.	® MM	3-02
❏ G-AIYR	Dragon Rapide ✈	ex HG691, Yatesbury SF. *Classic Lady*.	CW	3-02
❏ G-APAO	Tiger Moth ✈	ex R4922, 6 FTS, 7 EFTS.	CW	3-02
❏ G-AVGG	Cherokee 140	ex Leeds-Bradford. Crashed 10-8-70. Hulk.		2-00
❏ G-AZSC '43-SC'	Harvard IIB ✈	ex North Weald, PH-SKK, Dutch AF B-19, FT323, 43-13064.	GN	11-01
❏ ML407 'OU-V'	Spitfire Tr IX ✈	G-LFIX, ex Audley End, Goodwood, St Merryn, Strathallan, IAAC 162, G-15-175, ML407, 29 MU, 332, 485, 349, 341, 485. *Aon*. 485 Sqn colours.	CG	3-02
❏ XH328*	Vampire T.11	ex Bournemouth, Cranfield, Hemel Hempstead, Croxley Green, Bushey, Keevil, Exeter, 3 CAACU, 60. Arrived 1-00.	® JM	3-02

ELY on the A10 north-east of Cambridge
William Collins: Took delivery of an Andover fuselage from Bruntingthorpe, Leics, in July 2000.

❏ XS791*	Andover CC.2	ex Bruntingthorpe, Northolt, 32, 60, FEAF VIP Flt, 48, FECS, MECS, Abingdon SF. Fuse. Arr 22-7-00.	7-00

No.1094 Squadron, ATC: Located at the former RAF Hospital. Took on a 'Chippax' in May 2001.

❏ WG362*	Chipmunk T.10 PAX	8630M/8437M, ex Newton, Swinderby, Filton, Bir UAS, Wales UAS, Ox UAS, Swanton Morley SF, Carlisle SF, Mildenhall CF, 100, Edn UAS, 3 BFTS, 16 RFS, 3 BFTS, 7 RFS. Arr 5-01.	3-02

EVERSDEN on the A603 west of Cambridge
Last noted in April 1995, Emeraude G-BIVF was to be found at Northampton, Northants, by November 2001, ready to take to the air again. This listing is now long-in-the-tooth.

❏ G-ADJJ	Tiger Moth	ex BB819, 25 RFS, 28 EFTS, 1 EFTS, 9 EFTS,	
		G-ADJJ. CoA 20-3-75. Stored.	4-95
❏ G-AYBV	Tourbillon	unfinished homebuild project. Stored.	10-91
❏ G-BAXV	Cessna F.150L	ex Bredhurst, Eversden, Sandtoft. Crashed 25-7-82.	4-95
❏ G-BKKS	Mercury Dart	unfinished homebuild project. Stored.	4-95

GAMLINGAY on the B1040 south-east of St Neots

❏ G-ASAZ	Hiller UH-12E-4	ex N5372V. CoA 18-12-97. Stored.	2-00
❏ G-BBAZ	Hiller UH-12E	ex EC-DOR, G-BBAZ, N31707, CAF CH-112	
		112276, RCAF 10276. CoA 23-5-91. Stored.	2-00

GLATTON on the B660 south of Peterborough
The company Classic Aircraft moved out in 1998. Tomahawk 112 G-BGXN was reduced to components; Piranha G-BKOT, Silvaire G-BSYF and Grunau Baby CMY all moved on, destination(s) unknown. The Eagle is still stored externally, though losing a fight with the undergrowth!

❏ G-MJBN	Rainbow Eagle	stored.	7-95

GRANSDEN LODGE AERODROME north of the B1046 north-east of Gamlingay

❏ XA243	Grasshopper TX.1	ex St Athan 8886M, Bournemouth. Stored, poor.	12-01

HOUGHTON on the A1123 east of Huntingdon
Jon Wilson: Should keep his Canberra nose in the area.

❏ WJ567	Canberra B.2	ex Wyton, 100, 85, MinTech, 45, RNZAF,	
		45, 59, 149. Nose.	9-97

LITTLE GRANSDEN AERODROME south of the B1046, south of Great Gransden
Yak UK Ltd: Yak C-11 G-DYAK was flying by mid-2000 and delivered to Germany. Terrier 2 G-AYDW (last noted September 1997) returned to King's Lynn, Norfolk. Auster AOP.6 G-BKXP, Harvard IV G-BJST and the anonymous Tiger Moth, all moved to Thruxton, Hants, by mid-2001.
◆ Visits are *strictly* by prior arrangement only.

❏ G-AIRI	Tiger Moth	ex N5488, 29 EFTS, 14 EFTS,	
		20 ERFTS.CoA 9-11-81. Stored.	12-01
❏ G-ASZV	Nipper 2	ex 5N-ADE, 5N-ADY, VR-NDD. CoA 23-5-90.	9-97
❏ G-BIRI	CASA 1-131E	ex E3B-113. CoA 20-10-94. Stored.	9-99
❏ G-KEAC	Queen Air A80	ex G-REXY, G-AVNG, D-ILBO. CoA 18-8-89.	
		Dismantled, stored.	12-01
❏ LY-ALJ*	Yak-52	ex DOSAAF 132. Wreck, first noted 5-01.	12-01
❏ C-558	EKW C-3605	ex Wycombe AP, Lodrino, Swiss AF. Stored.	2-02

LITTLE STAUGHTON AERODROME south of the A45, west of Eaton Socon
By April 2000 Cessna F.150G G-AVGU had moved to Northampton, Northants. By 2001 Devon C.2/2 VP955 (G-DVON) had moved to Kemble, Glos.

❏ G-ARAU	Cessna 150	ex Willingham, Sibson, Land's End,	
		N6494T. Damaged 23-5-82.	9-96
❏ G-ARRG	Cessna 175B	ex Kimbolton, Great Yarmouth, N8299T.	
		Damaged 3-11-70. Fuselage.	2-00
❏ G-ARSB	Cessna 150A	ex Willingham, N7237X. CoA 10-6-88. Fuselage.	2-00
❏ G-BBVG	Aztec 250C	ex ET-AEB, 5Y-AAT. CoA 10-9-88. Derelict.	2-00
❏ SE-GVH	Tomahawk 112	ex Chessington. Stored.	2-00

MARCH on the A141 south of Wisbech
No.1220 Squadron Air Cadets: The Harrier nose should still be at their HQ. 'Parent' is Wittering.
❏ XZ990   Harrier GR.3   ex Wittering, 233 OCU, 3, 4, 3. Cr 14-5-92. Nose.   8-95

MOLESWORTH north of the A14, east of Thrapston
USAF Molesworth: With no recent sightings, the hulk of U-2R 68-10338 has been deleted.

PETERBOROUGH BUSINESS AERODROME or Conington, west of the A1, south of Wansford
❏ G-AVBP   Cherokee 140   Crashed 14-8-96. Stored.   4-97

PETERBOROUGH SPORT AERODROME or Sibson, east of the A1, south of Wansford
Aztec 250C G-ASHH was up and flying by September 2000.
❏ G-ARBN	Apache 160	ex EI-AKI, N3421P ntu. Damaged 8-86. Stored.	10-01
❏ G-ARMA	Apache 160G	ex Oxford, N4448P. CoA 22-7-77.	® 10-01
❏ G-ATMU*	Apache 160G	ex Beccles, Southend, N4478P. CoA 14-4-<u>90</u>.	
		Fuselage, in two sections.	10-01
❏ G-ATNV*	Comanche 260	ex N8896P. CoA 3-7-<u>93</u>.	® 9-01
❏ G-AWSD	Cessna F.150J	Damaged 16-10-87. Stored.	3-98
❏ G-AYRP	Cessna FA.150L	Crashed 1-8-87. Stored.	3-98
❏ G-BIHE	Cessna FA.152	Damaged 10-3-99. Stored.	10-01
❏ G-BDNR	Cessna FRA.150M	Damaged 22-1-92. Rebuild, wings of G-AYRP above.	10-01
❏ G-HUNY	Cessna F.150G	ex G-AVGL. Damaged 16-10-87. Stored.	10-97

ST IVES on the A1123 east of Huntingdon
David Collings: Pup G-AVDF moved to <u>Andover,</u> Hants, by March 2000, still in David's ownership.
❏ G-ADFV   Blackburn B-2   ex Breighton, E' Kirkby, Tattershall, Wigan, Caterham,
                        2893M, 4 EFTS, Hanworth. CoA 26-6-41.   off site ® 7-01

The Stirling Project: Former Stirling pilot Brian Harris, project leader Giuseppe Lombardi, and
others have established themselves to recreate the forward fuselage of a Short Stirling. An FN.5 nose
turret is already on hand. Work is underway on the instrument panel presently. A large amount of work
is being carried out on the engineering drawings and their re-creation.
◆   Visits by prior arrangement *only*. ✉ 9 Taylors Lane, Swavesey, Cambs, CB4 5QN ☎ 01954
    200326 e-mail stirling.project@tesco.net web http://homepages.tesco.net/~stirling. project/index.htm

Others: Airedale should still stored in the area.
❏ G-ASBY   Airedale   ex 'Eversden', Royston. CoA 22-3-80. Stored.   3-98

SOMERSHAM on the B1086 north of St Ives
The Enstrom that was in this general area was based upon the cabin of G-BATU with the tail from G-
JDHI and parts from other machines, including G-BACH. It had left the area by 1999 and is thought to
have formed the basis of the AA's travelling N-AAAS – see under <u>Basingstoke</u>, Hants.

WATERBEACH on the A10 north of Cambridge
No.39 Engineers Regiment: Not reported since June 1993, the reference to the anonymous Gazelle
AH.1 has been deleted. The Hunter reminds one and all of a different era at this location.
❏ WN904   Hunter F.2   ex Duxford, Newton 7544M, 257. Gate. 1 Sqn c/s.   5-01

WHITTLESEY on the A605 east of Peterborough
The Auster remains in long term store as a 'retirement project'.
❏ G-AOGV   J/5R Alpine   CoA 17-7-72. Stored.   12-97

WITTERING AIRFIELD on the A1 south of Stamford
RAF Wittering: The fuselage of AV-8B 162068 moved to Cottesmore, Leics, on 26th June 2000. It was followed by Spitfire F.21 LA255 which pursued 1 Squadron to Cottesmore, Leics, taking the 'low road' on 31st July 2000. The Harrier Maintenance Training School (HMTS) cherishes the GR.1. The newly-arrived T.4 will go on display outside 20 Squadron's HQ ①.

❑ XV279	Harrier GR.1	8566M, ex Farnborough, Culdrose, A&AEE. HMTS	3-01
❑ XV779	Harrier GR.3	8931M, ex 233 OCU, 3, Wittering SF, 3, 20, GR.1, 20, 4, 1. 20 Sqn colours by 11-00. Gate.	4-02
❑ XW923	Harrier GR.3	8724M, ex 1417 Flt, 233 OCU, 1, GR.1, 1. Nose. Crashed 26-5-81.	5-00
❑ XZ146*	'S' Harrier T.4	9281M, ex North Luffenham, Shawbury, 20, 233 OCU, Gutersloh SF, 233 OCU, 4. Arrived by 6-00. 20 Sqn c/s. ①	3-02

WOODHURST north of St Ives, west of the B1040
Chris Cannon: Should still have the Canberra nose.

❑ WE113	Canberra B.2	ex Wyton, 231 OCU, 100, 85, 98, 231 OCU. Nose.	7-97

WYTON AIRFIELD on the B1090 north-west of St Ives
RAF Museum Reserve Collection and Restoration Centre (RAFM): Having settled in to their temporary accommodation, a major coup was achieved in October 2000 with the donation of Miles Mohawk G-AEKW to the museum. By the summer of 2001 this had moved to the careful hands of Skysport at Hatch, Beds. Wyton was always to be a temporary venue while the impressive new facility at Cosford, Shropshire, was readied. Having perfected the act of upping sticks and moving out (honed to perfection during 2000 when Cardington, Beds, was vacated, the move westwards was achieved largely in November 2001. Several airframes have gone to 'deep store' at Stafford, Staffs.

Departures: Sycamore HR.12 WV783 to Rochester, Kent, during 2001. To Stafford, Staffs: Morane BB A301; anonymous FE.2b nacelle; Fi 103 (V-1) BAPC.237; Demoiselle REP BAPC.194. To Cosford, Shropshire: Dragon Rapide G-AHED; Farman F.141 F-HMFI; Blériot XXVII 433 from Hendon, Gtr Lon, 4-6-01, departed 9-11-01; Dolphin D5329; Hampden I P1344; Hawk Major DG590; Kittyhawk IV 'FX760'; Swordfish IV HS503 7-11-01; Spitfire F.21 LA226; Tempest TT.5 NV778 13-11-01; Spitfire F.22 PK664; Spitfire PR.XIX PM651; Spitfire XVI SL674; Vampire F.3 from Hendon, Gtr Lon, 7-1-00, departed 19-11-01; Sedbergh TX.1 VX275; Kestrel FGA.1 XS695; Phantom FGR.2 nose XT903; PT-19A Cornell 15195; Vampire FB.6 J-1172.

RAF Wyton:

❑ WJ633	'EF' Canberra T.17	ex St Athan, Wyton, 360, 231 OCU, 100. Forward fuselage with parts of PR.7 WT538.	9-98
❑ WT519	'CH' Canberra PR.7	ex 100, 13, A&AEE, 31. Dump.	2-00
❑ XH170	Canberra PR.9	8739M, ex 39, RAE, 58. Gate guardian.	3-01
❑ 162730*	AV-8B Harrier II	ex St Athan, USMC. Fuselage. Arrived 13-2-02.	2-02

CHESHIRE

CHELFORD on the A537 west of Macclesfield
On the very same piece of land that the erstwhile Macclesfield APS had their airframes, an airstrip and a carboot venue have appeared. On the former bit, a derelict Fuji lies.

❑ G-BCNZ*	Fuji FA-200-160	CoA 8-2-99.	5-00

CHESTER
Ian Starnes: (Previously listed under Sealand, Wales.) The 'JP' and trailer-mounted Vampire pod and both are kept in the vicinity.

| ❏ XD452 | '66' Vampire T.11 | ex Whixhall, Whitchurch, London Colney, Shawbury, 7990M, 3 FTS, 7 FTS, 1 FTS, 8 FTS, 5 FTS. Pod. | 2-02 |
| ❏ XR654 | Jet Provost T.4 | ex Barton, Chelford, Macclesfield, Bournemouth, Coventry, Puckeridge, Hatfield, Shawbury, CAW, 3 FTS, 6 FTS. Nose. | 2-02 |

A Vampire is stored, pod in one location and 'metal bits' in another, in this general area.

| ❏ XH312 | '18' Vampire T.11 | ex Knutsford, Woodford, Hawarden, St Athan, 8 FTS. | 12-97 |

HOOTON PARK south of Junction 6 of the M53, near Eastham Locks
Hooton Park Trust (HPT) / **Griffin Trust**: Vauxhall Motors handed over all three of the 'Belfast Truss' hangars to the HPT on 9th October 2000. The easterly hangar is still in use with the motorcar manufacturer and will be for some time to come. HPT are busy formulating a business plan for funding to restore the hangars and turn them into a heritage and education centre. This is being done in association with a series of organisations and private owners.
    Notes: The Aeroplane Collection (TAC) have two of their airframes here. Having moved the Auster over from Manchester, TAC's main operations are centred here – see below. The Tutor is on loan from Peter Storrar ①. Canberra B.2 WJ676 nose is on loan from Barry Jones ②. Hunter FGA.9 and Phantom noses are on loan from Mike Davey and Graham Sparkes ③. (Mike Davey built the Dragon Rapide FSM on show at Liverpool, Merseyside.) Griffin Trust has an Easy-Rider in store at Manchester, Gtr Man.
◆ By prior arrangement, plus regular special events. Access off M53, Junction 6 marked 'Eastham Oil Terminal'. Go north to a roundabout then turn right into South Road. ✉ Hooton Park Trust, The Hangars, West Road, Hooton Park Airfield, Ellsemere Port, L65 1BQ ☎ / **fax** 0151 327 4701

❏ G-AGPG*	Avro XIX Srs 2	ex Woodford, Brenzett, Southend, Pye, Ekco, Avro. CoA 13-12-71. Arrived by 6-00.	TAC	3-02
❏ G-AJEB*	J/1N Alpha	ex Manchester, Hooton, Warmingham, Brize Norton, Wigan, Cosford. CoA 27-3-69. Arr by 11-00.	TAC	3-02
❏ –*	T.8 Tutor	BGA.791, ex VM684. CoA 2-71. First noted 1-01.	①	1-02
❏ CCCP-19731	An-2 *Colt*	YL-LEU, ex Chester, Latvia, USSR. On loan. Dismantled ready for storage by 2-02.		2-02
❏ WF911	Canberra B.2	ex Charnock Richard, Bacup, Preston, Samlesbury, G-27-161, 231 OCU. Nose.		1-01
❏ WJ676*	Canberra B.2	ex Heswall, Stock, Wroughton, Colerne, Melksham, 7796M, 245, 35, 50. Nose. F/n 11-01.	②	1-02
❏ XE584*	Hunter FGA.9	ex Woodford, Barton, Chelford, Macclesfield, Bitteswell, G-9-450, 208, 8, 1. Nose. F/n 1-01.	③	1-02
❏ ZE352*	'G' F-4J(UK)	ex Stock, Foulness, Pendine, Laarbruch 9086M, 74, USN 153783. Nose. Arrived 24-2-01.	③	1-02
❏ –	BAPC.68 Hurricane FSM	ex 'H3426', Coventry, Great Bridge, Wembley, Lincoln, *Battle of Britain* 'P3975'.	⑧	1-02

The Aeroplane Collection (TAC): With the arrival of the Auster from Manchester, TAC's main activities are now located here. This is a case of second-time-around for TAC and Hooton. Apart from the machines noted above, TAC aircraft can be found under the following headings: Breighton, E Yorks (Fa 330A-1); Doncaster, S Yorks, (Sioux), Manchester, Gtr Man, (Avian, Dragon Rapide, Bensen, Roe Triplane) and Winthorpe, Notts (Chipmunk and McBroom).
✉ 12 Warren Hay, Wirral CH63 9TL **e-mail** keith_C84A@hotmial.com

MACCLESFIELD on the A523 south of Manchester
Macclesfield College of Further Education: Still have the Vampire in Park Street.

| ❏ XD624 | 'O' Vampire T.11 | ex CATCS, CNCS, Church Fenton SF, 19. | 8-99 |

MALPAS west of the A41, north-west of Whitchurch
No.617 Squadron Air Cadets: Inside Bishop Heber County High, 617 keep their Whirlwind.

❑ XK944   Whirlwind   ex Bristol, Lee-on-Solent, Fleetlands, Arbroath,
                 HAS.7   Fleetlands, A2607, Lossiemouth SF, Fleetlands,
                                 Yeovilton, 824, *Ark Royal* .   1-00

NANTWICH west of Crewe
Hack Green Secret Nuclear Bunker: Initially a World War Two radar station, it was rebuilt to become a labyrinthine bunker for regional government officials to run to if the 'balloon' went up and is now a three-level visitor centre. An appropriate 'Cold War' exhibit here is a **Phantom Preservation Group** FGR.2 nose. Details of the PRG can be found under Ruthin, Wales.
◆ 'Brown signed' off the A530 Nantwich to Whitchurch road. Open daily mid-March to end of October. Open weekends Nov, Jan, Feb, Mar. Closed all December. ✉ PO Box 127, Nantwich, Cheshire, CW5 8AQ ☎ 01270 629219 **fax** 01270 629218 **e-mail** coldwar@hackgreen.co.uk
❑ XV490   Phantom FGR.2   ex Bruntingthorpe, Wattisham, 74, 228 OCU,
                                    92, 56, 22, 92, 56, 23. Nose.   ®   2-02

STRETTON on the A49 south of Warrington
John Sykes: No recent news on the Jungmeister, but one of 'several' Jungmann projects underway has aspired to the UK civil register.
❑ G-BZJV   CASA 1.131L   ex Spanish AF E3B-367.   7-00
❑ ES1-16   CASA 1.133L   ex Spanish AF.   ®   3-94

WINSFORD on the A54 south of Northwich
Cheshire Fire Brigade Training School: Last noted in December 1993, the fuselage of Cessna F.150H G-AWFH has been consigned to LOST!

CORNWALL

BODMIN AERODROME east of the A30, north of Bodmin
❑ G-BFLM   Cessna 150M   ex N3017V. Crashed 14-1-97.   5-98
❑ G-BHJA   Cessna A.152   ex N4954A. Damaged 21-7-90. Fuselage.   6-99
❑ N7133J   Mooney M.20C   ex G-BJAK, OO-CAB, OO-VLB, N5814Q. Fuselage.   6-99

CALLINGTON on the A390 south-west of Tavistock
Complete with over-wing tanks, a Lightning is kept at this *private* location.
❑ XR755   'BA' Lightning F.6   ex Binbrook, 5, 5-11 pool.   7-01

CULDROSE AIRFIELD on the A3083 south of Helston
HMS *Sea Hawk* : The **School of Flight Deck Operations** (SFDO) is the main 'user' of *W&R* airframes on the base. Also here is the **Engineering Training School** (ETS).
     Departures: Skyraider AEW.1 WV106 was airlifted out by 18 Squadron Chinook HC.2 ZA671 to Yeovilton, Somerset, 6-12-00; Wessex HU.5 XT762 to Predannack, Cornwall, 6-12-00; Harrier GR.3 XV786 to Predannack, Cornwall, by 5-00

❑ WF225   Sea Hawk F.1   A2623 [2], ex A2645, FRU, 738, 802. Gate   2-01
❑ XM328   '650' Wessex HAS.3   A2644 [2], ex A2727, Wroughton, 737. *The Sow.* SFDO   9-01
❑ XP137   '711' Wessex HAS.3   A2634 [2], ex A2712, Culdrose,
                                     Lee-o-Solent, Wroughton, 737.   SFDO   9-01
❑ XR528*   Wessex HC.2   ex Predannack, St Mawgan, 60, 28,
                                     240 OCU. Arrived 5-12-00.   9-01

❏	XS876	'523'	Wessex HAS.1	A2626 [3], ex Lee-on-Solent, A2695, Wroughton, 771.	SFDO	9-01
❏	XS885	'512'	Wessex HAS.1	A2631 [2], ex A2668, 772.	SFDO	9-01
❏	XV359	'035'	Buccaneer S.2B	A2693 [2], ex Predannack, Lossiemouth, 208, 237 OCU, 12, 208, 12. 809 Sqn c/s. Displayed		2-01
❏	XV372*		SH-3D Sea King	ex Predannack, St Mawgan, Trowbridge, Yeovil, Lee-on-Solent, RAE, Westlands. Hulk. Arrived 5-12-00.		12-00
❏	XV657	'132'	Sea King HAS.5	A2600 [4], Fleetlands, Wroughton, 826. Tail of ZA135.	ETS	9-01
❏	XV741	'5'	Harrier GR.3	A2608 [3], ex A2607, Cosford, 233 OCU, 3, 233 OCU, 3.	SFDO	2-01
❏	XV753	'4'	Harrier GR.3	A2691 [2], ex Halton, Abingdon, 9075M, St Athan, 233 OCU, 1, 3, 233 OCU.	SFDO	2-01
❏	XV783		Harrier GR.3	A2609 [3], ex Lee-on-Solent, Culdrose SAH, Cosford, 233 OCU, 4, 3, 233 OCU, 1, 233 OCU, 1, 233 OCU, 1417 Flt, 233 OCU, 4, 20, 4.	SFDO	2-01
❏	XV808		Harrier GR.3	A2687 [2], ex 9076M, 233 OCU, 3, 20.	SFDO	2-01
❏	XW271		Harrier T.4	A2692 [2], ex Cosford, 4, 1, 233 OCU.	SFDO	2-01
❏	XX510	'69'	Lynx HAS.2	A2683 [2], ex Gosport, A2601, A2772, Lee-on-Solent, Foulness, Boscombe Down.	SFDO	9-01
❏	XZ145		Harrier T.4	A2610 [4], ex Shawbury, 20, 233 OCU, 3.	SFDO	7-01
❏	XZ243	'635'	Lynx HAS.3	A2613 [3], ex Gosport, Portland, Lee. Crashed 10-3-88.Cabin. Spares recovery.		9-01
❏	XZ969	'D'	Harrier GR.3	A2612 [3], ex A2610, Manadon, St Athan, 4, 1, 3.	SFDO	2-01
❏	XZ996	'3'	Harrier GR.3	A2685 [2], ex 1417 Flt, 4, 1417 Flt, 233 OCU, 1417 Flt, 233 OCU.	SFDO	7-01
❏	ZD667		Harrier GR.3	A2684 [2], 9201M, ex 1417 Flt, 233 OCU.	SFDO	9-01
❏	ZF641		EH-101 PP1	ex Fleetlands, Westland.	SFDO	9-01
❏	–		EH-101 EMU	ex Yeovil, avionics test.	SFDO	2-01

HELSTON on the A3083 north of Culdrose

Flambards Village Theme Park: The trend of 'down-sizing' the aircraft collection continues. The aircraft exhibits are part of a large multi-faceted theme-park. Canberra TT.18 WK122 and Sea Vixen FAW.2 XN647 were scrapped on site in late 2000 with their cockpits going to Bruntingthorpe, Leics.
♦ Open most days Easter to end of Oct 10am to 5pm. SAE brings details. Last admission 3.30pm. Signed off the A3083 south of Helston, next to RNAS Culdrose. ✉ Cornwall Aero Park, Clodgey Lane, Helston, TR13 0QA ☎ 01326 573404 **fax** 01326 573344 **e-mail** info@flambards.co.uk **web** www.flambards.co.uk

❏	G-BDDX		MW.2B Excalibur	only flight 1-7-76, built at Bodmin.	3-02
❏	WF122	'575'	Sea Prince T.1	ex Culdrose A2673, 750, Sydenham SF, Arbroath SF, Lossiemouth SF, 700Z Flt, Lossiemouth SF, FOFT, 750, Eglinton SF, 744.	3-02
❏	WG511		Shackleton T.4	ex Colerne, St Mawgan, MOTU, Kinloss Wing, MOTU, 120, 42. Nose.	3-02
❏	XA870		Whirlwind HAS.1	ex Predannack, Lee-on-Solent A2543, *Protector* Flt, 705, *Protector* Flt, 155, 848. Sectioned.	3-02
❏	XE368	'200'	Sea Hawk FGA.6	ex Culdrose SAH-3, Shotley A2534, 738, 806, 803, 899.	3-02
❏	XG831	'396'	Gannet ECM.6	ex Culdrose SAH-8, A2539, 831.	3-02
❏	XP350		W'wind HAR.10	ex Chivenor, 22, 225.	3-02
❏	XS887	'403'	Wessex HAS.1	ex Culdrose A2690, Wroughton, 771.	3-02
❏	–*		Concorde EMU	ex Filton, instrument layout trials.	3-02

LAND'S END on the A30 south-west of Penzance

Land's End: Suspended at a dramatic angle within the complex is a Bölkow 105. It has been given a new 'identity' to tie in with the *real* G-CDBS which belongs to the Cornwall Air Ambulance and is based at St Mawgan. G-BCXO was rebuilt with a new pod and flies on as G-THLS. Within can be found an all-yellow biplane which looks akin to a Sopwith Baby. A propeller is bolted straight on to what should be the firewall and while the tail carries a single float, there is no main undercarriage of any description. It is most *likely* to have come from the former Viv Bellamy 'stock' at the local aerodrome, but this is not cut-and-dried. Indeed, another theory is that is BAPC.137, auctioned by Christie's in October 1987 and once with Thorpe Park. Care to enter the fray?

◆ Open from 10am daily, closing times vary with the season. ✉ Land's End, Sennen, Penzance, TR19 7AA ☎ 0870 4580044 **fax** 01736 871812 **e-mail** info@landsend-landmark.co.uk **web** www. landsend-landmark.co.uk

❏ 'G-CDBS'	MBB Bö 105D	G-BCXO, ex 'G-BOND', D-HDCE. wfu 4-3-92.	3-02
❏ —*	'Sopwith'	first noted 8-01.	3-02

LAND'S END AERODROME or St Just, on the B3306 south of St Just

Storey TSR.3 G-AWIV was up and flying again by mid-1999. See above for another possible plot.

❏ G-BFNU	BN-2B-21	CoA 18-8-89. Fuselage, stored.	8-01
❏ '124'	Fokker D.VIII REP	G-BHCA. Crashed 21-8-81. Fuselage	8-01

LELANT on the A3074 south of St Ives

❏ G-ABTC	Comper Swift	CoA 18-7-84. *Spirit of Butler*. Stored.	11-93

LISKEARD on the A38 north-west of Plymouth

Castle Motors / Helicopters: The dramatically-posed Lightning graces the car park.

❏ G-USTA*	A.109A	ex G-MEAN, G-BRYL, G-ROPE, G-OAMH.	
		Damaged 27-3-99. Spares recovery.	6-01
❏ SX-HCF	A.109A Mk.II	ex Greece. Spares recovery.	6-01
❏ XS936	Lightning F.6	ex Binbrook, 5, 11, LTF, 5/11, LTF, 5, 11, 23.	12-01

PREDANNACK AIRFIELD off the A3083 south of Helston

Fleet Air Arm Fire School: *W&R17* (p39) recorded the arrival of a pair of Wessex in October 1998 and then declared that they were both tendered for scrap and removed the following year. Not so! XS866 and XS868 were made of stronger stuff! ① Early in 2001, several airframes were put up for tender - †.

Departures: Wessex HU.5C XS498 moved to Odiham, Hants, by late 2000; Wessex HU.5C XT463 arrived by 5-00, to Hixon, Staffs, 5-12-00; Gazelle HT.2 ZB648, last noted 11-98, thought perished; Sea King HAS.6 ZE419, last noted 9-96, thought perished.

❏ WT308		Canberra B(I).6	A2601, ex Culdrose, DRA Farnborough, A&AEE.	2-02
❏ XE668	'832'	Hunter GA.11	A2647 [2], Ex A2733, Culdrose SAH,	
			Yeovilton, FRADU, 738, 26, 4.	2-02
❏ XM868	'517'	Wessex HAS.1	A2630 [2], ex A2706, Lee-on-Solent, Wroughton, 737. †	2-01
❏ XM870		Wessex HAS.1	A2634 [2], ex A2712, Gosport, Lee-o-Solent, 772.	2-02
❏ XM874	'521'	Wessex HAS.1	A2629 [2], ex A2689, Lee, Culdrose, Wroughton, 771. †	2-01
❏ [XP160]	'521'	Wessex HAS.1	A2628 [2], ex A2650, Lee-on-Solent, Culdrose,	
			SAH-24. Poor state.	2-02
❏ XS516	'YQ'	Wessex HU.5	A2652 [2], ex Gosport, A2739, Lee-on-Solent, 845.	2-02
❏ XS522	'ZL'	Wessex HU.5	A2663 [2], ex Gosport, A2753, Lee-on-Solent,	
			Wroughton, 848.	2-02
❏ XS529	'461'	Wasp HAS.1	A2696 [2], ex A2743, Culdrose, Manadon,	
			Lee-on-Solent, 829, *Galatea* Flt. Poor state.	2-02
❏ XS866*	'520'	Wessex HAS.1	A2627 [2], ex Culdrose, Lee-on-Solent A2705	
			Wroughton, 771. Arrived 28-10-98. ① †	2-02

❑ XS868*		Wessex HAS.1	A2686 [2], ex Culdrose, Gosport, A2791, Lee-on-Solent, Fleetlands, A2691, Wroughton. Arrived 6-10-98.	①	2-01
❑ XS881	'046'	Wessex HAS.1	A2688 [2], ex A2675, Yeovilton, Wroughton, FAAM, Yeovilton, Culdrose.	†	2-01
❑ XT468	'628'	Wessex HU.5	A2667 [2], ex A2744, ex Culdrose, Gosport, Lee-on-Solent, Wroughton, 772.	†	2-02
❑ XT762*		Wessex HU.5	A2661 [2], ex Culdrose A2751, Lee-on-Solent, Wroughton, RAE. Arrived 6-12-00.		2-02
❑ XV786*	'S'	Harrier GR.3	A2611 [3], ex Culdrose, A2615, St Athan, 3, 4, 1, 4. Two sections.		2-02
❑ XX479	'563'	Jetstream T.2	A2611 [4], ex St Athan, 750, CFS, 5 FTS, Sywell, Radlett, G-AXXT.		2-02
❑ ZD631	'66'	Sea King HAS.6	A2621 [2], ex Gosport, Lee-on-Solent.		2-02

ST AUSTELL on the A390 north-east of Truro
Confirming *W&R17*, the nose of Short SC.9 XH132 moved to Italy by June 1999.

| ❑ WL756 | Shackleton AEW.2 | ex St Mawgan 9101M, 8, 204, 205, 37, 38. Nose. | 6-99 |
| ❑ XV237 | Nimrod MR.2 | ex St Mawgan, Kinloss W, 203, St Mawgan Wing. Forward Fuselage. | 4-99 |

ST MAWGAN AIRFIELD off the A3059, north-east of Newquay
RAF St Mawgan: SH-3D XV372 moved to Predannack, Cornwall, by September 2000 but moved again, to Culdrose, Cornwall, on 5th December 2000. It was replaced 13 months later. There is a sensational 'synthetic' fire trainer here that would appear to be a cross between a Harrier and a Sea King!

| ❑ WL795 | 'T' Shackleton AEW.2 | 8753M, ex 8, 205, 38, 204, 210, 269, 204. | 9-98 |
| ❑ XV709* | '263' Sea King HAS.6 | ex Gosport, 810, 706, 820, 826, 820, 814, 706. Arrived 15-1-02. Procedures trainer. | 1-02 |

Barry Wallond: Aviation artist Barry, acquired one of the former *Dark Blue World* Spitfire FSMs from Duxford and has it displayed in his garden.

| ❑ N3317* | Spitfire IX FSM | BAPC.268, ex Duxford, *Dark Blue World.* Arrived by 11-00. | 8-01 |

ST MERRYN AERODROME on the B3276 west of Padstow
The McCandless is the second user of the 'reggie'. See under Holywood, N Ireland for the other ①.

❑ G-ARTZ {2}	McCandless M4	Stored. CoA 13-10-69.	①	10-00
❑ 'G-ATCX'	Cessna 182A	G-OLSC, ex G-ATNU, EI-ANC, N6078B. Crashed 6-6-93. Fuselage.		10-00
❑ G-AWIF	Mosquito gyro	ex Husbands Bosworth, Shipdham, Tattershall Thorpe, Clitheroe. CoA 7-1-82.		6-98
❑ G-AXVN	McCandless M4	Stored.		10-00
❑ G-MLAS	Cessna 182E	ex Bodmin, OO-HPE, D-EGPE, N2826Y. Damaged 14-12-80. Para-trainer.		4-99

TREMAR north of the B3254, north of Liskeard
Roy Flood: The Sycamore is reported to have been sold in November 2000, with a destination of 'Wales' – details? ① Both the Lightning and Sycamore are/were kept within *private* grounds.

| ❑ XG544 | Sycamore HR.14 | ex Higher Blagdon, 32, MCS, 228, 275. | ① | 7-96 |
| ❑ XR751 | Lightning F.3 | ex Binbrook, 11, LTF, 29, 226 OCU, EE. | | 7-96 |

CUMBRIA

BARROW-IN-FURNESS
Martinis: The night-club in Cornwallis Street has a BD-5 Micro in store. Offers accepted!
❏ G-BDTT   Bede BD-5   ex Tattershall Thorpe, Bourne.   3-02

CARK AERODROME south-west of Grange-over-Sands
The local parachute club still uses its Cessna para-trainer.
❏ G-AWMZ   Cessna F.172H   ex Blackpool. Crashed 18-1-76. Para-trainer.   8-01

CARLISLE or Kingstown, on the A7 north of the City
The Luscombe is believed to still be in the area.
❏ G-AKTT   Silvaire 8A   ex N71852, NC71852. Crashed 6-7-91.   1-96

CARLISLE AIRPORT or Crosby-on-Eden, off the B629 east of Carlisle
Solway Aviation Museum and **Edward Haughey Aviation Heritage Centre**: Major changes here should be in place by the summer of 2002 and reflect the life injected into the airport in general by the new owner, Dr Edward Haughey. The museum has been granted a licence securing its future on the airport which has allowed it to expand both its facilities and its opening hours. An adjacent building to those already used by the museum will be turned into a restoration centre. In front of this a purpose-built display area of inter-connected pans will be built to house the aircraft exhibits. This will allow the airframes, including the Phantom and the Vulcan, to come off the 'airport' site and to move into close proximity with the display buildings. This is all great news for SAM, who have been based at Carlisle for over 40 years.
   Display space within the museum buildings will be enlarged with displays including wartime life, the 'Crosby Room' detailing the life and times of the airport and surrounding airfields, a major display devoted to the Blue Streak programme which was tested at nearby Spadeadam, and much more.
   Notes: SAS have a close relationship with Tom Stoddart, who owns Vulcan XJ823, and a share in the Sea Prince ①. The Grasshopper is composite, with parts of WZ824 – see Strathaven, Scotland ②.
◆ Open Mar to Oct Sundays Jun to Sep Saturdays also and July-Aug Fridays, same times. Open all Bank Hols. All days 10.30am to 5pm. ✉ 'Aviation House', Carlisle Airport, Crosby-on-Eden, Carlisle, CA6 4NW ☎ / **fax** / **info-line** 01228 573823 (the 'last three' honouring the Vulcan!) e-mail info@solway-aviation-museum.org.uk **web** www.solway-aviation-museum.org.uk

❏ G-APLG	J/5L Aiglet Trainer	ex Maryport, Bletchley, Romsey, Southend, Rettendon, Corringham, Felthorpe. CoA 26-10-68.	®	3-02
❏ G-AYFA	Twin Pioneer 3	ex Hooton Park, Warmingham, Sandbach, Shobdon, Prestwick, G-31-5, XM285, SRCU, 225, Odiham SF, 230. Nose.		3-02
❏ WE188	Canberra T.4	ex Samlesbury, 231 OCU, 360, 231 OCU, 360, 100,56, 231 OCU, Upwood SF, 231 OCU, Upwood SF, Waddington SF, Hemswell SF.		3-02
❏ WP314	'573' Sea Prince T.1	ex Preston, Hull, Syerston, Halton, 8634M, Kemble, 750, Sydenham SF, 750, Lossiemouth SF, Shorts FU, Brawdy SF, Lossie SF, 750.	①	3-02
❏ WS832	'W' Meteor NF.14	ex RRE Pershore, Llanbedr, 12 MU, 8 MU.		3-02
❏ WV198	'K' Whirlwind HAR.21	G-BJWY ex Firbeck, Warmingham, Chorley, Blackpool, Heysham, Carnforth, Gosport, Lee-on-Solent A2576, Arbroath, 781, 848, USN 130191.		3-02
❏ WZ515	Vampire T.11	ex Duxford, Staverton, Woodford, Chester, St Athan, 4 FTS, 8 FTS, 56, 253, 16.		3-02
❏ [WZ784]*	G'hopper TX.1	ex Thurrock. First noted 5-01.	②	3-02
❏ XJ823	Vulcan B.2	ex 50, Wadd Wing, 35, 27, 9/35, Wadd Wing, 230 OCU, MoA.	①	3-02
❏ XV259	Nimrod AEW.3	ex Stock, Chattenden, Abingdon, Waddington, Woodford, Kin Wing, St Mawgan Wing. Nose.		3-02

❑ XV406   'CK' Phantom FGR.2   ex Longtown, Carlisle, 9098M, St Athan, 29,
                                   23, 111, HSA, A&AEE, HSA. On loan.   3-02
❑ ZF583   Lightning F.53   ex Warton, RSaudi AF 53-681, G-27-51. RAF c/s. 3-02

Others: By August 2001 Tomahawk G-BNGS had moved to Tees-side, D&C. Cherokee 140 G-ATOO
was here by April 2000 but moved on to Blackpool, Lancs, during 2001.
❑ G-BRLO*   Tomahawk 112   ex N2397K, N9680N. CoA 1-7-99.   4-00

HAVERIGG south of Millom
RAF Millom Museum: Run by the **South Copeland Aviation Group**. The rear end of Chipmunk
WD377 can also be found in a composite at Dumfries ①. The wings of Vampire XD425 are on XD547
at Dumfries, Scotland ②.
◆ On the Bankhead Estate, North Lane, adjacent to HMP Haverigg. Open Sat, Sun, Mon, Wed and Fri
  10am to 5pm during the summer. Winter Sun only. Other times by appointment. ✉ c/o John Nixon,
  RAF Millom Museum, HMP Haverigg, Millom, Cumbria, LA18 4NA ☎ 01229 770340

❑ 'G-ADRX'   HM.14 'Flea'   BAPC.231, ex Torver, Ulverston.   9-01
❑ WD377   Chipmunk T.10   ex Dumfries, 12 AEF, Glas UAS, HCEU,
                              11 RFS, 2 BFTS. Cr 29-7-66. Cockpit.   ® ①   9-01
❑ XD425   'M' Vampire T.11 ex Dumfries, West Freugh, Stranraer, Woodford,
                              Chester, St Athan, 8 FTS, 5 FTS, 7 FTS,
                              202 AFS. Pod. 6 Sqn c/s.   ②   9-01
❑ XK637   '56' Vampire T.11 ex Royton, Woodford, Chester, St Athan,
                              4 FTS, 7 FTS.   ®   9-01
❑ XM660   Whirlwind   ex Sunderland, Almondbank, Fleetlands, Lee-on-
             HAS.7   Solent, Lossiemouth SAR Flt, 737, 700H, 824.   9-01
❑ XN597   'X' Jet Provost T.3 7984M, ex Firbeck, Levenshulme, Stamford, Firbeck,
                              Sunderland, Stoke-on-Trent, Bournemouth, Faygate,
                              2 FTS. Damaged 28-6-67. Nose.   9-01
❑ —   BAPC.260 HM.280   FAF colours. Touring exhibit.   9-01

SPADEADAM FOREST north of the B6318, north-east of Carlisle
RAF Spadeadam / Electronic Warfare Tactics Range (note change/correction of name): A
complex series of ranges centred around the former missile test/launch site. As can be seen below, the
Whirlwind is proving quite resilient! The Whirlwind was 'first noted' in April 2000 and again in
September of the following year, boomless and lying on its belly. T-33As noted in April 2000 were
coded as follows: '10', '11', '12', '18' and '80', against seven known to have been delivered. The
Mystères at that time were '01', '5' ('8-NW', No.262 or 282), '6', '8' ('NR'), '36', '60' ('8-NN'),
'63', '180', '04' ('NU'). That would appear to make nine of them against the previously held 'body
count' of eight. Sighting dates are left as before as only one tie-up is possible.

❑ XN387   W'wind HAR.9   ex Odiham 8564M, Wroughton, Lee-on-Solent SAR
                              Flt, Lossiemouth SF, 846, 719.   9-01
❑ FT-01   T-33A-1-LO   ex Prestwick, Belgian AF, 51-4041. Red stars.   3-95
❑ FT-02   T-33A-1-LO   ex Prestwick, Belgian AF, 51-4043.   —
❑ FT-06   T-33A-1-LO   ex Prestwick, Belgian AF, Neth AF M-44, 51-4231.   —
❑ FT-07   T-33A-1-LO   ex Prestwick, Belgian AF, Neth AF M-45, 51-4233.   —
❑ FT-10   T-33A-1-LO   ex Prestwick, Belgian AF, 51-6664.   —
❑ FT-11   T-33A-1-LO   ex Prestwick, Belgian AF, Neth AF M-47, 51-6661.   —
❑ FT-29   T-33A-1-LO   ex Prestwick, Belgian AF, 53-5753. Red stars.   3-95
❑ 61   Mystère IVA   ex Sculthorpe, FAF.   8-99
❑ 64   '36' Mystère IVA   ex Sculthorpe, FAF.   8-99
❑ 81   Mystère IVA   ex Sculthorpe, FAF.   7-96
❑ 139   Mystère IVA   ex Sculthorpe, FAF.   7-96
❑ 180   Mystère IVA   ex Sculthorpe, FAF.   6-99
❑ 184   '32' '63' Mystère IVA ex Sculthorpe, FAF.   6-99

❑	'8-NW' Mystère IVA	likely to be 262, (or 2̲8̲2̲)	4-00
❑	Mystère IVA	No.207?	7-96
❑ *	Mystère IVA	see above	7-96
❑ 98+10	Su-22M-4	ex Farnborough, Boscombe Down, LSK-LV 820.	4-00

W IND ER MER E on the A592 north of Bowness on Windermere
Windermere Steamboat Centre: (Note change of name.) As well as the waterglider, two other aeronautical items are within this superb collection; a Sunderland wing float, modified into a 'canoe'; and the MV *Canfly* a 1920s speedboat powered by a Rolls-Royce Hawk from the RNAS airship SST.3.
◆ Open daily mid-March to late October 10am to 5pm. Special events and exhibitions staged. Shop and tea room, good car parking. Steamboat cruises available. ✉ Rayrigg Road, Windermere, Cumbria, LA23 1BN ☎ 015394 4̲5̲5̲6̲5̲ **fax** 015394 48769. **web** www.steamboat.co.uk

❑ –	BGA.266 T.1 Falcon	Modified by Capt T C Patti̲n̲son DFC. f/f 3-2-43.	3-02

DERBYSHIRE

☛ Within the administrative county boundaries can be found the unitary authority of the City of Derby.

CHESTERFIELD on the A61 south of Sheffield
4x4 Car Centre: On the Dronfield Road, have a former Finningley 'JP' as an attraction.

❑ XM480	'02' Jet Provost T.3	ex Finningley, Halton 8080M, 6 FTS, 1 FTS.	3-02

DERBY
Derby Industrial Museum: Presents a staggering array of aero engines, nearly all of the home-spun Rolls-Royce variety, going from the Eagle to the RB.211 and is a must to visit. The rest of the museum – which is set in one of the world's first 'modern' factories, originally built in 1717 – has excellent displays on Derbyshire's industrial past. There are regular exhibitions and special events. The **Derbyshire Historical Aviation Society** works in support of the museum, on many other projects and stages regular meetings. (✉ Bill Harrison, 71 Mill Hill Lane, Derby, DE3 6SB e-mail williamharrison@netscapeonline.co.uk) The Rolls-Royce Heritage Trust, Derby and Hucknall Branch has many of its engines on show at the museum – see also below.
◆ Mon 11am to 5pm, Tue to Sat 10am to 5pm. Sun/Bank Hols 2pm to 5pm. ✉ Silk Mill Lane, off Full Street, Derby, DE1 3AR ☎ 01332 255308 **fax** 01332 716670 **web** www.derby.gov.uk/museums

Rolls-Royce Heritage Trust: Located within the new Rolls-Royce Learning and Development Centre in Willmore Road, the trust established an incredible heritage exhibition of aero engines and other memorabilia during the autumn of 2001 using engines, artefacts and input from all of the branches. As well as the engines etc, a Canberra B.15 nose is on show. This flew 'ops' during the Suez crisis, 1956.
◆ Open to groups by prior arrangement *only*. ✉ PO Box 31, Derby DE24 8BJ, ☎ 01332 249118, **fax** 01332 249727, **e-mail** richard.haigh@rolls-royce.com **web** www.rolls-royce.com

❑ WH960*	Canberra B.15	ex Nottingham, Bruntingthorpe, Cosford 8344M, Akrotiri Wing, 32, 9, 12. Nose.	3-02

Rolls-Royce Heritage Trust, Derby and Hucknall Branch and **Coventry Branch** (previously at Mickleover, Derbyshire) are busy establishing shared workshops and storage facilities in the former Light Alloy Foundry – also known as 'The Tram Sheds' – within a part of the extensive Rolls-Royce complex. The Coventry Branch's Macchi is in store here.
◆ By prior arrangement *only*, and occasional open days. ✉ Eric Neale, 18 Park Road, Duffield, Belper, Derbyshire, DE56 4GL.

❑ 0767*	MB.339AA	ex Mickleover, Filton, Yeovilton, Stanley, Argentine Navy. FAAM loan. Stored.	3-02

Adrian Marshall: See also Bruntingthorpe, Leics, for Adrian's Beech 18 projects.

❑ G-AIJZ	J/1 Autocrat	ex Hooton Park, Warmingham, Southend, Shobdon. Crashed 25-10-70.	11-95
❑ G-ASYN	Terrier 2	ex Southend, Sibson, Auster AOP.6 VF519, 661. Damaged 2-1-76.	1-96
❑	Auster 6A	ex Hedge End, Warmingham, Wigan, Handforth. Frame.	3-96
❑ –	Auster AOP.6 c/n 1908	ex Shoreham, Hedge End, Warmingham, East Kirkby, Sibson, Wigan, Handforth.	11-95

Others: The hulk of Spitfire XIV RM689 is stored at Hucknall, Notts.

DERBY AERODROME or Egginton, south of the A5132 between Egginton and Hilton Officially known under the heading of 'Derby' for a while, it is high time we noted this. By August 2000 Rattler Strike G-BKPG had arrived. It moved in mid-December to Winthorpe, Notts. The **Comet Racer Project Group** are making good progress with G-ACSP.
♦ Visits are possible *only* by prior arrangement. Details of membership of the support group can be had from ✉ Derby Airfield, Hilton Road, Egginton, Derby, DE65 6GU ☎ 01283733803 fax 01283 734829 web www.cometracer.co.uk

❑ G-ACSP*	DH.88 Comet	ex Stoke-on-Trent, Coventry / Staverton, Bodmin, Chirk, Portugal, CS-AAJ, E-1. *Black Magic.*	® 3-02
❑ G-AVLM	Pup 160	ex Shenstone, Tatenhill, Nottingham Airport, Chippenham. CoA 24-4-69. Stored.	1-02
❑ G-BHZS*	Bulldog 120	ex Botswana DF 0D5, G-BHZS. CoA 8-2-99.	8-01
❑ G-SACF	Cessna 152 II	ex G-BHSZ, N47125. Crashed 21-3-97. Wreck.	6-01

EGGINTON AERODROME
See Derby Aerodrome, above.

MICKLEOVER on the A516 west of Derby
Rolls-Royce Heritage Trust, Coventry Branch: The training centre here closed during 2000 and the Branch started a phased move to new, shared, premises in Derby. MB.339AA 0767 made the move to Derby, Derbyshire, during mid-2001.

RIPLEY on the A610 north-west of Nottingham
Anchor Supplies: In Peasehill Road, a Vampire and an armoured car tempt passers by to gaze on the myriad treasures on offer inside. The Vampire *may* be going indoors.
✉ Anchor Supplies Ltd, Peasehill Road, Ripley, DE5 3JG ☎ 01773 570139 **fax** 01773 570537 **e-mail** dean@anchor-supplies.lt.uk **web** www.anchor.supplies.ltd.uk

❑ XD382	Vampire T.11	ex Shawbury, Syerston 8033M, CATCS, CNCS, RAFC, 5 FTS, 206 AFS, 208 AFS.	2-02

SHARDLOW on the A6 south-east of Derby
The gyroplane is *thought* still stored here.

❑ G-ATGZ	Griffiths GH.4	stored. Unflown.	7-91

DEVON

☛ Within the administrative county boundaries are the unitary authorities of Plymouth and Torbay.

BARNSTAPLE
Tim Jones: Tim took delivery of the fuselage of JP T.5 XS231 on 9th June 2001. He notes with glee that, being Tim Andrew Jones and his 'JP' having been allocated G-ATAJ, he has the equivalent of a personalised number plate! Tim plans to acquire wings etc in due course.
◆ By prior appointment via e-mail timjones007@hotmail.com
❑ XS231* Jet Provost T.5 ex Ipswich, Bruntingthorpe, Bournemouth,
Scampton, Shawbury, A&AEE, G-ATAJ ntu.
Fuselage. Arrived 9-6-01 7-01

DUNKESWELL AERODROME north of Honiton
Dunkeswell Memorial Museum: Dedicated to the history of the airfield and its resident units, including the PB4Y-1 equipped FAW-7 of the US Navy. Core is a collection of local artefacts, amassed since the early 1980s by the founders, David Sharland, Darren Lillywhite and Rupert Fairclough. The Spitfire FSM is marked as 'BR600'. It is *not* the 'BR600' at Uxbridge, Gtr Lon or Sudbury, Suffolk ①.
◆ Mar to Oct, Tue to Sun 10am to 7pm. Nov to Feb, Sat and Sun 10am to 6pm. ✉ Dunkeswell Aerodrome, Honiton, Devon, EX14 0RA ☎ 01404 891943
❑ XE982 Vampire T.11 ex Hereford, St Athan 7564M, RAFC. 10-01
❑ 'BR600' Spitfire FSM fuselage. ① 7-99
❑ Gannet AS.x cockpit section. 7-99

Aerodrome: An organisation called **Flightaid** bases itself here, raising funds through a travelling 'roadshow' that includes a Wasp ①. They have a Cessna 'based' at Croydon, Gtr Lon, *qv*.
❑ G-AJAJ J/1N Alpha CoA 18-4-94. Stored. 4-99
❑ G-ASSY Turbulent ex Redhill. Damaged 8-5-83. ® 5-93
❑ G-BPRV Warrior II ex N4292G. Crashed 29-3-97. Cockpit. 7-99
❑ XT788 '316' Wasp HAS.1 G-BMIR, ex Faygate, Tattershall Thorpe, Wroughton. ① 1-01

EAGLESCOTT AERODROME west of the A377, north of Ashreigney
Aerodrome: The Currie Wot will re-appear in the guise of a scaled-down Pfalz D.VII! ① The nose of Lightning F.1A XM144 moved to Wycombe Air Park, Bucks.
❑ G-ARZW Currie Wot Crashed 12-2-88. ® ① 10-00
❑ G-BOLD Tomahawk ex N9740T. CoA 21-1-96. Stored. 10-00
❑ N24730 Tomahawk Dismantled. Stored. 10-00
❑ PH-NLH Hunter T.7 ex Goff's Oak, Marlow, Exeter, NLR Amsterdam,
Neth AF N-320, XM126 ntu. Nose. 10-00
❑ WT744 '868' Hunter GA.11 ex Yeovilton, FRADU, 738, 247, AFDS. 8-01
❑ WT867 Cadet TX.3 ex Syerston, 626 VGS. Stored. 8-01
❑ XA289 Cadet TX.3 ex Syerston, 636 VGS. Stored. 8-01

EXETER
Arden Family Trust: The late Bertram Arden's airframes are held in careful store in the general area.
❑ G-AALP Surrey AL.1 CoA 17-5-40. 12-97
❑ G-AFGC BA Swallow II ex BK893, GTS, CLE, RAE, G-AFGC. CoA 20-3-51. 12-97
❑ G-AFHC BA Swallow II CoA 20-3-51. 12-97
❑ G-AJHJ* Auster V ex NJ676, 83 GCS, 440. CoA 27-6-49. 12-97

Others: A Seafire project has joined the Spitfire.
❑ RR232 Spitfire IX G-BRSF, ex Lancing, Winchester, Nowra,
Bankstown, Point Cook, Cape Town, Ysterplaat,
SAAF 5632, RR232, 47 MU, ECFS. 12-01

❑ RX168*   Seafire III   G-BWEM, ex Andover, Norwich, Battle,
                                   Dublin, IAAC 157, RX168.   12-01

EXETER AIRPORT on the A30, east of the city at Clyst Honiton

Classic Jet Aircraft Company (CJAC) / **Hunter Flying Club**: To mark the 50th anniversary of the first flight of the Hunter prototype, WB188, on 20th July 1951 from Boscombe Down in the hands of Neville Duke, CJAC painted newly-arrived GA.11 WV256 in the famed 'duck egg green' colours in early June 2001. With the support of a wide series of organisations, including *FlyPast*, 'WB188' flew to Boscombe for a re-enactment with Neville Duke looking on. After that, it appeared at a number of airshows and similar events. Not content with *one* WB188, on 25th July 2001 Classic Jet unveiled a *second* in the form of GA.11 XF300, this time in the overall red colours of the Mk.3 record-breaker. This will take centre stage in 2003 to celebrate the world-record flight on 7th September 1953. BAE Systems will supply a pointed nose to make the aircraft as realistic-looking as possible. (The *real* WB188 can be found at Tangmere, West Sussex.)

    Notes: CJAC operate several Hunters for other owners, as follows: PR.11 WT723 for Belgian-based Stick and Rudder Aviation (who are also working on T.7 XL601 in Belgium, see under 'Departures'); GA.11 XE685 on behalf of David Hayes and F.6A XF516 for Peter Hellier. These are marked ±. CJAC occasionally uses St Mawgan, Cornwall, for winter storage, but for the purposes of this entry all aircraft are noted under this heading.

    Departures: All Hunters, GA.11 XE685 (G-GAII) to North Weald, Essex, 6-99 but returned 21-5-00 ①; T.8C XF357 (G-BWGL) flew to Bournemouth, Dorset, on 8-4-00 for repaint and then on to Duxford, Cambs, on 29-5-00; T.7 XL601 to Belgium 1-99; T.7A XL613 (G-BVMB) was first flown 3-3-01 following restoration – it departed by air to South Africa 17-6-01; GA.11 XF368 (G-BZRH) arrived from Shawbury, Shrop, on 12-2-01, followed by T.8B XF967 (G-BZRI) from Cranwell, Lincs, on 16-2-01. Both departed for South Africa 17-6-01.

◆ Visits possible *only* by prior arrangement. web www.classicjets.co.uk

❑ 'WB188'* ✦		Hunter GA.11	G-BZPB, ex WV256, Shawbury, Yeovilton, FRADU, 738, 229 OCU, 26. Arrived 13-2-01. Prototype colours, pale green, from 6-01.		1-02
❑ 'WB188'*		Hunter GA.11	G-BZPC, ex Shawbury XF300, Yeovilton, FRADU, 130, 234, 71. Arrived 14-2-01. Record-breaker red colours from 7-01.		1-02
❑ WT722	'878'	Hunter T.8C	G-BWGN, ex Shawbury, Yeovilton, FRADU, 764, 703, 26, 54.		1-02
❑ WT723	'866'	Hunter PR.11 ✦	G-PRII, ex N723WT, A2616 [3], Culdrose, FRADU, Lossiemouth SF, 14.	±	1-02
❑ WT799*		Hunter T.8C	ex North Weald, Ipswich, Shawbury, FRADU, FRU, 759, RAE, 4, 11. Arrived 19-1-01. Stored.		2-02
❑ XE665	'876'	Hunter T.8C ✦	G-BWGM, ex Shawbury, Yeovilton, FRADU, 764, Jever SF, 118.		1-02
❑ XE685	'861'	Hunter GA.11 ✦	G-GAII, ex Yeovilton, FRADU, 738, 98, 93.	± ①	1-02
❑ XE689*	'864'	Hunter GA.11 ✦	G-BWGK, ex North Weald, Exeter, Shawbury, Yeovilton, FRADU, 234, 130, 67. Arr 21-5-00.		1-02
❑ XF321		Hunter T.7	A2734, ex Yeovilton, Manadon A2648, A2734, RAE, 56, 130. Spares.		1-02
❑ XF516	'19'	Hunter F.6A ✦	G-BVVC, ex Cranwell 8685M, 2 TWU, 1 TWU, TWU, 229 OCU, 56, 92, 66. 234 Sqn, TWU, c/s.	±	1-02
❑ XJ639*	'H'	Hunter F.6A	ex Ipswich, Ipswich aerodrome, Cranwell 8687M, 1 TWU, TWU, 229 OCU, 4. Arr 9-2-01. Stored.		2-02
❑ XL573*		Hunter T.7	G-BVGH, ex North Weald, Exeter, Shawbury, 237 OCU, Laarbruch SF, 237 OCU, 4 FTS, 229 OCU, FCS. CoA 13-6-01. Arr 20-1-01.		1-02
❑ XL592	'Y'	Hunter T.7	8836M, ex Scampton, 1 TWU, TWU, 229 OCU. Stored.		1-02
❑ XL602		Hunter T.8M ✦	G-BWFT, ex Shawbury, Yeovilton, FRADU, 759, 764.		1-02

Airport: Like many airfields, Exeter has become a storage centre for airliners, in this case largely HS/BAe 146s and ATRs. As we close for press, none can be listed as long-termers. The Auster is assumed to be still in the area, but the listing is somewhat dated now.

❑ G-AOIY	J/5G Autocar	CoA 26-8-90.	off-site	6-98
❑ G-AVXJ	HS.748-2A	ex Emerald, CAAFU. CoA 22-8-98. Spares.		2-02
❑ G-BAUR	F.27-200	ex JEA, PH-FEP, 9V-BAP, 9M-AMI, VR-RCZ ntu, PH-FEP. CoA 5-4-96. Fuselage.		2-02
❑ [G-BORM]	HS.748-2B	ex RP-C1043, V2-LAA, VP-LAA, 9Y-TDH. Dump.		2-02

IVYBRIDGE on the A38 east of Plymouth
Tony Thorne: Work continues on the Skeeters. XL738 is a composite with the boom of XM565 ①. The collection of rotorcraft has grown somewhat, including an Adams-Wilson acquired in Leicestershire.

❑ G-ATWT*	Napier-Bensen	ex Narborough, G-29-3. wfu 31-1-77.		8-01
❑ G-BIVL*	Bensen B.8M	ex St Merryn. CoA 29-4-87.		8-01
❑ XL738	Skeeter AOP.12	ex Middle Wallop, Fleetlands, Middle Wallop, Southampton, Middle Wallop 7860M, 651, HTF.	® ①	8-01
❑ XL763	Skeeter AOP.12	ex Ottershaw, Southall, Wroughton, 15/19 Hussars, 2 Div, 654, 1 Wing.		8-01
❑ –*	Hobbycopter	ex 'Leicestershire'.		8-01

Others: Work on the Stampe is believed to continue.

❑ G-STMP	SNCAN SV-4A	ex St Merryn, F-BCKB.	®	5-93

KINGSBRIDGE on the A381 north of Salcombe

❑ G-AVXB	Bensen B.8	ex Swansea, G-ARTN. CoA 23-6-87.	10-98

OKEHAMPTON on the A30 west of Exeter
Terrier 2 G-ARSL was flying by 2000. No news of the Series 1.

❑ G-ARNO	Terrier 1	ex Northampton, Stamford, Nympsfield, Auster AOP.6 VX113, 651, 662. CoA 19-6-81.	®	7-97

PLYMOUTH CITY AIRPORT or Roborough, on the A386 north of Plymouth
Plymouth Executive Aviation: Barry Pover sold up and moved to the land of the *flying* Lightnings! Pitts S-2A G-PEAL and the nose of Lightning F.6 XR747 certainly moved on – destination unknown.

YARNSCOMBE north of the B3227, west of Atherington

❑ G-BBAK*	MS.894A Rallye	ex D-ENMK ntu. CoA 8-8-98.	9-00

DORSET

☛ Within the administrative boundaries of Dorset are the unitary authorities of Bournemouth and Poole.

BOURNEMOUTH
Bill Hamblen: Clearing up the destinations of the two Harvards that were held here: Mk.IIb FX442 returned here from Fordingbridge, Hants, and then moved to Hawkinge, Kent; Mk.IIb cockpit KF488 had turned up at the Bournemouth Aviation Museum, Bournemouth, Dorset, by July 2000. The fuselage frame of J/1 Autocrat G-AJPZ had appeared briefly at Stoke-on-Trent, Staffs, before going to Newark-on-Trent, Notts, by October 2001.

Streetwise Safety Centre: Among the 'attractions' at the awareness training centre in Bournemouth is a Twin Squirrel about to 'land' on a Police helicopter pad.
❑ 'S-WISE' AS.355 Squirrel ex PAS Gloucestershire, N354E, F-GIRL. 2-00

BOURNEMOUTH AIRPORT or Hurn, west of the A338, north of the city
De Havilland Aviation (DHA): De Havilland Aviation (see also under Swansea and Bridgend, Wales) are the A8-20 approved maintenance organisation for their own and other resident jets and operate in association with the Bournemouth Aviation Museum – see below. Sea Vixen XP924 was reflown on 16th February 2001, in readiness for the airshow season. Tragically, its much-heralded debut season was over-shadowed by the horrific weekend of 2nd/3rd June at Biggin Hill. On the 2nd Venom G-GONE landed with its wheels-up, but with no injury to the pilot. (It was soon repaired and flying again.) Later in the day, XP924 was displaying with Vampire T.55 U-1234 (G-DHAV) when the latter dived into the ground, killing pilot AM Sir Kenneth Hayr and engineer Jonathon 'Jim' Kerr. New Zealand-born Ken Hayr had become a legend within the RAF and was well regarded in the 'warbird' world as well. Jim Kerr lived for flying and was co-owner of Vampire XE920. He moved to Swansea at the birth of DHA and was a major part in the success of the operation. Both are sorely missed. Shattered by the loss of men and machine, DHA's personnel realised that the best tribute to Ken and Jim would be to carry on the good work. The Sea Vixen continued to wow crowds throughout the 2001 season and looks set to do the same again in 2002. (On the 3rd at Biggin Hill, The Fighter Collection's P-63 crashed fatally – see under Duxford, Cambs.)
◆ Aircraft viewable during normal museum opening hours – subject to engineering and operational conditions – see below. ✉ DHA Bridgend, St Mary's Golf Club, Bridgend, CF35 5EA ☎ 01656 861100 **fax** 01656 863400 **e-mail** enquiries@dehavilland.net **web** www.dehavilland.net

Bournemouth Aviation Museum (BAM) Operated by the Bournemouth Aviation Charitable Foundation. Note that other light aircraft 'lodge' within, but only 'long-termers' are noted here. De Havilland Aviation – see above – operates within the building, looking after its own, and other jets.
Notes: BAM owns Hunter XG160 and Grasshopper WZ798, all others are on loan from individuals or organisations. Some of these are as follows: The Dragon Rapide and 'JP5' G-BWOF are owned and operated by Phil Meeson (PM); the BAC 111 is on loan from European Aviation (EAL); Hunter T.68 G-HVIP is owned by German national Dr Karl Theurer, who trades as Golden Europe Jet Ltd (GEJ). The nose of Vulcan XH537 is on loan from Paul Hartley. It will be restored and painted in an early Mk.2 colour scheme ①. Of John Hallett's (JH) airframes, three are reported to be moving on – ➡.
Departures: Hunter T.7 G-VETA flew to Kemble, Glos, 13-11-00; Buccaneer S.2B nose XK527 moved to Fleetlands, Hants, by 9-00; Vampire T.11 XH328 to Duxford, Cambs, 1-00.
◆ Daily Apr to Sep 10am to 5pm, Oct to Mar, 10am to 4pm ✉ BAM, Hangar 600, Bournemouth International Airport, Christchurch, BH23 6SE ☎ 01202 580858 **web** www.aviation-museum.co.uk

❑ G-AGSH	Rapide 6 ✈	ex Lower Upham, EI-AJO, G-AGSH, NR808. BEA colours, *Gemma Meeson*.	PM	3-02
❑ G-AVMN*	BAC 111-510ED	ex AB Airlines, European, BA, BEA. Last flown 15-2-99. Towed over 4-5-01.	EAL	3-02
❑ G-BEYF	Herald 401	ex Channel Express, RMAF FM1022. On loan.		3-02
❑ G-BWOF	Jet Provost T.5	ex North Weald, XW291, Shawbury, 6 FTS, RAFC, CFS.	PM	3-02
❑ G-GONE	Venom FB.50 ✈	ex Chester, Bournemouth, Swiss AF J-1542. Yellow colours by 5-01.	DHA	3-02
❑ G-HUEY	Bell UH-1H	ex Cranfield, Argentine Army AE-413, 73-22077. CoA 5-10-98.		3-02
❑ G-HVIP	Hunter T.68 ✈	ex Swiss AF J-4208, G-9-415, RSweAF Fv34080. GEJ		3-02
❑ N7SY	Sea Prince T.1	ex G-BRFC, North Weald, Bourn, WP321, Kemble, 750, 744.	JH	3-02
❑ 'K5673'*	Isaacs Fury III ✈	G-BZAS. *Spirit of Dunsfold*. Arrived 8-11-00.		3-02
❑ KF488*	Harvard IIb	ex Bournemouth, Wimborne, Sandhurst, Avex. Cockpit. First noted 7-00		3-02
❑ RT486* PF-A'	Auster 5 ✈	G-AJGJ, ex RT486, 43 OTU. Arrived 11-00.		3-02
❑ WM167	Meteor TT.20 ✈	G-LOSM, ex HOC, Blackbushe, RAE Llanbedr, 228, Colerne CS, 228 OCU.		3-02

❑	WT532	Canberra PR.7	ex Airport, Lovaux, Cosford, 8890M / 8728M, RAE		
			Bedford, 13, Wyton SF, 58, 31, 13, 80. Nose.		3-02
❑	WZ798*	G'hopper TX.1	ex Bournemouth School. Stored. First noted 6-01.		3-02
❑	XE920*	'A' Vampire T.11 ✈	G-VMPR, ex Swansea, Chester, Sealand, 8196M		
			Scampton, Henlow, Shawbury, CATCS, 8 FTS,		
			5 FTS, 1 FTS. 603 Sqn c/s. Arr 2-4-01.	DHA	3-02
❑	[XG160]	Hunter F.6A	G-BWAF, ex 'RJAF', Scampton 8831M,		
			1 TWU, 229 OCU, 111, 43. Stored.		3-02
❑	XH537*	Vulcan B.2MRR	ex Bruntingthorpe, Ottershaw, Camberley,		
			Abingdon 8749M, 27, 230 OCU, MoA. Nose.		
			Arrived 29-10-01.	①	3-02
❑	'XJ771'	Vampire T.55 ✈	G-HELV, ex '215' Sion, Swiss AF U-1215.		
			RAF colours.		3-02
❑	[XM697]	'S' Gnat T.1	G-NAAT, ex Dunsfold, Bournemouth, Woking,		
			HSA, A&AEE, HSA.	JH ➠	1-02
❑	XP924*	Sea Vixen D.3	G-CVIX, ex Swansea, Llanbedr, RAE, FRL,		
			RAE, ADS, 899, 893. *Lt Marcus Edwards RN.*		
			Arrived 29-5-00. Reflown 16-2-01.	DHA	3-02
❑	XR537	'T' Gnat T.1	G-NATY, ex Cosford 8642M, Reds, 4 FTS.	®	3-02
❑	XX897*	Buccaneer	ex airfield, DRA Bedford, RAE, RRE. Tornado nose.		
		S.2B(mod)	European Airlines colours. Towed over 1-6-01.		3-02
❑	E-402	Hunter F.51	ex Kemble, Bournemouth, Macclesfield,		
			Dunsfold, G-9-433, RDanAF Esk.724.	JH ➠	2-02
❑	503	MiG-21PF	G-BRAM, ex North Weald, Hungarian AF.	JH ➠	2-02
❑	1211*	SBLim-5	G-BWUF, ex Duxford, Polish AF. Korean c/s.		
		(MiG-17)	Arrived 20-2-02.		3-02
❑	C-552*	EKW C-3605 ✈	G-DORN, ex HB-RBJ, SwissAF C-552. Arr 9-1-01. JH		2-02
❑	–	Hunter T.7	ex Biggin Hill, 'G-ERIC', Bournemouth,		
			Leavesden, Elstree, Hatfield. Nose of XJ690. 'Gate'.		3-02

Source Classic Jet Flight / Lindsay Wood Promotions Ltd: Gnat T.1 XS100 was entered in the Philips auction of 16th March 2000, reaching £9,200. It departed by road on 10th May 2000, going initially to Fyfield, Essex. The collection, in part or in whole, was advertised for sale, in early 2002.

❑	[FLV]	L-13 Blanik	BGA.3354, ex Eaglescott, D-1355. *Jenny.* Fuselage.		3-02
❑	'VT871'	Vampire FB.6 ✈	G-DHXX, ex 'LZ551/G', Southampton, Swiss AF		
			J-1173. 54 Squadron colours by 6-98.		3-02
❑	'VV612'	Venom FB.50 ✈	G-VENI, ex 'WE402'. Swiss AF J-1523.		
			Prototype colours by 8-99.		3-02
❑	'WR360'	Venom FB.50 ✈	G-DHSS, ex Swiss AF J-1626. White 60 Sqn c/s.		3-02
❑	'WR410'	Venom FB.50 ✈	G-DHUU, G-BMOD ntu, ex Swiss AF J-1539.		
			6 Sqn colours, Suez stripes. First flown 17-7-96.		3-02
❑	'WR410'	'N' Venom FB.54	G-BLKA, ex Bruntingthorpe, Cranfield,		
			G-VENM ntu, Swiss AF J-1790. Stored.		3-02
❑	'WR421'	Venom FB.50 ✈	G-DHTT, G-BMOC ntu, ex Swiss AF J-1611. Red c/s.		3-02
❑	WZ553	'40' Vampire T.11	G-DHYY, ex Bruntingthorpe, Cranfield, Lichfield,		
			Winthorpe, South Wigston, Bruntingthorpe,		
			Loughborough, East Midlands, Liverpool, Woodford,		
			Chester, St Athan, 4 FTS, 7 FTS, 202 AFS. Stored.		3-02
❑	'WZ589'	Vampire T.55 ✈	G-DHZZ, ex Southampton, Swiss AF		
			U-1230. 20 Sqn colours by mid-2001.		3-02
❑	'XE897'	Vampire T.55 ✈	G-DHVV, ex Southampton, Swiss AF		
			U-1214. 54 Sqn colours.		3-02
❑	'XG775'	Vampire T.55 ✈	G-DHWW, ex Southampton, Swiss AF U-1219.		
			Navy FOFT c/s, as Sea Vampire T.22.		3-02
❑	XR954	'30' Gnat T.1	ex Ipswich, Halton 8570M, 4 FTS, CFS, 4 FTS.		3-02
❑	J-1573	Venom FB.50 ✈	G-VICI, ex HB-RVB, G-BMOB ntu, Swiss AF.		4-01
❑	J-1629	Venom FB.50	ex Dubendorf, Swiss AF. Stored.		3-02
❑	J-1649	Venom FB.50 ✈	ex Dubendorf, Swiss AF. Stored.		3-02

Airliners: A cull of One-Elevens to record: -510ED G-AVMI (last flown 8-9-99), 2-02; -510ED G-AVMK 1-02 and sections moved to Gravesend, Kent; -510ED G-AVMP stored by 5-01, 2-02; -510ED G-AVMR, 3-4-01; -510ED G-AVMV 5-9-00; -510ED G-AVMW 23-1-02; -510ED G-AVMX 1-9-00; -521FH G-HKIT 30-3-01; -518FG G-IIIH 4-4-01; -524FF VR-BEA 7-9-00; -414EG 5N-BAB 8-00 (see under Alton, Hants, for a likely – partial - destination). BAC 111-527FK VR-BEB was moved to the fire crews on 27th September 2000 – see below. BAC 111-510ED G-AVMN last flew on 15th February 1999, it was towed over to the museum (see above) 4th May 2001. Electra EI-CHX was scrapped by February 2002.

❏ G-AVMH	BAC 111-510ED	ex BA, BEA. Stored.	6-01
❏ G-AVMJ	BAC 111-510ED	ex Filton, BA, BEA. CoA 17-11-94. Cabin trainer.	6-01
❏ G-AVMP*	BAC 111-510ED	ex European, BA, BEA. Stored by 5-01.	6-01
❏ G-AVMS*	BAC 111-510ED	ex European, BA, BEA. Stored by 5-01.	12-01
❏ G-AVMY*	BAC 111-510ED	ex European, BA, BEA. Stored by 5-01.	6-01
❏ G-AVMZ*	BAC 111-510ED	ex European. Last flight 30-10-01. Stored.	10-01
❏ G-AWYV*	BAC 111-501EX	ex 5N-OSA ntu, European, BA, BEA. Stored by 5-01.	6-01
❏ G-CEAA	Airbus A300B2	ex F-WQGQ, F-BUAI, Air Inter. Stored.	11-01
❏ G-CEAB	Airbus A300B2	ex F-WQGS, F-BUAH, Air Inter, F-WLGC, F-WLGB. Stored.	2-00
❏ G-CHNX*	Electra 188AF	ex Channex, EI-CHO, -G-CHNX ntu, N5535. Withdrawn by 10-01. Spares.	1-02
❏ ZS-SDA*	Airbus A300B2	ex South African, F-WLGA. *Blesbok*. Arrived 22-5-01. Spares.	2-02
❏ ZS-SDD*	Airbus A300B2	ex South African, F-WUAX. *Rooibok*. Arrived 7-5-01. Spares.	2-02
❏ XA-PBA*	Boeing 737-2H6	ex TAESA, XA-APB, PK-IJD, 9M-MBG, 9M-ARG. Arrived 22-4-01. Spares.	2-02
❏ XA-TLJ*	Boeing 737-2H6	ex TAESA. Arrived 25-5-01. Spares.	2-02

Others: Herald 210 G-SCTT was scrapped on 1st September 2000. Vampire FB.6 G-SWIS was exported, believed to New Zealand, during 2001. The nose of A300B2 F-BVGB had gone from the dump by mid-2000. The hulk of P-2 Kraguj 30151 moved to Fordingbridge, Hants, by February 2001. Buccaneer S.2B(m) XX897 was resprayed in European Airlines colours and towed over to the museum, above, on 1st June 2001. One of the former Indonesian Air Force Hawks is used as a source of spares.

❏ G-ASOX	Cessna 205A	ex ?, Newcastle, N4856U. CoA 1-8-92.	2-02
❏ G-ATPD	HS.125-1B/522	ex 5N-AGU, G-ATPD. CoA 14-10-98.	12-01
❏ G-AXAU	T Comanche 160C	ex N8613Y. CoA 8-3-86. Stored.	2-00
❏ G-BAVS*	AA-5 Traveler	fuselage. CoA 8-11-94. First noted 8-00.	2-02
❏ G-BBFC	AA-1B Trainer	fuselage. Damaged 9-6-96.	2-02
❏ G-BDCE	Cessna F.172H	ex Bruntingthorpe, N6137Y. Fuselage. Dam 1-99.	2-00
❏ G-BUTT	Cessna FA.150K	ex G-AXSJ. Fuselage. Damaged 1-99.	2-00
❏ N44DN*	Malibu 350P	crashed 8-7-00. Stored.	2-02
❏ SX-BFM*	Navajo	ex Southampton, N4504J. Crashed 23-6-99. Fuselage. First noted 12-01.	3-02
❏ VR-BEB*	BAC 111-527FK	ex airliner store, RP-C1181, PI-C1181. Fire crews. Towed over 27-9-00.	2-02
❏ WJ992	Canberra T.4	ex DRA Bedford, RAE, 76. Fire dump.	2-02
❏ LL-5313*	Hawk T.53	ex Indonesian Air Force. Spares. First noted 1-02.	1-02
❏ [J-4083]	Hunter F.58	G-EGHH, ex JHL, Swiss AF. Stored.	2-02

BOVINGTON off the A352 near Wool, west of Wareham

Tank Museum: Houses the world's finest international collection of armoured fighting vehicles.
◆ Open daily (except Xmas) 10am to 5pm. Special events throughout the year. ✉ Tank Museum, Bovington, Dorset, BH20 6JG ☎ 01929 405096 fax 01929 405360 e-mail admin@ tankmuseum.co.uk web www.tankmuseum.co.uk or www.tiger-tank.com

❏ TK718	GAL Hamilcar I	ex Beverley, Christian Malford.	3-02
❏ XM564	Skeeter AOP.12	ex 652, CFS, 12 Flt, 652.	3-02

CHRISTCHURCH on the A35 east of Bournemouth
Sea Vixen FAW.2 XJ580 moved to Tangmere, W Sussex, on 27th June 2000.

COLEHILL north of the A31, north-east of Wimborne Minster
St Michael's Middle School: Nothing on the school's had plaything, the fuselage and tail of what is thought to be a Stampe with a propeller described as 'of dubious origins'.

❏ 'G-OFLY'   'Biplane'   see notes   9-98

COMPTON ABBAS AERODROME south-east of Shaftesbury
Two long-termers are best deleted from here: F.150G G-AVCT (last noted December 1997) and FRA.150L G-BBKF (June 1996).

❏ G-AZRV*   Arrow 200   ex N2309T. Crashed 30-12-00. First noted 2-01.   1-02

DORCHESTER
Wessex Aviation and Transport: Three aircraft have left the store, Dragon Rapide G-ACZE had moved to Haverfordwest, Wales, by March 2000; Hornet Moth G-ADUR and Leopard Moth G-AIYS had both moved on during 2000. *Uniform-Romeo* moved to Spanhoe Lodge, Northants, and returned to the air on 13th July 2001. The remainder, including the Stearman which did not leave, contrary to *W&R17*, are presumed undisturbed.

❏ G-ABEV	DH.60G Moth	ex N4203E, G-ABEV, HB-OKI, CH-217. CoA 19-10-97.	7-01
❏ G-AFOB	Moth Minor	ex Old Warden, X5117, 10 OAFU, StA UAS, 613, G-AFOB. CoA 11-5-93.	7-01
❏ G-BMNV	SNCAN SV-4L	ex Booker, F-BBNI. CoA 8-6-94.	7-01
❏ N4712V	PT-13D Kaydet	ex 42-16931.	7-01
❏ T5672	Tiger Moth	G-ALRI, ex ZK-BAB, G-ALRI, T5672, 7 FTS, 21 EFTS, 7 FTS, RAFC, 4 EFTS. CoA 19-8-94.	7-01

GALLOWS HILL on a minor road between Bere Regis and Wool, north of Bovington Camp
Dorset Gliding Club: A trio of 'retired' military gliders at this delightful location.

❏ WB922*	Sedbergh TX.1	ex Rufforth, Syerston, 615 VGS, Benson, St Athan, CGS. Stored. First noted 6-00.	12-01
❏ WZ755*	FSC G'hopper TX.1	BGA.3481. Ex Brunton, Barnstaple. Stored. First noted 5-98. Stored.	12-01
❏ XP492*	FSB G'hopper TX.1	BGA.3480. Ex 2 MGSP, Locking, Taunton, Greater Malvern. Stored. First noted 11-98.	12-01

POOLE on the A35 west of Bournemouth
Two 'Sheds' (well, one's a 'Super Shed') are to be found in two different locations in the area.

❏ G-BGNG*	Short 330-200	ex Bournemouth, Gill, N330FL, G-BGNG. Fuselage. Here since 1996.	1-02
❏ G-DASI*	Short 360	ex Guernsey, Gill, G-14-3606. Fuselage. Arr 1-01.	1-02

STALBRIDGE on the A357 south-west of Shaftesbury
The Moth Minor Coupe is under restoration to open top format.

❏ G-AFNI   Moth Minor   ex Woodley, W7972, 100 GCF, Foulsham SF, 241, G-AFNI. CoA 26-5-67.   ® 12-99

DURHAM and CLEVELAND

☛ The unitary authorities of Hartlepool, Middlesbrough, Redcar and Cleveland and Stockton-on-Tees, and Darlington form the region.

STANLEY on the A693 west of Washington
'By February 2000 Cherokee 140 G-ATOO was flying again' - quote from *W&R17*, p52. Err... no!
More like it moved to <u>Carlisle</u>, Cumbria and it was not with Jason Howe!

TEES-SIDE AIRPORT or Middleton St George, south of the A67, east of Darlington
International Fire Training Centre: At the Serco-operated school, as well as the real airframes also here is a convincing mock-up of a Tornado, complete with 9 Squadron badge, used for burning practice along with a 747 front fuselage, a 'Boeing 737', a light aircraft and a 'helicopter' mock-up.

❏ G-ARPO	Trident 1C	ex BA, BEA. CoA 12-1-86. Whole.	7-01
❏ G-AVFJ	Trident 2E	ex BA, BEA. CoA 18-9-83. Poor state.	7-01
❏ G-AWZR	Trident 3B-101	ex BA, BEA. CoA 9-4-86. Poor state.	7-01
❏ G-AWZS	Trident 3B-101	ex BA, BEA. CoA 9-9-86. Whole.	7-01
❏ G-AZLP	Viscount 813	ex BMA, SAA ZS-CDT. CoA 3-4-82. Fuselage.	3-02
❏ G-AZLS	Viscount 813	ex BMA, SAA ZS-CDV. CoA 9-6-83.	3-02
❏ 'G-JON'	Short 330-100	G-BKIE, ex Newcastle, G-SLUG, G-METP, G-METO, G-BKIE, C-GTAS, G-14-3005. CoA 22-8-93.	3-00
❏ XP330	W'wind HAR.10	ex Stansted, 21, 32, 230, 110, 225. Poor state.	3-00

Others: The land on which the Lightning stood was required for further airport development and FRA Aviation offered to take care of it. It was moved in March 2001 and 'unveiled' on its new (and secure) site on the airport on 5th July 2001 ①. Viscount G-AZNC is used by the airport fire services for non-destructive training. Cessna 170B G-BCLS moved to <u>East Kirkby</u>, Lincs, by July 2001.

❏ G-AZNC	Viscount 813	ex BMA, G-AZLW ntu, SAA, ZS-SBZ, ZS-CDZ.		3-02
❏ G-BNGS*	Tomahawk 112	ex Carlisle, Tees-side, Carlisle, N2463A. Damaged 5-87. Spares.		3-02
❏ XR749 'DA'	Lightning F.3	ex Chop Gate, Leuchars 8934M, 11, LTF, 11, LTF, Binbrook pool, 29, 226 OCU, 56, EE. Overstressed 17-2-87. LTF c/s. FRA 'guardian'.	①	3-02

Off-site: P-51D-20-NA 41 (G-LYNE) was exported to the USA during late 2001.

YEARBY on the B1269 south of Redcar
Acro Engines and Airframes Ltd: Two Bölkow Juniors are under composite rebuild.

❏ G-APYB*	Nipper III	CoA 212-6-<u>96</u>.	®	3-02
❏ G-ASFR	Bö 208A-1	ex D-EGMO. CoA 29-3-90.		3-02
❏ G-BAMG*	Ganagobie	unfinished project. Stored.		3-02
❏ G-BHUO*	Evans VP-2	unfinished project. Stored.		3-02
❏ G-OOSE*	Rutan VariEze	unflown project. Damaged, stored.		3-02
❏ D-EFNO	Bö 208A-1	–	off-site ®	3-02

ESSEX

ANDREWSFIELD AERODROME or Great Saling, north of the A120, west of Braintree

❏ G-ASXC	SIPA 903	ex F-BEYK. CoA 28-7-94.	®	1-99
❏ G-AYUI	Cherokee 180F	ex N8557, G-AYUI. CoA 5-11-93. Stored.		11-01
❏ G-AZOT	Seneca 200	ex Sibson. Landing accident -98.		4-00
❏ G-BOON	Lance II	ex N361DB. Crashed 10-10-97. Wreck.		5-01
❏ 319	Mystère IVA	ex Sculthorpe, French Air Force.		1-02

AUDLEY END AERODROME off the B1383, west of Saffron Walden
Historic Flying Ltd (HFL): When Spitfire XVIII SM845 (G-BUOS) flew for the first time on 7th July 2000 it clocked up HFL's tenth Spitfire restoration. Mk.IX MK912 (G-BRRA) made its first flight on 8th September 2000. By late April 2001, HFL had completed relocation to a brand-new facility at Duxford, Cambs, shared with ARCo. Involved in the move were the following: Spitfires MK912 (G-BRRA)on 8th September 2000, RN201 (G-BSKP), SM845 (G-BUOS) on 7th July 2000 and Chipmunk T.10 WK522 (G-BCOU). Two others remain stored, off-site, in the area.

☐ JG891	Spitfire Vc	ZK-MKV, ex Auckland, RAAF A58-178, 79, RAF JG891. Accident 1-44. Stored.	off-site 3-02
☐ TB252	Spitfire XVI	G-XVIE, ex Braintree, Bentley Priory 8073M, Leuchars, Boulmer, Acklington, Odiham, 7281M, 7257M, 61 OTU, 350, 341, 329, 84 GSU. Stored.	off-site 3-02

Others: The Humming Bird project G-EBQP moved to Hatch, Beds.

☐ F-BGCJ	Tiger Moth	G-BTOG, ex France, French AF, NM192. Stored.	4-99

BRAINTREE on the A120 east of Colchester
In the general area are salvaged Spitfires - shot down within 72 hours of one another – plus a Seafire from Malta. All three are substantial remains and one day will form restoration projects.

☐ N3200*	Spitfire Ia	ex Sandown, Calais, 19. Shot down 27-5-40. Stored. Arrived 22-2-02.	3-02
☐ P9374*	Spitfire Ia	ex Sandown, Calais, 92. Shot down 24-5-40. Stored. Arrived 22-2-02.	3-02
☐ MB293*	Seafire IIc	ex Sandown, Malta, 879, 887, A&AEE. Stored. Arrived 22-2-02.	3-02

CHELMSFORD
No.276 Squadron Air Cadets: In Meteor Way, off the Chelmsford-Harlow road, keep their T.7.

☐ WH132	'J' Meteor T.7	7906M, ex Kemble, CAW, CFS, CAW, 8 FTS, 207 AFS.	9-00

Others: Glen Newman *should* still keep a Hunter nose in the area.

☐ XG209	'66' Hunter F.6	ex Stock, Halton, Cranwell, Halton 8709M, 12 DFLS, 111, 14. Nose.	2-96

David Collins: David has started work in this area on a long-term project to build a full-size model DH Hornet, using many original components. David is co-operating with Mark Reeder (see under Fyvie, Scotland) and would like to hear from others who may be able to help. **e-mail** dcollins103@hotmail.com

CHIPPING ONGAR north of the A414, west of the town
Blake Hall 'Ops' Room and Airscene Museum: The hall is well known for its gardens, but also has within it a splendid array of artefacts centred around the hall's history as being the Operations Centre for Sector E when the 'ops' room at North Weald was dispersed from the airfield.
◆ Easter to October Sundays and Bank Holidays 11am to 5pm.

CLACTON-ON-SEA
East Essex Aviation Museum (EEAM) **and Museum of the 1940s**: Located within one of the fine Martello towers that dot the coastline, EEAM includes a fine array of recovery items and other memorabilia. Dominating the contents is the fuselage of P-51D *Little Zippie*. Recovered during 1999 and on show is the substantial wreckage of 339th FG P-51D 44-15560 which crashed at Frinton-on-Sea.
◆ Within Point Clear caravan park. Open Monday 7pm to 10pm and Sunday 10am to 2pm all year. Jun to Sep Wed 10am to 2pm, plus Sunday 10am to 4pm and Bank Holidays. ✉ Roger Barrell, 37 Brookland Road, Brantham, Essex, CO11 1RP

☐ 44-14574	P-51D-10-NA	ex 479th FG *Little Zippie*. Crashed off-shore 13-1-45.	2-00

Locally: A collector acquired two airframes during 2000. Hunter FGA.9 XG254 arrived on 10th October 2000 but moved to Flixton, Suffolk, on 19th February 2002. The 'JP' is also for disposal.

❑ XR670*	Jet Provost T.4	8498M, ex Odiham, Brize Norton, Halton, SoRF, CATCS, 3 FTS, 1 FTS, 2 FTS, 7 FTS, CFS.	12-01

CLACTON AERODROME west of Clacton, east of Jaywick
Clacton Aero Club: Operate the Classic Wings joy-riding fleet – see under Duxford, Cambs. The hulks of Cessnas F.172E G-ASUH and 172N G-BKRB are both thought to have gone.

CLAVERING on the B1038 south-west of Saffron Walden
No news on the scrapyard at Starling's Green and its Cessna fuselage.

❑ G-AXWF	Cessna F.172H	ex Clacton, Andrewsfield. Dbr 26/27-11-83. Fuselage.	7-95

COLCHESTER
Charleston Aviation Services: Craig Charleston's workshop in the area specialises in Bf 109s.

❑	Sea Fury FB.11	composite, parts from G-AGHB, G-FURY and *possibly* T.20S D-CIBO.		3-94
❑ LA546	Seafire F.46	ex Newport Pagnell, Newark. Substantial parts.		3-02
❑ 7485*	Bf 109F-4	ex Russia.	®	3-02
❑ 8147	Bf 109F-4	ex Lancing, Russia, 6/JG54.	®	3-02
❑ 15458*	Bf 109G-2	ex Russia.	®	3-02

Others: Glenn Mitchell is *thought* still to have his Canberra nose section in the area.

❑ WE168	Canberra PR.3	ex Manston 8049M, 231 OCU, 39, 69, 540. Nose.	4-90

EARLS COLNE AERODROME on the B1024 south of Earls Colne, east of Halstead
Hawker Restorations Ltd (HRL): Earls Colne was the flying base for HRL, but they moved out by mid-2001. (See also their workshop at Sudbury, Suffolk.) Sea Hurricane X AE977 (G-TWTD) arrived from Sudbury and made its first flight on 7th June 2000. It left for the USA as N33TF in late 2001 having operated out of Duxford, Cambs, for a while. Seafire III PP972 (G-BUAR) moved to Martham, Norfolk. Bf 109E 1342 (G-BYDS) was acquired by the Flying Heritage Collection of Seattle, Washington, USA, and was exported.

Others:

❑ G-AOZL	J/5Q Alpine	ex Southend. CoA 28-5-88.	®	9-01

EAST TILBURY on a minor road east of Tilbury
Thameside Aviation Museum (TAM): Located within the Coalhouse Fort 1860s Victorian Casemate Fortress, TAM is dedicated to aviation archaeology excavations carried out from the early 1970s to date. The MiG-21UM is now owned by TAM, as is the newly-arrived Gnat nose, which is also ex-Air Defence Collection. Its identity is confirmed ①.
♦ At Coalhouse Fort, 'brown signed' from A13. TAM open last Sun of the month and Bank Hols, Mar to Oct 11am to 4.30pm. Other times by arrangement. (Details of Coalhouse Fort ☎ 01375 844203) ✉ Coalhouse Fort, East Tilbury, Essex ☎ 07860 134946 **e-mail** museum@aviationmuseum.co.uk **web** www.aviationmuseum.co.uk

❑ WG471*	Chipmunk T.10 PAX	ex Bury St Edmunds, 8210M, Stowmarket, Leeming, Abn UAS, 1 FTS, 6 FTS, 220 OCU, Aston Down CF, MCCS, 4 SoTT, Nott UAS, Leeds UAS, 19 RFS, 24 RFS, 3 BFTS, 16 RFS, 4 BFTS.		3-02
❑ XM692*	Gnat T.1	ex Boscombe Down, Robertsbridge, Salisbury, Southampton, Fareham, Folland. Nose.	①	3-02
❑ 0446	MiG-21UM	ex Salisbury, Farnborough, Egyptian AF. Nose.		3-02

EASTWOOD on the A1015 north of Leigh-on-Sea
No.2431 Squadron Air Cadets: Canberra B.15 nose WT502 moved to <u>Manston</u>, Kent, on 14th October 2000.

FOULNESS ISLAND on a minor road north-east of Great Wakering
Defence Science and Technology Laboratory, Shoeburyness (DS&TL — yet still another name change, effective from 1st July 2001. See under Boscombe Down, Wilts, for still more interesting alphabetic contortions): The range functions in a smaller enclave, at the north-east of the 'island', beyond Courtsend. *W&R16* (p61) recorded Buccaneer S.2B XW541 being used for destructive testing and wrote it out of the book. This was premature! It was scrapped sometime between June and November 2000 and the cockpit moved to Stock, Essex, thence to Ingatestone, Essex, and from there to <u>Welshpool</u>, Wales. This almost certainly accounts for the anonymous 'Bucc' noted under this heading in *W&R17* (p55). By early 2001, the two former Pendine F-4J(UK)s, ZE350 and ZE352 had moved to <u>Stock</u>, Essex.

❏ XT272	Buccaneer S.2	ex Pendine, Farnborough, Bedford.	6-98
❏	F-4	cockpit section	3-00

FYFIELD on the B184 north of Chipping Ongar
During 2000 a Skeeter and a Gnat arrived here.

❏ XK482*	Skeeter AOP.10	G-BJWC, ex Northampton, Blackpool, Heysham, Horsham, Ottershaw, Middle Wallop 7840M, HTF, HS, MoS.	6-01
❏ XS100*	'57' Gnat T.1	ex Bournemouth, Ipswich, Halton 8561M, 4 FTS. Arrived 10-5-00.	3-02

GREAT DUNMOW on the A120 west of Braintree
Paul and **Andy Wood**: Should still have their Hunter.

❏ WP185	Hunter F.5	ex Abingdon, Hendon, Henlow 7583M, 34, 1. Stored.	2-96

GREAT WALTHAM on the A130 north of Chelmsford
Peter Lee: The Messenger restoration continues. A small part of G-AHUI and a wing section from North Ireland, are helping in this project. Airworthy Gemini G-AKHP is now with Adrian Brook.

❏ G-AKEZ	Messenger 2A	ex 'RG333', Higher Blagdon, Bristol. CoA 15-11-68. ®	10-01

HALSTEAD north-east of Braintree
Rebuild of the Auster and Tiger is *thought* to continue.

❏ G-AJUL	J/1N Alpha	CoA 11-9-81.	® 12-90
❏ G-APBI	Tiger Moth	ex Audley End, EM903, 2 FIS, 26. Crashed 7-7-80.	® 12-90

INGATESTONE on the A12 south west of Chelmsford
A private collector here acquired four airframes from Welshpool, Wales, during the summer of 2001. Vampire XE864 is fitted with the wings of XD435 ①. See under Foulness, Essex, for the story of a 'Bucc' nose that staged through here.

❏ WF145*	Sea Hawk F.1	ex Welshpool, South Molton, Salisbury, Torbay, Brawdy, Abbotsinch, RAE, A&AEE.	7-01
❏ XD235*	Scimitar F.1	ex Welshpool, Southampton, Ottershaw, Foulness, FRU, 803. Nose.	7-01
❏ XD599*	'A' Vampire T.11	ex Welshpool, Shobdon, Caernarfon, Bournemouth, Blackbushe, Staverton, Stroud, CATCS, RAFC, 1.	7-01
❏ XE864*	Vampire T.11	ex Welshpool, Shobdon, Stretton, Kibworth, Firbeck, Studley, Chester, Woodford, St Athan, 8 FTS, 7 FTS, 1 ANS, CFS, 4 FTS.	① 7-01

LAINDON north of the A127, near Basildon

❑ G-AFGE*	Swallow II	ex BK894, CLE, RAE, G-AFGE. CoA 27-7-98.	
		Maggie. Stored. First noted 6-01.	8-01
❑ G-ARXP	Luton Minor	CoA 17-10-95. Stored.	8-01

NORTH WEALD AERODROME off the A414, junction 7, M11 east of Harlow

Aces High Flying Museum: Aviation film work has again been enjoying an 'up' with Dakotas to the fore in terms of 'stardom'. As with other elements of this superb aerodrome, the Aces High area hosts a series of airworthy 'modern' light aircraft. These are not given here.

Notes: The CASA 2-111 continues its restoration. It has been sold to a US collector, very probably Seattle-based ①. The pages of *W&R* have recorded the comings and goings of a gutted helicopter fuselage here, variously described as a 'JetRanger; or an 'Enstrom'. From around December 2000 the beast was back! And it has remained a consistent resident. Inspection confirms it not just to be an Enstrom, but an F-280 Shark and D-HGBX at that ②. The Auster AOP.9 and Beech 18 are owned by Edwards Brothers Aviation (EBA). C-47A N47FK is operated by **The Dakota Trust** (DT): ✉ PO Box 96, Reading, RG7 4EH ☎ 0118 9831776 **fax** 0118 9833744 **e-mail** dakinfo@eurofly.co.uk **web** www.dakotatrust.com It spends a lot of time at Bournemouth, Dorset.

◆ Visits strictly by prior appointment *only.* ✉ Aces High Flying Museum (NW) Ltd, North Weald Aerodrome, Epping, CM16 6AA.

❑ G-AWHB	CASA 2-111	ex Royston, Southend, Spanish AF B2I-57.	® ①	9-01
❑ 'G-ESKY'	Aztec 250D	G-BADI ex N6885Y. CoA 29-10-92. Hulk.		3-02
❑ G-CSFT	Aztec 250D	ex G-AYKU, N13885. CoA 3-12-94. Hulk.		9-01
❑ [D-HGBX]	Enstrom F-280	hulk. First noted (again!) 12-00.	②	9-01
❑ N47FL	C-47A-20-DK ✈	ex Elstree, EC-FIN, EC-659, N7164E,		
		C-GCTE, C-GXAV, N92A ntu, C-GXAV,		
		CAF 12952, RCAF 968, 42-93203.		1-01
❑ N2700	C-119G-FA	ex Manston, 3C-ABA, Belg AF CP-9, 12700. Nose.		9-01
❑ (N3455)*	C-47B-35-DK	ex North Weald, Sandtoft, North Weald, Exeter,		
		G-AMSN, EI-BSI, N3455, SU-BFZ, N3455,		
		G-AMSN, KN673, 240 OCU, 1382 TCU,		
		45 GCF, 44-77047. Arrived by 4-01.		3-02
❑ N96240	Beech D.18S	ex Rochester, Spain, Wellesbourne Mountford,		
		Blackbushe, G-AYAH, N6123, RCAF 1559.		
		The Name of the Game Is..	EBA	3-02
❑ [6W-SAF]*	C-47A-65-DL	ex North Weald, Woodley, Kew, Cranfield, F-GEFU,		
		Le Bourget, Senegalese AF, USAF MAAG Brussels,		
		USAAF 42-100611. Nose. Arrived by 4-01.		9-01
❑ 'FL586'*	C-47B-10-DK	ex Pinewood, *Sword of Honour*, OO-SMA, N99346		
'AI-N'		ntu, Belg AF K-1 OT-CWA, 43-49240. Fuselage.		3-02
❑ XN437	Auster AOP.9	G-AXWA, ex ?, Lashenden, Welling, Biggin		
		Hill, Luton, Odiham, Maghull, Hoylake,		
		St Athan, Kenya.	EBA ®	12-00
❑ '0710'	'TG' Dakota 3 ✈	N147DC, ex G-DAKS, Duxford, '10884', 'KG374',		
		Airline 'G-AGHY', TS423, RAE, Ferranti, Airwork,		
		Gatow SF, 436, 1 HGSU, 42-100884.		
		Early USAAF colours by 9-00.		3-02
❑ '292912'	C-47A-35-DL ✈	N47FK, ex Elstree, EC-FNS, EC-187, N2669A,		
'L4-S'		C-FEEX, CF-EEX, N308FN, N3PG, N3W, N7V,		
		NC49538, 42-23838. USAAF c/s by 9-00.	DT	9-01
❑ 430861	TB-25J-NC	N9089Z, ex Duxford, 'HD368', G-BKXW ntu,		
		Southend, Biggin Hill, N9089Z, 44-30861.		
		Bedsheet Bomber.		3-02

Flying 'A' Services / Wizzard Investments Ltd: The hangar remains tantalisingly enigmatic! Catalina N285RA is registered to the Randsberg Corporation of the USA ①. Given that some of the aircraft are believed to be within the six ISO containers within, the listing below is believed to be accurate! It will be seen that several items considered 'elsewhere' are here, hence 'tidying' things up considerably. They are noted with the traditional asterisk as 'new' but are likely to have been here some time. The bulk of the cockpit of Lancaster X KB994 is also here – see under Sandtoft for more Lancaster/Lincoln jottings ②. A second P-51 is stored is *likely* N513PA, but could also be N7098V ③. During June 2000 a Fi 156 Storch or MS.500/505 coded 'ZE+RA' was noted inside the hangar. This is believed to have come from La Ferté Alais, France, and is also thought to have transitted to the USA. This could have been the genuine Fi 156 that became N436FS or it may be MS.500 N43FS - your call! Fw 190A 1227 (G-FOKW) moved to Martham, Norfolk, where the Seafire project is also located. F6F-5K Hellcat N79863 left by road on 12th July 2001, bound for the USA.

◆ Visits by prior appointment *only*.

❑ N285RA	PBY-6A Catalina	ex G-BPFY, Biggin Hill, North Weald, N212DM, G-BPFY, N212DM, G-BPFY, C-FHNH, F-ZBAV, N5555H, N2846D, BuNo 64017.	①	3-02
❑ NL314BG*	P-51D-25-NA	ex ?, Bournemouth, Biggin Hill, USA, C-GZQX, CF-BAU, N51N, N169MD, N6337T, RCAF 9567, 44-73140. *Petie 2nd*. Stored, dismantled.		1-02
❑ N909WJ	FM-2 Wildcat	ex Earls Colne, Lelystad (?), Bournemouth, Biggin Hill, USA, USN 5613. Stored.		1-02
❑ N9950*	P-40N Warhawk	ex ?, Biggin Hill, USA, USAAF 44-7983. Stored.		1-02
❑ NH238*	Spitfire IX	G-MKIX, ex ?, Bournemouth, Biggin Hill, Bitteswell, N238V, Harlingen, Hemswell, Winthorpe, Southampton, Andover, COGEA OO-ARE, Coxyde, Belg AF SM-36, Dutch AF H-60, Sealand, 76 MU, 9 MU, 49 MU, 84 GSU. Stored, dismantled.		1-02
❑ KB994*	Lancaster B.10	ex Bedford, Exeter, Canada, Pigeon Lake, Edmonton, RCAF. Nose.	②	1-02
❑ RW386	Spitfire XVI	G-BXVI, ex ?, Audley End, Biggin Hill, Bitteswell, Blackbushe, St Athan, Halton 6944M, 58 MU, 604. Stored, dismantled.		1-02
❑ SM969	'D-A' Spitfire XVIII	G-BRAF, ex ?, Bournemouth, Biggin Hill, Bitteswell, Blackbushe, New Delhi, Indian AF HS877, RAF SM969, 47 MU, India, ACSEA, 76 MU. CoA 23-9-93. Stored, dismantled.		1-02
❑ *	P-51D	Stored, dismantled.	③	1-02

Intrepid Aviation: The collection was put up for sale during August 2000 and the aircraft are slowly moving on P-51D 474008 (G-SIRR) flew to Duxford, Cambs, on 6th July 2001 for storage.

Here is an appropriate place to pay tribute to a fine pilot and great character who flew the Intrepid P-51 with much style. Norman Lees was killed in Spitfire Tr.IX PV202 (G-TRIX) at Goodwood, Sussex, on 8th April 2000. Norman was teaching a South African, who had just acquired the aircraft, to convert to it. Norman flew Sea Kings – among others – with the Royal Navy and had a considerable amount of time on the RNHF Firefly. He was a founder member of the Harvard Formation Team and flew 'warbirds' for a whole range of operators. A man always keen to help others and with a keen sense of humour, we miss him greatly.

❑ G-BRVE	Beech D.17S ✈	ex N1139V, NC1139V, FT475, 44-67724, 23689 ntu.	3-02
❑ G-BRVG	SNJ-7 ✈	ex Staverton, N830X, N4134A, Bu90678, 42-85895.	3-02
❑ G-BVOK	'55' Aerostar Yak-52 ✈	ex DOSAAF.	10-97
❑ N4596N	PT-13D Kaydet ✈	ex 42-17782. *US Mail* colours.	3-02

Robs Lamplough / Fighter Wing Display Team: (See also Filton, Glos.)
◆ Visits *strictly* by prior arrangement only.

❑ G-BMJY	'07' SPP C.18M ✈	ex La Ferté Alais, Egyptian AF 627.	10-97
❑ G-TAFI	Jungmeister ✈	ex Breighton, N2210, HB-MIF, Swiss AF U-77.	3-96
❑ LV-RIE	Nord 1002	ex Duxford, Kersey, Argentina. Stored.	9-00
❑ N999PJ	Paris 2 ✈	ex F-BJLY.	9-00
❑ 'EN398'	Spitfire IX FSM	BAPC.184, ex Duxford, Huntingdon.	9-00
❑ KZ191	Hurricane IV	ex Fowlmere, Israel, 351, 1695F, AFDU.	9-01
❑ 152/17	Fokker Dr.I REP	G-ATJM, ex Duxford, Rendcomb, North Weald, Duxford, N78001, EI-APY, G-ATJM. CoA 10-9-93. ®	9-01

❏ J-1758	Venom FB.54	G-BLSD, ex N203DM, Cranfield, G-BLSD, SwAF.	3-02
❏ 'DR628' 'PB1'	Beech D.17S	N18V, ex NC18, Bu32898, FT507, 44-67761. Stored.	9-00
❏ '114'	Noralpha	G-BSMD, ex F-GDPQ, F-YEEE, F-YCZK, CAN-11,	
		Fr military No 139. *Luftwaffe* c/s. CoA 4-5-96.	9-01
❏ 472216	P-51D-20-NA ✈	G-BIXL, ex Duxford, Ein-Gedi, Israeli AF/DF 43,	
'HO-<u>M</u>'		RSweAF Fv26116, 44-72216. *Miss Helen*,	
		352nd FG colours by 5-01.	5-01

The Jet Centre / Military Jet Partnership: As before, only aircraft under long-term maintenance or held in store here are listed. **Departures**: Jet Provosts T.3A XM478 (G-BXDL) and XR673 (G-BXLO) were flying by 2000. Hunter T.8C WT799 to Exeter, Devon, 19-1-01; Hunter F.6A XG172 to Norwich, Norfolk, 2-2-01; Hunter nose ET-272 to Wolverhampton, W Mids, 19-12-00.

❏ OJ9	Strikemaster 87	G-BXFR, ex Ipswich, Binbrook, Botswana DF,	
		Kenyan AF 604, G-27-194.	4-99
❏ N36TH*	T-33AN	G-BYOY, N333DV, N134AT, N10018,	
		N134AT,RCAF 21231. First noted 12-00.	® 3-02
❏ 1121*	Strikemaster 80A	ex Humberside, RSaudiAF, G-27-232. F/n 9-01.	9-01

North Weald Airfield Museum: Based at 'Ad Astra' House, located at the former main gate of the station, with a very impressive memorial dedicated to al those who served at 'Weald and another to the Norwegians who flew from the there in the foreground. All of 'Ad Astra House' is now the museum's. The material on display is superb – an important place of pilgrimage.
◆ 'Ad Astra' House is off Hurricane Way, from North Weald *village* – ie the B181 – not via the aerodrome. Open Sat and Sun noon to 5pm. Other times by arrangement. Tours of the airfield can also be arranged. ✉ 'Ad Astra House', Hurricane Way, North Weald Aerodrome, Epping, CM16 6AA. ☎ 01992 523010 e-mail Arthur1@btinternet.com web http://fly.to/northweald

'The Squadron' / North Weald Flying Services (NWFS): Only airframes stored or under long-term work are listed under this heading. Cadet TX.3 XE796 was sold in the Netherlands.
◆ Visits by prior permission *only*. A series of fly-ins are staged during the season. ✉ North Weald Airfield, Epping, Essex, CM16, 6AA ☎ 01992 52 4510 fax 01992 52 2238.

| ❏ 143 | MS.733 Alcyon | ex Wycombe AP, F-BLXV, Fr No.143. | ® 3-02 |

Others: Joining the Sprints has been a quartet of Opticas. The former No.39 Restoration Group Meteor languishes at the north end. Fellow Sea Vixen FAW.2 XN691 was scrapped on site on 26th July 2001. The 'JP' nose is with a private collector and kept locally.

❏ [G-BXIY]*	Blake Bluetit	ex Old Warden, BAPC.37, Winchester.	® 9-01
❏ G-BMPF*	OA.7 Optica	ex Bournemouth. CoA 14-1-9<u>3</u>. Stored.	9-01
❏ G-BMPL*	OA.7 Optica	ex Farnborough, Bournemouth. CoA 2-8-97. Stored.	9-01
❏ G-BOPR*	OA.7 Optica	ex Bournemouth (?). Stored.	9-01
❏ G-FLSI	Sprint 160	ex Stansted, Bournemouth. Stored.	9-01
❏ G-SAHI	Sprint 160	ex Stansted, Bournemouth. CoA 30-4-94. Stored.	9-01
❏ G-70-503	Sprint 160	G-BXWU, ex Stansted, Bournemouth. Stored.	9-01
❏ G-70-505	Sprint 160	G-BXWV, ex Stansted, Bournemouth. Stored.	9-01
❏ EC-FVM*	OA.7 Optica	ex Farnborough, Bournemouth, G-BOPO. Stored.	9-01
❏ [WM224]	Meteor TT.20	ex 'WM311' North Weald village, East Dereham,	
		Swanton Morley 8177M, 5 CAACU, 3 CAACU,	
		3/4 CAACU, AWA, 29, 228 OCU.	9-01
❏ XS181*	'F' Jet Provost T.4	ex Bletchley, Desborough, Bruntingthorpe, Halton	
		9033M, Shawbury, CATCS, RAFC, 3 FTS.	
		Nose. Arrived 9-01.	9-01

RAYLEIGH on the A1095 north-west of Southend-on-Sea
The Cockpit Collection: Nigel Towler's collection is located variously within the region. The wings of Vampire WZ608 can be found on WZ518 at Sunderland, N&T ①. The nose of Valiant BK.1 XD857 moved to Manston, Kent, by June 2000. The cockpit of Canberra B.2 WD954 moved to Hendon, Gtr Lon, by mid-2001.

◆ The collection is scattered in various locations and, accordingly, visits are *not* possible.
❑ WZ608   Vampire T.11   ex Market Harborough, Lutterworth, Bitteswell,
                             Woodford, St Athan, 3 CAACU, 5 FTS, 266,
                             Fassberg SF, 11 Vampire Flt, 5, Wunstorf SF, 266.   ①   4-00
❑ 'WZ826'   Valiant BK.1   XD826, ex Cardiff-Wales, Abingdon, Stratford,
                             Cosford, 7872M, 543, 232 OCU, 138, 90, 7.   4-00
❑ XH560   Vulcan B.2   ex Marham, Waddington, 50, Wadd W, 27,
                             Akrotiri Wing, Cott W, Wadd W, Cott W,
                             230 OCU, 12, MoA, 230 OCU.   4-00
❑ XH669   Victor K.2   ex Waddington 9092M, 55, 57, Witt Wing, A&AEE.   4-00
❑ XH670   Victor B.2   ex East Kirkby, Tattershall, Woodford, Radlett, MoA.   4-00
❑ XN795   Lightning F.2A ex Foulness, RAE Bedford, A&AEE, BAC.   4-00
❑ XS421   Lightning T.5   ex Foulness, RAE, 23, 111, 226 OCU.   4-00

No.1476 Squadron Air Cadets: In Connaught Road.
❑ '1476'   Cessna F.172H   G-BOVG, ex Southend, OO-ANN, D-ELTR.
                             Damaged 1991.   2-02
❑ XG325   Lightning F.1   ex Southend, Wattisham, Foulness, A&AEE. Nose.   9-99

RETTENDON on the A130 south-east of Chelmsford
'The Wheatsheaf': Locals call it 'The Pink Pub' – note it is a distance outside the village.
❑ XP399   Whirlwind   ex Kettering, Glastonbury, Hadfield,
             HAR.10   Pyrton Hill, 32, 1563 Flt, 230.   2-02

RIDGEWELL on the A1017 south-east of Haverhill
Ridgewell Airfield Commemorative Museum / 381st Bomb Group Memorial Museum:
Established in USAAF Station No.167's former hospital buildings. A series of displays - including the
Tony Ince Collection — are dedicated to the 381st and to the RAF units that operated from the base, 90
Squadron among others.
◆ Second Sunday of each month, April to September, 11am to 5pm. Other times by arrangement. ✉
   Ridgewell Airfield Commemorative Association, 'White Wings', Ashen Road, Ovington, Sudbury,
   CO10 8JX ☎ or 01787 277310 or 07881 518572

SOUTHEND AIRPORT or Rochford, on the B1013 north of Southend-on-Sea
Vulcan Restoration Trust (VRT): A building has been acquired on-site and this is being converted
into a workshop and store. The intention is to open a Vulcan Visitors' Centre in the second half of 2003.
As might be imagined, VRT members have thrown themselves into the effort to return XH558 to the
skies, with their charitable trust status helping considerably in streamlining the fund-raising effort.
◆ Occasional open and 'up-and-running' days. Other times by appointment. VRT publish the excellent
   Vulcan News. ✉ Richard Clarkson, VRT, 39 Breakspears Drive, St Pauls Cray, Orpington, BR5
   2RX. **e-mail** richard.clarkson@avrovulcan.com **web** www.avrovulcan.com
❑ XL426   Vulcan B.2   ex Waddington, VDF , Waddington SF, 50, 617, 27,
             G-VJET   617, 230 OCU, 617, 230 OCU, 617, 230 OCU,
                             617, 230 OCU, Scampton Wing, 83.   3-02

Airport: Still more airliners – of all sizes – have had the 'chop' here: BAC 111-208AL 5N-HTC and
Belfast G-BFYU in August 2001; HS.748-2A/238 G-AVXI and Bandeirante G-LOOT in November
2001. (At least 5N-HTC, G-AVXI and short-termer Short 330 G-SSWT were 'processed' to Stock,
Essex.) Work started on Boeing 707-341C 4K-AZ3 during early March 2002. Luscombe G-AKUL was
airworthy by early 2002. Navajo T G-BMGH became N189SA in November 2000 and was flying.
Boeing 707-351B P4-FDH became N707CA and departed on 19th July 2001. Clearing up a note in
W&R17 (p69), it was noted that Auster G-AOZL moved to Audley End, Essex. This was not so, it
moved to Earls Colne, Essex, where that edition had correctly placed it!

❑ G-AOHL   Viscount 802   ex BAF, BA, BEA. CoA 11-4-80. Fuselage.   3-02
❑ G-ATAA   Cherokee 180C   Damaged 12-9-86. Wreck.   3-02

☐ G-ATRP	Cherokee 140	Damaged 16-10-81. Wreck.	3-02
☐ G-AYEI	Navajo T	ex N6730L. CoA 11-5-89. Fire dump.	3-02
☐ G-BEPS*	Belfast	ex G-27-13, XR368, 53. Last flight 30-3-01.	3-02
☐ G-BNNI*	Boeing 727-276	ex Sabre Airways, VH-TBK. *LadyPatricia*.	
		Arrived 1-11-01. Stored.	3-02
☐ G-BPEL	Warrior 151	ex C-FEYM. CoA 8-2-92. Wreck.	3-02
☐ G-BTYT*	Cessna 152 II	ex N24931. CoA 20-3-99. Stored. F/n 12-00.	3-02
☐ G-BXTH*	Gazelle HT.3	ex XW866, Shawbury, 2 FTS, CFS.	
		Arrived 11-98. Stored.	3-02
☐ G-CHTT	Varga Kachina	ex Elstree. Crashed 27-4-86. Spares.	3-02
☐ EL-AKJ	Boeing 707-321C	N2NF ntu, ex Omega, PP-BRR, EL-AKJ,	
		9Q-CSW, 5N-TAS, N864BX, OB-R1243,	
		HK-2473X, N473RN, N473PA. Stored.	3-02
☐ F-GFLD	King Air C90	ex HB-GGW, I-AZIO. Stored.	3-02
☐ N150JC*	Bonanza A35	ex Andover, Wick, N8674A. Damaged 18-6-83.	
		Stored.	3-02
☐ 5N-HHH*	BAC 111-401AK	ex HZ-NB2, N5024. Stored. Arrived 4-01.	3-02
☐ 9Q-CBW	Boeing 707-329C	ex 9Q-CBS, OO-SJO. Stored.	3-02

SOUTHEND-ON-SEA
Adventure Island: On Marine Parade is Lost City Adventure Golf, which has a novel putting hazard.

☐ G-AZRX	Horizon 160	ex Great Yarmouth, Tattershall Thorpe (?), F-BLIJ.	
		Crashed 14-8-91. Wreck.	2-02

SOUTH WOODHAM FERRERS on the A132 north of Rayleigh
A Canberra T.22 nose *should* still be kept in the area.

☐ WT525	'855' Canberra T.22	ex Stock, St Athan, FRADU, 17, 80. Nose.	2-94

STANSTED AIRPORT north of the A120 east of Bishop's Stortford M11, junction 8
Since at least mid-1999 dismantled Cherokee Lance 300 G-GOMM was stored inside the Inflite hangar. It had gone by November 2000. (CoA expired 24th June 1998.) The fire crews have a realistic-looking, steel plate, BAe 146-ish fuselage to torch.

☐ G-AWZU	Trident 3B-101	ex Heathrow, BA, BEA. CoA 3-7-85. *Tina*.	2-02
☐ G-IOIT	TriStar 100	ex Classic Airways, G-CEAP, SE-DPM,	
		G-BEAL. Flew in 13-4-98. Stored.	10-01
☐ VR-BMB	HS.125-400B	ex VR-BKN, I-GJBO, G-AYLI, G-5-11. Stored.	5-01

STAPLEFORD TAWNEY AERODROME on the A113 south of the M11/M25 junction
With 75% of the references here now very long-in-the-tooth, it is time to put a LOST! warning out!

☐ G-AZTO	Seneca 200-2	ex Linley Hill, N4516T. Crashed 27-8-92. Spares.	7-93
☐ G-BHUP	Cessna F.152	ex Tattershall Thorpe. Crashed 17-5-89. Fuselage.	10-93
☐ G-BOIP	Cessna 152 II	ex Tattershall T', Staverton, N49264. Dam 11-1-90. ®	9-93
☐ G-ORDN	Arrow II	ex G-BAJT. CoA 9-4-96. Fuselage. Dump.	6-00

STOCK on the B1007 south of Chelmsford
Hanningfield Metals / H&M Sales: Canberra PR.9 nose XH177 moved to <u>Corby</u>, Northants, by mid-2000. Sea Vixen D.3 XN657 was 'processed' by June 2000, the cockpit moving on to <u>Yateley</u>, Hants. Wessex HU.5 XS479 was scrapped during 2000. Two former Foulness, Essex, F-4J(UK)s came here for processing. The two cockpit sections were retained. ZE350 moved on to a collector within the county, then moved to an unknown location further west. The other, ZE352, moved to <u>Hooton Park</u>, Cheshire, on 24th February 2001. See under Southend, Essex, for recent airliner activity.

☐ G-BOPW*	Cessna A.152	ex Manston, Firbeck, Northampton, N4922A.	
		Damaged 30-8-95.	10-00

❏ XH175	Canberra PR.9	ex St Athan, 1 PRU, 39, 58. Nose, travelling exhibit.	2-01
❏ XT677	Wessex HC.2	8016M, ex Brize Norton, Lyneham, Thorney Island, 18. Crashed 25-4-68.	12-99
❏ XV399	Phantom FGR.2	ex Wattisham, 56, 228 OCU, 29, 41, 2. Nose.	12-99

STONDON off the A128 south-east of Chipping Ongar
It is believed that the remains of the 'one-off' Tawney Owl G-APWU moved on during 2001.

THURROCK on the A13, north end of the Dartford Crossing
Thurrock College: Grasshopper TX.1 WZ784 moved to <u>Carlisle</u>, Cumbria, by mid-2001.

WEST HANNINGFIELD west of the A130, south of Chelmsford
The B-2 hulk is believed still held at the car breakers' yard at Temple Farm.

| ❏ G-ACBH | Blackburn B-2 | ex Wickham Bishops, Downham, Ramsden Heath, Brentwood 2895M. Fuselage. CoA 27-11-41. | 1-96 |

WEST HORNDON west of Basildon, south of the A127
Buccaneer Preservation Society (BPS): The BPS share in XX894 at Kemble, Glos, is diminishing as the BSC takes on the major share of the aircraft – *qv*.
✉ Ricky Kelley, 47 Freshwell Gardens, West Horndon, Essex, CM13 3NE.

| ❏ XW550 | Buccaneer S.2B | ex Stock, St Athan, 16, 15. Nose. | ® 3-98 |

WEST THURROCK near Purfleet, north of the Dartford Bridge

❏ G-ASUE	Cessna 150D	ex N6018T. CoA 1-8-90. Stored.	6-94
❏ G-AYFJ	Rallye Club	ex F-BKZR. CoA 18-5-92. Stored.	6-94
❏ G-BTKT	Warrior 161	ex Southend, N429FT, N9606N. Cr 8-8-95. Stored.	3-98

GLOUCESTERSHIRE

☛ Within the administrative county regional boundaries can be found the unitary authorities of City of Bristol and South Gloucestershire.

ASTON DOWN AIRFIELD south of the A419 west of Cirencester
Cotswold Gliding Club: By late 2000, T.21B FFZ had moved to <u>Oakhill</u>, Somerset. The fuselage of Sedburgh WB981 had arrived here by May 2001, but moved to Keevil, Wilts, in September 2001.

❏ ASS		EoN Baby	BGA.628, ex G-ALRU. Crashed 28-5-71. Stored.	6-01
❏ CVX	'3'	Kestrel 19	BGA.1851. Stored.	7-99
❏ CWV	'Z'	Rhonlerche II	BGA.1873. Ex D-8226. CoA 5-94. Stored.	6-01
❏ DVW	'590'	ASW 20	BGA.2424. Stored.	7-99
❏ EQP	'158'	DG-202/17	BGA.2869. Crashed 12-7-92. Stored.	6-01
❏ FMD		Ka 7 Rhonadler	BGA.3362, ex D-2877, HB-603. Dam 6-5-92. Stored.	6-01
❏ XP493		Grasshopper TX.1	ex Syerston. Last flight 9-8-84.	1-02

BRISTOL
Bristol Industrial Museum: As well as the Sycamore, there is a fabulous array of Bristol aero engines on show – many having been restored by the Rolls-Royce Heritage Trust, Bristol Branch – see below. Also here is a 'walk-through' engineering mock-up of Concorde.

◆ Apr to Oct, Sat to Wed 10am to 5pm; Nov to Mar Sat and Sun *only*, 10am to 5pm ✉ Prince's Wharf, Bristol BS1 4RN ☎ 0117 9251470 **fax** 0117 9297318 **e-mail** andy_king@bristol-city.gov.uk **www** bristol-city.gov.uk/museums

❏		Concorde EMU	ex Filton. Forward fuselage.	3-02
❏	XL829	Sycamore HR.14	ex 32, MCS, Khormaksar SAR Flight.	3-02

Bristol Plane Preservation Unit (BPPU): Jim Buckingham and friends operate the well-known 'Miles Duo'. The Messenger can be seen around and about at airshows and fly-ins.

◆ Visits to the strip are *not* possible, but both aircraft can be seen in the air regularly.

❏	G-AKKB	Gemini 1A	CoA 19-9-98.	6-99
❏	'RG333'	Messenger 2A ✈	G-AIEK, ex Miles 'B' condition U-9.	6-99

Brunel Technical College: The Beagle 206 is owned by the Midland Air Museum of Coventry, Warks, and is on temporary loan ①. The College has airframes at Bristol Airport, Somerset – *qv*. Although somewhat dated, the entries are believed current.

❏	G-ASWJ	Beagle 206-1	ex Halton 8449M, Rolls-Royce. CoA 30-1-75.	① 11-95
❏	G-ATHA	Apache 235	ex Bristol Airport, N4326Y. CoA 7-6-86.	6-91
❏	G-AVDR	Queen Air B80	ex Bournemouth, Shobdon, Exeter, A40-CR, G-AVDR. CoA 30-6-86.	6-91
❏	G-AVVW	Cessna F.150H	ex Bristol Airport. CoA 31-5-82.	6-91
❏	G-AWBW	Cessna F.172H	ex Bristol Airport, Compton Abbas. Dam 20-5-73.	6-91

City Museum and Art Gallery: The Bristol Boxkite reproduction remains the main aeronautical attraction at the Museum, although there are other aviation artefacts. It 'flies' in the foyer.

◆ Every day including Sundays, 10am to 5pm. ✉ Queen's Road, Clifton, Bristol, BS8 1RL ☎ 0117 9223571 **fax** 0117 9222047 **e-mail** general_museums@bristol_city.gov.uk **web** www.bristol-city.gov.uk/museums

❏	–	BAPC.40 Boxkite repro	ex Old Warden, *Those Magnificent Men...*	3-02

Others: A long-term project for **Tim Cox** and team at their workshop in the general area is the Miles Sparrowjet for the Dunkerley family. All the 'metal' leavings from the M.77 conversion and salvaged metal parts from the fire hulk will be used to recreate G-ADNL and its days as an M.5. It is too early yet to list in a 'formal' manner. See under West Chiltington, W Sussex, for a *possible* airframe 'donor' for this project. See also Ramsbottom, Lancs, for the family Spitfire. PT-17 Kaydet G-BSGR had moved to Kemble, Glos, by August 1998.

❏	G-AETG	Aeronca 100	ex Hanwell, Booker. Crashed 7-4-69.	® 9-01
❏	G-AEWV	Aeronca 100	.ex Hanwell. Fuselage frame, other parts. Spares.	9-01
❏		'252' Cadet TX.1	BGA.427, ex Stoke-on-Trent, Firbeck, Bickmarsh, RAFGSA.258.	9-01
❏	EI-ALU	Avro Cadet	ex New Castle, Dublin, G-ACIH. Arrived by mid-2000.	9-01

CAM on the A4136 south-west of Stroud

Hurricane II G-BWHA moved to Sudbury, Suffolk.

CHELTENHAM

Nick Parker: Cherishes his Scimitar nose.

❏	XD215	Scimitar F.1	ex Ottershaw, Foulness, Culdrose A2573, 764B, 800, 803, A&AEE. Nose.	3-02

Others: Pilatus P.2-06 G-BONE was flying again by early 2000.

CHIPPING CAMPDEN on the B4081 north of Stow on the Wold

The former Boscombe Down Comet nose is still kept in the area.

❏	XV814	Comet 4	ex Boscombe Down, RAE, BOAC, G-APDF. Nose.	6-01

FILTON AIRFIELD south of the M5 at Patchway, north of Bristol
Rolls-Royce Heritage Trust - Bristol Branch (RRHT): The Branch has an astounding collection of aero engines, centred on two former test-beds that used for Proteus work within the R-R plant. As well as Bristol and Bristol Siddeley engines and Rolls-Royce (from 1966), de Havilland engines and archive from the former Leavesden Branch are also here.
◆ By prior permission *only*. ✉ Rolls-Royce Heritage Trust, Peter Pavey, 23 Morley Avenue, Mangotsfield, Bristol, BS16 9JE

Rolls-Royce: AV-8B Harrier is believed to be as given, but may be 162071.

❑ 162074	AV-8B Harrier	ex Wittering, AMARC, VMA-231. Stripped hulk.	2-00

Airfield: The Rolls-Royce (RR) Spitfire PR.XIX is based here. Robs Lamplough (RL) continues to base his Mk VIII here. His Commander 112, G-BFZM, was flying again by 2000. See also under North Weald, Essex, for the bulk of Robs' collection. The Canberra is a composite, with the starboard wing of Q497, see under Dumfries, Scotland ①. The Sea Devon acts as a source of spares for Compton Abbas-based Dove G-HBBC ②.
Most of the Airbus A300s awaiting or hoping to undergo freighter conversion care of BAE Systems are too transient for the likes of *W&R*, but one has proved particularly long-term. With many thanks to Andrew Appleton, we can keep a good eye on them. A300B4-2C N6254X became the 27th freighter conversion and was delivered to Tradewinds on 30th March 2000, becoming N501TR; A300B4-203 RP-C8883 became the 31st conversion, it was also delivered to Tradewinds, on 15th November 2000, becoming N505TR. As with many other places following 11th September 2001, Filton has found itself the host of mothballed airliners, including Air 2000 Boeing 757s and A320s and Virgin Sun A320s and A321s. Hopefully, all will not become subject matter for this book.

❑ G-AVDS	Queen Air B80	ex Bristol, Bournemouth, Exeter, A40-CS, G-AVDS. CoA 26-8-77. Dump	1-02
❑ G-BBDG	Concorde 100	CoA 1-3-82. BA spares, stored.	2-01
❑ S7-AAW	A300B4-2C	ex HS-THH, HS-TAX, HS-TGH, F-WNDC. Stored.	2-02
❑ 'MT928' 'ZX-M'	Spitfire VIII ✈	G-BKMI, ex Huntingdon, Duxford, Australia, RAAF A58-671, MV154, 82 MU, 6MU. 145 Sqn colours.	RL 3-02
❑ PS853*	'C' Spitfire PR.XIX ✈	G-RRGN, ex East Midlands, Filton, G-MXIX, North Weald, Coningsby, BBMF, West Raynham, CFE, North Weald SF, Biggin Hill SF, THUM Flt, 16, 268, 16.	RR 3-02
❑ WH665	'J' Canberra T.17	ex Samlesbury, Cosford 8736M, 360, RNZAF, 45, 10. Dump	① 3-02
❑ XK896	Sea Devon C.20	G-RNAS, ex Gloucestershire, North Coates, Gloucestershire, 781, Hal Far SF, 781. CoA 3-7-84. Spares.	② 1-02

GLOUCESTERSHIRE AIRPORT or Staverton, on the B4063 west of Cheltenham
Jet Age Museum: operated by the **Gloucestershire Aviation Collection** (GAC). Re-developments at the airport meant that at the end of 2000, Jet Age had to vacate their wartime hangar (once used by Flight Refuelling?) and move on – for the second time in their history. Their final day open to the public was staged on 1st October. The bulk of the 'hardware' was moved in a very hectic time in the period 28th December to 1st January, 2001. Prior to this the pods of Vampire NF.10 WM729 and Venom FB.4 WR539 returned to London Colney, Herts. Three separate sites were used for storage. The main one was at Bentham, Glos, but in July 2001 GAC had to vacate this site – also in double-quick time. They succeeded in gaining external storage space back at Gloucestershire Airport and this is currently how the bulk of the collection remains. Because of this situation, all of the collection continues to be listed under this heading. Former Bentham airframes are marked ß. The Sea Venom is living the life of a split-personality, the pod is in store off-site, the wings are with the rest of the external stored airframes at the airport ①. Meteor F.8 WH364 is held in open store at Kemble, Glos, (*qv*). Active fund-raising continues to achieve the ultimate goal of moving into the refurbished double 'Belfast' hangar at Brockworth (or Hucclecote), Glos. This is a freehold gift from the developer of the site, Arlington.

◆ Aircraft in store at various locations. Access *not* possible at present. **e-mail** noel.griffiths@virgin.net
web www.jetagemuseum.org

❑	N5914		Gladiator II	ex Norway, 263. Crashed 2-6-40. Stored.	off-site	8-01
❑	'V6799'		Hurricane FSM	BAPC.72, ex 'V7767', Bournemouth, Sopley, Bournemouth, Brooklands, North Weald, Coventry, *Battle of Britain*. 501 Sqn c/s. Stored.	off-site	8-01
❑	EE425		Meteor F.3	ex Yatesbury, Earls Colne, Andrewsfield, Foulness, MoS, 206 AFS, 210 AFS, 206 AFS, 63, 266, 1, 222. Nose. Stored.	off-site	8-01
❑	VM325		Anson C.19	ex Coventry, Halfpenny Green, WCS, NCS, WCS, TCCF, Upavon CF, 173, 4 FP. Stored.	ß	8-01
❑	WF784		Meteor T.7	ex Quedgeley, Kemble 7895M, 5 CAACU, CAW, FTU, 130, 26. Stored.	ß	8-01
❑	WK126	'843'	Canberra TT.18	ex Hucclecote, N2138J ntu, St Athan, FRADU, 100, 9. Stored.	ß	8-01
❑	WS807	'N'	Meteor NF.14	ex Yatesbury, Watton 7973M, Kemble, 1 ANS, 2 ANS. 46 Squadron c/s. Stored.	ß	8-01
❑	XD506		Vampire T.11	ex Thrupp, Staverton, Swinderby, Finningley 7983M, CATCS, CNCS, 5 FTS, 206 AFS. Stored.	ß	8-01
❑	XD616		Vampire T.11	ex London Colney, Hoddesdon, Old Warden, Woodford, Chester, St Athan, 8 FTS, 1 FTS, 8 FTS, 65. Pod. Stored.	ß	8-01
❑	XE664		Hunter F.4	ex Marlborough, ?, HSA, 26. Nose. Stored.	off-site	8-01
❑	XG331		Lightning F.1	ex Hucclecote, Barton, Chelford, Long Marston, Innsworth, Staverton, Foulness, A&AEE, makers. Nose. Stored.	off-site	8-01
❑	XG691		Sea Venom FAW.22	ex Hucclecote; Helston, Chilton Cantello, Yeovilton, FRU, 891, 894. Stored.	off-site ①	8-01
❑	XH903		Javelin FAW.9	ex Hucclecote, Innsworth 7938M, Shawbury, 5, 33, 29, 33, 23. Stored.	ß	8-01
❑	XM569		Vulcan B.2	ex Enstone, Cardiff, 44, Wadd Wing, 27, Cott Wing, 27. Nose. Stored.	ß	8-01
❑	XV165		Buccaneer S.2B	ex Hucclecote, Heathrow, Stock, Shawbury, 12. Nose. Stored.	ß	8-01
❑	XW264		Harrier T.2	ex Hucclecote, Innsworth, Dowty, Boscombe Down, HSA. Damaged 11-7-70. Nose. Stored.	off-site	8-01
❑	XX889		Buccaneer S.2B	ex Enstone, St Athan, 12, 208, 12, 16. 208 Sqn c/s. Stored.	ß	8-01
❑			McBroom Arion	ex Hucclecote. Hang-glider. Stored.		2-00
❑	—	BAPC.259	Gamecock REP	under construction.	off-site	8-01
❑	—		Typhoon I	ex Twyford, Chippenham. Cockpit.	off-site	8-01

Airport: Meteor T.7 WL349 is owned by Gloucester and Cheltenham Councils ①. Dove 8 G-OEWA moved to Kemble, Glos, by July 2000.

❑	G-AVVF	Dove 8	CoA 11-2-88. Dump. Changed location 3-98.		8-01
❑	G-AXPA	Pup 100	ex Bidford, D-EATL, G-AXPA, G-35-116. CoA 4-11-87.		1-00
❑	G-WACO	Waco UPF-7	ex N29903, NC29903. Crashed 15-4-89.	®	1-98
❑	G-WILY	Rutan LongEZ	CoA 6-6-96. *Time Flies*. Stored.		8-97
❑	—	BN-2	nose for trials work.		4-99
❑	WL349	'Z' Meteor T.7	ex Kemble, 1 ANS, 2 ANS, CFE, 229 OCU.	①	8-01
❑	XR442	Sea Heron C.1	G-HRON, ex Yeovilton, 781, G-AORH. Stored.		4-99

INNSWORTH west of the B4063, near Parton, north-east of Gloucester
Cotswold Aircraft Restoration Group (CARG): In January 2001 CARG announced that they would have to be leaving Innsworth, their base since formation in April 1979. Accordingly, some

restructuring was needed and the decision was taken to stop their long-founded 'supply missions' and their role of acting at 'maintenance unit' to UK – and wider – heritage organisations. The move proper will come about in mid-2002. The Fairey Ultra-Light for The Helicopter Museum, Weston-super-Mare ① and the Monospar for the Newark Air Museum, Winthrope, Notts ②. Edwards Helicopter G-ASDF and the anonymous Primary glider moved to Kington, H&W.

Departures: First visual effect of the 'drawdown' was the removal of their 'flagship' airframe, Auster AOP.9 XR267 (G-BJXR) to Melton Mowbray, Leics.
◆ Visits to the workshop are possible by prior application *only*. ✉ Steve Thompson, CARG, Kia-Ora, Risbury, Leominster, Herefordshire, HR6 0NQ

❑ G-AOUJ	Fairey ULH	ex Weston-super-Mare, Harlow, White Waltham, XJ928. CoA 29-3-59.	® ①	3-02
❑ VH-UTH	Monospar ST-12	ex Winthorpe, Australia.	® ②	3-02
❑ R9371	Halifax II	ex local, 10. Crashed 9-3-42. Cockpit.		3-02

RAF Innsworth: Personnel and Training Command HQ, the Meteor graces the main entrance.

❑ VW453	'Z' Meteor T.7	8703M, ex Salisbury Plain, Hullavington, Takali, 604, 226 OCU, 203 AFS. Gate.	3-02

KEMBLE AIRFIELD on the A429 south-west of Cirencester
Bristol Aero Collection (BAC) Opened on a regular basis in Easter 2000. Their work of expanding and consolidating their collection to glory the Bristol Aeroplane Company and its associates continues, as do negotiations to establish a base at or near Filton. What the Brigand lacks in substance, it more than makes up for in significance. The Bristol 173 is a great achievement – much praise to the RAF Museum for giving the 'nod' to its first-ever public display as a museum piece. It arrived on the 50th anniversary of its first flight at Filton and was greeted by its test-pilot, 'Sox' Hosegood.

Notes: BAC work closely with the Britannia Aircraft Preservation Trust (BAPT – see below) and host their Series 101 nose and all of *Charlie-Fox*. The latter will become a 'walk-through' exhibit. The Beagle 206 started life as the Bristol 220 and is on loan from the Science Museum ①. The Brigand is highly appropriate and on loan from Unimetal Industries via the North East Aircraft Museum ②. The Bristol 173 is on loan from the RAF Museum ③. The Harrier used the BSE Pegasus ④, while the Jindivik represents the first application for the BSE (*née* Armstrong Siddeley) Viper ⑤. Scout N5419 moved to Yeovilton, Somerset, on 30th November 1998. The type will be replaced in due course.
◆ Open Easter and every Sun mid-Apr to Oct 10am to 4pm. Parties at other times by arrangement. ✉ A1 Hangar, Kemble Airfield, Cirencester, GL7 6BA ☎ 01285 771204, or ☎ / **fax** 0117 950 0908 **web** www.bristolaero.com

❑ 'G-EASQ'	Babe III REP	BAPC.87, ex Banwell, Stoke, Hemswell, Cleethorpes, Selby.		3-02
❑ G-ALRX	Britannia 101	ex Banwell, Boscombe Down, WB473 ntu, VX447 ntu. Crashed 4-2-54. Nose.	BAPT	3-02
❑ G-ANCF	Britannia 308F	ex Banwell, Brooklands, Manston, 5Y-AZP, G-ANCF, LV-GJB, LV-PPJ, G-ANCF ntu, G-14-1, G-18-4, N6597C ntu, G-ANCF. CoA 12-1-81. Dism.	BAPT	3-02
❑ G-ARRM	Beagle 206-1X	ex Banwell, Brooklands, Shoreham, Duxford, Shoreham. CoA 28-12-64.	①	3-02
❑ G-ATDD	Beagle 206-1	ex Filton, Wroughton, South Kensington, Leeds. Damaged 6-73. Nose.	①	3-02
❑	Concorde EMU	ex Brooklands. Test shell, nose. Plus cabin mock-up.		3-02
❑ RH746*	Brigand TF.1	ex Sunderland, Failsworth, CS(A), ATDU Gosport, Bristol, ATDU, A&AEE, Bristol. Fuselage. Arrived 19-4-01.	②	3-02
❑ XF785	Bristol 173 Srs 1	ex Cosford, Henlow 7648M, G-ALBN. Arr 3-1-02.	③	3-02
❑ XJ917 'S-H'	Sycamore HR.14	ex Banwell, Helston, Wroughton, CFS, 275.		3-02
❑ XV798	Harrier GR.1	ex Banwell, Foulness, PCB rig, Dunsfold, 20, 233 OCU. Cr 23-4-71. Wing from T.2 XW264.	④	3-02
❑ A92-708	Jindivik 3	ex Llanbedr.	⑤	3-02

Britannia Aircraft Preservation Trust: See above for two of the trust's airframes.

✉ BAPT, Roger Hargreaves, 8 Mill Park, Park Road, Burgess Hill, Sussex, RH15 8ET

❑ XM496   Britannia 253   ex Lanseria, EL-WXA, Transair Cargo 9Q-CJH, Aerocaribbean CU-T120, Afrek, G-BDUP, Kemble, XM496 99/511. *Jack / Regulus.*   3-02

Buccaneer Supporters Club (BSC) / **Buccaneer Engineering**: In October 2000 BSC took on Buccaneer XX894 on long term loan from the Buccaneer Preservation Society (see under West Hordon, Essex) and aims to ultimately buy out the remaining shares that BPS holds in the aircraft. Buccaneer Engineering is BSC's restoration arm and is working to get '894 taxiable. Between the two organisations, they seek to help support the preservation of Buccaneers where-ever they may be. BSC have acquired on long-term loan XW544 – see under Shawbury, Shropshire – which is due to travel to Bruntingthorpe, Leics, in the summer of 2002.

◆ Visits by prior arrangement. ✉ Nigel Goodall, 32 The Haven, Inkpen Road, Kintbury, Hungerford, RG17 9TY ☎ 07773 173111 **e-mail** buccaneerclub@hotmail.com **web** www.buccaneerclub.co.uk

❑ XX894   '020' Buccaneer S.2B   ex Bruntingthorpe, St Athan, 208, 16, 12, 208, 12.   2-02

Delta Jets: A thriving selection of jets, restored and maintained from this super airfield. As with several other locations within this work, the bulk of the jets here are owner-operated and not part of a collection as such. From this edition, the listing will be restricted to aircraft on long-term restoration or storage.

    Departures: Meteor F.8 VZ467 (G-METE) departed for Cranfield, Beds, on 18-6-00. Hunter T.7 XL565 moved to Bruntingthorpe, Leics, on 21-3-02. Hunter T.8C WV322 (G-BZSE) arrived from Cranwell, Lincs, 14-2-01. Owned by Chris Perkins, it was air-tested on 13-3-02. Buccaneer S.2B XW986 has been acquired by Graham Pringle. It was air-tested on 29th March 2002 in readiness for ferrying to Cape Town, South Africa, where it will be maintained by the Thunder City operation on behalf of Graham ①.

◆ Visits by prior arrangement *only*. Occasional open days/airshows staged. **web** www.deltajets.com

❑ XF995	'K'	Hunter T.8B	G-BZSF, ex Cranwell, 9237M, ex 208, 12, Laarbruch SF, 237 OCU, Honington SF, 237 OCU, FAA, 229 OCU, 245, 247. Arrived 16-2-01.	2-02
❑ XL577	'W'	Hunter T.7	G-BXKF, ex Navenby, Cranwell 8676M, 2 TWU, 237 OCU, 1 TWU, TWU, 229 OCU.	® 2-02
❑ XL578	'77'	Hunter T.7	ex Norwich, Bruntingthorpe, Cranfield, St Athan, 1 TWU, TWU, 229 OCU. Stored.	2-02
❑ XL586		Hunter T.7	ex Ipswich, Colsterworth, Shawbury, BAe Warton, 1 TWU, 2 TWU, 1 TWU, 229 OCU.	2-00
❑ XL591		Hunter T.7	ex Ipswich, Colsterworth, Shawbury, 237 OCU, 208, 237 OCU, 208, 237 OCU, 4 FTS, RAE, 4 FTS, 229 OCU, FCS.	8-01
❑ XP502*		Gnat T.1	ex Ipswich, St Athan 8576M, 4 FTS. Red Arrows c/s. First noted 2-01. Dismantled.	2-02
❑ XS209	'29'	Jet Provost T.4	ex Gloucestershire, Halton 8409M, St Athan, Kemble, Shawbury, CAW. '5 MU' tail marking.	2-02
❑ XW986		Buccaneer S.2B	ex Wellesbourne Mountford, West Freugh, Boscombe Down, RAE.	① 3-02
❑ XX467		Hunter T.7	G-TVII, ex Perth, 1 TWU, Jordan AF 836, Saudi AF 70-617, G-9-214, XL605, 66, 92.	2-01

Others: By July 2001 Meteor T.7(mod) WF877 (G-BPOA) had moved to Washington, W Sussex. Meteor F.8 WH364 is held in store for the planned Jet Age Museum – see under Gloucestershire Airport, Glos .

❑ G-AJOE	Messenger 2A	ex Gloucestershire, Innsworth, 'RH378'. Stored.	10-01
❑ G-AKUE	Tiger Moth	ex Chilbolton, ZS-FZL, CR-AGM, Port AF. Crashed 2-1-89. Stored.	2-00
❑ G-APSO	Dove 5	ex Coventry, Cumbernauld, Carlisle, Shobdon, N1046T ntu. CoA 8-7-78. Fuselage.	8-01
❑ G-ARJB	Dove 8	ex Cumbernauld, Carlisle, Rocester, East Midlands. CoA 10-12-73. *Exporter.*	8-01

❏ G-ASIP	Auster 6A	ex Oaksey Park, Innsworth, Staverton, Nympsfield, Heathrow, VF608, 12 Flt, 652, 1904 Flt, Hague Air Attaché. Damaged 7-5-73. Frame.		8-98
❏ G-ATKI	J3C-75 Cub	ex N70536, NC70536. Crashed 14-11-93.	®	8-98
❏ G-AXCN	Rallye Club	ex Thruxton. Wrecked 16-10-87.		7-99
❏ G-AXRU	Cessna FA.150K	ex Withybush. CoA 10-12-87.	®	7-97
❏ G-AZMN	Airtourer T5	ex Oaksey Park, Bristol, Glasgow. Crashed 23-6-87.		8-98
❏ G-BDFX	Auster 5	ex Oaksey Park, F-BGXG, TW517, 661. Cr 10-10-93.		8-01
❏ G-BFEH	SAN D.117A	ex F-BITG. CoA 30-9-94.	®	7-99
❏ G-BSGR*	PT-17 Kaydet	ex Bristol, EC-ATY, N55050, 42-16558.		7-99
❏ G-DDCD*	Dove 8	G-OEWA, ex Staverton, Biggin Hill, G-DDCD, G-ARUM. CoA 7-10-91. Stored.		12-00
❏ VP955*	Devon C.2/2	G-DVON, ex Little Staughton, Cranfield, G-BLPD ntu, VP955, 207, 21, C.1 WCS, MCS, 31, Upavon SF, Hendon SF, MEAF, Malta CF. CoA 29-5-96. Stored.		10-01
❏ WH364	Meteor F.8	8169M, 601, Safi SF, Takali SF, Idris SF, Takali SF, Safi SF, 85. Stored.	①	2-02
❏ XA880*	Devon C.2	G-BVXR, ex RAE, RRE, TRE. Stored.		10-01

MORETON-IN-MARSH on the A44 north-east of Cheltenham
Wellington Aviation Museum: Gerry Tyack's superb collection of artefacts, together with aviation art and prints (many for sale) is always worth a visit. Among the impressive array is the tail section of Wellington L7775 of 20 OTU which crashed near Braemar 23rd October 1940.
◆ Open 10am to 12.30am and 2pm to 5.30pm daily. On the A44 west of the town, signed. ✉ British School House, Moreton-in-Marsh, GL56 0BG ☎ 01608 650323 **web** www.wellingtonaviatio.org

Home Office Fire and Emergency Training Centre: A convincing purpose-built 'airliner' is used for burning exercises. The second Hunter referred to in *W&R17* is a nose section and was kept indoors, and is confirmed as the former Halton FGA.9 XE597. It moved to Bromsgrove, H&W, on 19th March 2003. By June 2001 Sioux AH.1 XT141 – confirmed as ex Brize Norton – had been sold on.

❏ G-AZDZ	Cessna 172K	ex Firbeck, Fownhope, Warmingham, Southend, 5N-AIH, N1647C, N84508. Crashed 19-9-81.	2-02
❏ G-BAPF	Viscount 814	ex Southend, SE-FOY, G-BAPF, D-ANUN. CoA 13-6-90.	2-02
❏ G-BKRD	Cessna 320	ex Sandtoft, D-IACB, HB-LDN, N2201Q. Cr 5-11-90.	6-01
❏ G-BLHL	Emeraude	ex Hooton Park, Warmingham, Wigan, East Kirkby, Tattershall, Chinnor, Booker, F-BLHL, F-OBLM. Crashed 4-8-81. Frame.	8-98
❏ G-BNJJ	Cessna 152 II	ex Stamford area, Spanhoe, Nayland, Cranfield. Damaged 18-5-88. Hulk.	6-01
❏ G-BPAD	Seneca 200T	ex N21208. Crashed 15-7-92. Crash scene.	6-01
❏ G-BPJT	Cadet 161	ex Oxford, N9156X. Crashed 12-7-92. Wreck.	8-98
❏ G-SULL	Saratoga SP	ex Stamford, Spanhoe, N82818. Crashed 1-2-95.	8-98
❏ WT804 '831'	Hunter GA.11	ex Culdrose A2646, A2732, , Shawbury, FRADU, Lossiemouth, 247. Pole mounted, nose in ground.	2-02
❏ XM404	Jet Provost T.3	ex Halton, Newton, 8055BM, Shawbury, 3 FTS, 2 FTS.	2-02
❏ XP150	Wessex HAS.3	ex Lee-o-S A2764, Wroughton, 829, *Antrim* Flt.	2-02
❏ XP680	Jet Provost T.4	8460M, ex St Athan, CAW, 6 FTS. 'Crash' scene.	6-01

NYMPSFIELD AERODROME off the B4066, south-west of Stroud
By August 2001 Grasshopper BGA.4361 was fully rigged and ready to go. Fellow WZ796 was noted as being wings and tailplane only, and should be deleted.

❏ *	T.8 Tutor	BGA.1745, ex XE760, VM539. Stored.	8-01
❏ WZ831	Grasshopper TX.1	ex Locking, Reading, Halton, Lightwater. Stored.	8-01

QUEDGELEY east of the A38 south of Gloucester
Hunter Restoration Flight: HRF have to leave the site by mid-2002 and in preparation for this staged a fund-raising sale of parts, spares etc on April 14. The three aircraft will have to leave shortly afterwards. The Hunter is thought to be the last surviving RAF whole airframe to have taken part in the Suez operation and has been restored in Operation MUSKETEER markings. It is hoped that it may find a very appropriate home. WP190 and the former WAM Lightning are owned by Raymond Hansed, while the Meteor is owned by John Holder, Sandy Mullen and Raymond Hansed. The Lightning is in the markings of F.6 XR753 'A', 23 squadron. The *real* XR753 can be found at Leeming, N Yorks ①.

❑ WP190	'K'	Hunter F.5	ex Hucclecote, Stanbridge 8473M, Upwood, Finningley, Bircham Newton 7582M, Nicosia, 1. 1 Sqn colours, Suez stripes.	®	3-02
❑ WS774		Meteor NF.14	ex Fearn, Ely, Upwood 7959M, Kemble, 1 ANS, 2 ANS. Stored.		2-00
❑ 'XR753'	'A'	Lightning F.53	ZF578, ex Cardiff-Wales, Warton, RSAF 53-670, G-27-40. 23 Squadron colours.	①	3-02

RENDCOMB AERODROME east of the A435 north of Cirencester
◆ Access on a *strictly* prior permission basis.

❑ [XB-RIY]	PT-17	ex Hatch, Sudbury. Stored.	7-01
❑ –*	PT-17	fuselage frame, stored.	7-01

HAMPSHIRE

☛ Within the administrative county boundaries of Hampshire can be found the unitary authorities of the City of Portsmouth and the City of Southampton.

ALDERSHOT on the A325 south of Farnborough
Parachute Regiment and Airborne Forces Museum: Devoted to the exploits of paratroop and glider-borne forces, the museum stages regular special displays and events.
◆ Open Mon to Fri 10am to 4.30pm - last admission 3.45pm. Sat, Sun and Bank Hols 10am to 4pm. Closed Xmas period. Other times by prior arrangement. Note that photography is not permitted within the museum. ✉ Browning Barracks, Aldershot, Hampshire, GU11 2DS ☎ 01252 349619 fax 01252 349203 e-mail airborneforcesmuseum@army.mod.uk.net

❑ KP208	'YS'	Dakota IV	ex Kemble, AFNE, Air Adviser New Delhi, AFNE, HCCF, 24, MEAF, USAAF 44-77087.	3-02
❑		Hotspur II	nose section.	3-02
❑		Horsa II	nose section.	3-02

Keogh Barracks: Took on a pair of Wessex airframes in April 2001 for exit training.

❑ XR501*		Wessex HC.2	ex Gosport, Shawbury, 22, 72, 18, 1 FTU, A&AEE. Arrived 25-4-01.	4-01
❑ XS515*	'N'	Wessex HU.5	ex Gosport, A2658 [2], A2747, Lee-on-Solent, 845. Arrived 25-4-01.	4-01

ALTON on the A31 south-west of Farnham
Air Salvage International: The yard here specialises in airliner salvage. ASI also have a 'Shed' at nearby Lasham, Hants – *qv*. Great news is the survival of HS.748 nose G-ARAY. This was last noted at Lasham in December 1995 with the note that it may have gone to the Hampshire Fire Service. See under Bournemouth, Dorset, for a candidate for the BAC One-Eleven.

❑ G-ARAY*	HS.748-1/100	ex Lasham, Dan-Air, OY-DFV, PI-C784, G-ARAY, PP-VJQ, YV-C-AMC, G-ARAY. Nose.	1-02

❏ G-BITW	Short 330-100	ex Coventry, G-EASI, G-BITW ntu, G-14-3070. CoA 9-6-98. Fuselage.	1-02
❏ G-OHIG	Bandeirante	ex G-OPPP, XC-DAI, PT-SAB. CoA 30-4-96. Fuselage.	4-02
❏ G-OJEM	HS.748-2B/378	ex Stansted, Emerald, ZK-MCH, G-BKAL, 9N-ADF,G-BKAL,V2-LDK, D-AHSD, G-BKAL. *Tashy's Kite*. Nose. Crashed 31-3-98.	1-00
❏ A6-SHK*	BAe 146-100	ex UAE Gov, G-BOMA, G-5-091. Fuse, scrapping.	4-02
❏ EI-EXP	Short 330-100	ex G-BKMU, SE-IYO, G-BKMU, G-14-3092, EI-BEH, EI-BEG, G-BKMU, G-14-3092. Fuselage.	1-00
❏ OY-BNM*	Bandeirante	ex Bournemouth, N5071N, G-BFZK. F/n 7-00.	7-00
❏ OY-MUB*	Short 330-200	ex Bournemouth, Muk Air, G-BITX, G-14-3069. Fuselage. First noted 7-01.	4-02
❏ _*	BAC 111	ex Nigerian. Cockpit.	1-02

ANDOVER

Aerofab Restorations: The wonderful team here continue to work their magic. Chrislea Super Ace G-AKVF and Cessna F.150H G-AWOT both arrived by road from Kilkerran, Scotland, on 16th March 2000. The 'Ace made her first flight on 2nd September 2000 with 'WOT following in early 2001. By September 2001 Bonanza A35 N150JC had moved by road to Southend, Essex. Also by this time, Seafire III moved to Exeter, Devon. The Pup fuselage 'KK327' listed in *W&R17* (pp69) is best described as an 'extreme forward fuselage' and is also best deleted.

❏ G-AVDF	Pup 200	ex St Ives, Brooklands, Shoreham, Duxford, Shoreham. CoA 22-5-68. Stored for owner.	4-02
❏ G-AWKM	Pup 100	ex Swansea. CoA 29-6-84. Stored.	10-01
❏ G-AXZO*	Cessna 180	ex N3639C. CoA 8-12-99. Wreck. F/n 6-00.	® 10-01
❏ G-BGZJ	Tomahawk 112	ex Halfpenny Green. Damaged 5-8-90. Stored.	10-01
❏ G-BOPX*	Cessna A.152	ex N761BK. CoA 24-1-98.	10-01
❏ XX623*	'M' Bulldog T.1	ex Newton, CFS, York UAS. EM UAS. Crashed 26-7-95. Wreck. First noted 3-01.	4-02
❏ XX657*	'U' Bulldog T.1	ex Newton, 2 FTS, Cam UAS. Overstressed 22-11-98. First noted 3-01.	4-02
❏ XX669*	'5' Bulldog T.1	ex Llantrisant, Bruntingthorpe, Cosford 8997M, 2 FTS, Birm UAS, Man UAS. Damaged 6-9-88. Hulk. First noted 3-01.	10-01
❏ G-102	Bulldog 122	ex Ghana AF. Stored.	4-02
❏ G-108	Bulldog 122	ex Ghana AF, G-BCUP.	4-02

Durney Collection: No sooner was the Dragon Rapide sent off to LOST! in *W&R17* (p69) than confirmation came of its existence - albeit stored outside and in very poor state.

❏ G-ALAX	Dragon Rapide	ex Old Warden, Luton, RL948, ERS, 27 GCF. CoA 8-3-67. Composite. Stored, poor state.	2-99

BASINGSTOKE on the M3 north-east of Winchester

Automobile Association: Have a travelling Enstrom in their colours which we shall list here, under their headquarters. It is believed to be based upon the former Somersham, Cambs, hybrid, with the cabin of G-BATU with the tail from G-JDHI and other parts from other machines, including G-BACH. The 'registration' comes from National Air Ambulance Service' – the AA being a major supporter of regional helicopter operations. The 'N-' prefix is to avoid confusion with the Northumbria Ambulance Service's Twin Squirrel G-NAAS.

❏ 'N-NAAS'*	Enstrom F-28	composite. Travelling airframe.	6-01

BLACKBUSHE AERODROME on the A30 west of Yateley.

❏ [G-XIIX]	Robinson R-22	CoA 21-3-97. Pole-mounted.	8-01

BRAMLEY south-east of Tadley, east of the A340
Army Training Estate (ATE) **Home Counties**: The number of airframes here had swollen somewhat, but by 2001 health and safety restrictions put most up for disposal. The following had gone by early 2002, possibly to a location in Devon: Whirlwind HAR.10 XK970, from Odiham, Hants, by August 1998; Scout AH.1 XP191; Scout AH.1 XP853 from Arborfield, Berks, by July 2000; Wessex HU.5 XT467 from Odiham, Hants, by July 2000.

❑ XP856	Scout AH.1	ex Middle Wallop.	7-00
❑ XZ300	'L' Gazelle AH.1	ex Middle Wallop.	7-00

CHILBOLTON AERODROME east of the A3057, south of Andover
Hampshire Light Plane Services: By September 2000 the cabin of Silvaire 8F G-AKTM had moved on. Torquil Norman's former Australian DH.84 is under restoration.

❑ G-ECAN*	DH.84 Dragon I	ex VH-DHX, VH-AQU, RAAF A34-59.	®	4-02
❑ G-BEPF	SNCAN SV-4A	ex Warminster, Raveningham, F-BCVD. Stored.		4-02
❑ G-FORD	SNCAN SV-4C	ex F-BBNS. Crashed 16-7-96. Stored.		4-02
❑ N1134K	Silvaire 8AE	ex NC1134K. Crashed 28-8-96. Spares.		5-01

Others: Hiller UH-12E G-BEDK was crated and exported (Greece?) circa 1997. Evans VP-2 G-BTSC is no longer here, thought in the East Midlands.

❑ G-REPM	Tomahawk 112	ex N2528D. CoA 9-10-95. Stored.	4-02

FARLEY on the A27 north of Southampton
The Cessna 336/337 store has not been reliably sighted since early 1992. For the record they were/are: 336 G-ASLL, 336 G-ATAH, 337B G-BBBL, T.337D G-BNNG and 336 N1721Z. This strip is one and the same as that listed under Romsey, Hants – *qv*.

FARNBOROUGH
Prince's Mead Shopping Centre: The SE.5A still 'flies' above the shoppers.

❑ 'D276'	'A' SE.5A REP	BAPC.208, built by AJD Engineering.	12-00

FARNBOROUGH AIRFIELD east of the A325, north of Aldershot
Farnborough Air Sciences Trust (FAST): The Trust was formed in late 1993 to save the listed buildings known as the Main Factory Site (some of which date from 1905) in the north-eastern corner of the former RAE site. This area includes wind tunnels and other major items. Fund raising is underway with a view to establishing a 'high-tech' science and aerospace visitor centre. Airframes on site so far are used for travelling displays. The balloons are on loan from BPG at Lancing, West Sussex – *qv* – ①. The Lightning nose is on loan from Hugh Trevor ②.
♦ By prior arrangement *only* at present. Membership details from ✉ FAST Association, 11 Coleford Bridge Road, Mytchett, Camberley, Surrey, GU16 6DH

❑ G-BKIK	Cameron DG-19	ex Lancing. CoA 4-9-88. (Helium Airship). Stored.	①	3-02
❑ OO-JAT	Cameron Zero 25	ex Lancing. Stored.	①	3-02
❑ WT309	Canberra B(I).6	ex Wycombe Air Park, Boscombe Down, Farnborough, Boscombe Down, A&AEE, HS. Nose.		2-00
❑ WV383*	Hunter T.7	ex Boscombe Down, DERA, RAE, 28, Jever SF, Gutersloh SF, F.4 RAFFC. Arrived 13-4-00. On loan.		4-00
❑ XS932*	Lightning F.6	ex Shoreham, Bruntingthorpe, Rossington, Binbrook, 5, 11, 56, 11. Nose. Arrived 29-6-01.	②	6-01
❑ 'U-1215'	Vampire T.11	XE998, ex Wisbech, Huntingdon, Horley, Charlwood, Biggin Hill, Warmingham, Wigan, Woodford, Chester, St Athan, 8 FTS, 4 FTS, 8 FTS. On loan		4-00

Defence Science and Technology Laboratory / QinetiQ (DS&TL – yet still another name change, effective from 1st July 2001. See under Boscombe Down, Wilts, for more interesting alphabetic contortions): Lynx HAS.1 XX910 moved to <u>Weston-super-Mare</u>, Somerset, on 5th December 2000.

❏	XP516		Gnat T.1	ex 8580M, 4 FTS. Stored.		3-01
❏	XV344		Buccaneer S.2C	ex Boscombe Down, Farnborough, RAE. *Nightbird*. Gate.		2-02
❏	XW241		Puma (SA.330E)	ex RAE Bedford, F-ZJUX. Stored.		2-02
❏	XW566		Jaguar T.2	ex RAE, A&AEE. Stored.		2-02
❏	XW934	'Y'	Harrier T.4	ex 20, 233 OCU, 1.		2-02
❏	XX907		Lynx AH.1	ex RAE. Static tests.		2-02
❏	*		Mil Mi-24	ex ? Stored.		2-02
❏	*		MiG-23 / -27	ex ? Stored.		2-02

Elsewhere: By May 2001 at least Opticas G-BMPL and EC-FVM had moved to North Weald, Essex.

FLEET on the A323 north-west of Aldershot
'**Dakotas**': Those noshing are surrounded by large chunks of C-47A N9050T.

❏	N9050T	C-47A-10-DK	ex Thruxton, Hal Safi, 5N-ATA, PH-MAG, G-AGYX, KG437, 42-92656. Nose.	3-96

FLEETLANDS on the B3334 south of Fareham
RNAY Fleetlands Museum: The collection was wound up by late May 2001 – probably a victim of 'contractorisation' having no place for heritage in the 'bottom line'. Curator Graham Cooper did an exceptional job and there are many who have benefited by his courtesies and researches. Sea Vixen FAW.1 XJ481 moved to Yeovilton, Somerset, on 29th November 2001. The nose of Buccaneer S.2B XK527 arrived from Bournemouth, Hants, by May 2000, but left in April 2001 for 'Scotland'.

❏	WV838*	Sea Hawk FGA.4	ex Bruntingthorpe, Chippenham, Fleetlands. Cockpit. Arrived 21-11-00.	11-00

Defence Aviation Repair Agency (DARA): The Training Centre (TC) maintains several airframes for instruction. **Departures**: Wessex HC.2 XR502 to Colsterworth, Lincs, 3-4-00; XR518 to Shawbury, Shrop, 9-00; Wessex HC.2 XR523 (and XV724) to Shawbury, Shrop, 4-01, the last of their type in store here; Wessex HC.2 XT604 to Colsterworth, Lincs, 5-4-00; Wessex HC.2 XT607 to Shawbury, Shrop, 2-4-01. Additionally, Wessex HU.5 XT766 arrived from Gosport, Hants, 9-10-00 but was found to be too decayed for use, it was scrapped in late 11-00.

❏	XS539	'435'	Wasp HAS.1	A2640 [2], ex A2718, Lee, 829 *Endurance* Flt.	TC	5-00
❏	XS569		Wasp HAS.1	A2639 [2], ex A2717, Wroughton, NATIU, 703.	TC	5-00
❏	XT434	'455'	Wasp HAS.1	A2643 [2], ex A2723, Lee-on-Solent, 829.	TC	5-00
❏	XT480	'468'	Wessex HU.5	A2603 [2], ex A2617, Wroughton, 847. Gate		4-01
❏	XT780	'636'	Wasp HAS.1	A2638 [2], ex A2716, Wroughton, 703.	TC	5-00
❏	XX440		Gazelle AH.1	A2702 [2], ex 665, 3 Regt, 12F, 669.	TC	5-00
❏	XZ213		Lynx AH.1	TAD.213, ex Wroughton, Middle Wallop, Wroughton, 659.	TC	5-00
❏	XZ307		Gazelle AH.1	A2703 [2], ex 665, 662, 663, 654, GCF.	TC	5-00
❏	XZ318*		Gazelle AH.1	ex Yeovil, Fleetlands. DBR 2-1-97. Arr by 8-00.		1-02
❏	ZA733		Gazelle AH.1	A2704 [2], ex 665, 664, BATUS.	TC	5-00
❏	ZH257*		CH-47C Chinook	ex Wattisham 9217M, Fleetlands, Wroughton, Fleetlands, Brize Norton, Fleetlands, Portsmouth, St Athan, Stanley, Argentine Army AE-520. Rear of ZA704. Under rebuild. Arrived 6-00.		1-02
❏	QP31		Lynx HC.28	ex Almondbank, Wroughton, Qatar Police.	TC	10-99

FORDINGBRIDGE west of the A338, south of Salisbury
The report in *W&R17* (p71) about Harvard II FX442 going to Kent was correct, but see under Bournemouth, Dorset, for the full picture. To the north of the town, Kraguj 30151 appeared from Bournemouth by February 2001 for use as a plaything outside a house. It moved to Shoreham, W Sussex on 25th February 2002.

GOSPORT on the B3333 south of Fareham

HMS *Sultan*:: **Air Engineering and Survival School**: The wholly fictitious unit, 760 Squadron, 'operates' the airframes here and has given some airframes codes in the '2xx' series. Wessex HAS.3 XS122 is used by the medical school at **Fort Grange** (FG).

Departures: Wessex HC.2 XR501 arrived by 4-01, to Aldershot, Hants, 25-4-01; Wessex HU.5 XS515 to Aldershot, Hants, 25-4-01; Wessex HU.5C XT463 to Predannack by 5-00; Wessex HU.5 XT766 to Fleetlands, Hants, 9-10-00; Sea King HAS.6 XV709 arrived 20-9-99, moved to St Mawgan, Cornwall, 14-1-02; Harrier GR.3 XW630 to Yeovilton, Somerset, 17-5-00

❑ XP110	'55'	Wessex HAS.1	A2636 [2], ex A2714 [2], A2728, Lee-on-Solent, Fleetlands. ABDRT	8-01
❑ XR499	'W'	Wessex HC.2	A2710 [2], ex Fleetlands, 72, A&AEE.	8-01
❑ XR516	'WB'	Wessex HC.2	A2709 [2], ex Shawbury, 2 FTS, 18.	8-01
❑ XR508*	'B'	Wessex HC.2	'XR499', ex Shawbury, 72, 18, 28. Arrived 12-9-00.	8-01
❑ XR520		Wessex HC.2	A2708 [2], ex Shawbury, 22, 72. SAR yellow.	8-01
❑ XR523*	'M'	Wessex HC.2	ex Shawbury, Fleetlands, 72. Arrived 15-1-02.	1-02
❑ XS122	'655'	Wessex HAS.3	A2632 [2], ex A2707, Lee-on-Solent, Manadon, Wroughton, 737. FG	8-01
❑ XS485		Wessex HU.5C	A2635 [3], ex Shawbury, Akrotiri, 84, FAA.	8-01
❑ XS488*	'XK'	Wessex HU.5	ex Wattisham, Halton, Wroughton, 846. Arr by 4-01.	8-01
❑ XS489	'R'	Wessex HU.5C	ex Ballymena, Odiham, Wroughton, 845, 707, 846, 848. ABDRT	8-01
❑ XS496		Wessex HU.5	A2675 [2], ex A2763, Lee-on-Solent, 772.	8-01
❑ XS507	'627'	Wessex HU.5	A2674 [2], ex A2762, Lee-on-Solent, 772.	8-01
❑ XS510	'626'	Wessex HU.5	A2676 [2], ex A2765, Lee-on-Solent, 772.	8-01
❑ XS511	'YM'	Wessex HU.5	A2660 [2], ex A2750, Lee-on-Solent, 845.	8-01
❑ XS513	'419'	Wessex HU.5	A2681 [2], ex A2770, Lee-on-Solent, 772. ABDRT	8-01
❑ XS514	'YL'	Wessex HU.5	A2653 [2], ex A2740, Lee-on-Solent, 845.	8-01
❑ XS517	'©'	Wessex HU.5C	A2625 [3], ex Shawbury, Akrotiri, 84, FAA. ABDRT	8-01
❑ XS520	'YF'	Wessex HU.5	A2659 [2], ex A2749, Lee-on-Solent, 845.	8-01
❑ XS568	'441'	Wasp HAS.1	A2637 [2], ex A2715, Fleetlands, 829.	8-01
❑ XT453	'A/B'	Wessex HU.5	A2666 [2], ex A2756, Yeovilton, Lee-on-Solent, 845.	8-01
❑ XT455	'U'	Wessex HU.5	A2654 [2], ex A2741, Lee-on-Solent, 845.	8-01
❑ XT458	'622'	Wessex HU.5	A2679 [2], ex A2768, Lee-on-Solent, 772.	8-01
❑ XT466	'XV'	Wessex HU.5	A2617 [4], ex Weeton 8921M, Cosford, Wroughton, 847.	8-01
❑ XT474	'820'	Wessex HU.5	A2695 [2], ex Detmold, Wroughton, 820, 771, ETPS, A&AEE, 846. Hulk.	8-01
❑ XT484	'H'	Wessex HU.5	A2655 [2], ex A2742, Lee-on-Solent, 845.	8-01
❑ XT485	'621'	Wessex HU.5	A2680 [2], ex A2769, Lee-on-Solent, 772.	8-01
❑ XT602		Wessex HC.2	A2706 [2], ex Shawbury, 22, 72, 78, Muharraq SAF Flt, 78.	8-01
❑ XT761		Wessex HU.5	A2678 [2], ex A2767, Lee-on-Solent, Wroughton.	8-01
❑ XT764	'G'	Wessex HU.5	A2694 [2], ex Gütersloh, Detmold, Wroughton, 845, 847, 707. Hulk.	8-01
❑ XT765	'J'	Wessex HU.5	A2665 [2], ex A2755, Lee-on-Solent, 845.	8-01
❑ XT771	'620'	Wessex HU.5	A2673 [2], ex A2761, Lee-on-Solent, 772.	8-01
❑ XV370	'260'	SH-3D Sea King	A2682 [2], ex A2771, Lee-on-Solent, Yeovil, G-ATYU.	8-01
❑ XV371	'261'	Sea King HAS.1	A2699 [2], ex Boscombe Down, A&AEE.	8-01
❑ XV625	'471'	Wasp HAS.1	A2649 [2], ex A2735, Lee-on-Solent, Culdrose, Manadon, 815.	8-01
❑ XV642	'259'	Sea King HAS.2A	A2614 [3], ex A2613, Lee-on-Solent, Yeovil, A&AEE, Yeovil, A&AEE, Yeovil.	8-01
❑ XV643*	'262'	Sea King HAS.6	ex Culdrose, 819, 849, 819, 814, 820, 824, 814, WHL, A&AEE. Arrived by 3-00.	8-01
❑ XV653*	'513'	Sea King HAS.6	ex 810, 706. Arrived 19-7-01.	8-01

❏ XV654	'05'	Sea King HAS.6	A2698 [2], ex Fleetlands, 819. Crashed 21-7-93.	8-01
❏ XV655*	'270'	Sea King HAS.6	ex 814, 819, 826, 845, 826, 814, 826, 819, 737, 824. Arrived 20-11-00.	8-01
❏ XV659*	'510'	Sea King HAS.6	ex Fleetlands, 810, 814, 819, 706, 826, 824, 819, 814, FTU, 824. First noted 12-00.	8-01
❏ XV660*	'269'	Sea King HAS.6	ex Culdrose, 819, 810, 706, 810, 819, 810, 826, 810, 824, 706. Arrived 11-12-00.	8-01
❏ XV663*		Sea King HAS.6	ex Fleetlands, 819, 810, 820, 819, 737, 706, 826. First noted 12-00.	8-01
❏ XV665*	'507'	Sea King HAS.6	ex 810, 820, 810, 824, 826. Arrived 16-2-00.	8-01
❏ XV675*	'701'	Sea King HAS.6	ex 819, 706, 824, 814, 706, 819, 814, 737, 819. First noted 4-01.	8-01
❏ XV677*	'269'	Sea King HAS.6	ex Fleetlands, 814, 820, 810, 819, 814, 820, 819. First noted 10-99.	8-01
❏ XV669	'410'	Sea King HAS.1	A2602 [4], ex Culdrose, Fleetlands 820. Mr Walter.	8-01
❏ XV696*	'269'	Sea King HAS.6	ex Culdrose, 814, 819, 826, 825, 814, 820. Arrived 18-1-01.	8-01
❏ XV701*	'268'	Sea King HAS.6	ex 814, 820, 706, 810, 819, 706, 814, 824. Arrived 20-11-00.	8-01
❏ XV705*	'821'	Sea King HU.5	ex Fleetlands, 771, 819, 706, 819, 814, 824. F/n 3-01.	8-01
❏ XV708*	'501'	Sea King HAS.6	ex 810, 819, 706, 819, 706, 820, 737. F/n 4-01.	8-01
❏ XV710*	'264'	Sea King HAS.6	ex 814, 820, 814, 819, 824. Arrived 26-7-99.	8-01
❏ XV712*	'266'	Sea King HAS.6	ex 814, 820, 814, 820, 810, 820, 706, 826, 706, 814. Arrived 20-11-00.	8-01
❏ XV713*	'018'	Sea King HAS.6	ex Fleetlands, 820, 810, 706, 826, 810, 814, 820. First noted 3-00.	8-01
❏ XV720		Wessex HC.2	A2701 [2], ex Fleetlands, SARTU, 22, 18.	8-01
❏ XV724*		Wessex HC.2	ex Shawbury, Fleetlands, 22, SARTS, 18. Arrived 15-1-02.	11-01
❏ XV725	'C'	Wessex HC.2	A2707 [2], ex Shawbury, 72, 18.	8-01
❏ XZ579*	'707'	Sea King HAS.6	ex 819, 820, 814, 820, 819, 824, 826, 824. Arrived 20-7-01.	8-01
❏ XZ581*	'269'	Sea King HAS.6	ex Fleetlands, 810, 826, 819, 814, 824, 826, 706, 814. First noted 3-00.	8-01
❏ XZ930	'Q'	Gazelle HT.3	ex Shawbury, 2 FTS, CFS. Arrived by 11-00.	8-01
❏ ZA126*	'504'	Sea King HAS.6	ex 810, 706, 820, 810, 820. Arrived 19-7-01.	8-01
❏ ZA127*	'509'	Sea King HAS.6	ex 810, 706, 810, 826, 810, 706, 820. Arr 19-7-01.	8-01
❏ ZA129*	'502'	Sea King HAS.6	ex Fleetlands, 810, 820, 826, 706. F/n 4-01.	8-01
❏ ZA131*	'271'	Sea King HAS.6	ex 814, 820, 826, 810, 826. Arrived 20-11-00.	8-01
❏ ZA136*	'18'	Sea King HAS.6	ex 820, 706, 820, 819, 706, 824, 814, 826. Ditched 4-9-98. Arrived 19-9-00.	8-01
❏ ZF649*		EH-101 PP5	ex Yeovil. Arrived 22-12-00.	8-01
❏ ZD633*	'014'	Sea King HAS.6	ex 820, 810, 814, 810, 820, 706. Arr 19-1-01.	8-01
❏ ZG817*	'702'	Sea King HAS.6	ex 819, 810. First noted 4-01.	8-01
❏ ZG818*	'707'	Sea King HAS.6	ex Fleetlands, 819, 814. First noted 3-00.	8-01
❏ ZG819*	'265'	Sea King HAS.6	ex 814, 820. Arrived 20-11-00.	8-01
❏ ZG875*	'013'	Sea King HAS.6	ex Yeovilton, 820, 819, 814. Crashed 12-6-99. Wreck. First noted 10-00.	8-01

Bernie Salter:

❏ FM118	Lancaster B.10	ex Shilo, Nanton, Brandon, RCAF. Nose.	8-01

Gosport Aviation Society / Gosport Aviation Museum Trust: The society maintains a collection of photographs, artefacts and display boards largely devoted to the history of aviation in the Gosport area at the **Royal Naval Armaments Museum**.
✉ GAS, c/o Royal Naval Armaments Museum, Priddy's Hard, Gosport, PO12 4LE ☎ 02392 422115

HAMBLE south-east of Southampton
Hamble Aerostructures: On the B3397 into Hamble, opposite 'The Harrier' public house, can be found the Gnat, still guarding the former Folland plant.

❏ XM693	Gnat T.1	ex Abingdon, Bicester 7891M, A&AEE.	4-00

HEDGE END on the A334 east of Southampton
Classic Vintage Aircraft Services (CVAS): The Auster is at a workshop in the general area.

❏ G-AKXP	Auster 5	ex Hatfield, Claygate, NJ633, 29 EFTS, 22 EFTS, 659, HS. Crashed 9-4-70.	6-95

Others: The former BCAR Terrier 1 frame has been sold in 'Essex' – any offers?

HOOK north of the M3, near Junction 5

❏ G-AJXC	Auster 5	ex TJ343, 652, 655. CoA 2-8-82. Dam 16-10-87.	10-96

LASHAM AERODROME west of Golden Pot, north-west of Alton
Second World War Aircraft Preservation Society (SWWAPS): As well as the aircraft and artefact collection, SWWAPS offers great views of the intensive gliding activity on the airfield. The Meteor NF.13 is a complex composite, with the centre section, wings and tailplane from Israel, the nose from TT.20 WM234, latterly at Arborfield, and rear fuselage of F.8 VZ462 from Biggin Hill ①.
♦ Located to the east of the gliding headquarters, on the north side of the airfield. Open Sun and Bank Hols 10am to 6pm (or dusk if first) and other times by arrangement. ✉ Bob Coles, 8 Barracane Drive, Crowthorne, Berks, RG45 7NU.

❏ 'VH-FDT'	DHA Drover II	G-APXX, ex Blackbushe, Southend, G-APXX, VH-EAS.		3-02
❏ 4X-FNA	Meteor NF.13	ex Israel, IDF-AF, WM366, A&AEE, RRE.	①	3-02
❏ VR192	Prentice 1	G-APIT, ex Biggin Hill, Southend, VR192, 1 ASS, 6 FTS, CFS, 2 FTS, Blackburn's. CoA 7-9-67.		3-02
❏ WF137	Sea Prince C.1	ex Yeovilton, Culdrose SF, Shorts FU, Arbroath SF, 781. 'Admiral's Barge' c/s.		3-02
❏ WH291	Meteor F.8	ex Kemble, 229 OCU, 85, CAW, 257.		3-02
❏ WV798 '026'	Sea Hawk FGA.6	ex Chertsey, Culdrose A2557, FRU, 801, 803, 787.		3-02
❏ XK418	Auster AOP.9	ex Basingstoke, Thruxton, Middle Wallop 7876M, 654.		3-02
❏ XM833	Wessex HAS.3	ex Lasham, Wroughton.		3-02
❏ E-423	Hunter F.51	ex Elstree, Bitteswell, Dunsfold G-9-444, Dan AF.		3-02
❏ 22+35	F-104G	ex Manching, JbG34, KE+413, DD+105.		3-02

Others: The Shorts 360 is held by ASI of Alton, Hants – *qv*. PBY-5A VR-BPS moved by road to Lee-on-Solent, Hants, on 11th March 2001.

❏ G-BLGB	Short 360-100	ex BRA / Loganair, G-14-3641. Damaged 9-2-98.	7-01

LEE-ON-SOLENT AIRFIELD east of the B3385, south of Fareham
W&R16 'wrapped up' the navy days of this wonderful airfield. Thankfully aviation has remained alive here and the former base was chosen as the headquarters for the **Super Catalina Restoration** operation. After extensive work on their hangar, the Lasham 'Cat' arrived in March 2001 with restoration starting again. The former Greenpeace example arrived in November 2001.
♦ Visits possible *only* by prior permission. web www.supercatalina.com

❏ N423RS*	PBY-5A Catalina	ex Duxford, Greenpeace, C-FJJG, CF-JJG,	
	✈	N4002A, USN 48423. Arrived 10-11-01.	11-01
❏ VR-BPS*	PBY-5A Catalina	ex Lasham, Hamble, Duxford, '9754', G-BLSC, 'JV928', Barkston Heath, South Africa, C-FMIR, N608FF, CF-MIR, N10023, Bu46633. Crashed 27-7-98. Arrived 11-3-01.	® 3-01

MIDDLE WALLOP AIRFIELD on the A343 south-west of Andover
Museum of Army Flying (MoAF): The museum's superb GAL Hotspur re-creation was officially unveiled on 13th December 2001. The six-year project completes the 'set' in terms of examples of major assault glider types on show at 'Wallop. Incorporating the rear fuselage of HH379 and as many original bits as possible, the project was largely new-build. It has adopted the identity and colours of an example that flew with the Shobdon-based 5 Glider Training School ①.
   Notes: The AFEE 10/42 is centred upon an original Jeep and is on loan from the Wessex Aviation Society ②. Largest Horsa airframe on show is 'KJ351' which is an amalgam of LH208, TL659 and 8569M ③. Another nose section and other large Horsa sections can be found on display within Hayward Hall ④. Several sections are held in store. The battered centre fuselage of TL659 is currently at Shawbury, Shropshire, along with other parts, to act as a reference for a project there. The Hamilcar (made up of parts from NX836 and TK718) is a 'walk-through' exhibit, currently under restoration. Mannequins and workbenches inside the capacious fuselage cheerfully 'hide' this work-in-progress! ⑤
   W&R17 (page 73) wrote the Grasshopper out as 'departed', not so it remains stored in the rafters! ⑥ The ML Utility inflatable aircraft had three wing options, 'Clouy', 'Delta' and 'Gadfly', all three are in store ⑦. The Prospector is a composite ⑧. MoAF aircraft out on loan are as follows: Gazelle XW276 at Winthorpe, Notts, Pucará A-528 at Sunderland, T&W; and Skeeter AOP.12 XL770 at Southampton.
◆ 10am to 4.30pm every day - last entry 4pm. Also within is 'Choppers' cafe (renamed and now with an AH-64 Apache 'pub' sign on the A343) offering commanding views of the activity on the airfield.
✉ Middle Wallop, Stockbridge, SO20 8DY ☎ 01980 674421 **fax** 01264 781694 **e-mail** daa@flying-museum.org.uk **web** www.flying-museum.org.uk

❑ G-AXKS		W-Bell 47G-4A	ex Bristow, ARWF, G-17-8. CoA 21-9-82.		1-02
❑ 'B-415'		AFEE 10/42 REP	BAPC. 163, ex Wimborne.	②	10-01
❑ P-5		Rotachute III	8381M, ex Henlow. On loan from RAFM.		1-02
❑ 'N5195'		Sopwith Pup	G-ABOX, ex Redhill. On loan. CoA 18-6-90.		1-02
❑ 'T9707'		Magister I	ex Cardington, Manchester, Hendon 8378M, G-AKKR, 'T9967', T9708, 51 MU, 16 EFTS, 239. CoA 10-4-65.		1-02
❑ 'KJ351'		Horsa II	BAPC.80, fuselage.	③	1-02
❑ 'HH268'		Hotspur II REP	BAPC.261. Unveiled 13-12-01.	①	1-02
❑ TJ569		Auster 5	G-AKOW, ex PH-NAD, PH-NEG, TJ569, 652, 660, 659. CoA 26-6-82.		1-02
❑ TK777		Hamilcar I	ex Christian Malford. Forward fuselage.	⑤	1-02
❑ WG432	'L'	Chipmunk T.10	ex AFWF, LAS, Bri UAS, 19 RFS, Cam UAS, 4 BFTS.		10-01
❑ WJ358		Auster AOP.6	G-ARYD, ex Perth, WJ358, 651, 657, 1913 Flt.		1-02
❑ WZ721		Auster AOP.9	ex 4 RTR, 656, 6 Flt. *Dragon.*		1-02
❑ WZ772		G'hopper TX.1	ex Halton, 1 MGSP, Brentwood. Stored.	⑥	1-02
❑ XG502		Sycamore HR.14	ex gate, Wroughton, Bristol, JEHU.		1-02
❑ XK776		ML Utility Mk 1	ex Cardington. On loan.	⑦	1-02
❑ XL813		Skeeter AOP.12	ex ARWF, 4 Regt, 9 Flt.		1-02
❑ 'XM819'		Prospector	ex Durrington. Composite.	⑧	1-02
❑ XP821 'MCO'		Beaver AL.1	ex Shawbury, Kemble, St Athan, Defence Attaché, Laos, 130 Flt, 30 Flt RASC, 656. White/grey c/s.		1-02
❑ XP822		Beaver AL.1	ex Duxford, 'Wallop, Shawbury, Kemble, 132 Flt, 667, 18 Flt. 'Gate'.		10-01
❑ XP910*	'D'	Scout AH.1	ex SEAE. Crashed 13-9-89.	⑧	1-02
❑ XP847		Scout AH.1	ex AETW, Wroughton, Yeovil.		1-02
❑ XR232		Alouette AH.2	ex Historic Flight, Wroughton, A&AEE, Middle Wallop, EW&AU, 656, A&AEE, 16 Flt, 6 Flt.		1-02
❑ XT108	'U'	Sioux AH.1	ex Duxford, Yeovilton, 'Wallop, D&T Flt, 'Wallop.		1-02
❑ XV127		Scout AH.1	ex Fleetlands, Chelsea, Wroughton, 655.		1-02
❑		Scout CIM	ex AETW. Kid's plaything.		1-02
❑ ZA737*		Gazelle AH.1	ex 1 Rgt, 847, Fleetlands 'hack', 670, ARWS. Arrived by 12-99.		1-02
❑ '998-8888'		UH-1H 'Huey'	ex Greenford, Middle Wallop, Fleetlands, Stanley, Argentine Army AE-406, 72-21491. US Army c/s.		1-02

☐ AE-409	'656'	UH-1H 'Huey'	ex Duxford, Middle Wallop, 656, Stanley,		
			Argentine Army, 72-21506.		1-02
☐ 111989		L-19A Bird Dog	N33600, ex Fort Rucker, Alabama.		1-02
☐ '243809'		CG-4A	BAPC.185, ex Burtonwood, Shrewsbury. Fuselage.		1-02
☐		Horsa II	Fuselage.	④	10-01
☐		Horsa II	Cockpit.	④	10-01

Army Air Corps Historic Aircraft Flight / Army Air Corps Reserve Collection Trust
(RCT): The Trust was formed to support the Flight. Some aircraft within the Trust are on loan, including Tiger Moth G-AOHY. The Trust's Beaver XP772 (G-BUCJ) is at Duxford, Cambs.
◆ *Not* available for public inspection, but does 'do the rounds' of the airshow circuit.

☐ G-AOHY		Tiger Moth	ex Shobdon, Land's End, Elmdon, N6537,		
			Dyce SF, Ringway SF, 11 RFS, 11 EFTS,		
			35 ERFTS. CoA 20-8-60.	RCT ®	3-97
☐ N6985		Tiger Moth ✈	G-AHMN, ex 2 EFTS, 22 EFTS, Andover SF. Loan.		3-98
☐ XL814		Skeeter AOP.12 ✈	ex 1 Wing, 2 Wing, 651.		3-98
☐ XP242		Auster AOP.9 ✈	G-BUCI. Ex AFWF.		3-98
☐ XP820		Beaver AL.1 ✈	ex 7 Regt, 667, 132 Flt RCT, 130 Flt RCT,		
			30 Flt RASC, 11 Flt, 656.		9-01
☐ XR244		Auster AOP.9 ✈	ex AFWF.		9-01
☐ XR379		Alouette AH.2 ✈	ex Almondbank, 667, 16F, 6(A) Flt.		9-01
☐ XT131	'B'	Sioux AH.1 ✈	ex D&T Flight.		9-01
☐ XT626	'Q'	Scout AH.1	ex 666, Wroughton, 656, BATUS, 656, 663.		9-01

No.2 Training Regiment, Aircrew Technical Training Detachment / No.70 Aircraft Workshops (ACW): Technical training here is now a detachment of SEAE at Arborfield, Berks, which see. Three airframes serve in this role, within Stockwell Hall. The Sioux on the gate has its complex side. The plate in the cockpit gives it as WA-S-179, which makes it XT827, latterly a 'spares ship' with the Historic Flight ①.

Departures: Scout AH.1 XP854 to Wattisham, Suffolk, by 2-01; Scout AH.1 XP910 moved to the museum, above, by late 2001; Gazelle AH.1 XW900 to Arborfield, Berks, by 3-00; Gazelle AH.1 ZB668 arrived from Arborfield, Berks, 7-99 but returned to Arborfield, Berks, by 2-01.

☐ WZ724		Auster AOP.9	7432M, ex 'WZ670', 656, FEAF.		
			Tan/brown colours. Gate.		10-01
☐ XP893		Scout AH.1	ex Wroughton, Garrison Air Sqn, 3 CBAS,		
			655, 666, 656. ABDR. 70 ACW.		3-00
☐ XR436		SARO P.531-2	ex MoAF, A&AEE. ABDR.		7-90
☐ XR630		Scout AH.1	ex 658, 664, 666, 664. Hulk.		6-98
☐ 'XT123'	'D'	Sioux AH.1	XT827, ex Wroughton, Yeovilton, Coypool,		
			3 CBAS. Composite. Gate.	①	3-00
☐ XT151		Sioux AH.1	ex ARWF. Stored.		11-97
☐ XT638	'N'	Scout AH.1	ex Fleetlands, 666. Gate.		10-01
☐ XV131	'Y'	Scout AH.1	ex Wroughton, 660, 665,.653, D&TS. ABDR. 70 ACW.		3-00
☐ XV629		Wasp HAS.1	ex Wroughton, 703. ABDR.		5-94
☐ XX443	'Y'	Gazelle AH.1	ex 658, 662, 663, 3 Regt, 669, 659. Cr 28-9-97. SEAE.		4-98
☐ QP32		Lynx HC.28	TAD.016, ex Middle Wallop, Almondbank,		
			Wroughton, Qatar Police. SEAE.		4-98

ODIHAM AIRFIELD on the A32 south of Odiham
RAF Odiham: Travel back to *W&R12* (p65). This records Whirlwind HAR.10 XK970 leaving on 17th July 1987 for somewhere. The rampant optimism in the phrase "doubtless someone is putting pen to paper even now..." was rewarded in July 2000, via an e-mail. Of such is the long arm of *W&R* and the pace of progress! Mention of XK970 is to be found under Bramley, Hants, in this edition. It is not known if it went somewhere else in between. The hulk of Wessex HU.5 XT467, last noted in May 1997, also gravitated to Bramley, Hants. The base 'parents' Chipmunk T.10 PAX WK570, currently located at Southampton, Hants, and 'JP' T.4 cockpit XP677 at East Grinstead, West Sussex. There is a

very realistic, but very much 'synthetic' Chinook burning rig on the dump. Jet Provost T.4 XR670 was tendered during mid-2000 and moved to Clacton, Essex. Chinook HC.1 ZA676, last noted here in July 1999, had moved on to Wattisham, Suffolk, by June 2000.

❏ XR453	'A' Whirlwind HAR.10	8883M, ex Foulness, 2 FTS, CFS, 230, 1563 Flt, CFS. Gate	4-01
❏ XS498*	'WK' Wessex HU.5C	9277M, ex Predannack, Gosport A2641 [3], Shawbury, Akrotiri, 84, FAA. 'Joker'. (Tail from HC.2 XT601) Dump, first noted 4-01.	5-01
❏ ZA678	'EZ' Chinook HC.1	9229M, ex Fleetlands, 7, N37023. Crashed 24-7-89.	6-01

Steve Markham: A SIPA is stored locally.

❏ G-AWLG	SIPA 903	ex F-BGHG. CoA 22-8-79. Stored.	12-97

PETERSFIELD on the A3 north of Havant
Churchers College: Grasshopper TX.1 XA225 moved to Keevil, Wilts, on 27th February, 2001.

POPHAM AERODROME on the A303 west of North Waltham

❏ G-ARTY	Cessna 150B	ex Perth, N7382X. CoA 6-10-68.	8-96
❏ G-ATKU	Cessna F.172G	ex Hinton-in-the-Hedges. Damaged 20-7-91. Fuselage.	1-97
❏ G-BPDJ	Mini Coupe	ex N13877. CoA 28-10-91. Stored.	1-02
❏ G-BSTV	Cherokee Six	ex N4069R. Stored.	4-00
❏ G-MTBC	Gemini Flash 2	CoA 11-5-92. Stored.	5-98

PORTSMOUTH
Marine Salvage Ltd: Lightning F.53 moved to Charlwood, Surrey, by May 2000. By July 2000 F.53 ZF581, along with the wings of ZF585, had moved out. Initial reports said to Rochester, but certainly by late 2001 it was to be found in Rotterdam being re-assembled for display. F.53 ZF592 moved to Norwich, Norfolk, on 6th February 2002.

❏ XM369*	'C' Jet Provost T.3	8084M, ex Harry Pounds, East Wretham, Halton, Shawbury, 2 FTS.	5-01

Royal Navy Diving School: The Wessex is still kept in a deep lake off Horsea Island.

❏ XT760	Wessex HU.5	A2669 [2], ex Fleetlands.	1-00

Others: The Canberra nose listed here is more accurately located in Southampton, Hants, *qv*. Jet Provost T.3 XM369 at the Harry Pounds scrapyard, was with Marine Salvage (see above) by May 2001. Listed under Jordans' yard in *W&R17*, HS.125-1B XW930 had gone by 1998.

ROMSEY on the A27 north-west of Southampton
A farm strip in this general area holds a variety of inmates. (See under 'Farley', Hants.) Cessna 185A OO-RGM became G-BWMC and was flying again by 2001.

❏ G-AWUH	Cessna F.150H	CoA 16-7-94. Stored.	2-01
❏ G-AXCX	Pup 150	ex G-35-046. CoA 10-7-94. Stored.	5-00
❏ G-BAPM	Fuji FA.200-160	CoA 4-5-98. Wreck.	2-01
❏ G-BFJJ*	Evans VP-1	CoA 23-6-96. Stored.	2-01
❏ G-BHDO	Cessna F.182Q	Forward fuselage. Crashed 7-5-89.	1-96
❏ G-BNHE	ARV Super 2	CoA 7-8-99. Stored.	2-01
❏ EC-AOZ*	PA-20-150 Pacer	G-BXBB, ex N1133C.	® 9-01
❏ N5052P*	Comanche 180	ex Nuthamstead, Panshanger, G-ATFS, N5052P.	® 9-01
❏ OO-VPC	Cessna 185A	Stored.	1-96

SOPLEY on the B3347 north of Christchurch
Contrary to *W&R17* (p76), Auster G-AJPZ did not move north — see under Bournemouth, Dorset.

SOUTHAMPTON

Hall of Aviation: For some considerable period of time, museum staff have been in negotiation to relocate the museum within the planned heritage development at a former ship repair yard at Marchwood. To date these plans have yet to be finalised.

Notes: Several airframes are on loan, the SR.A.1 from the Imperial War Museum ②, the Sandringham from the Science Museum ①. The Tiger Moth is a composite, with parts from G-AOAC and G-AOJJ ③. The museum has an excellent relationship with **424 Squadron, Air Cadets** (424). The unit have their headquarters within the museum complex, although not open to the public. All but one of 424's airframes are their own, ie not MoD property. Within their HQ are several impressive procedure trainers and simulators, including a three-axis 'JP' cockpit which may be wholly 'synthetic' but may also owe its origins to a Mk.3 or Mk.4, although it is emblazoned 'T Mk 5-A' (*sic*).

♦ Open daily *except* Mondays and over Christmas, 10am to 5pm (Tue to Sat) and 2pm to 5pm (Sun) ✉ Albert Road South, Southampton, SO1 1FR ☎ 023 80635830 **fax** 023 80223383 **e-mail** aviation@spitfireclub.com **web** www.spitfireonline.co.uk

❑ 'G-ADZW'*	HM.14 'Flea'	BAPC.253, ex Sandown, Lake, Isle of Wight. Arrived 5-00.			3-02
❑ G-ALZE	BN-1F	ex Cosford, Kemble, Bembridge.			3-02
❑ VH-BRC	Sandringham 4	ex Lee-on-Solent, VP-LVE *Southern Cross*, N158C, VH-BRC, ZK-AMH, JM715.	①		3-02
❑ N248	Supermarine S.6A	ex Cowes, Southampton, Henlow, Southampton Pier, 'S1596', Eastleigh, Calshot, RAFHSF.			3-02
❑ 'N546'	Wight Quad'plane	BAPC.164, ex Wimborne. Repro.			3-02
❑ 'C4451'	Avro 504J REP	BAPC.210, built by AJD Engineering.			3-02
❑ 'K5054'*	Spitfire REP	G-BRDV, ex Sandown, Keevil. CoA 18-2-95. Arr 5-00.			3-02
❑ BB807	Tiger Moth	G-ADWO, ex Wimborne.	③		3-02
❑ PK683	Spitfire F.24	ex Kingsbridge Lane, Kemble, Colerne, Changi 7150M, Singapore Aux AF.			3-02
❑ TG263	SARO SR.A.1	ex Duxford, Staverton, Cranfield, G-12-1, TG263.	②		3-02
❑ WK570	Chipmunk T.10 PAX	8211M, ex Bournemouth Airport, Hamble, 663, Hull UAS, 663, RAFC. .		424	3-02
❑ WM571	Sea Ven FAW.22	ex Wimborne, Staverton, ADS, 831B, HS.			3-02
❑ WZ753	Grasshopper TX.1	ex Halton, Emanuel School, London.			3-02
❑ XD332 '194'	Scimitar F.1	ex Helston, Culdrose SAH-19, Lee-on-Solent A2574, 764B, 736, 807, 804. Stored, outside.			3-02
❑ XD596	Vampire T.11	ex Calmore, St Athan 7939M, CATCS, CNCS, 5 FTS, 4 FTS.		424	3-02
❑ XJ476	Sea Vixen FAW.1	ex Boscombe Down, A&AEE. Nose.		424	3-02
❑ XK740	Gnat F.1	ex Hamble, Cosford 8396M, Bicester, Church Fenton, MoS, Filton.			3-02
❑ XL770	Skeeter AOP.12	ex Middle Wallop, Shrivenham 8046M, Wroughton, 15/19 Hussars, 652, 654.			3-02
❑ XN246	Cadet TX.3	ex Syerston, 617 GS.			3-02
❑	Swift CIM	—			3-02
❑	Jet Provost CIM	marked 'CRAN 22/2'.		424	3-02
❑ — BAPC.7	SUMPAC	ex Old Warden, Southampton. Man-powered aircraft.			3-02
❑ — BAPC.215	Airwave HG	prototype.			3-02
❑ —	HM.14 'Flea'	ex Rayleigh. Unfinished.			3-02

Aero Antiques and AeroTech Ltd: During early 2001 two of the Tiger Moth projects took to the air again: G-AHPZ and G-APPN. The DH.71 Tiger Moth (monoplane) project is currently 'on ice' ①. The DH.34 project is based on original wings, all else is new built and was previously with Russavia ②. Tiger Moth G-DHTM is effectively a 'from new' project ③.

❑ G-ECDX	DH.71 REP	Under construction.	①	1-00
❑ G-ACET	DH.84 Dragon	ex Bishop's Stortford, AW171, Ringway SF, 6 AACU, G-ACET.	②	1-00

❑ G-AFSW	Chilton DW.2	ex Chilton Manor. Unflown. Stored.		1-00
❑ G-AHMM	Tiger Moth	ex EM870, 25 ETFS. Crashed 10-7-54.	®	1-00
❑ G-ALJL	Tiger Moth	ex T6311, Fairford SF, 38 GCF, Tarrant Rushton SF, 11 OTU, 25 PEFTS. CoA 28-9-50.	®	1-00
❑ G-AMIU	Tiger Moth	ex Membury, Wycombe Air Park, T5495, 16 EFTS, 54 OTU, Church Fenton SF. Crashed 15-10-69. Stored.		1-00
❑ G-ANFP	Tiger Moth	ex Fownhope, London Colney, Denham, Rush Green, N9503, 2 RFS, 7 RFS, 2 RFS, 4 RFS, 4 EFTS. CoA 1-7-63. Frame.	®	1-00
❑ G-ARTH	Super Cruiser	ex EI-ADO. CoA 21-4-95. Stored.	®	1-00
❑ G-DHTM	Tiger Moth	Under construction.	③	1-00
❑ DR613	GM.1 Wicko	G-AFJB, ex COA, ATA, G-AFJB. CoA 12-7-63.	®	11-01

Frank Lund: Previously listed under 'Portsmouth', Frank keeps his Canberra nose in the area.
❑ WT536	Canberra PR.7	ex Bruntingthorpe, Cosford, 8063M 80, 31, 13, 17. Nose.	6-01

The World's End: A large pub-cum-night-club has – among other things – an 'Avro 504' hanging from the ceiling in the main bar area. The fuselage looks relatively convincing – while the lettering ICE PATROL does not, but the wings are truncated and poorly prepared. More details appreciated.
❑ —*	'Avro 504' FSM	first noted 12-99.	12-99

Others: Of the Austers believed held in the area, two have been moved into the LOST! column: J/1N G-AHHU (last noted 12-91) and J/1N G-AIGF (12-96). Auster 5 G-ANLU is thought to have moved to 'Yorkshire' for restoration. A collector in the general area has two Vampires and a Gannet.
❑ WN411	Gannet AS.1	ex Abbotsinch, 820. Fuselage.	5-01
❑ 'XD614' '65'	Vampire T.11	WZ572, ex Southampton museum, Leeming, 8 FTS, 7 FTS, 202 AFS. Pod.	5-01
❑ XH318 '64'	Vampire T.11	ex Calmore, Southampton, Ferndown, 7761M, Shawbury, RAFC.	5-01

SOUTHAMPTON AIRPORT or Eastleigh, at the A335/M27 junction north of the City
❑ G-BKBH	HS.125-600B	ex 5N-DNL, G-5-698, 5N-DNL, 5N-NBC, G-5-698, G-BKBH, G-5-698, TR-LAU, G-BKBH, G-BDJE, G-5-11. Dump.	2-02
❑ N6NE	JetStar 731	ex VR-CCC ntu, N222Y, N731JS, N227K, N12R, N280R. Damaged 27-11-92. Non-destructive.	2-02

THRUXTON AERODROME north of the A303 west of Andover
Military Helicopters Ltd: Have a 'niche' in Scout and Wasp work. Most only rotate (ugh!) through here, but XV123 is more long term. By February 2002 XW613 was airworthy and awaiting a customer.
❑ XV123*	Scout AH.1	ex Ipswich, Weston-super-Mare, Fleetlands.	®	12-01

Others:
❑ G-AOAA	Tiger Moth	ex Chilbolton, DF159, 24 GCF, 1 RS, 1 GTS, 20 PAFU, 5 GTS. Crashed 4-6-89.	®	9-97
❑ G-BKXP*	Auster AOP.6	ex Little Gransden, Royston, Oakington, Belgian AF A-14, VT987.	®	6-01
❑ G-BJST	Harvard IV	ex Little Gransden, Coventry, *Empire of the Sun*, ItAF MM53795.	®	6-01
❑ —*	Tiger Moth	ex Little Gransden, Cranfield, VAT et al.	®	6-01

TITCHFIELD on the A27 west of Fareham
Melvyn Hiscock: The climax approacheth – sort of!
❑ G-BVLK	Cloudster	ex Thruxton, Sudbury, N25403, NC25403.	®	10-01

YATELEY on the B3272 west of Camberley
Mick Long: Keeps three cockpits in the general area.

❏ WP977*	Chipmunk T.10	G-BHRD, ex Crowland, Doncaster, Stamford, Burford, 9M-ANA, VR-SEK, WP977, Malayan Aux AF, Rufforth SF, Man UAS, Lpl UAS, 63 GCF, QUAS, Man UAS. Crashed 21-1-97.	6-01
❏ WZ876*	Chipmunk T.10	G-BBWN, ex Twyford, Tattershall Thorpe, Lon UAS, 1 AEF, Lon UAS, Biggin Hill SF, Lon UAS, Ox UAS, Birm UAS, MCS, 31. Forward cockpit.	6-01
❏ XN657*	Sea Vixen D.3	ex Stock, Llanbedr, RAE, FRL, RAE, ADS, 899, 893. Cockpit.	6-01

HEREFORDSHIRE and WORCESTERSHIRE

☛ Unitary status was granted to Herefordshire and Worcestershire from 1st April 1998. *W&R* will keep the two counties under the same banner while adding the 'Shires' to their titles!

BIRLINGHAM on the A4104, east of the B4080 to the west of Evesham
Graham Revill: This *private* collection is unchanged.

❏ WF299	Sea Hawk FB.3	WF299, ex 'WN105', Helston, St Agnes, Topcliffe, Catterick 8164M, Lee-on-Solent, A2662, A2509, Culdrose SAH-8, 802, 738, 736. Composite.	8-01
❏ WH166	Meteor T.7	ex Digby 8052M, CFS, 5 CAACU, CAW, 4 FTS, 205 AFS, 210 AFS, 208 AFS.	8-01
❏ [WZ425]	Vampire T.11	ex Cardiff-Wales, Woodford, Chester, St Athan, 5 FTS, RAFC, 229 OCU, CGS.	8-01
❏ [XE979] '54'	Vampire T.11	ex Stonehouse, Woodford, Chester, St Athan, 1 FTS, 8 FTS, RAFC.	8-01
❏ XF526 '78' and 'E'	Hunter F.6	ex St Athan, Halton 8679M, Laarbruch SF, 4 FTS, 229 OCU, 56, 43, 56, 63, 66.	8-01
❏ XN632	Jet Provost T.3	ex Eaglescott, Chivenor, St Athan 8352M, Kemble, Shawbury, 3 FTS.	8-01

BREDON on the B4080 south of Pershore
T-6G G-BTKI was cancelled as sold in the USA during May 2000.

BROMSGROVE on the A448 north-west of Redditch
Bob Dunn and **Brian Barrett**: Both members of the Wolverhampton Aviation Group, took delivery of a Canberra nose during late 2000. Having got the hang of it, they then went for a Hunter!

❏ WJ865*	Canberra T.4	ex Stamford, Stock, Farnborough, ETPS. Nose. Arrived 12-00.	12-01
❏ XE597*	Hunter FGA.9	8874M, ex Moreton-in-Marsh, Halton, Bentley Priory, Brawdy, 1 TWU, 2 TWU, TWU, 229 OCU, West Raynham SF, 1, 54, MoA, 208, 56, 63, 66. Nose. Arrived 19-3-02.	3-02

DEFFORD on the A4104 south-west of Pershore

❏ G-BOKW	Bö 208C Junior	ex G-BITT, F-BRHX, D-EEAL. CoA 3-11-95.	4-98
❏ G-BPAO	Air Command 503	CoA 8-8-91. Stored.	4-98
❏ G-MNAF	Pegasus XL-R	CoA 3-95. Stored.	4-98

EVESHAM on the A435 south of Redditch
HMS *Explorer:* In Honeybourne Road, South Littleton, the Sea Cadets have a Wessex HAS.1.
❏ XS886   '27' Wessex HAS.1   ex Birmingham, Lee-on-Solent A2685,
                                   Wroughton, 771.   2-02

FOWNHOPE on the B4224 south-east of Hereford
Ross Aviation Services (RAS): The anonymous JetRanger Navajo fuselage E18-2 have moved on.

HEREFORD on the A49 south of Leominster
A local enthusiast has a pair of Hunters. Turbulent G-AREZ has 'moved on'.
❏ XG252   'U' Hunter FGA.9   8840M, ex Cosford, 1 TWU, 2 TWU, 1 TWU,
                                   TWU, 45, 8, Wittering SF, MoA, 54, 66.   7-00
❏ XL563   Hunter T.7   9218M, ex Kempston, Farnborough, IAM, MoA, mkrs.   8-99

KINGTON south of the A422, east of Worcester
Martin Aubrey: Has taken on two airframes from CARG at Innsworth, Glos – *qv* ①. The Edwards is owned by Computair Consultants, the glider was designed in Gloucestershire an is similar in design to the SG.38, Dagling etc but with a metal fuselage frame ②.
❏ G-ASDF*   Edwards Helic   ex Innsworth, Woking, Coulsdon.   ®①   3-02
❏ *   Primary glider   ex Innsworth, 'Glos'.   ®②   3-02

MADLEY on the B4352 west of Hereford
❏ G-ADWJ   Tiger Moth   ex Shobdon, Defford, BB803, 9 EFTS,
                                   20 EFTS, 12 EFTS, G-ADWJ.   ®   6-97

MALVERN WELLS on the A449 south of Great Malvern
Peter Ward: A 'Flea' is kept in the area.
❏ 'G-ADYV'   HM.14 'Flea'   BAPC.243, ex 'A-FLEA', Leigh-on-Sea.   8-95

SHOBDON AERODROME north of the A44 west of Leominster
Shobdon Aircraft Maintenance (SAM) moved out during 2000. It is assumed that the bulk of the Cessna 150s etc moved out as well, perhaps to North Wales. Only two elements have 'surfaced': Cessna 150E G-ATAT to Hull, E Yorks; Jet Provost T.3 XM355 to Bruntingthorpe, Leics. That leaves the following unaccounted for: Tiger Moth G-ANNE; F.150F G-ATMN; F.150G G-AVHN; F.150F G-AWAV; F.150H G-AWCK; F.150H G-AWEO; F.150H G-AWGY; F.150H G-AWLJ; 150J G-AYRK; F.150L G-BAXX; F.150H G-BFGW; Tiger Moth G-BNDW; F.150G G-JWDS; 172RG F-GDPA. A Cessna cockpit, doubtless from the SAM 'stock' is on dump, close to runway 27's southern edge.
❏ G-BEPN   Pawnee 235D   ex N54877. Crashed 11-2-78. Fuselage frame. Dump.   5-01
❏ *   Cessna F.150   cockpit. Dump. First noted 8-00.   5-01

UPPER HILL between the A4110 and the A49 south of Leominster
Sheppards Surplus and Garden Centre: The Swift still guards the entrance to this amazing emporium while the Whirlwind moulders in a yard at the rear.
❏ WK275   Swift F.4   ex Hatfield, Filton, C(A). Displayed.   2-02
❏ XP360   'V' W'wind HAR.10   ex Sunderland, Warmingham, Lasham,
                                   Fawkham Green, CFS, 225. Stored.   2-02

WORCESTER
John Hancock: Should still have his Canberra nose.
❏ WK118   Canberra TT.18   ex Stock, Wyton, 100, 7, 59, 103. Nose.   3-96

HERTFORDSHIRE

BERKHAMSTED on the A4251 west of Hemel Hempstead
Stuart McKay: Is the driving force of the **de Havilland Moth Club** uniting all who restore, own, operate or just love DH biplanes. As well as the annual Woburn fly-in, they produce by far and away the best magazine of any 'type' organisation anywhere in the UK – *The Moth*. Tiger Moth G-AMTK was sold in Italy in 2000.
✉ De Havilland Moth Club, 23 Hall Park Hill, Berkhamsted, Herts, HP4 2NH.

❏ G-AVPD	Jodel D.9 Bebe	ex Langley. CoA 6-6-75.	12-99

CHESHUNT on the A10 north of Junction 25 of the M25

❏ G-AOBV	J/5P Autocar	ex Laindon, Stapleford Tawney, Benington. CoA 7-4-71.	10-97

CLOTHALL COMMON on the A507 south-east of Baldock

❏ G-APYU	Tri-Traveler	ex Moreton-in-Marsh. Crashed 23-4-72. Stored.	10-99

ELSTREE AERODROME north of Junction 4, M1
Inspection of the dump area revealed a population explosion! Note that the 'accepted' state of things for AA-5s G-OBSF and G-ODAE are that the latter was a rebuild of the former! ①

❏ G-ASON	Twin Comanche	ex N7273Y ntu. CoA 30-11-91. Stored.		1-00
❏ G-AXGC	MS.880B Rallye	CoA 12-5-88. Stored.		9-95
❏ G-BSCR*	Cessna 172M	ex N12693. Crashed 19-6-99. Dump.		6-00
❏ G-NGBI*	AA-5B Tiger	ex G-JAKK, G-BHWI, N3752E. Crashed 12-7-90. Fuselage. Dump.		6-00
❏ G-OBSF*	AA-5A Cheetah	ex G-ODSF, G-BEUW, N6158A. Damaged 8-2-97. Fuselage. Dump.	①	6-00
❏ G-ODAE*	AA-5A Cheetah	ex G-OBSF, G-ODSF, G-BEUW, N6158A. Fuselage. Dump.	①	6-00
❏ C-FQIP*	Lake LA-4-200	ex N1068L. Stored. First noted 6-00.		11-01
❏ ST-AHZ	Navajo 310	ex G-AXMR, N6558L. Fire dump.		6-00
❏ 'KM.174'	Fokker S.11-1	G-BEPV, ex PH-ANK, MLD 174, KLu E-31. CoA 15-4-93. Dutch Navy colours.	®	10-00
❏ —*	Cherokee	fuselage, dump. Last letter 'H'.		6-00
❏ —*	AA-5	fuselage, dump. Last letter 'X'.		6-00

HATFIELD
Galleria: The Comet still 'flies' inside the mall. (The 'real' – ie hugely reconstructed – G-ACSS can be found at Old Warden, Beds, and see under St Albans, Herts.)

❏ 'G-ACSS'	DH.88 FSM	BAPC.257. *Grosvenor House.*	3-02

Gerry Atwell and **Frank Telling**: No news on the HM.21 – inbound for LOST!?

❏	Mignet HM.21	ex Agonac, France. Stored.	10-94

University of Hertfordshire: The Jetstream test-shell is used as a teaching aid within the campus. It is described as the third example built which would *probably* make it the whole static airframe laid down in early 1967 between G-ATXI (c/n 199/02) and G-ATXJ (c/n 200/03).

❏	Jetstream 1 EMU	ex Radlett. Fuselage.	1-97

HATFIELD AIRFIELD west of the A1 at Hatfield
Two aircraft are in open store for the Mosquito Aircraft Museum – see under London Colney, Herts ①. The fuselage of Trident 1E-140 G-AVYE - believed at some stage to have been used for special forces training until the site became a trading estate and film set – is thought to have been scrapped in 2000.

With filming of the series *Band of Brothers* complete, by mid-2001 Dakota N3455 and the nose of C-47A 6W-SAF moved to <u>North Weald</u>, Essex. In late 2000 Dove 8 G-AREA made the move to <u>London Colney</u>, Herts. This leaves just the Trident 3B-101, looking increasingly forlorn and now awaiting disposal. It is owned by the de Havilland Heritage Centre at London Colney.

❏ G-AWZO   Trident 3B-101   ex Heathrow, BA, BEA. CoA 13-2-86.   3-02

HEMEL HEMPSTEAD on the A414 west of St Albans
The Vampire Collection: Alan Allen still keeps his Vampire pod in the area.
◆ Visits by prior arrangement *only*. ✉ Alan Allen, 201 High Street Green, Hemel Hempstead, HP2 7AA. **e-mail** alan.allen@lineone.net
❏ WZ581   '77' Vampire T.11   ex Ruislip, Bushey, Keevil, Exeter, 3/4 CAACU,
                                      229 OCU, 233 OCU, 25. Pod.   3-02

HITCHIN on the A505 north-east of Luton
Philip Leaver: (Previously listed under Luton, Beds.) The GR.1 is thought to have been a 'spare' with the cockpit number FL/R 41H 725624, and – contrary to previous thinking – not a damaged 'flyer'.
❏   Harrier GR.1   ex Llantrisant, Welshpool, Stafford,
                                      Abingdon, Hamble. Nose.   3-02
❏ XV759   'O' Harrier GR.3   ex Bruntingthorpe, Barnstaple (?), Welshpool,
                                      Llantrisant, Pendine, St Athan, 233 OCU, 1417F,
                                      233 OCU, 1, 233 OCU, 1, 233 OCU. Nose.   3-02

Others: The Martin Monoplane project is thought still to be underway here. The wings are being used on the Humming Bird project, to be found at Hatch, Beds.
❏ G-AEYY   Martin Monoplane ex Bishop's Stortford, Meir.   ® 4-92

KINGS LANGLEY on the A41 north of Watford
❏ XM708   Gnat T.1   ex Locking, Halton 8573M, 4 FTS, CFS, HS.   3-02

LEAVESDEN south of Abbots Langley, north of the A41
Studios: Eon Productions have a travelling 'roadshow' dedicated to James Bond. Part of the display is the Bede 'Acrostar' (BD-5J) used in *Octopussy*. The nose of Hunter F.6A XJ676 is believed to have been scrapped. (See also Iver Heath, Bucks.)
❏   Bede BD-5J   ex *Octopussy*.   1-98

LONDON COLNEY off the A6 between London Colney and South Mimms
De Havilland Heritage Museum (DHHM) incorporating the **Mosquito Aircraft Museum** and administered by the De Havilland Aircraft Museum Trust. The Transport Trust's Restoration Award for 2000 went to the Queen Bee project, picking up a cheque for £750 on 31st March 2001. The prototype Mosquito has entered a comprehensive restoration, with assistance coming from a wide variety of sources, including Marshall Aerospace and Rolls-Royce ①. On 9th May 2001 another Horsa section was added to the collection. This one – a 15ft mid-section having been a former house at Wallingford, Oxon.
   Notes: The de Havilland-built Cierva C.24 is on loan from the Science Museum ②. Mosquito FB.6 TA122 is being rebuilt using the wing of TR.33 TW233 acquired in Israel ③. The Chipmunk PAX will be turned into an educational exhibit and fitted with a sectioned Gipsy Major 10 Mk.2 and the rear fuselage of fellow WG418 ④. The DH.88 Comet FSM was built for use in the film *The Great Air Race*, it will re-appear in the colours of G-ACSP *Black Magic* ⑤. The Comet SIM is a nose section that was built at the same time as the noses for the first two prototypes and was used for structural tests. It then went to the DH Servicing School and was later converted into a simulator. It is now fitted with Mk.4 instrumentation ⑥. At nearby Hatfield DHM's Trident 3B G-AWZO is pending disposal. See under Fyvie, Scotland, for an ambitious and long term project.
◆ Open from first Sun of Mar to last Sun of Oct, Tue, Thu and Sat 2pm to 5.30pm, Sun and Bank Hols 10.30am to 5.30pm. Last admission 4.30pm ✉ PO Box 107, Salisbury Hall, London Colney, St Albans, AL2 1BU ☎ 01727 822051 **fax** 01727 826400 **web** www.dehavillandmuseum.co.uk

❑ G-ABLM	Cierva C.24	ex Hatfield. CoA 16-1-35.	②	3-02
❑ G-ADOT	Hornet Moth	ex Hatfield, Old Warden, Stoke Ferry, Stapleford, Houghton-on-the-Hill, X9326, 5 GCF, 23 OTU, 24 GCF, 6 AONS, Halton SF, 2 CPF, G-ADOT. CoA 5-10-59.		3-02
❑ G-AFOJ	Moth Minor	ex Navestock, E-1, E-0236, G-AFOJ. CoA 27-8-69. *Bugs 2.*	®	3-02
❑ G-AKDW	Dragon Rapide	ex Aviodome, Amsterdam store, F-BCDB, G-AKDW,YI-ABD, NR833. *City of Winchester.*	®	3-02
❑ G-ANRX	Tiger Moth	ex Belchamp Walter, N6550, SLAW, 25 EFTS, 18 EFTS, 241, 14 EFTS, 56 ERFTS. CoA 20-6-61. Crop duster. *Border City*		3-02
❑ G-AOTI	Heron 2D	ex Biggin Hill, Exeter, G-5-19. CoA 24-6-87.	®	3-02
❑ G-AREA*	Dove 8	ex Hatfield. CoA 8-9-87. Arrived late 2000.		3-02
❑ G-ARYC	HS.125 Srs 1	ex Hatfield, Filton, R-R. CoA 1-8-73.	®	3-02
❑ G-AVFH	Trident 2	ex Heathrow, BA, BEA. Forward fuselage.		3-02
❑ F-BGNX	Comet 1XB	G-AOJT, ex Farnborough, F-BGNX. Fuselage.		3-02
❑ D-IFSB	Dove 6	ex Hatfield, BFS, D-CFSB, Panshanger, G-AMXR, N4280V.		3-02
❑ W4050	Mosquito I proto	ex Hatfield, Chester, Radlett, E-0234.	® ①	3-02
❑ LF789 'R2-K'	Queen Bee	BAPC.186, ex 'K3584', Hadfield, Droylsden, Redhill, St Athan, Pilotless A/c Unit, Manorbier, St Athan.	®	3-02
❑ TA122 'UP-G'	Mosquito FB.6	ex Soesterberg, 4, 2 GCS, 48, 4, 605, 417 ARF. 605 Sqn colours.	③	3-02
❑ TA634 '8K-K'	Mosquito TT.35	ex Liverpool, G-AWJV, Aldergrove, 3 CAACU, APS Schleswigland, APS Ahlorn, APS Sylt, 4 CAACU. 571 Sqn colours.		3-02
❑ TJ118	Mosquito TT.35	ex Elstree, Exeter, 3/4 CAACU, 3 CAACU. Nose.		3-02
❑ WP790 'T'	Chipmunk T.10	G-BBNC, ex Rush Green, WP790, Bir UAS, Wales UAS, PFTS, AOTS, 1 ITS, RAFC, Man UAS, G&S UAS, Stn UAS, 24 GCF, 5 RFS, 17 RFS.		3-02
❑ WP927 PAX	Chipmunk T.10	8216M, ex Ashton-under-Lyne, Woodvale, Ashton-under-Lyne, Crosby, Hamble G-ATJK, MCS, Oxf UAS, Lon UAS, Detling SF, Lon UAS.	④	3-02
❑ WM729*	Vampire NF.10	ex Gloucestershire, London Colney, Ruislip, Bingley, Bradford, Church Fenton, CNCS, 2 ANS, 25, 151. Nose. Arr by 12-00. Stored.	®	3-02
❑ WR539*	Venom FB.4	ex Gloucestershire, London Colney, Fownhope, Cardiff, 'Midlands', Cosford, 8399M, Kai Tak, 28, 60. Nose. Arrived by 12-00. Stored.	®	3-02
❑ WX853	Venom NF.3	ex Debden 7443M, Shawbury, 23.	®	3-02
❑ XG730 '499'	Sea Ven FAW.22	ex Southwick, Portsmouth, Lee-on-Solent, ADS, Sydenham, 893, 894, 891. 894 Sqn colours.		3-02
❑ XJ565	Sea Vixen FAW.2	ex RAE, 899, 893, 766B. '127-E', 899 Sqn c/s.		3-02
❑ XJ772 'H'	Vampire T.11	ex Brooklands, Wisley, Shawbury, CATCS, 1 FTS, 8 FTS, RAFC, RNorAF 15018 'XP-G'.	®	3-02
❑ XK695	Comet C.2(R)	ex Stock, Newton 9164M, Duxford, Wyton, 51, 216, G-AMXH. Nose.		3-02
❑ J-1008	Vampire FB.6	ex Hatfield, Swiss AF.		3-02
❑ J-1632*	Venom FB.50	G-VNOM, ex Cranfield, Bridgend, Bruntingthorpe, Cranfield, Swiss AF. Arrived 2-02.		3-02
❑ –*	DH.88 FSM	BAPC.216, ex 'G-ACSS', St Albans, Kings Langley, Wroughton, Australia. Arr by 9-01.	® ⑤	3-02
❑ –	Comet 2 SIM	ex Wroughton, Crawley.	⑥	3-02
❑ – BAPC.232	Horsa I / II	composite fuselage.		3-02

Microlight strip: Typhoon G-MJJF was flying again by 2000.

NUTHAMSTEAD AERODROME east of the B1368, south-east of Royston
By February 2001, Comanche 180 N5052P had moved to Romsey, Hants.

PANSHANGER AERODROME east of Welwyn Garden City, south of the B1000
❑ G-BSKC	Tomahawk 112	ex OY-PJB, N748RM, C-GRQI. Crashed 2-6-96.	6-97
❑ G-DTOO	Tomahawk 112	ex Seething. Crashed 9-7-94.	9-00

RUSH GREEN AERODROME west of the A1(M), west of Stevenage
Gordon Spooner's Messenger G-AJWB moved to Hatch, Beds, for flight test. It first flew on 19th December 2001 and will be based at Earls Colne, Essex.

ST ALBANS
Eric Littledike: Acquired the former Science Museum Pilcher REP and is working to restore it.
❑ –*	BAPC.57 Pilcher Hawk REP	ex Wroughton, Hayes, South Lambeth. Built 1930.	® 11-01

Microlight strip: One of the anonymous Cessnas here as now been identified as G-AZZX. DH.88 FSM 'G-ACSS' moved to London Colney, Herts, by mid-2001.
❑ G-AZZX	Cessna FRA.150L	damaged 28-2-87. Stored, spares use.	9-00
❑ N7263S	Cessna 150H	Stored.	® 9-00
❑ N13253	Cessna 172M	Stored, spares use.	9-00
❑	Cessna F.150K	c/n 71427. Stored, spares use.	6-99

WATFORD
Sundowner hulk G-BARI and the scrapyard it was in are both no more.

ISLE OF MAN

ISLE OF MAN AIRPORT or Ronaldsway, north-east of Castletown
Aeroservice (IoM) Ltd: During September 2001, Percival Q6 G-AFFD started to make the move to Northampton, Northants, for continued restoration. Other references here are now long-in-the-tooth.
❑ G-AJEE	J/1 Autocrat	ex Compton Abbas. CoA 10-7-89.	® 8-92
❑ G-APSZ	Cessna 172	ex Barton, N6372E. Damaged 2-3-84. Stored.	6-96
❑ G-BCGA	Seneca 200-2	ex Panshanger, N41975. Crashed 18-12-77. Fuselage.	6-96

Airport: On display inside the terminal is the one-off Eider Duck single-seater, tail-less (how appropriate for the land of the Manx cat!) pusher. A scale model was tested in the 1960s at Cranfield. This prototype was built with assistance from Peel Cars. It never flew.
❑ G-AZRG	Aztec 250D	ex Aldergrove, N6536Y. CoA 8-7-93. Dump.	7-96
❑ –*	Eider Duck	See above. First noted 7-01.	7-01

JURBY AERODROME west of Andreas
❑ G-ACLL	Leopard Moth	ex AW165, AFEE, 7 AACU, 6 AACU, Ringway SF. CoA 6-12-95. Stored.	10-96
❑ CEV	Bergfalke II	BGA.1492. CoA 12-93. Stored.	10-96

ISLE OF WIGHT

BEMBRIDGE AERODROME on the B3395 south-west of Bembridge
Britten-Norman Historians Preservation Society:
◆ Visits *strictly* by prior permission: ✉ 32 Budesbury Road, Staines, TW18 2AX
❑ G-AVCN BN-2A ex Puerto Rico, N290VL, F-OGHG, G-AVCN. 4-01

B-N Group: (Note the new name of the resurrected company.) Still languishing in woods is the
original fuselage of the currently operational Royal Oman Police Turbo-Islander, which was extensively
rebuilt here in 1991 ①. The Trislander will act as a pattern airframe for the re-opened Trislander 'line' for
China ②. Islander AL.1 ZG994 was stripped of spares and moved to St Athan, Wales, in May 2001.
❑ [G-BVYE] BN-2B-20 Over-stressed 28-8-96. Stored. 4-01
❑ G-BVHX* BN-2T-4R Radar-nosed, fuselage. First noted 4-00. Tests. 4-01
❑ A40-CT BN-2T ex G-51-2201, G-BOMC. Crashed 25-6-90.
 Original fuselage, less tail. Derelict. ① 1-02
❑ 6Y-JQK Trislander G-BEVV, ex Cumbernauld, 6Y-JQK,
 G-BNZD, G-BEVV. Fuselage. ② 4-01

COWES on the A3020, north of the island
Cliftongrade Ltd: The scrap dealers still use the cockpit to advertise their business.
❑ XT863 'AS' Phantom FG.1 ex Abingdon, 43, 111, 892, 767. Nose. 1-02

NEWPORT on the A3054, middle of the island
Stored in the area in two separate places are two homebuilds, their status believed unchanged.
❑ G-AZJE Minicab ex Sandown. CoA 7-7-82. Stored. 12-01
❑ G-BCMF Levi Go-Plane one and only flight 16-11-74. Stored. 1-98

SANDOWN on the A3055 south of Ryde, east coast
Airframe Assemblies: The company moved premises within Sandown during early 2001. Airframe
Assemblies continue to produce fine and detailed work, specialising in wings for several Spitfire projects
and some Messerschmitt Bf 109 projects. The fuselage of Buchón G-BWUE was redelivered to
Breighton, E Yorks, on 20th November 2000 with the wings following on 17th November 2001.
During September 2001 the pod/centre section of the Focke-Wulf Fw 189 arrived for restoration work
here. Previously listed under Sandtoft, Lincs, this incredible restoration project is now centred here. The
Focke Wulf Fw 189 Society exists to support the project, details of the latter via: PO Box 5840,
Brightlingsea, CO7 0QY, **e-mail** ken@fockewulf189.com ① Work on the Spitfire IX is nearing
completion.
❑ BH238* Hurricane IIb ex Front Line Sandown, Russia, Soviet AF. Wreck.
 Arrived 6-00. Stored. 1-02
❑ RW382* Spitfire XVI N382RW, ex USA, Audley End, Braintree, Uxbridge
 8075M, Leconfield, Church Fenton 7245M, C&RS,
 3 CAACU, 604. Wreck, stored. Arrived 24-8-01. 1-02
❑ TA805 Spitfire IX G-PMNF, ex Battle, South Africa, SAAF, 234, 183. ® 1-02
❑ 2100* Fw 189A-1 G-BZKY, ex Sandtoft, Lancing, USSR,
 'V7+1H' Luftwaffe. Crashed 4-5-43. Arrived 26-9-01. ® ① 1-02

SANDOWN AERODROME north of the A3056, west of Sandown
Former **Front Line Aviation Museum:** Clearing up the entries: 'Flea' 'G-ADZW' to Southampton,
Hants, 5-01; Klemm Kl 35D G-BWRD believed returned to Germany; M.1D Sokol G-BWRG to
Germany 17-5-00; Aeronca K G-ONKA operating from "the mainland" by 2000; PZL Gawron SP-CHD
believed returned to Germany, but possibly moved on to 'Essex'; Spitfire REP 'K5054' (G-BRDV) to
Southampton, Hants, 5-01; Magister V1075 (G-AKPF) flew off to Shoreham, W Sussex, on 10-5-00
then to Earls Colne, Essex, and later settled upon Old Warden, Beds; Hurricane IIb wreck BH238 to
Sandown, above; Meteor F.8 'WF714' (WK914) and Hunter F.4 WV276 moved to Scampton, Lincs,
by 6-00; Hunter F.51 'XF314' (E-412) to Wycombe Air Park, Bucks, by 6-00; anonymous Easy Rider

powered hang-glider status unknown; Spitfire FSM cockpit 'JE-' status unknown; anonymous Fi 103 (V-1) FSM status unknown, but Weybourne, Norfolk, in with a chance!; wrecks of P-40E 41-13570 to local storage and then to the USA 29-9-00; anonymous P-39Q wreck to the USA 1-6-00.

Others: Firemaster G-NACL had gone by April 2001, possibly to Turkey. The remains of Cherokee 140 G-OHOG had been removed by early 2001.

❑ G-AMVP	Tipsy Junior	ex OO-ULA. Damaged 4-7-93.	® 12-01
❑ G-BHMR	Stinson 108-3	ex F-BABO, F-DABO, NC6352M. CoA 23-11-90.	12-01
❑ G-NRDC	Fieldmaster	ex Old Sarum. CoA 17-10-87. Fuselage.	12-01
❑	Fieldmaster EMU	ex Old Sarum. Stored.	12-01

SHANKLIN

An amusement arcade on the seafront has a Rallye as an attraction. It comes complete with skeletal pilot!

❑ G-BIRB	MS.880B Rallye	ex Manston, Firbeck, Carlisle, Hooton Park, Moston, Carlisle, F-BVAQ. CoA 16-6-90.	1-02

YARMOUTH on the A3054 west of Newport

A private collector took delivery of a Vampire T.11 pod during 2001.

❑ XE921*	'64' Vampire T.11	ex Welshpool, Stoke-on-Trent, Barton, Firbeck, Retford, Firbeck, Keevil, Exeter, 3/4 CAACU, 1 FTS, CFS. Pod.	10-01

KENT

ASHFORD on the M20 west of Folkestone

The Jackaroo is thought unchanged. Grasshopper TX.1 WZ816 (HJJ) is thought to be in Surrey.

❑ G-ANFY	Jackaroo	ex NL906, 9 RFS, 23 EFTS, 9 FTS. CoA 25-5-68.	1-96

BREDHURST or Farthing Corner, south of Junction 4 of the M2, south of Gillingham

❑ G-ARWH	Cessna 172C	ex Golders Green, Fenland, N1466Y. CoA 28-4-86. Spares.	5-99

BRENCHLEY east of the B2160, east of Royal Tunbridge Wells

❑ G-ATKH	Luton Minor	ex Rochester. CoA 24-6-92. Stored.	1-96
❑ G-AYXO	Luton Major	ex Beeston Rylands. Stored.	1-96

BRENZETT on the A2070 north-west of New Romney

Brenzett Aeronautical Museum Trust (BAMT): Occupying buildings to the west of the Brenzett (or Ivychurch) Advanced Landing Ground (ALG), the museum was awarded £5,000 from the Wolfson Foundation in early 2001. The money was put to repair of the roof and other building upgrades. Opening in Easter 2002 was a new display room which has been named 'Pam's Memory Lane' in memory of BAMT stalwart Pam Beckley who sadly passed away in November 2001.

◆ Open Sat and Sun from Easter to end of Oct, also Bank Holidays, 11am to 5.30pm. Also open Jul until end of Sep Wed-Thu-Fri 11am to 5.30pm. ✉ Ivychurch Road, Brenzett, Romney Marsh, TN29 0EE ☎ 01797 344747 or 01233 627911 **web** www.ket2do.com/brenzettaeronautical

❑ G-AMSM	Dakota 4	ex Booker, Brenzett, Duxford, Brenzett, Lydd, Skyways, Eagle, Starways, KN274, TCDU, 77, St Eval SF, Azores SF, 43-49948. Damaged 17-8-78. Nose. Silver City colours.	3-02

❏ V7350	Hurricane I	ex Robertsbridge, 85. Crashed 29-8-40. Cockpit.	3-02
❏ WH657	Canberra B.2	ex Godalming, RAE, 231 OCU.	3-02
❏ XK625	Vampire T.11	ex Firbeck, North Weald, Southend, Woodford,	
		St Athan, 8 FTS, 7 FTS.	3-02

CANTERBURY

BB Aviation: Bill Baker and friends work on a Canberra nose. *Likely* identity for this is WJ581 ①.
✉ Bur Oak, Bossingham, near Canterbury, Kent, CT4 6DX.

❏ —	BAPC.17	Woodhams Sprite	ex Manchester, Hooton Park, Wigan, Irlam,	
			Wigan, Liverpool, Leamington Spa. Incomplete.	2-00
❏		Canberra PR.7	ex Cardiff-Wales, WAM, CTTS St Athan. Nose. ® ①	2-00

CHATHAM east of Rochester
Chatham Historic Dockyard Trust: Amongst the ships, lurk two naval aircraft.
◆ North of the A231, signed. Open late Mar to late Oct daily 10am to 6pm. Feb, Mar and Nov Wed,
Sat and Sun 10am to 4pm. Closed Dec and Jan. ✉ Chatham Historic Dockyard, Chatham ME4 4TZ
☎ 01634 823800 **fax** 01634 823801 **e-mail** info@chdt.org.uk **web** chdt.org.uk

❏ WG751	Dragonfly HR.3	ex Gosport, Condover, Ramsgreave, Ancoats,	
	'710'	*The Last Caravan*, Wisbech, Blackbushe,	
		Fleetlands, 705. 705 Squadron colours.	3-02
❏ XL500	Gannet AEW.3	A2701, ex Culdrose, Lee-on-Solent, Culdrose,	
		Dowty-Rotol, Culdrose, Lossiemouth, 849.	3-02

Royal Engineers Museum: There is much to interest the aviation enthusiast here including the medals
etc of James McCudden VC DSO* MC* MM and many other artefacts. The history of military aviation in
the UK from 1880 with balloons, through to man-lifting kites and airships to the Air Battalion of the
Royal Engineers of 1912 is all well charted. The wing of a Cody monoplane, on loan from the RAeS, is
also on display. The Sioux is still in store off-site.
◆ On the B2004 to the north of Chatham. Mon to Thu 10am to 5pm, Sat, Sun and Bank Hols 11.30am
to 5pm. *Not* open on Fridays. ✉ Prince Arthur Road, Gillingham, Chatham, ME4 4UG ☎ 01634
406397 **fax** 01634 822371 **e-mail** remuseum.rhqre@gtnet.gov.uk **web** www.royalengineers.org.uk

❏ —		Vulcan hang-glider —	3-02
❏ XT133		Sioux AH.1	ex Arborfield, Middle Wallop 7923M. Stored.	3-02
❏ XZ964	'D'	Harrier GR.3	ex St Athan, 1417F, 233 OCU, 3, 233 OCU, 1.	
			Ninja One. 1417 Flight colours.	3-02
❏ —		Military balloon	basket only. RAFM loan.	3-02

No.1404 Squadron Air Cadets: In Boundary Road, still have their Chipmunk.

❏ WZ846	Chipmunk T.10	8439M, ex G-BCSC, Bicester, Manston, Wales UAS,	
		AOTS, 202, 228, CFE, W Raynham SF, G&S UAS,	
		Bri UAS, 1 AEF, St Athan, Nott UAS, 63 GCF,	
		Edn UAS, S'tn UAS. Fuselage and wings.	5-00

CHATTENDEN on the A228 north of Rochester
Defence Explosives Ordnance Disposal School: The 'JP' is in the Lodge Hill Camp site.

❏ XM410*		Jet Provost T.3	8054AM, ex North Luffenham, Halton, Shawbury,	
			RAFC, 7 FTS, 2 FTS. First noted 8-01.	8-01
❏ XT907	'W'	Phantom FGR.2	9151M, ex 74, 228 OCU. EOD.	8-01
❏ —	BAPC.158	Fieseler Fi 103	held inside the camp.	5-00
❏ —	BAPC.159	Ohka 11	held inside the camp.	5-00

CHISLET north of the A28 south-east of Herne Bay
Piper Super Cruiser G-AXUC was flying again by mid-2000.

❏ N3188H	Ercoupe 415C	ex NC3188H. Damaged 7-92. Stored.	12-00

DOVER
Dover Museum: Among a wide sweep of exhibits is a full-size V-1 reproduction. Other items of interest include a small piece of Blériot's cross-Channel Type XI and a piece from the first bomb ever to drop on the UK - Dover, Christmas 1914.
◆ Open daily 10am to 5.30pm. ⊠ Market Square, Dover, CT16 1PB ☎ 01304 201066 fax 01304 241186 e-mail museumenquiries@dover.gov.uk web www.dover.gov.uk/museum/home.htm
❑ –*   Fieseler Fi 103 REP —   7-00

FAVERSHAM on the A2 east of Sittingbourne
No.1242 Squadron Air Cadets: *Should* still have their Hunter. 'Parent' is Manston.
❑ XG226   Hunter F.6A   ex Manston, Faygate, Catterick 8800M, 1 TWU,
                                TWU, 229 OCU, 92, 66, 92. Nose.   5-96

GRAVESEND on the A226 east of Dartford
A collector keeps two Buccaneer noses in the area.
❑ XN928*   Buccaneer S.1   ex Manston, Bruntingthorpe, Cardiff, St Athan
                                8179M, 736, 809, 801. Desert pink,
                                Glenfiddich, *Jaws* and *Liz*. Nose.   10-01
❑ XV352*   Buccaneer S.2B   ex Manston, Stock, St Athan, Lossiemouth,
                                237 OCU, 208. Nose.   10-01

Gravesend Police College: The college has taken on large sections of a BAC 111.
❑ G-AVMK*   BAC 111-510ED   ex Bournemouth, BA, BEA. Sections arrived 1-02.   1-02

HAWKINGE on the A260 north of Folkestone
Kent Battle of Britain Museum: The depth and intensity of the displays is exceptional, especially when remembering that the museum occupies buildings used during the Battle of Britain by the famous RAF station. The Spitfire IX FSM has a real counterpart, at Coningsby, Lincs ①. Note that the full-size models are occasionally repainted with new identities and it is not easy to keep track of them!
◆ Daily Easter to end Sept 10am to 5pm and October 11am to 4pm. Signed off the A260. Note that photography is not permitted within the museum.⊠ Aerodrome Road, Hawkinge Airfield, Folkestone, CT18 7AG ☎ 01303 89340

❑ 'D-3-340'	Grunau Baby	ex Ramsgate. True identity unknown.	8-01
❑ 'K5054'	Spitfire proto REP	ex Luton, Lowestoft, Luton.	6-00
❑ 'P3059'	Hurricane FSM	BAPC.64, ex Chilham Castle, *Battle of Britain*,	8-01
❑ 'N2532'*'GZ-H'	Hurricane FSM	BAPC.272, new build, arr by 4-00. 32 Sqn colours.	8-01
❑ 'N3313' 'KL-B'	Spitfire FSM	BAPC.69, ex Higher Blagdon, Stoneleigh, *Battle of Britain*. 54 Sqn colours.	8-01
❑ 'N7033'*	Harvard IIb	ex FX442, Bournemouth, Fordingbridge, Bournemouth, Sandhurst, Hullavington, 501, 226 OCU, 203 AFS, 61 OTU.	6-00
❑ 'P2921'*'GZ-L'	Hurricane FSM	BAPC.273, new build, arr by 4-00. 32 Sqn colours.	8-01
❑ 'P3059' 'SD-N'	Hurricane FSM	BAPC.64, ex Chilham Castle, *Battle of Britain*, 501 Sqn colours.	4-98
❑ 'P3208' 'SD-T' '	Hurricane FSM	BAPC.63, ex 'L1592', Higher Blagdon, *Battle of Britain*. 501 Sqn colours.	8-01
❑ 'P3679' 'GZ-K'	Hurricane FSM	BAPC.278, new build, arr by 4-00. 32 Sqn colours.	8-01
❑ 'MK356''2I-V'	Spitfire IX FSM	—	① 8-01
❑	Hurricane FSM	ex Lowestoft. 'RF-U' 303 Squadron colours.	4-98
❑ '425/17'	Fokker Dr I FSM	BAPC.133, ex Winthorpe, Higher Blagdon.	8-01
❑ — BAPC.36	Fi 103 (V-1) FSM	ex Old Warden, Duxford, Old Warden.	8-01
❑ BAPC.66	'Bf 109' FSM	ex '1480', Chilham Castle, *Battle of Britain*.	8-01
❑ BAPC.67	'Bf 109' FSM	ex Coventry, North Weald, Newark, *Battle of Britain*.	8-01
❑ BAPC.74	'Bf 109' FSM	ex '6357', Higher Blagdon, *Battle of Britain*.	8-01

Peter Smith: Peter has a Chipmunk PAX on loan at Brooklands, Surrey. The Typhoon project continues to progress. EJ922 includes the rear fuselage of a Sea Fury FB.11 ①. Adding to the considerable cache of parts are the remains of R7708 (609 Squadron, 'friendly fire' victim 31st October 1942 crashed Pegwell Bay) The **Hawkinge Airfield Youth Club** are working on the former Manston BE.2 rep now that the 'Hurricane' has moved on ②.

Departures: Both the anonymous 'Gunbus' FSM and the PT-19 Cornell frame-based 'Hurricane' recreation have 'moved on' – no details. *W&R17* (pp88) reported 'Gunbus' FSM '2882' BAPC.234 as having been disposed off, it is now known to have gone High Halden, Kent, and then to Sleap, Shrop.

◆ Airframes are stored in a variety of places and visits are not possible. ✉ Peter Smith, 1 Daniels Terrace, St Luke's Walk, Hawkinge, CT18 7EF e-mail peter-tiffy9.freeserve.co.uk

❏ G-AAXK	Klemm L 25	ex Sevenoaks, CoA 29-11-60. Damaged 3-62. Fuse.		3-02
❏ EJ922	Typhoon Ib	ex Manston, Brooklands, Sevenoaks, Biggin Hill, Southend, Brooklands, Brownhills, 3. Cockpit, for fitting to rear fuselage of a Sea Fury.	①	3-02
❏ –	'SE.5A' FSM	ex Sevenoaks, Coventry. Poor state.		3-02
❏ –	Typhoon I	ex Manston, Brooklands, Sevenoaks, Innsworth, Leeds, Cheltenham, Kemble. Cockpit.		3-02
❏ –	BAPC.117 BE.2c FSM	ex Manston, Sevenoaks, Brooklands, North Weald, BBC *Wings*. Stored.	②	3-02
❏ –	BAPC.190 Spitfire FSM	ex Barton, Chelford, 'K5054', Sevenoaks. Poor state.		3-02

HIGH HALDEN on the A28 south-west of Ashford
Richard Hukins: Vampire T.11 XE995 is reported to have been broken up for spares. See also under Washington, West Sussex.

IVYCHURCH north of the A259, east of New Romney
❏ G-BEOD	Cessna 180	ex Errol, OO-SPZ, D-EDAH, SL-AAT, N3294D. Crashed 29-6-89.	3-97

LASHENDEN AERODROME or Headcorn, on the A247 south of Headcorn
Lashenden Air Warfare Museum (LAWM): An appeal for a new display building is due to be launched in mid-2002. Within the extensive display buildings can be found well-presented material on the wartime Lashenden and Kent in general. The Lightning nose was split vertically for use in the sci-fi film *Wing Commander*. It is on loan from Mike Coleman ①. The Reichenberg V-1 carries a manually-operated fuel pump. The museum have the remains of the rudder pedals, control column and their cockpit mountings plus the aileron controls and mountings. All of this adds up to impressive physical evidence that this was one of 175 built at either Dannenberg or Pulverhof ②. Whirlwind HAS.7 XN380 moved to Manston, Kent, 23rd October 2001.
◆ Sun and Bank Hols 10.30am to 6pm, Easter until end of Oct. Sun 10.30am to 3.30pm Nov to Easter. Other times by prior arrangement. ✉ Lashenden Aerodrome, Ashford, TN27 9HX ☎ 01622 890226 or '206783 fax 01622 206783 e-mail lashairwar@aol.com

❏ WZ450	Vampire T.11	ex North Weald, Birmingham, Sealand, Wrexham, Woodford, Chester, Shawbury, RAFC, 233 OCU, 202 AFS. Pod.		3-02
❏ WZ589	'19' Vampire T.11	ex Woodford, Chester, St Athan, 56.		3-02
❏ ZF587*	Lightning F.53	ex Reading, Portsmouth, *Wing Commander*, Portsmouth, Stretton, Warton, RSAF 215, 53-691, G-27-61. Arrived 17-5-01. Nose.	①	3-02
❏ 84	'8-NF' Mystère IVA	ex Sculthorpe, French AF.		3-02
❏ 63938	'11-MU' F-100F-16-NA	ex Sculthorpe, French AF.		3-02
❏ 100549	Fa 330A-1	ex Manchester, Liverpool, Blackpool, Lavenham, Hullavington, Biggin Hill, Farnborough.		3-02
❏ –	BAPC.91 Fi 103R-IV	ex Horsham, Farnborough.	②	3-02

Aerodrome: Going back to *W&R17* (p89) BN-2T G-OTVS was scrapped on site in 1999 and therefore did not go to Gloucestershire Airport. Colt 108 G-ARKP ended 21 years on the ground when it flew again in December 2001. Cessna F.172H G-AWGJ was scrapped in late 2000. Super Cub 95 G-NICK moved on during 2000, no 'forwarding address'. The hulk of Cherokee Arrow II G-TOBE was broken up in September 2001 with more elements going on the dump.

❏ G-AHAV	J/1 Autocrat	ex HB-EOM ntu. CoA 21-6-75. Stored.	off-site	3-02
❏ G-ARHL	Aztec 250	CoA 23-11-79. Stored.		3-02
❏ G-ARBZ*	Turbulent	Damaged 17-7-99. Stored.		7-00
❏ G-ARZM	Turbulent	ex Chessington, Headcorn. Crashed 23-6-91.		3-02
❏ G-ASAM	Turbulent	ex Chessington, Headcorn. Crashed 23-6-91.		3-02
❏ G-AZZP*	Cessna F.172H	ex LN-RTA. Crashed 8-6-97. Stored.		3-02
❏ G-BMCS*	Tri-Pacer 135	ex 5Y-KMH, VP-KMH, ZS-DJI. CoA 15-7-01. Stored.		3-02
❏ G-BSPC	SAN D.140C	ex F-BMFN. CoA 31-10-85. Stored.		3-02
❏ A-806	Pilatus P.3-03	G-BTLL, ex Swiss AF. CoA 23-6-94. Stored.		3-02

LYDD AIRPORT south of New Romney, at the end of the B2075, beyond Lydd itself

❏ G-ASER*	Aztec 250B	ex Smeeth, Biggin Hill. Crashed 14-9-72. Dumped.	3-01

MANSTON AIRPORT or London (Manston) Airport, on the A253 west of Ramsgate
Hurricane and Spitfire Memorial Building: The superb Hurricane and Spitfire dominate the exhibition – both examples of the workmanship of Medway APS, Rochester. 'BN230' is a composite, with parts from Mk.II Z3687 (SOC with RAE 9th April 1951) and Mk.IIc PG593 (crashed 21st February 1945) ①. There is a wealth of other material to see and the superb 'Merlin' cafeteria to sample. The Allied Air Forces Memorial Garden opened in June 2001.

◆ Open daily, Apr to Sep 10am to 5pm, Oct to Mar 10am to 4pm. Closed 25th-27th Dec and 1st Jan. Signed off the A253 Ramsgate road. ✉ Manston Road, Ramsgate, Kent, CT12 5DF ☎ / fax 08143 821940 e-mail pete@spitfire752@freeserve.co.uk web www.spitfire-museum.com

❏ 'BN230'	Hurricane II	LF751, ex Rochester, Bentley Priory, Waterbeach		
	'FT-A'	5466M, 27 OTU, 1681 BDTF. 43 Sqn colours.	①	3-02
❏ TB752	Spitfire XVI	8086M, ex Rochester, Manston 7256M / 7279M,		
	'KH-Z'	Lyneham, 5 CAACU, 103, 102 FRSs, 403, 66.		
		Val (port). 403 Sqn colours.		3-02

RAF Manston History Museum: The museum faced a possible move of site within the airport complex during 2000, but this did not transpire. With this news, the opportunity was taken to *double* the display area and the new undercover area will accommodate all of the airframes. Established in the old MT building, the museum is run by the RAF Manston History Society. The museum concentrates on the 80 plus year history of Manston, both military and civil.

Departures: Cessna A.152 G-BOPW to <u>Stock</u>, Essex by 10-00; noses of Buccaneer S.1 XN928 and S.2B XV352 to <u>Gravesend</u>, Kent; BE.2c FSM BAPC.117 to <u>Hawkinge</u>, Kent.
◆ Adjacent to the Hurricane and Spitfire Memorial. Open daily Mar to Oct 10am to 4pm. Weekends Nov to Mar 10am to 4pm.✉ Manston Road, Manston, Ramsgate, CT12 <u>5DF</u> ☎ 01843 82<u>5</u>224 e-mail museum@raf-manston.fsnet.co.uk web www.raf-manston.fsnet.co.uk

❏ HB-NAV	'A' Pup 150	ex Stock, Henley-on-Thames, Henlow, Redhill,		
		G-AZCM. <u>Blue</u>/white c/s. Forward fuselage.		3-02
❏ 'VM791'	Cadet TX.3	XA312/8876M. Ex Kenley.		3-02
❏ 'WD615'	Meteor TT.20	WD646, ex North Weald, Birmingham, Cosford		
		8189M, 5 CAACU, 3/4 CAACU, AWA, CSE.		
		85 Sqn, NF.11 colours.		3-02
❏ WK638*	Chipmunk T.10	G-BWJZ, ex 9 AEF, RAFC, 9 AEF, York UAS,		
		1 FTS, 1 AEF, Ox UAS, 1 RFS.		
		Crashed 22-8-99. Sapres. Arrived 11-01.		3-02
❏ WP772	Chipmunk T.10	ex Lyneham, Colerne, Abingdon, St Athan,		
		Middle Wallop, BFWF, QUAS, Hull UAS,		
		17 RFS. Damaged 4-5-98.		3-02

☐ WT205*		Canberra B.15	ex Eastwood, Foulness, MoA, 9. Nose.	
			Arrived 14-10-00. On loan.	3-02
☐ XA231		Grasshopper TX.1	8888M, ex Stockport, 'Sealand', Cosford,	
			Warwick, Kimbolton, Petersfield.	3-02
☐ XD857*		Valiant BK.1	ex Rayleigh, Foulness, 49. Nose. Arrived by 6-00.	3-02
☐ XJ727	'L'	Whirlwind	ex Dishforth, Halton 8661M, 2 FTS, CFS,	
		HAR.10	1310 Flt, 228, 22.	® 3-02
☐ XL190		Victor K.2	9216M, ex St Mawgan, 55, 232 OCU,	
			Witt Wing, 139. Nose.	3-02
☐ XN380*		Whirlwind HAS.7	ex Lashenden, Wroughton, 705, 771, 829, 824,	
			825. SAR c/s. Spares. Arrived 13-10-01.	3-02
☐ XS482	'A-D'	Wessex HU.5	ex DSFCTE, Farnborough, A&AEE.	3-02

Defence Fire Services Central Training Establishment (DFSCTE): DFSCTE operates as an RAF Enclave, 'parented' by RAF Odiham. Boeing 707-351 D2-TOU were scrapped by September 2000 but the nose lived on until it was acquired by an Irish company for conversion into a Boeing 737 simulator in late 2000. During July 2001 Andover E.3A XS643 were scrapped. Early in 2002 Hunter FGA.9 XJ695 was scrapped.

☐ WK124	'CR'	Canberra TT.18	9093M, ex Wyton, 100, 7, 213, 59, 103.	2-02
☐ XR503*		Wessex HC.2	ex Boscombe Down, Gosport A2705 [2], RAE,	
			A&AEE, MoA. Tail of XT463.	8-01
☐ XS714	'P'	Dominie T.1	9246M, ex Finningley, 6 FTS, RAFC, CAW.	2-02
☐ XV411	'L'	Phantom FGR.2	9103M, ex 56, 92, 19, 92, 14. Scorched.	2-02
☐ XV864		Buccaneer S.2B	9234M, ex 12, 237 OCU, 16.	2-02
☐ XW870*	'F'	Gazelle HT.3	ex Shawbury, 2 FTS, CFS. Arrived 29-11-01.	2-02
☐ XW922		Harrier GR.3	8885M, ex Laarbruch, Brüggen, Foulness, Enfield,	
			233 OCU, 1, 233 OCU, 1. Crashed 19-11-85.	2-02
☐ XX655*	'V'	Bulldog T.1	ex Colerne, Bri UAS, 2 FTS. First noted 8-01.	2-02
☐ XZ966	'G'	Harrier GR.3	9221M, ex Cottesmore, St Athan, 1417 Flt,	
			4, 1417 Flt, 233 OCU, 1, 1417, 1.	2-02
☐ ZE353	'E'	F-4J(UK)	9083M, ex 74, USN 153785.	2-02
☐ ZE360	'O'	F-4J(UK)	9059M, ex 74, USN 155529.	8-01

Airport: It is sometimes difficult to assess if an airliner is merely 'laid up' or stored going on dereliction. Boeing 707-328C P4-ESP had been completely removed by the scrapmen by early 2001. The former Southend B-26C is known to be stored close by ①

☐ EL-AKU		Boeing 707-347C	ex ZS-NLJ, 9J-AFT, HR-AMA, TT-EAP, TT-WAB,	
			B-2425, N707PD, EI-BLC, N1502W, TF-VLG,	
			N1502W. Spares.	12-00
☐ N4806E		B-26C Invader	ex Southend Airport, Rockford (Illinois), 44-34172,	
			Davis-Monthan, 3 BW, 17 BW, 7 ADW. Stored.	① 12-96
☐ TF-ABW		Boeing 747-128	ex Iberia, C-GCIS, TF-ABW, F-BPVF. Cockpit.	2-02

MARGATE on the A28 north of Ramsgate
Helicharter / Summit Aviation moved out of this location to Manston, Kent. The eclectic trio of helicopters noted here in August 1998 are unaccounted for. (AB.212s 405 and 420 plus a Bö 105.)

PADDOCKWOOD on the B2160 north-east of Royal Tunbridge Wells
Historic Aircraft Collection of Jersey Ltd: See under Duxford, Cambs, and St Leonards-on-Sea, East Sussex, for the closely-related Aero Vintage.

ROCHESTER AERODROME on the A229 south of Rochester
Medway Aircraft Preservation Society Ltd (MAPS): Spitfire I K9942 was handed over officially to the RAF Museum in a ceremony here on 31st October 2000. The restoration work and research effort

on this beauty has been incredible. The Spitfire was installed at Hendon, Gtr Lon, on 7th December 2000. MAPS then had a brief 'rest', but it was not for long! They took on the restoration of the starboard wing of Tempest TT.5 NV778 (see Cosford, Shrop) ready for it moving into the 'Milestones of Flight' hall at Hendon, Gtr Lon, and a Northrop target drone The Sycamore is being return to ASR guise for the RAF Museum and is due for completion in early 2003.

◆ The workshop is open to the public on Sun, Mon and Wed 9am to 1pm. Airport rules must be observed – the threshold of Runway 34 needs negotiating ✉ Lewis Deal, 15 Amethyst Avenue, Chatham, ME5 9TX ☎ 01634 865028 **fax** 01634 204992

❑	G-36-1	SB.4 Sherpa	ex Duxford, Staverton, Bristol, Cranfield, G-14-1. Fuse. ® 3-02
❑	WV783*	Sycamore HR.12	ex Wyton, Cardington, Fleetlands, Henlow, 7841M,
			HDU Old Sarum, CFS, ASWDU, G-ALSP ntu.	3-02

Others: Held in storage here is a former Burmese Spitfire.

| ❑ | UB441 | Spitfire IX | ex USA, Myanmar, Burmese AF, Israeli DF/AF 2020 |
| | | | Czech AF, RAF ML119, 1. Arr in UK 10-00. Stored. | 3-02 |

SEVENOAKS

| ❑ | G-APJZ | J/1N Alpha | ex St Albans, 5N-ACY, VR-NDR ntu, G-APJZ. |
| | | | Crashed 10-11-75. | ® 12-97 |

SHOREHAM west of the A225 north of Sevenoaks

Shoreham Aircraft Museum (SAM): A superb museum based upon SAM's extensive number of 'digs', all beautifully researched and presented. Also on show are some of the paintings of SAM's leading light, Geoff Nutkins. The cockpit of Spitfire XVI TB885 is not available for inspection.

◆ Open May to Sep Sun only 10am to 5pm, or by prior arrangement. ✉ High Street, Shoreham Village, Sevenoaks, Kent, TN14 7TB ☎ 01959 524416 **web** www.s-a-m.freeserve.co.uk

| ❑ | TB885 | Spitfire XVI | ex Kenley, *Reach for the Sky* as 'R1247', |
| | | | Cosford. | off-site 3-00 |

SMEETH on the A20 east of Ashford

Around August 2000, Aztec 250B G-ASER left its long-term home here and turned up at Lydd, Kent..

LANCASHIRE

☛ Within the administrative boundaries are two unitary authorities, Blackburn and Blackpool.

ADLINGTON on the A6 south of Chorley

By late 2001 Whirlwind HAS.7 XK911 had moved, perhaps to the Gloucestershire area.

BACUP on the A671 north of Rochdale

Neil Dykes:

❑	—		Flexiform h-glider	ex local area.	4-96
❑	—	BAPC.192	Weedhopper	ex Hooton Park, Warmingham.	4-96
❑	—	BAPC.193	Whing Ding	ex Hooton Park, Warmingham.	4-96

BLACKPOOL AIRPORT or Squires Gate, off the A584 south of Blackpool

Airport: Turning to *W&R17* (p92), disregard the comment about Cherokee G-AVWG, which still lingers here ①. The 'truncated' Islander 'G-FOXY' – complete with folding wings – is used as a travelling fund raiser by the Blackpool North Round Table and kept at the airfield. It is a classic 'cut and shut' being the front end and tail section of a 'drowned' BN-2B! ② Aztec 250C G-BBTL left by road during August 2001, destination unknown.

❑ G-ANWB	Chipmunk 21	ex G-5-17. CoA 8-3-91. Stored.		7-97
❑ G-ARCI	Cessna 310D	ex N6966T. Damaged 22-8-86. Stored.		9-01
❑ G-ARTT	MS.880B Rallye	CoA 29-5-94. Stored.		7-97
❑ G-ATOO*	Cherokee 140	ex Carlisle, Stanley. CoA 24-9-84.		7-01
❑ G-ATMI*	HS.748-2A/225	ex Emerald, VP-LIU, G-ATMI, VP-LIU, G-ATMI, VP-LIU, G-ATMI. *Old Ben.* CoA 18-5-00. Stored.		7-00
❑ G-AVWE	Cherokee 140	ex Stanley, Biggin Hill. CoA 22-4-82.		8-00
❑ G-AVWG	Cherokee 140	Damaged 11-12-88. Stored.	①	8-00
❑ G-AWKP*	CEA DR.253	Damaged 8-6-98. Stored. First noted 4-00.		10-00
❑ G-AWUA	Cessna P.206D	ex Thruxton, N8750Z. Damaged 16-10-87.		8-00
❑ G-BBTL	Aztec 250C	ex N6525Y. CoA 14-8-89. Stored.		9-01
❑ G-BCBM	Aztec 250C	ex N5854Y. Damaged 14-7-91. Stored.		7-97
❑ G-BJZX*	Grob G-109	ex D-KGRO ntu. Stored. First noted 4-00.		10-00
❑ G-BMIY	Great Lakes	ex G-NOME. CoA 27-8-87. Stored.		7-97
❑ G-BMJG*	Arrow 200	ex ZS-TNS, ZS-FYC, N9345N. Cr 11-10-98. F/n 4-00.		10-00
❑ G-BSPF	T.303 Crusader	ex OY-SVH, N3116C. Wreck.		9-99
❑ G-BTEF	Pitts S-1	ex N88PR. CoA 6-6-92. Stored.		2-97
❑ 'G-FOXY'	BN-2B-26	G-BLDX, ex Barrow, Air Furness. *Charlie.* Crashed 21-8-87. Travelling 'exhibit'.	②	2-97
❑ G-LYDD	Navajo 300	ex Lydd, G-BBDU, N6796L. Dam 17-7-91. Fuselage.		10-00
❑ G-TAIL*	Cessna 150J	ex N60220. Crashed 1-9-98. Stored. First noted 4-00.		10-00
❑ c/n 2073	ATP	ex Chadderton. Dump. First noted 4-96.		10-00
❑ XL391	Vulcan B.2	ex 44, 101, 44, 9/35, BCDU, MoA.		7-01

CAPERNWRAY on the A6 north of Carnforth
Both of the choppers are in the depths of the diving school's lake... or should be!

❑ WP503	'901' Dragonfly HR.3	ex Malton, Storwood, Cleethorpes, Elsham Hall, Stansted, RAE, North Coates, Lee-on-Solent, Lossiemouth SF.	4-96
❑ XS491	'XM' Wessex HU.5	ex Firbeck, Stafford, Wroughton, 845.	2-00

CHARNOCK RICHARD on the A49, south-west of Chorley
Dave Stansfield: Artefacts from the former Pennine Aviation Museum are kept in the area. The Albemarle is best described as '1½ nose sections' plus some other pieces. Dave is hard at work on these with the long-term aim of creating a fitted out cockpit. Also here is the 'tilting' nose section of the CG-4A Hadrian at Elvington, N Yorks (*qv*), the latter wearing a mock-up nose section.
◆ Not available for public inspection. ✉ 54 Hillcrest Avenue, Cliviger, Burnley, BB10 4JA.

❑ —	Albemarle	ex Bacup, Carlisle, Westnewton. Frames.	8-01

CHIPPING north of Longridge, itself north east of Preston
Bowland Forest Gliding Club: "T.8 BGA.1759 is believed to have moved on" said p93 of *W&R17*. How right that was! To be more specific, it gravitated to <u>Wolverhampton</u>, West Midlands.

CHORLEY on the A6 south of Preston
Botany Bay Village: Correcting *W&R17* (p93) Sycamore HR.14 XG540 lasted through to the autumn of 2000 before wholly expiring. Prior to this it had provided spares for the examples at Doncaster, S Yorks, and Flixton, Suffolk. Robinson G-IBED had moved on by April 2001.
◆ Open 9am to 5.30pm daily. North of Hartwood, access off the B6228. ✉ Canal Mill, Botany Brow, Chorley, PR6 9AF ☎ 01257 261220

❑	G-OBAY*	JetRanger	ex Blackpool, G-BVWR, C-GNXQ, N4714R.		
			Crashed 5-1-01. First noted 4-01.		7-01
❑		Pegasus Q	'trike', no wings.		1-99
❑	'A4850'	SE.5A scale	BAPC.176, ex Barton, Firbeck, Pontefract.		8-99
❑	'N5177'	'Sopwith 1½ Str	ex Barton, 'B9708', Chelford, Coventry.		3-00
❑	XN385	Whirlwind	ex Bruntingthorpe, Bournemouth, Wroughton, Culdrose,		
		HAS.7	Wroughton, HS, A&AEE, 771, 824, 825, 824.		6-01
❑	XP688	'E' Jet Provost T.4	ex Bruntingthorpe, Halton 9031M, Shawbury,		
			CATCS, CAW, RAFC.		6-01
❑	J-1712	Venom FB.54	ex Bournemouth, Swiss AF. Pod.		3-01

International Fire Training Centre: At Washington Hall, still have their Whirlwind.

| ❑ | XN298 | '10' Whirlwind HAR.9 | ex Warmingham, Stoke, Bournemouth, Yeovilton, | |
| | | | Wroughton, Lee SAR Flt, Fleetlands, Lee, 846, 848. | 3-01 |

Royal Ordnance: Jet Provost T.5A XW363 moved to Samlesbury, Lancs, by October 2000, but moved on to <u>Warton</u>, Lancs, on January 12, 2001.

COCKERHAM on the A588 between Lancaster and Fleetwood

The Black Knight Parachute Centre have a Cessna para-trainer. A microlight is store.

| ❑ | G-ARZE | Cessna 172C | ex Blackpool. Damaged 11-9-76. Para-trainer. | 8-01 |
| ❑ | G-MWWE | Team Minimax | CoA 23-7-97. Stored. | 7-99 |

ECCLESTON on the B5250 south of Leyland

Bygone Times Antique Warehouse:

◆ Open 9am to 5.30pm daily. ✉ Grove Mill, The Green, Eccleston, PR7 5PD ☎ 01257 451889 **fax** 01257 451090.

❑	'F-OTAN-6'	Noralpha	G-BAYV, ex Barton, Chelford, Sevenoaks, Booker,	
			Hawkinge, Maidstone, Ford, F-BLTN, French AF.	
			Crashed 23-2-74. Fuselage.	1-99

KENDALL on the A6 east of Windermere

A collector here took delivery of a 'JP' procedure trainer in 2001.

| ❑ | * | Jet Provost T.3 | ex Welshpool, Elvington, Linton-on-Ouse. | 7-01 |

PRESTON on the A56 north of Bury

Marsh Lane Technical School: Have a Harrier for instruction. It is a complex composite, with the nose section of XV281, the centre fuselage of XW272 and the rear of a P.1127 test-rig ①.

| ❑ | XV281* | Harrier GR.1 | ex Samlesbury, Dunsfold, Boscombe Down, | | |
| | | | A&AEE, BSE, Dunsfold. Arrived 3-01. | ① | 3-01 |

RAMSBOTTOM on the A56 north of Bury

Alan Dunkerley: The Spitfire project located in the general area. See also under Bristol, Glos.

| ❑ | SM520 | Spitfire IX | G-BXHZ, ex Oxford, Pretoria, SAAF. | 11-01 |

SAMLESBURY AIRFIELD on the A59 east of Preston

BAE Systems: Harrier GR.1 composite XV281 arrived here from Dunsfold, Surrey, in August 2000 for preparation work. It moved to <u>Preston</u>, Lancs, in March 2001.

❑	WH914	Canberra B.92	G-27-373, ex frustrated Argentine AF B.62, 231 OCU,	
			35, 76, 50, 61, 100. Dismantled and stored.	9-91
❑	WT537	Canberra PR.7	ex 13, 31, 17. Displayed.	4-01
❑	ZF580	Lightning F.53	ex RSAF 53-672, G-27-42. Displayed.	3-01

THORNTON-CLEVELEYS north of the A585, north of Blackpool

❏ WP839	Chipmunk T.10	G-BZXE, ex Newton, 8 AEF, 2 FTS, PFTS, Liv UAS, St A UAS, CUAS, 231 OCU, Birm UAS, 10 AFTS. ® 4-97

WARTON AIRFIELD on the A584 west of Preston

BAE Systems: Also on site are the **BAE Systems North West Heritage Group** (NWHG): The group now have three airframes on site. Please note that inspection is *not* possible without prior permission. The former Saudi T.55 nose is a mobile exhibit.

The Strikemaster composite uses the nose of a 'spare' BAC.167, centre-section from an engineering mock-up, the rear end from 'JP' Mk 3 XN634, a wing from a 'JP3' and a wing from a 'JP5' ①. Two airframes continue to serve with the renamed Overseas Customer Training Unit (OCTU).

Departures: Jaguar T.2 XX830 fuselage to <u>Coltishall</u>, Norfolk, 6-7-00; Canberra T.4 fuselage Q497 to Dumfries, Scotland, by 8-01.

❏ XS928	'AD'	Lightning F.6	ex BAe, Binbrook, 5-11, 56, 11, 56, 74, 5, 11. 5 Squadron colours, displayed.	NWHG 9-01
❏ XV147		Nimrod proto	ex Farnborough, Woodford, A&AEE. Fuselage.	9-01
❏ XV263		Nimrod AEW.3	ex Bournemouth, Finningley 8967M, Waddington, JTU, Woodford, St M Wing, 203. Nose	9-01
❏ XW363*	'36'	Jet Provost T.5A	ex Samlesbury, Preston, Warton, RAFC, 6 FTS, 1 FTS. Arrived 12-1-01.	NWHG 9-01
❏ ZA359	'B-55'	Tornado GR.1	ex TTTE.	OCTU 9-01
❏ [ZF596]		Lightning T.55	ex Portsmouth, Stretton, Warton, RSAF 233, 55-715, G-27-71. Nose	NWHG 9-01
❏ ZH200		Hawk 200	ex BAe.	OCTU 9-01
❏	c/n 06402	Comet 4	ex Woodford. Fuselage.	4-97
❏		Strikemaster	ex SSU. Dump	① 9-01

No.967 Squadron Air Cadets: On the Bank Lane site.

❏ WT520	Canberra PR.7	ex Lytham St Annes, Eaglescott, Burntwood, Swinderby, 8184M, 8094M, CAW, 31, 17, 1, 17, 31, 80. Nose. 9-01

LEICESTERSHIRE

☛ Within the administrative county boundaries of Leicestershire are two unitary authorities, Leicester City and Rutland. Rutland is Rutland County Council District Council but is referred to 'in short' as Rutland County Council. As such, it remains firmly within the county bounds of Leicestershire with the name conferring a little 'kidology' to local feelings!

BRUNTINGTHORPE AERODROME between the M1 and the A50 south of Leicester

☛ The Bruntingthorpe site is large and aircraft are listed below under their nominal 'keepers'. It is possible to find aircraft 'owned' by one heading parked in an area 'operated' by another. Please note also that admission on the regular Sundays openings need not necessarily provide access to *all* areas.

British Aviation Heritage - Cold War Jets Collection (BAH) / **Vulcan Operating Company** (VOC) / **C Walton (Aviation Division) Ltd**: Fund-raising for the 'Vulcan to the Sky' project continued apace throughout 2001 and work on the aircraft under Marshall Aerospace of Cambridge with the support of BAE Systems and a whole host of original equipment manufacturers (OEMs) made great strides.

Take strides beyond the photo-spread for more Bruntingthorpe, on page 129

BEDFORDSHIRE

Hunter F.1 WT612
Henlow, August 2001
David E Thompson

ANEC II G-EBJO
Old Warden, June 2001
Tim R Badham

Safir 91D G-SAFR
Cranfield, July 2000
Andy Wood

98

BEDFORDSHIRE

Bristol F.2b 'D7889'
Old Warden, June 2001
Tim R Badham

BUCKINGHAMSHIRE

Lightning F.1A XM144
Wycombe Air Park, May 2000
Alf Jenks

BERKSHIRE

Martinet TT.1 TF-SHC
Woodley, October 2001
David J Burke

CAMBRIDGESHIRE

L.100-30 TR-LBV
Cambridge Airport, April 2000
Roger Richards

MS.505 Criquet G-BPHZ
Duxford, February 2001
Col Pope

Tiger Moth R5136
Duxford, July 2001
Ken Ellis

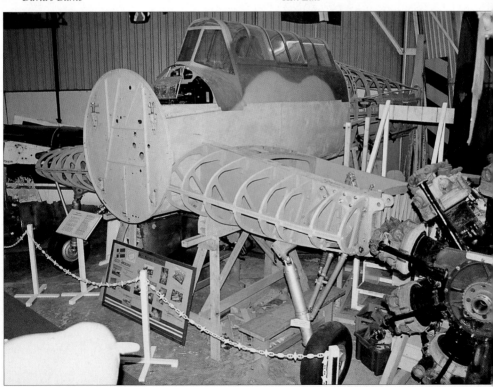

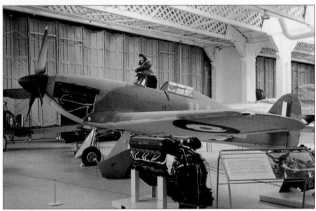

CAMBRIDGESHIRE

Lancaster X KB889
Duxford, May 2001
Roger Richards

Hurricane FSM 'Z2315'
Duxford, July 2001
Ken Ellis

Hastings C.1A TG528
Duxford, May 2001
Roger Richards

CAMBRIDGESHIRE

Spitfire F.24 VN485
Duxford, May 2001
Roger Richards

NA-64 Yale 3349
Duxford, September 2001
Col Pope

Silver Star Mk.3 '42161'
Duxford, July 2001
Col Pope

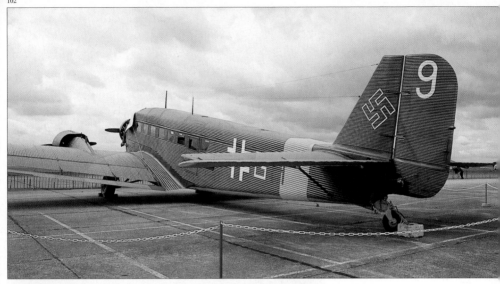

CAMBRIDGESHIRE

Amiot AAC.1 'V4+GH'
Duxford, June 2001
Alf Jenks

Strikemaster Mk.80 1108
Duxford, June 2001
Col Pope

F-15A Eagle 76-0020
Duxford, April 2001
Alf Jenks

CAMBRIDGESHIRE

Apache 160 G-ARBN
Peterborough Sport, September 2000
Andy Wood

Apache 160G G-ATMU
Peterborough Sport, September 2000
Andy Wood

Harrier GR.3 XV779
Wittering, April 2001
Jarrod Cotter

CHESHIRE

J/1N Alpha G-AJEB
Hooton Park, April 2001
Alf Jenks

F-4J(UK) ZE352
Hooton Park, July 2001
Mark A Jones

CORNWALL

Lightning F.6 XS936
Liskeard, December 2001
Richard Tregear

CORNWALL

Jetstream T.2 XX479
Predannack, August 2001
Richard Tregear

Spitfire FSM 'N3317'
St Mawgan, August 2001
Jarrod Cotter

CUMBRIA

Whirlwind HAR.9 XN387
Spadeadam, April 2000
David E Thompson

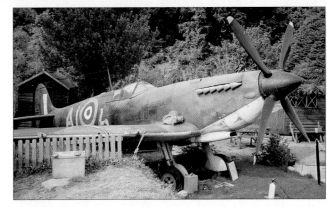

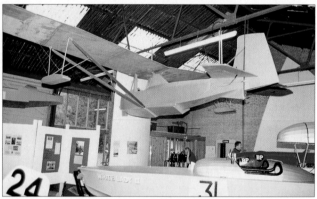

CUMBRIA

Su-22M-4 98+10
Spadeadam, April 2000
David E Thompson

Slingsby T.1 Falcon BGA.266
Windermere, October 2001
Ken Ellis

DEVON

Jet Provost T.5 XS231
Barnstaple, June 2001
Tim Jones

DORSET

HS.125-1B/522 G-ATPD
Bournemouth, December 2001
Es Robinson

Airbus A300B2 G-CEAA
Bournemouth, November 2001
Jon Wickenden

BAC 111-510ED G-AVMN
Bournemouth, May 2001
Ian Haskell

DORSET

Sea Vixen D.3 XP924 (G-CVIX)
Bournemouth, 29th May 2000
Baz Manning

L.188CF Electra EI-CHX
Bournemouth, September 2001
Baz Manning

Buccaneer S.2B(mod) XX897
Bournemouth, July 2001
Ian Haskell

DORSET

Hunter F.6 XG164
Poole, November 2001
Tony McCarthy

Arrow 200 G-AZRV
Compton Abbas, September 2001
Tony McCarthy

DURHAM AND CLEVELAND

Trident 3B-101 G-AWZR
Tees-side Airport, April 2001
Kevin Bowen

DURHAM AND CLEVELAND

Viscount 813 G-AZLP
Tees-side Airport, March 2000
David E Thompson

Short 330-100 'G-JON'
Tees-side Airport, March 2000
David E Thompson

ESSEX

Blake Bluetit G-BXIY
North Weald, September 2001
Ken Ellis

ESSEX

C-119G N2700 and Enstrom F.280
North Weald, September 2001
Ken Ellis

Aztec 250D 'G-ESKY'
North Weald, September 2001
Ken Ellis

C-47s 6W-SAF (nose),
N3455, 'FL586'
North Weald, September 2001
Duncan Parnell

ESSEX

Hurricane IV KZ191
North Weald, October 2001
Tim R Badham

Alcyon No.143
North Weald, September 2000
Alf Jenks

Belfast G-BFYU
Southend, April 2001
Phil Whalley

ESSEX

Bandeirante G-LOOT
Southend, June 2001
Ian Haskell

GLOUCESTERSHIRE

Brigand TF.1 RH746
Kemble, January 2002
Tim R Badham

Meteor T.7 VW453
Innsworth, September 2000
J P Longbottom

114

GLOUCESTERSHIRE

Bristol 173
Kemble, January 2002
Tim R Badham

Devon C.2/2 VP955 and Dove 8 G-AI
Kemble, August 2001
Tony McCarthy

Hunter T.7 XL578
Kemble, August 2000
Duncan Parnell

HAMPSHIRE

Short 330-200 OY-MUB
Alton, July 2001
Ian Haskell

Wessex HU.5 XT467
Bramley, May 2000
Bob Dunn

Enstrom F.28 'N-AAAS'
Basingstoke, July 2001
(at Membury Services)
Tony McCarthy

HAMPSHIRE

Jaguar T.2 XW566
Farnborough, January 2002
Mike Lynn – QinetiQ, via John Phillips

Bucanneer S.2C XV344
Farnborough, January 2002
QinetiQ, via John Phillips

Harrier T.4 XW934
Farnborough, January 2002
Mike Lynn – QinetiQ, via John Phillips

HAMPSHIRE

Sea King HAS.6 XV713
Gosport, August 2001
Tony Wood

Wessex HC.2 XR520
Gosport, August 2001
Tony Wood

EH.101 PP5 ZF649
Gosport, August 2001
Tony Wood

HAMPSHIRE

Hotspur II REP 'HH268'
Middle Wallop, December 2001
Jarrod Cotter

Whirlwind HAR.10 XR453
Odiham, April 2001
Roger Cook

Beaver AL.1 XP822
and Scout AH.1 XP910
Middle Wallop, October 2001
Ken Ellis

119

HAMPSHIRE

Chris Tena Mini Coupe G-BPDJ
Popham, December 2001
Brian Roffee

ISLE OF MAN

Eider Duck
Isle of Man Airport, June 2001
Lloyd P Robinson

HEREFORDSHIRE

Swift F.4 WK275
Upper Hill, August 2000
Ken Ellis

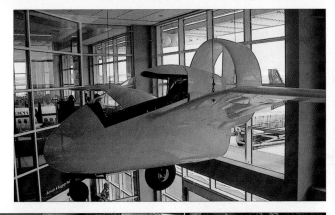

ISLE OF WIGHT

BN-2T-4R G-BVHX
and Islander AL.1 ZG994
Bembridge, April 2001
Chris Michell

KENT

Harrier GR.3 XZ964
Chatham, September 2001
Steve Barker

Jet Provost T.3 XM410
Chattenden, August 2001
Steve Barker

KENT

Phantom FGR.2 XT907
Chattenden, August 2001
Steve Barker

Chipmunk T.10 WP772
Manston, August 2001
Bob Parnell

Hurricane FSMs 'N2532' and 'P2921'
Hawkinge, June 2000
Kent Battle of Britain Museum

KENT

Bulldog T.1 XX655
Manston, August 2001
Mark A Jones

Wessex HU.5 XS482
Manston, August 2001
Bob Parnell

Harrier GR.3 XZ966
Manston, January 2001
David J Burke

LANCASHIRE

Vulcan B.2 XL391
Blackpool, October 2001
David S Johnstone

LEICESTERSHIRE

Jet Provost T.4 XP686
North Luffenham, July 2000
Tim Trehewey

Hunter F.6A 'XJ673'
Cottesmore, July 2001
Jarrod Cotter

LINCOLNSHIRE

Phantom FGR.2 XV497
Coningsby, August 2001
Mark A Jones

Provost T.1 WW388
Hemswell, February 2001
J P Longbottom

Lightning T.5 XS416
Grainthorpe, April 2001
J P Longbottom

LINCOLNSHIRE

Hunter FGA.9 'XG193'
Hemswell, February 2001
J P Longbottom

Rallye G-JENS
Skegness, July 2001
Andy Wood

Mystère IVA No.101
Hemswell, February 2001
J P Longbottom

LINCOLNSHIRE

Geronimo PH-NLK
Skegness, July 2001
Andy Wood

GREATER LONDON

Tiger Moth T7793
Croydon, January 2001
Tim R Badham

Trident 3B-101 G-AWZK
London Airport, September 2001
Kevin Bowen

GREATER LONDON

P-51D Mustang '472218'
South Lambeth, December 2001
Duncan Parnell

Spitfire I R6915
South Lambeth, December 2001
Duncan Parnell

Camel 2F1 N6812
South Lambeth, December 2001
Duncan Parnell

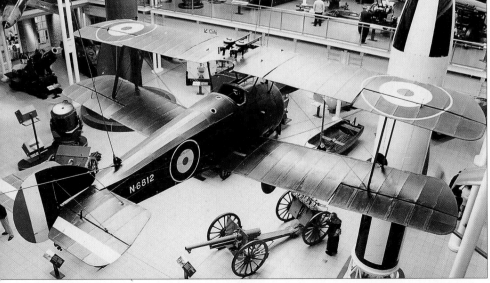

128

GREATER MANCHESTER

Trident 1C 'G-SMOKE'
Manchester Airport, March 2001
Barry Abraham

MERSEYSIDE

Dragon Rapide FSM 'G-AEAJ'
Liverpool, September 2001
Don Ellis

WEST MIDLANDS

B&P P.6 FSM 'X-25'
Wolverhampton, August 2001
Alf Jenks

Bruntingthorpe, continued from page 96

Following the tragedy in New York on 11th September 2001, fund raising was halted as a mark of respect and the decision was taken to repaint XH558 in its original anti-flash white colour scheme of July 1960 with the motto 'The Power for Peace'. Activities resumed in the new year with the working party from Marshall Aerospace stripping the aircraft down for full inspection. On 23rd March it was announced that it was not feasible to fly the Vulcan in the 50th anniversary year (2002) but that the next phase of the project was expected to be achieved by the beginning of the summer. This will be the achievement of an A8-20 recognition from the CAA, allowing XH558 to follow a self-monitoring restoration path once procedures have been agreed. This will considerably ease the cash burdens of the project. The vista of that delta back in the sky is as real as ever...

Supporting XH558 is the **XH558 Club** which also unites lovers of Vulcans every-where. They publish a superb journal and stage meetings and events. ✉ XH558 Club, Paul Hartley, 19 Bowling Green Drive, Hook, RG27 9TZ info hotline: 01426 965302 web: www.vulcan558club.demon.co.uk

Notes: The Valiant nose is on loan from a private collector from the north-east of England ①. The Jaguar is on loan from a US owner. It may eventually travel to Florida ②.

Departures: Vulcan B.2 nose XH537 moved to Bournemouth, Dorset, 29-10-01. TriStar TF-ABP was scrapped 11/12-3-02, leaving just three RB211s as evidence by the end of the month. The forward fuselage section moved to Iver Heath, Bucks, on 13-3-02.

◆ Open every Sunday 10am to 4pm. Other times by prior arrangement – ☎ Caroline Richmond 0116 2478030. Please note that there are *no* catering facilities on the airfield. 'Rolling Thunder' days staged when several aircraft are fired up and taxied, often in association with other operators on the airfield. Details of these events widely published in the aviation press. ✉ C Walton (Aviation Division) Ltd / Vulcan Operating Co, Bruntingthorpe Airfield, Lutterworth, LE17 5QS ☎ 0116 2478030 fax 0116 2478031 web www.tvoc.co.uk

❑ G-CPDA	Comet 4C	ex XS235, Boscombe Down, DTEO, A&AEE, BLEU. *Canopus.*		3-02
❑ F-BTGV	'1' Super Guppy 201	ex Airbus Skylink, N211AS.		3-02
❑ 9L-LCI*	LET 410	stored. First noted 6-01.		3-02
❑ XD875	Valiant B.1	ex Marham, Firbeck, Coventry, Cosford, 7, 138, 207, SAC Bombing Sqn, 207, 49, 207. Nose.	①	3-02
❑ XH558	Vulcan B.2	G-VLCN, ex Waddington, VDF, Marham, Waddington, 50, Wadd Wing, A&AEE, Wadd Wing, 27, 230 OCU, 27, Wadd Wing, 230 OCU.	ℝ	3-02
❑ XM715	Victor K.2	ex 55, 232 OCU, 543, 232 OCU, 100, 139. *Teasin' Tina.*		3-02
❑ XX900	Buccaneer S.2B	ex St Athan, 208, 12, 208, 216, 12, 208.		3-02
❑ XZ382	'GH' Jaguar GR.1 and 'FO'	8908M, ex Coltishall, Halton, Shawbury, 14, 17. 54 Sqn c.s stb, 41 pt. 'Gate guardian'.	②	3-02
❑ 85	'8-MV' Mystère IVA	ex East Midlands, Sculthorpe, Fr AF. Stored.		3-02
❑ 1018	Iskra 100	G-ISKA, ex Polish AF.	ℝ	3-02

Beech Restorations and **Tomcat T6 Restorations:** Adrian Marshall, Philip Turland and friends are restoring G-BKRN to airworthy status with G-BKRG as a source of spares. (See also under Derby, Derbyshire.) Their new project is a former French Air Force T-6G. In Algeria, the French knew such armed Texans as 'Tomcats' because of their growl – hence the registration.

◆ Aircraft exhibited at open days and special events. Otherwise visits by prior arrangement only. ✉ 14 Hallam Close, Moulton, Northampton NN3 7LB ☎ 01604 790901 fax 01604 492946 e-mail philipstudfast@netscapeonline.co.uk web www.beechrestorations.com

❑ G-BKRN	Beech D.18S	ex Cranfield, Perth, Prestwick, CF-DTN, RCAF inst A675, RCAF 1500. CoA 26-6-83. US Navy c/s. *Naval Encounter.*		3-02
❑ '122351'	Beech C-45G	G-BKRG, ex North Weald, Duxford, N75WB, *Octopussy,* N9072Z, 51-11665. Spares use.		3-02
❑ 114700*	T-6G-NT Texan	G-TOMC, ex Stoke-on-Trent, Eccleshall, North Weald, Coventry, *Empire of the Sun,* La Ferté Alais, FAF. Arrived 20-10-02.	off-site ℝ	3-02

Lightning Preservation Group (LPG): Work continues on keeping their two machines 'live' and LPG undertakes regular 'running' days, all well advertised. While planning permission for the erection of the QRA shed has been approved by Harborough District Council, fund-raising still needs a boost. Dig deep and help out!
◆ Regular open days, otherwise by prior appointment *only*. ✉ 66 Stoneage Close, Bognor Regis, PO22 9QW e-mail htrevor@tesco.net web www.lightnings.org.uk

❑ XR728	'JS' Lightning F.6	ex Binbrook, 11, LTF, 5, 56, 23, 11, 23. Taxiable.	3-02
❑ XS904	'BQ' Lightning F.6	ex BAe Warton, Binbrook, 5-11 pool. Taxiable.	3-02

Phoenix Aviation: Continue a lively trade, particularly in nose sections. Gnat T.1 XP540 is on loan to Arbury College, Cambridge, Cambs. The nose of Sea Vixen XN647 is being held for collector Robin Phipps ① – see under Coventry, Warks, for his Buccaneer nose.
   Departures: Sea Hawk FGA.4 WV838 cockpit to Fleetlands, Hants, 21-11-00; Hunter F.6A XK149 to the USA 10-4-00; Gnat T.1 XR569 left for the USA 16-12-00; Andover CC.2 fuselage XS791 to Ely, Cambs, 22-7-00; Harrier GR.3 ZD668 left on 10-6-00, initially for Lowestoft, Suffolk. It was registered to a Belgian owner as G-CBCU but is believed bound for Washington state, USA.

❑ G-APFG	Boeing 707-436	ex Cardington, Stansted, British Airtours, BOAC. CoA 24-5-81. Nose.		3-02
❑ [G-AYKA]* 'AY'	Baron 55A	ex Shoreham, Elstree, HB-GEW, G-AYKA, D-IKUN, N8683M. Crashed 18-6-89. Converted to a car! Arrived 11-9-01.		3-02
❑ G-KEAB*	Queen Air B80	ex Shoreham, Manston, G-BSSL, G-BFEP, F-BRNR, OO-VDE. Fuselage. Arrived 11-9-01.		3-02
❑ WK122*	Canberra TT.18	ex Helston, Samlesbury, 7, 15, 61. Nose. Arr 10-1-01.		3-02
❑ WV795	Sea Hawk FGA.6	ex Cranfield, Bruntingthorpe, Bournemouth, Bath, Cardiff-Wales, Culdrose A2661, Halton 8151M, Sydenham, 738, 806, 700.		3-02
❑ XE327	'644' Sea Hawk FGA.6	ex King's Langley, Llangennech A2556, Sydenham, 738.		3-02
❑ 'XF324'	Hunter F.51	E-427, ex Brough, Holme-on-Spalding Moor, Brough, Dunsfold, G-9-447, Danish AF, Esk.724. RAF 92 Sqn 'Blue Diamonds' colours.		3-02
❑ XF844	'70' Provost T.1	ex Farnborough, RAE, 6 FTS.		3-02
❑ XH136	'W' Canberra PR.9	ex Cosford 8782M, 1 PRU, A&AEE, 39, 13, 58, MoA. Nose.		3-02
❑ XH592	'L' Victor B.1A	ex Cosford 8429M St Athan, 232 OCU, TTF, 232 OCU, Honington Wing, 15. Nose.		3-02
❑ XJ494	Sea Vixen FAW.2	ex Kings Langley, Farnborough, FRL, A&AEE, HSA, Sydenham, 899, Sydenham, 892.		3-02
❑ XL565*	Hunter T.7	ex Kemble, Ipswich, Colsterworth, Shawbury, Lossiemouth, FRADU, 237 OCU, 4 FTS, 208, 8, West Raynham SF, 8, 1417F, 8, mkrs. Arr 21-3-02.		3-02
❑ XN647*	Sea Vixen '707' FAW.2	ex Helston, Culdrose SAH-10, A2610, 766, 899. Cockpit. Arrived 12-12-00.	①	3-02
❑ XS217	'O' Jet Provost T.4	ex Halton 9029M, Shawbury, CATCS, CFS, RAFC.		3-02
❑ XV328	'BZ' Lightning T.5	ex Cranfield, Binbrook, LTF, 5, LTF, 5, 29.Nose.		3-02
❑ XV751*	Harrier GR.3	ex Charlwood, Lee-on-Solent A2672, A2760, 3, 1, 3, 20, 233 OCU. Grey c/s, Royal Navy titles. Arrived 13-2-01.		3-02
❑ XW270	Harrier T.4	ex Cranfield, Wittering, 4, 1, 233 OCU, 1, 233 OCU. Wing from XV748.		3-02
❑ J-4091	Hunter F.58	ex FSt7/FSt9, Swiss AF.		3-02

Others: A series of machines are held on the aerodrome by private individuals or organisations: Canberra B(I).8 WT333 is with Roger Wintle and Arthur Perks. It was built as a B(I).8 but was later fitted with the cockpit from B.2 WK135 ①. Classic Aviation Projects Canberra B.2/6 WK163 (G-BVWC) flew to Coventry, Warks, 26th March 2000, to be based. Their B.2/6 G-BVIC (= Great Britain,

Mk VI Canberra) was built as a B.6 and was then fitted with the cockpit from B.2 WG788 and is stored here ②. 'JP' XM355 is owned by Alan Witt and will be restored to taxiable condition ③. (See also under Barton, Gtr Man.) 'JP' XN584 with Malcolm and Sarah Bent. It is under restoration to taxiable status. The wings of XN584 are fitted to T.4 XP627 at Sunderland, N&T. ④. The Harrier nose is with Graham Smith ⑤. (See also Wigston, Leics.) John and Mark Wood took delivery of an anonymous Auster frame, this will form the basis of a 'flyer' ⑥.

Departures: Chipmunk T.10 PAX WP845 went to Canada; Harrier GR.3 nose XW763 moved to Wigston, Leics; Lightning T.55 nose ZF595 to the USA 22-5-01.

❏ WT333		Canberra B(I).8	G-BVXC, ex DRA Farnborough, DRA Bedford, RAE, C(A).	①	3-02
❏ XH568		Canberra B.2/6	G-BVIC, ex DRA Bedford, RAE, MoA. CoA 30-1-97. Stored	②	3-02
❏ XM355*	'D'	Jet Provost T.3	ex Shobdon, Cambridge, Bruntingthorpe, Halton 8229M, Shawbury, 1 FTS, 7 FTS, CFS. Arrived 10-5-01.	③	3-02
❏ XN584	'E' and '88'	Jet Provost T.3A	ex Halton 9014M, 1 FTS, CFS, RAFC, CFS, RAFC, TWU, RAFC.	®④	3-02
❏ XV810	'K'	Harrier GR.3	9038M, ex 233 OCU, 4, 20. Nose.	⑤	3-02
❏ _*		Auster	frame. Arrived 22-10-01.	⑥	3-02

BURBAGE on the B578 south-east of Hinckley
Midland Helicopters: A shop on the Sapcote Road, specialising in the sale of model, radio controlled, helicopters, was displaying a wrecked Scout by January 2001.

❏ XT630*	'X'	Scout AH.1	G-BXRL. Crashed 16-10-99.	2-01

COALVILLE on the A511 north-west of Leicester
Snibston Discovery Park: Within can be found a host of fascinating material on the industrial and transport heritage of the county. Items acknowledging aircraft manufacture in Leicestershire are the Auster AOP.9 and a sectioned Whittle turbojet. Other airframes are in store and listed under this heading as a 'port of convenience'. They are not available for inspection. Leicestershire Museums' Arts and Records Service maintain an extensive Auster archive, including original manufacturer's drawings. (Contact Peter Stoddart on 0116 2765532 Monday 2pm to 4.30pm or on 0116 2775932.) See under Winthorpe, Notts, for Auster G-AGOH.
◆ Daily 10am to 5pm, except Xmas and a week in January for maintenance. Signed off the A511. ✉ Ashby Road, Coalville, Leicestershire, LE67 3LN ☎ 01530 278444 **fax** 01530 813301 **info-line** 01530 813256 **e-mail** snibston@leics.gov.uk

❏ G-AFTN*	Taylorcraft Plus C2	ex Heavitree, HL535, 43 OTU, 652, 651, G-AFTN. CoA 1-11-57.	®	3-02
❏ G-AIJK	Auster J/4	ex Leicester, Stratford. CoA 24-8-68. off-site		3-02
❏ VZ728	Desford Trainer	G-AGOS, ex Perth, Strathallan, Thruxton, RAE. CoA 28-11-80. Stored.		3-02
❏ XP280	Auster AOP.9	ex Leicester, St Athan, 2 Wing, Queen's Dragoon Guards, 2 RTR, 651. On display.		3-02

COTTESMORE AIRFIELD north of the B668, north-east of Oakham
RAF Cottesmore: 'Rutland International' now has no less than four 'historics' on it. The Spitfire F.21 is owned by the 1 Squadron Association and kept in a hangar. The Hunter is kept in the 4 Squadron hangar. Both appear outside when needed. Harrier XW917 adorns the 'inner' gate and is painted in joint 3 (port) and 4 (starboard) Squadron colours, while XW924 is displayed outside the 3 Squadron hangar (the most westerly) in their markings. Cottesmore is another base to take on a 'synthetic' fire crash rescue rig, in this case it is of the combined 'Harricopter' sort - *W&R16* carries an illustration.

❏ LA255*	Spitfire F.21	6490M, ex Wittering West Raynham, Cardington, Tangmere, 1. Arrived 31-7-00.	7-01

❑ 'XJ673'	Hunter F.6A	XE606/8841M, ex Laarbruch, 1 TWU, TWU, 229 OCU, 92, 74, 65, 54, CFE. 8737M ntu. Arr 11-99.	7-01
❑ XW917	Harrier GR.3	8975M, ex Laarbruch, 3, 4, 3. SOC 3-4-88. 'Gate'	7-01
❑ XW924	Harrier GR.3	9073M, ex Laarbruch, Halton, 3, 4, 1, 233 OCU, 4.	7-01
❑ 162068*	AV-8B Harrier	9250M, ex Wittering, AMARC, VMAT-203. Fuselage. Arrived 26-6-00.	6-00

DISEWORTH on the B5401 south of East Midlands Airport
Joe Goy: The Buccaneer is thought to still be resident.

❑ XV337	Buccaneer S.2C	ex Stock, St Athan, Abingdon 8852M, A&AEE, 208, A&AEE, 809, 800. Nose.	11-99

DONINGTON CIRCUIT or Donington Park, near to East Midlands Airport
A Spitfire FSM is mounted on a dramatic 'wishbone' plinth over-looking the Craner Curves.

❑ –	'K-W' Spitfire FSM	—	4-01

EAST MIDLANDS AIRPORT or Castle Donington junction 24 M1, on the A453
Aeropark: On 9th August 2001 the Aeropark opened up again on the north side of the airport with much help from East Midlands Airport, DHL and bmi british midland (the new lower case incarnation of the famed airline). The aircraft are displayed with plenty of space amid a great viewing area.
Vampire T.11 XD459 incorporates the wings and tail feathers from XE872 ①. Correcting *W&R17* (p131) Meteor F.8 composite WE925 was *not* part of the collection. The centre section was briefly on site with the bulk of the airframe stored in Norfolk. It is believed destined for Australia.

◆ Open Thu (10.30am to 5pm), Sat (noon to 5pm) and Sun (103.0am to 5pm) April to October, and Thu and Sun 10.30am to 5pm in the winter. Also Bank Holidays other than Christmas. ◙ Supporting the Aeropark and the airframes is the **East Midlands Airport Volunteers Association**. Contact: J Sandland, 37 Wigginton Road, Tamworth, B79 8RL.

❑ G-APES	Merchantman	ex Hunting, ABC, BEA. CoA 2-10-95. *Swiftsure*. Nose.	3-02
❑ G-BEOZ	Argosy 101	ex ABC, N895U, N6502R, G-1-7. CoA 28-5-86.	3-02
❑ G-FRJB	SA.1 Sheriff	ex Sandown. Incomplete and unflown. off-site ®	3-02
❑ WH740	'X' Canberra T.17	ex Cosford 8762M, 360, RNZAF, Upwood SF, 40, 18.	3-02
❑ WL626	'P' Varsity T.1	G-BHDD, ex Coventry, 6 FTS, 1 ANS, 2 ANS, 201 AFS.	3-02
❑ XD459	'63' Vampire T.11	ex Bruntingthorpe, Long Marston, Bennington, Cranfield, Bushey, Keevil, 3/4 CAACU, 229 OCU, 233 OCU, 151, 253, 56. ® ①	3-02
❑ XG588	Whirlwind Srs 3	VR-BEP, ex Cuckfield, G-BAMH, Redhill, XG588, 705, 701, *Warrior* Flt, *Albion* Flt. SAR c/s. off-site ®	3-02
❑ XL569	'SC' Hunter T.7	ex Abingdon, Cosford 8833M, 2 TWU, 1 TWU, 12, 216, 237 OCU, Laarbruch SF, 15, 237 OCU, 12, MinTech, 2 TWU, 1 TWU, TWU, 229 OCU.	3-02
❑ XM575	Vulcan B.2	G-BLMC, ex 44, Wadd Wing, Scampton Wing, 617.	3-02
❑ XV350	Buccaneer S.2B	ex Shawbury, Warton, RAE.	3-02
❑ ZF588	'L' Lightning F.53	ex Warton, RSAF 53-693, G-27-63. 74 Sqn c/s.	3-02

Airport:

❑ TC-ALM	Boeing 727-230	ex Air Alfa, TC-IKO, TC-JUH, TC-ALB, N878UM, D-ABDI. Fire training.	3-02

HINCKLEY off the A47 south-west of Leicester
Douglas Boston-Havoc UK Preservation Trust: Undergoing restoration is the 'birdcage' nose of a Boston IIIA, originally an A-20C operated by 22 Squadron, RAAF, in the Pacific 1943-45. In

storage awaiting a UK sponsor is a 13ft section of forward fuselage and the 'attack' nose from A-20G 43-9628, plus a fully restored A-20G Martin gun turret, all gifted by 23 Squadron, RAAF. Also held are an inner mainplane, rear fuselage and tailplanes from RAF Boston III Z2186, main and nose landing gear, a Boston-fit Wright Cyclone plus DB-7 Havoc and Boston IV instrument panels.
◆ Please note that visits are always possible by prior arrangement. ✉ Dick Nutt, 17 Hinckley Road, Barwell, Leics, LE9 8DL ☎ 01455 845517

❏ 43-9628	A-20G-30-DO	ex RAAF Museum, Papua New Guinea, USAAF. Forward fuselage.	® 3-02

Hurricane and Aircrew Collection: Steve Milnthorpe's Hurricane is based on a remanufactured Mk.IIa DR348 which was shipped to Russia in October 1941. Originating as Mk I P3717, it flew during the Battle of Britain with 253 and 257 Squadrons with at least one confirmed 'kill' to its credit.
◆ Visits are *only* possible by prior arrangement.

❏ P3717	Hurricane I	ex Russia, Mk IIA DR348, 8 FTS, 55 OTU, 43, 257, 253, 238. Composite.	® 2-00

HUSBANDS BOSWORTH AERODROME south of the A427, south of the village

❏ G-BDCC*	Chipmunk 22	ex WD321, DH. Damaged. First noted 8-01.	11-01
❏ G-MNGO	Hiway Skytrike	CoA 3-89. Stored.	6-98
❏ XK790	Grasshopper TX.1	ex Halton. Stored.	7-00

LEICESTER
John Poyser: John has built a full-size Spitfire IX and keeps it at his home in the city.

❏ –*	'JE-J' Spitfire FSM	fuselage.	1-02

LEICESTER AERODROME or Leicester East, or Stoughton, south-east of Leicester
RN Aviation: J/1 Autocrat G-AGVG was flying again by July 2000 powered by a Lycoming O-360.

❏ G-AEXZ	J-2 Cub	CoA 2-11-78.	off-site ® 8-92
❏ G-AHLK	Auster III	ex NJ889, 43 OTU. CoA 21-9-97.	® 6-01
❏ G-AMTD*	J/5F Aiglet Tnr	ex EI-AVL, G-AMTD. Crashed 7-8-93. Frame.	6-01
❏ G-APTU*	Alpha 5	CoA 8-6-98. Stored.	6-01
❏ G-ARDJ	Auster D.6/180	crashed 30-5-86. Stored.	6-01

LOUGHBOROUGH on the A6 north of Leicester
Charnwood Museum: Within the museum the 1956 King's Cup winning Auster J/1N 'flies' as a memorial to the wonders worked at nearby Rearsby. Restoration was undertaken by a team led by Ron Neal from Leicester Aerodrome with input from the International Auster Club.
◆ Mon to Sat 10am to 4.30pm, Sun 2pm to 5pm. Exhibitions and special events ✉ Granby Street, Loughborough, LE11 3QU ☎ 01509 233754, **fax** 01509 268140 **e-mail** charnwood@leics.gov.uk

❏ G-AJRH	'7' J/1N Alpha	ex Leicester area, Harrogate, Wigan. CoA 5-6-69.	3-02

University: Department of Aeronautical, Automotive Engineering and Transport Studies.

❏ ZF534	BAe EAP	ex Warton.	3-00

MELTON MOWBRAY on the A607 north-east of Leicester
Auster Nine Group: Have workshops in the general area. Beagle E.3 G-ASCC was flying again by May 2000, joining XR417 (G-AVXY) and XN441 (G-BGKT). By September 2001 Auster AOP.9 XR246 (G-AZBU) was at North Coates, Lincs. Auster AOP.9 XN412 moved to Winthorpe, Notts.

❏ G-AYUA	Auster AOP.9	ex Bruntingthorpe, Cranfield, Bushey, Luton, Sibson, XK41<u>6</u>, Middle Wallop, 7855M, 651, 19 MU.	12-96
❏ XR267*	Auster AOP.9	G-BJXR, ex Innsworth, Staverton, Congresbury, St Athan, 655, 652. Arrived by 1-01.	1-01
❏ XP282	Auster AOP.9	G-BGTC, ex XP282. Damaged 2-10-96. Stored.	7-97

David Hall: Also in the area, David is working on an Auster 4.
❑ G-AJXY*   Auster 4   ex Ipswich, MT243.   ® 6-01

NORTH LUFFENHAM north of the A6121 south-west of Stamford
St George's Barracks: Within is an enclave on the eastern side of the former airfield for the **RAF Explosive Ordnance Disposal** unit, a sub-site from EOD at Wittering, Cambs. The Hunter is mostly hangar-bound and has had the nose cone removed to render it more MiG-looking, aided considerably by the red stars it carries! It is used by EOD to simulate a fully-armed 'defector' complete with 'strange' weaponry to assess and then disarm ①.
    Departures: Jet Provost T.3 XM410 to Chattenden, Kent, by mid-2001; Harrier T.4 XZ146 to Wittering, Cambs, by 12-00.

❑ [XG194]	'69'	Hunter FGA.9	8839M, ex Cosford, 1 TWU, TWU, 229 OCU, 1, 92, 111, 43. Soviet red stars.	① 3-02
❑ [XN554]		Jet Provost T.3	8436M, ex Halton, St Athan, Shawbury, CFS.	3-02
❑ XN579		Jet Provost T.3A	9137M, ex Shawbury, 1 FTS, 7 FTS, 1 FTS, RAFC,TWU, RAFC.	3-02
❑ XP344	'H723'	Whirlwind HAR.10	8764M, ex Cranwell, Finningley, Chivenor, 22, SAR Wing, CFS. French roundel, olive drab.	3-02
❑ XP629		Jet Provost T.4	9026M, ex Halton, Shawbury, CATCS, SoRF, CAW, 2 FTS.	3-02
❑ XP686		Jet Provost T.4	8502M, ex Halton, 8401M, CATCS, 6 FTS, CAW, CATCS, CAW, 3 FTS.	3-02
❑ [XS186]		Jet Provost T.4	8408M, ex Halton, St Athan, Kemble, Shawbury, CAW.	3-02
❑ [XT905]	'P'	Phantom FGR.2	9286M, ex Coningsby, 74, 228 OCU, 29, 228 OCU, 31, 17.	3-02
❑ XV804	'O'	Harrier GR.3	9280M, ex Winterbourne Gunner, 4, 3, 1, 3, 4, 233 OCU, 1417F, 233 OCU.	3-02

OAKHAM on the A606 west of Stamford
Restoration is underway on a Globe Swift.
❑ G-BFNM*   Globe Swift   ex Tatenhill, Nottingham Airport, N78205.   ® 12-01

SHAWELL south of Lutterworth, east of the A5
The Wessex is still at the paintball assault course.
❑ XT770   'P' Wessex HU.5   ex Bruntingthorpe, Halton 9055M, Wroughton, 845.   2-02

STANFORD north-east of Rugby, near Swinford
Stanford Hall and **Percy Pilcher Museum:** Within the stables block is a small display devoted to the life and times of Percy Pilcher RN, including a Hawk REP. Although a reproduction this Hawk is probably the most representative of the pioneering craft, including the original, which can be found at East Fortune, Lothian. As well as the hall itself, there is a small, but impressive, motorcycle museum in the out-buildings.
◆ Sat and Sun, Easter to end of Sep 1.30pm to 5.30pm (last admission 5pm), also Bank Holidays and Tue following, same times. Regular special events in the grounds - SAE for details. ✉ Stanford Hall, Lutterworth, LE17 6DH. ☎ 01788 860250 fax 01788 860870 e-mail enquiries@stanfordhall.co.uk web www.stanfordhall.co.uk
❑   BAPC.45 Pilcher Hawk REP ex Coventry, Bitteswell.   2-00

STONEY COVE on the B581 east of Hinckley
Within the waters of the diving school are Wessex HU.5 XT768 (down at 70ft); the forward fuselage of Viscount 814 G-AWXI (down at 23ft) and Partenavia P.68C G-LOUP (down at 60ft).

WIGSTON south-east Leicester
Graham Smith: Has moved on of his Harrier cockpits here. The other is at Bruntingthorpe, Leics.
❑ XW763*   Harrier GR.3   ex Bruntingthorpe, Wigston, Bruntingthorpe,
                                   Duxford, St Athan, 9041M / 9002M, 1,
                                   1453 Flt, 3, 4, 3. Nose. .   2-03

LINCOLNSHIRE

☛ Within the administrative county boundary of Lincolnshire can be found the unitary authorities of North Lincolnshire (centred around Scunthorpe) and North East Lincolnshire (centred around Grimsby and Immingham).

BARKSTON HEATH AIRFIELD on the B6403 north of Grantham
RAF Barkston Heath: A Minicab is under restoration here while the Canberra just hangs on.
❑ G-AWUB*   Minicab   ex Boston, F-PERX. CoA 23-10-80.   Ⓡ 11-01
❑ WT339   Canberra B(I).8 8198M, ex Cranwell, 16, 3, 14, 88. Dump.   4-02

BINBROOK on the B1203 north-east of Market Rasen
Charles Ross: As Chairman of the Lightning Association (see below) it is hardly surprising to find that Charles has an example in his garden and a small museum dedicated to the subject. As well as the F.6 here, Charles owns F.1A XM192 at Hemswell, Lincs, and F.6 nose XS899 at Coltishall, Norfolk.
◆ Admission by prior arrangement *only* - see below for contact address.
❑ XR725   'BA' Lightning F.6   ex Rossington 'TVI725', Binbrook, 11,
                                   5, LTF, 5, 56, 74, 5, 23.   2-02

BINBROOK AIRFIELD north of the B1203, north of the village
Lightning Association (LA): As well as regular events, the LA publishes *Lightning Review*, their journal covering all aspects of Lightning history and technical documentation. XR724 is kept operational and undertakes engine runs plus occasional taxis.
◆ Annual open day and other times for LA members. Visits by prior permission *only*. ✉ Lightning Association, c/o Charles Ross, Chestnut Farm House, Ludford Road, Binbrook, Market Rasen, LN8 6DR ☎ 01472 398705, **fax** 01472 399391
❑ XR724   Lightning F.6   ex G-BTSY, Shawbury, BAe Warton, 5, 11,
                                   5, 11, 5, LTF, 11.   10-01

Global Aviation (GA): The main hub is Humberside Airport, Lincs, where maintenance is carried out on the large fleet of UK private-owner 'JPs'. By the end of 2001, Global had cleared their store here.
Departures: Further to *W&R17*, Jet Provost T.3A XN470 (G-BXBJ) moved to the Dubai Men's College for use as an instructional airframe during late 1999; and Jet Provost T.3A XN510 (G-BXBI) moved to Ipswich, Suffolk. 'JP' T.3A XM349 is unaccounted for. Gnat T.1 XR541 moved to Humberside Airport, Lincs.

Others: Canberra nose WJ565 moved to the Louth, Lincs, avia a brief stop at North Coates.

BOSTON
A *private* workshop in this general area *should* continue to hold some 'long-termers' with an over-riding French accent. Falconar F-11 G-AXDY and Nord 3400 No.37 (G-ZARA) have moved on.
❑ G-AXGA   Super Cub 95   ex Tattershall Thorpe, PH-NLE, PH-CUB ntu,
                                   RNethAF R-51, 52-2447. Crashed 26-12-86.   8-90
❑ G-AYVT   Brochet MB.84   ex Tattershall Thorpe, Sunderland, F-BGLI.
                                   Damaged 28-6-77   8-90

❑ G-PULL   Super Cub 150   ex Tattershall Thorpe, PH-MBB, ALAT 18-5356.
                             Crashed 13-6-86. Frame.   8-90
❑ F-BBGH   Brochet MB.100   ex F-WBGH. Stored.   8-90
❑ F-PFUG   Adam RA-14   Stored.   8-90

Others: A collector should have the nose of the former Coningsby Lightning F.2A.
❑ XN774   Lightning F.2A   ex Coningsby 8551M, 92, 19. Nose.   1-99

BOSTON AERODROME or Wyberton, on the A1121 west of Boston
The aerodrome had closed by the end of 2001. Tiger Cub 440 G-MJSP was noted stored by August
1998 but had moved to North Coates, Lincs, by December 2000. Fellow G-MMFT (CoA expired 23rd
January 1995) was also stored here, first noted in March 1999. It moved to its owners home but was
destroyed in an act of arson in November 2001.

CLEETHORPES south of Grimsby
A pair of microlights are stored in the town.
❑ G-MJUZ*   Dragon 150   ex North Coates. CoA 28-2-87. Arrived 11-<u>98</u>.   1-02
❑ G-MMAI*   Dragon 150   ex North Coates. CoA 13-7-97. Arrived 11-<u>98</u>.   1-02

COLSTERWORTH on the A1 north of Stamford
During April 2000 a well-known dealer in former MoD vehicles had taken delivery of a pair of Wessex.
❑ XR502*   'Z' Wessex HC.2 ex Fleetlands, 60, 72, WTF, 18, 1 FTU. Arr 3-4-00.   4-01
❑ XT604*   Wessex HC.2   ex Fleetlands, 22, 103, 78, Muharraq SAR Flt, 78.
                             Arrived 5-4-00.   4-01

CONINGSBY AIRFIELD on the B1192, south of Horncastle
Battle of Britain Memorial Flight (BBMF) and **Visitor Centre**: Major changes to the airfield to
get it ready for the Eurofighter Typhoon may cause some disruption to the operation of BBMF with a
possible 'bolt-hole' of Barkston Heath, Lincs, planned. As *W&R* goes to press, it is hoped that the flight
can co-exist with the construction work and continue to be based at the airfield. The Chipmunks are
maintained under contract by PropShop at Duxford, Cambs.
◆ Open Monday to Friday except Bank Holidays 10am to 4.30pm with the last guided tour at 3.30pm.
Please note: although booking is not required to attend the Visitor Centre, it is advisable as it may
be that the Flight in whole or in part are positioning to a show. **Lincolnshire's Lancaster
Association** support the Visitor Centre, the BBMF and PA474 in particular. Details from: 31,
Knaton Road, Carlton-in-Lindrick, Worksop, Notts, S81 9HJ.✉ BBMF Visits, RAF Coningsby,
Lincoln LN4 4SY ☎ 01526 344041

❑ P7350   Spitfire IIa ✈   ex *Battle of Britain* G-AWIJ, Colerne, 57 OTU,
            'XT-D'   CGS, 64, 616, 603, 266. 603 Sqn c/s, *Blue Peter*.   3-00
❑ AB910   Spitfire Vb ✈   ex *Battle of Britain*, BBMF, G-AISU, 29 MU, RWE,
            'ZD-C'   527, 53 OTU, 402, 242, 133, 130, 222. 222 Sqn c/s.   4-01
❑ LF363   Hurricane IIc ✈ ex Audley End, Coningsby, Biggin Hill SF, 41,
            'US-C'   41 GCF, Waterbeach SF, Odiham SF, Thorney
                             Island SF, FCCS, Middle Wallop SF, 61 OTU, 41
                             OTU, 62 OTU, 26, 63, 309, 63. 56 Sqn colours.   4-01
❑ 'MK178'   Spitfire XVI   TE311/7241M, ex EP&TU, 'X4474', France,
            'LZ-V'   Abingdon, Henlow, Wattisham, CAACU, 103 FRS,
                             102 FRS, 83 GSU. Stored.   9-01
❑ MK356   Spitfire IX ✈   ex St Athan, Abingdon, 5690M St Athan, Henlow,
            '2I-V'   Bicester, Hawkinge, Halton, 84 GSU, 443.
                             443 Sqn c/s.   4-01
❑ 'MK673'   Spitfire XVI   TB382/7244M ex EP&TU, 'X4277', Abingdon,
            'SK-E'   Henlow, Ely, Middleton St George, 602. 165 Sqn c/s.   9-01

☐ PA474 'QR-M'	Lancaster I ✈	ex 44, Wroughton, Cranfield College, RAE, FRL, 82. 61 Sqn c/s, *Mickie the Moocher*. H2S scanner.	4-01
☐ PM631 'S'	Spitfire PR.XIX ✈	ex THUM Flt, Buckeburg SF, 206 OCU, 203 AFS. 681 Sqn colours.	4-01
☐ PS915 'UM-G'	Spitfire PR.XIX ✈	ex Samlesbury, Preston, Brawdy, St Athan, Coningsby, Brawdy, Leuchars 7548M/7711M, West Malling, Biggin Hill, THUM Flt, 2, PRDU, 541. 152 Sqn c/s.	4-01
☐ PZ865 'Q'	Hurricane II ✈	ex Hawker Siddeley G-AMAU. 5 Sqn SEAC c/s.	4-01
☐ WG486 'G'	Chipmunk T.10 ✈	ex Newton, Gatow SF, ARWF, 3 AEF, Bri UAS, 3 AEF, Bri UAS, Liv UAS, PFS, 1 FTS, ITS, AOTS, ITS, RAFC, MECS, 114, 651, 657, 2 FTS, 63 GCF, 9 RFS, 5 BFTS.	4-01
☐ WK518 'K'	Chipmunk T.10 ✈	ex Newton, 1 AEF, Lon UAS, Hull UAS, Leeds UAS, Hull UAS, Coltishall SF, FWS, Cam UAS, Hull UAS, Cam UAS, Mcr UAS, Lpl UAS, 63 GCF, RAFC.	4-01
☐ ZA947 'YS-H'	Dakota III ✈	ex DRA, RAE, Farnborough, West Freugh, 'KG661', RCAF 661, 42-24338. 77 Sqn colours.	4-01

RAF Coningsby: The Phantom 'cull' continued on 20th July 2001 when F-4J(UK) ZE354 was scrapped. XV497 *may* be heading south-west for a change of duty...

☐ XT891 'Z'	Phantom FGR.2	9136M, ex 74, 228 OCU, 56, 228 OCU, 29, 228 OCU, 29, 228 OCU, 29, 228 OCU, 56, 228 OCU, 6, 54, 228 OCU, 54. Gate, 228 OCU c/s.	9-01
☐ XV497 'W'	Phantom FGR.2	ex 56, 92, 19, 92, 23, 56, 228 OCU, 17. Decoy.	8-01
☐ XW528 'AN'	Buccaneer S.2B	8861M, ex St Athan, 15. Poor state by 3-00.	3-00
☐ ZA254	Tornado F.2	9253M, ex Warton, BAe trials. Wingless.	8-01

CRANWELL AIRFIELD on the A17/B1429 north-west of Sleaford
RAF Cranwell: The Jetstream nose is located in the Simulator Building complex on the flight line ①. The Chinook is used by the RAFC Navigator and Airman Aircrew School ② and is located within Trenchard Hall. Gnat T.1 XR571 departed on 14th January 2001 back to Scampton, Lincs.

☐ BKC		DFS Weihe	BGA.1021, ex SE-SNE, Fv 8312. CoA 9-96. Stored.	2-00
☐ BTV		DFS Weihe	BGA.1230, ex RAFGGA. CoA 5-93. Stored.	2-00
☐ EHB		Schleicher Ka 3	BGA.2689, ex Dishforth, RAFGGA.559. CoA 4-89.	2-00
☐ 'P8448' 'UM-D'		Spitfire FSM	BAPC.225, ex Swanton Morley. 52 Sqn c/s.	7-01
☐ XW353 '3'		Jet Provost T.5A	9090M, ex 3 FTS, RAFC, CFS, 3 FTS, RAFC. 'Gate'	7-01
☐ XX477		Jetstream T.1	8462M, ex Finningley, Little Rissington, CFS, G-AXXS. Cr 1-11-74. Cockpit, procedure tnr. ①	7-01
☐ XZ138		Harrier GR.3	9040M, ex SIF, St Athan, 1, 233 OCU, 1453 Flt, 1, 3, 4, 3. Cockpit only, Trenchard Hall.	11-97
☐ ZA717 'C'		Chinook HC.1	9238M, ex St Athan, Fleetlands, 78, 7 1310F, 18. Crashed 25-7-89. Fuselage. ②	7-01

Aircraft Maintenance Instruction Flight (AMIF) and **Airframe Technology Flight** (ATF): For training, AMIF operates as the fictional '284 (Training) Squadron'. Phillips staged another sale on behalf of the Defence Disposal Sales Agency on 29th November 2000 in London with the Hunters at last going under the hammer - after a couple of false starts while their MDAP-funded past was ironed out. They are given in lot order as follows: type, serial, date last flown, flying hours, high bid, departure:

Hunter T.8B	XF995	11-4-94	5,515	£15,000	to Kemble, Glos, 16-2-01 as G-BZSF
Hunter T.8B	XF967	5-4-93	5,422	£24,000	to Exeter, Devon, 16-2-01 as G-BZRI
Hunter T.8C	WV322	5-5-91	5,209	£28,000	to Kemble, Glos, 14-2-01 as G-BZSE

Hunter T.7A XL568 was allocated for the RAF Museum and held in store until 28th February 2002 when it moved to Cosford, Shropshire.

☐ XX141 'T'	Jaguar T.2A	ex 16, 6, Cranwell, 6, 226 OCU, 6 JOCU.	7-01
☐ XX396* 'N'	Gazelle HT.3	8718M, ex EPTT, St Athan, Abingdon, Henlow, 2 FTS. Crashed 30-6-81. F/n 1-01.	7-01

❏ XX747	'08'	Jaguar GR.1	8903M, ex Halton, Shawbury, Gibraltar Det,		
			6, 20, 31, 226 OCU. Gulf pink c/s, *Sadman*.	ATF	7-01
❏ XX821	'P'	Jaguar GR.1	8896M, ex Coltishall, 41, 14, 17, 226 OCU, 17.		7-01
❏ XX962	'e'	Jaguar GR.1B	ex Coltishall, 6, 17, 20, 17.		7-01
❏ XX965	'C'	Jaguar GR.1A	ex Coltishall, 16, 226 OCU, 54, 14.		7-01
❏ XZ119	'FG'	Jaguar GR.1A	ex Coltishall, 41.		7-01
❏ XZ132	'C'	Harrier GR.3	9168M, ex St Athan, 4, 1, 1351F, 1,		
			233 OCU, 1, 3.	ATF	7-01
❏ XZ358	'L'	Jaguar GR.1A	ex Coltishall, 41. 41 Sqn colours.		7-01

RAF Exhibition Production and Transportation Team (EPTT): Operated under contract by Hunting Contract Services, the airframes are based on a former airfield about ten miles to the south-west. EPTT is 'parented' by the Cranwell-based Directorate of Recruitment and Selection and, for that reason, the 'fleet' is listed under this heading. Access to the 'detached' site is not possible and indeed many of the airframes spend their time in 'transit camps' elsewhere to minimise vehicle usage. As well as the airframes listed below, EPTT have two Eurofighter Typhoon cockpit mock-ups, both of which include interactive segments. These two and a Hercules exhibit – the latter owing more to Crane Fruehauf than to Lockheed – are not considered as deserving of a 'formal' listing. EPTT Gazelle HT.3 XX396 came to Cranwell 'proper', settling with AMIF - see above.
   Departures: Bulldog T.1 'XX530' (XX637) to Glasgow, Scotland, in 2000; Jaguar GR.1 FSM 'XX725' (BAPC.150) to Oman during late 2000.

❏ XM191		Lightning F.1	8590M, ex St Athan, Abingdon, 7854M, Wattisham,	
			111.Crashed 9-6-64. Nose. Shark's mouth c/s. Stored.	7-00
❏ 'XV238'	'41'	Comet 1	ex St Athan, Abingdon, G-ALYW, Farnborough,	
			Heathrow, BOAC. In Nimrod MRA.4 guise.	7-00
❏ 'XX226'	'74'	Hawk T.1 FSM	BAPC.152, ex St Athan, 'XX262', Abingdon,	
			'XX162'. 74 Sqn c/s.	7-00
❏ 'XX253'		Hawk T.1 FSM	BAPC.171, ex St Athan, 'XX297', Abingdon,	
			'XX262'. Red Arrows colours.	6-01
❏ XX753		Jaguar GR.1	9087M, ex St Athan, Abingdon, Shawbury,	
			226 OCU, 6.	Nose. 7-01
❏ XZ135		Harrier GR.3	8848M, ex St Athan, Abingdon, 4. Nose.	7-00
❏ 'XZ363'	'A'	Jaguar GR.1 FSM	BAPC.151, ex St Athan, Abingdon, 'XX824'. Cockpit.	7-00
❏ 'ZA556'		Tornado GR.1	BAPC.155, ex St Athan, 'ZA368' 'ZA446' Abingdon,	
		FSM	'ZA600', 'ZA322'. Grey colours, 13 Sqn c/s.	6-01
❏ 'ZH139'	'01'	Harrier GR.7 FSM	BAPC.191, ex St Athan, 'ZD472', Abingdon.	7-01

Cranwell Aviation Heritage Centre: Located close to the base, the centre charts the history of Cranwell and gives notes on the other airfields on the Lincolnshire Airfields Trail. With a souvenir shop, flight simulator and archive film show, it is an excellent stop-off when visiting Cranwell and/or the trail.
◆ Open May to Sep, 10.30am to 4.30pm, Wed, Thu and Sun. Signposted just off the A17 (to the south of RAF Cranwell) on the minor road to North and South Rauceby. ✉ Tourist Information Centre, Advise Services building, Moneys Yard, Carre Street, Sleaford, NG34 7TW ☎ 01529 414294 or '488490 **e-mail** info@n-kesteven.gov.uk

❏ XE946		Vampire T.11	ex Cardington, Henlow, 7473M,	
			Habbaniya SF, Nicosia SF. Pod.	3-02
❏ XP556	'B'	Jet Provost T.4	ex Bruntingthorpe, Halton 9027M, Shawbury,	
			CATCS, SoRF, 6 FTS, RAFC.	3-02

CROFT west of Skegness

❏		AZK T.8 Tutor	BGA.789, ex Skegness, VM650. Stored.	5-93
❏ NJ703		Auster 5	G-AKPI, ex Skegness, Humberside, 652, 660. Stored.	5-93

CROWLAND AERODROME on the A1073 north of the town, south of Spalding

❏ G-ARUR*		Cherokee 160	crashed 14-9-92. Fuselage.	4-00

DIGBY east of the B1188 north of Sleaford
RAF Digby: Is guarded by a Spitfire-on-a-stick. Within the historic station the operations room has been lovingly restored to its former wartime glory and is a joy to behold.
◆ Open every Sun May to Sep, at 11am, guided tours only. ☎ 01526 327503, fax 01526 327560 – weekdays between 8am and 5pm.

❑ 'MJ832'	Spitfire FSM	BAPC.229, ex 'L1096', Church Fenton.	
'DN-Y'		City of Oshawa, 416 Sqn colours.	6-99

EAST KIRKBY on the A155 west of Spilsby
Lincolnshire Aviation Heritage Centre (LAHC): The whole centre is run by Fred and Harold Panton as a memorial to their brother Christopher, who was killed on the Nuremberg raid – and as a memorial to Bomber Command as a whole. Other displays include the famous restored and equipped watch tower, the RAF Escaping Society, a blast shelter, 'Blitz' display and much more. A memorial chapel has recently been opened. Lancaster NX611 took on the codes 'CM-V' during February 2001 for film work for BBC TV drama entitled *Night Flight*. This involved some spectacular high-speed taxi runs! ① There is also a great 'NAAFI'!

Two other groups are based within the LAHC: **Lincolnshire Aircraft Recovery Group** (LARG): 'Prize' exhibit is the very substantial Spitfire BL655. LARG have a wide array of artefacts on show. The already impressive collection is ever-increasing, as more aircraft are recovered. There are permanent memorials to the crews of Lancasters ME473 and ND572 as well as the crew of Albemarle V1610, shot down over Lincolnshire. ✉ Dave Stubley, 33 Grosvenor Road, Frampton, Boston, PE20 1DB **e-mail** djstubley@aol.com **Lincolnshire Aviation Preservation Society** (LAPS): Main project is the painstaking restoration of AE436, the Brian Nicholls Hampden Project and Proctor IV NP294. ✉ LAPS, 154 Park Street, Grimsby, DN32 7NS ☎ 01472 362285 **e-mail** chatersgr@grimsby.ac.uk
◆ Open Easter to Oct Mon to Sat 9.30am to 5pm, last admission 4pm; Nov to Easter Mon to Sat 10am to 4.30pm, last admission 3pm. NB *not* open on Sundays. Acting in support of the taxiable Lancaster is the **East Kirkby Lancaster Association** - subscribing helps in the upkeep of the aircraft and brings benefits, including an annual newsletter. Details via the address below. ✉ East Kirkby, near Spilsby, Lincs, PE23 4DE ☎ 01790 763207 **fax** 01790 763677 **e-mail** enquiries@lincsaviation.co.uk **web** www.lincsaviation.co.uk

❑ AE436	Hampden I	ex Coningsby, Henlow, Sweden, 144. Crashed 4-9-42. Forward fuselage, etc.	LAPS ®	3-02
❑ BL655	Spitfire Vb	ex Dorrington Fen, 416, 129, 341, 164, 602, 416. Crashed 1-7-43. Substantial fuselage section.	LARG	3-02
❑ NP294	Proctor IV	ex Tattershall, Friskney, Poynton, Andover, Cosford, 4 RS, 2 RS.	LAPS ®	3-02
❑ NX611 'DX-C' *and* 'LE-C'	Lancaster VII	G-ASXX, ex Scampton, 8375M, Blackpool, Hullavington, Lavenham, Biggin Hill, Aéronavale WU-15, St Athan, Llandow. *Just Jane*, 57 Sqn c/s to stb and 630 Sqn to port. City of Sheffield.	①	3-02
❑ WH957	Canberra E.15	ex Bruntingthorpe, Cosford 8869M, 100, 98, Akrotiri Wing, 32, Hemswell SF, Upwood SF, 21, 542, 617. Nose. 'Hands-on' exhibit.		3-02
❑ –	BAPC.90 Colditz Cock REP	ex Duxford, Higher Blagdon, BBC.		3-02

Airfield: A Cessna 170 is under restoration.

❑ G-BCLS*	Cessna 170B	ex Tees-side, N8094A. CoA 27-1-83.	®	3-02

FENLAND AERODROME or Holbeach St Johns, west of the B1168, west of the village
Cessna F.172M G-BBJY was flying by mid-1999. See LOST! for the resurfacing of the 'missing' MS.317 G-BPLG.

❑ G-AREL*	Caribbean 150	ex N3344Z. CoA 22-8-98. Stored	4-00

GAINSBOROUGH north-west of Lincoln
The Tempests arrived at a workshop in this general area (and *not* at Hibaldstow, Lincs) by January 2000. *Mike-Tango* should move for flight test later in 2002. The Shturmoviks are the next major project here, out of the three hulks will come a static example and a flyer.

❏ G-BZHL	Harvard IIB	ex Egypt, FT118, USAAF. Arrived 4-01.		®	3-02
❏ G-WGHB*	T-33A/N	ex Sandtoft, Portsmouth, Southampton, Coventry, Duxford, Southend, CF-EHB, CAF 21640, 133640. CoA 13-6-77. Stored.		off-site	3-02
❏ 354* G-BZNK	MS.315E D2	ex France, F-BCNK, French AF. Arr mid-2001.		®	3-02
❏ MW763*	Tempest II 'HF-L'	G-TEMT, ex Sandtoft, Brooklands, Chichester, India, IAF HA586, RAF MW763.		®	3-02
❏ HA604*	Tempest II	G-PEST, ex Sandtoft, Brooklands, Chichester, India, IAF, RAF MW401. Stored.		off-site	3-02
❏ *	G-BZVW Il-2M3	ex Lancing, Russia. Stored.			3-02
❏ *	G-BZVX Il-2M3	ex Lancing, Russia. Stored.			3-02
❏ *	Il-2	ex Lancing, Russia. Stored.			3-02

GLENTHAM on A631 west of Market Rasen
Alan Ellis: Keeps his Vampire T.11 pod in the area.

❏ XD595	Vampire T.11	ex Altrincham, Woodford, Chester, St Athan, 1 FTS, Oakington SF, 7 FTS, 4 FTS. Pod.	11-99

GOOLE on the A614, south of Howden
No.2357 Squadron ATC: With their headquarters in Pasture Road, keep a 'JP', last heard of at Finningley. It is trailer-mounted and 'does the rounds'.

❏ XS216*	Jet Provost T.4	ex Finningley, 6 FTS, CAW. Dam 7-5-73. Nose.	6-01

GRAINTHORPE on the A1031 west of North Somercotes
The aircraft and artefact collection of the Grimsby-Cleethorpes Aircraft Preservation Group relocated to a *private* location in the area by September 2001. The nose of Lightning T.5 XS457 is thought to belong to the Lincolnshire Aircraft Preservation Group.
◆ Visits by prior arrangement *only*.

❏ XR757*	Lightning F.6	ex New Waltham, Rossington, Binbrook, 5-11 pool, 23, 5. Nose. Arrived 7-4-01.	10-01
❏ XR770* 'AA'	Lightning F.6	ex New Waltham, Laceby, Binbrook, 11, 5-11 pool, 56, 23, 74. Arrived 6-01.	10-01
❏ XS416*	Lightning T.5	ex New Waltham, Rossington, Binbrook, 5, LTF, 11, 74, 226 OCU, MoA. Arrived 7-4-01.	10-01
❏ XS457*	Lightning T.5	ex North Coates, New Waltham, Laceby, Binbrook, 5, 11, 5, LTF, 11, 226 OCU. Nose.	10-01
❏ A-011*	A.35XD Draken	ex New Waltham, Danish AF Esk.729. Arr 2-01.	10-01
❏ 22+57*	F-104G	ex New Waltham, Skegness, Laceby, Binbrook, Manching, JbG34, DD+239, KE+438. Arr 2-01.	10-01

HAXEY off the A161, north-west of Gainsborough
Andrew Exton: Should still have the Lightning nose.

❏ XR759	Lightning F.6	ex Rossington 'TVI759', Binbrook, 5-11 pool, 56, 74, 5. Nose. 56 Sqn colours.	10-95

HEMSWELL on the A631, east of Gainsborough
Bomber County Aviation Museum (BCAM): The Hunter is a composite, with the nose section of GA.11 WT741 and parts from XG297 ①. The Lightning F.1 is on loan from Charles Ross ② while the

F.3 is on loan from John Jennings ③. Sycamore HR.14 XG506 moved to Doncaster, S Yorks, by November 2000 for spares recovery.
◆ Off the A631 at Hemswell Cliff, follow signs for antiques centre. Open Sun and Bank Hols 11am to 6pm or by prior arrangement. ✉ Martin Chiappini, 10a Partridge Drive, Rothwell, LN7 6BH.web www.lineone.net/~bcam

❏ G-AEJZ		HM.14 'Flea'	BAPC.120, ex Cleethorpes, Brough. Stored.		3-02
❏ WJ975	'S'	Canberra T.19	ex Cleethorpes, Cambridge, 100, 7, 100, 85, West Raynham TFF, 228 OCU, 44, 35, 231 OCU.		3-02
❏ WW388	'O-F'	Provost T.1	ex Firbeck, Long Marston, Cardiff-Wales, Llanelli, Chinnor, Chertsey, Cuxwold, Chessington, Halton 7616M, 2 FTS.		3-02
❏ XD445	'51'	Vampire T.11	ex Cleethorpes, Hatfield, Woodford, Chester, St Athan, 4 FTS, 5 FTS, Buckeburg SF.		3-02
❏ 'XG193'		Hunter FGA.9	XG195, ex Macclesfield, Bitteswell, HSA G-9-453, 208, 1, 19. Black Arrows colours.	①	3-02
❏ XM192	'K'	Lightning F.1A	ex Binbrook, Wattisham 8413M, Wattisham TFF, Binbrook TFF, 226 OCU, 111. 111 Sqn c/s	②	3-02
❏ XP557	'72'	Jet Provost T.4	ex Firbeck, Bruntingthorpe, Halton 8494M, 6 FTS, RAFC.		3-02
❏ XP706		Lightning F.3	ex Strubby, Binbrook 8925M, LTF, 11, 5, LTF, 23, 111, 74.	③	3-02
❏ 101	'8-MN'	Mystère IVA	ex Cleethorpes, Sculthorpe, FAF.		3-02

HIBALDSTOW AERODROME on the B1206 south of Brigg
The Tempests and T-33 did *not* come here from Sandtoft, Lincs, see under Gainsborough, Lincs.

❏ G-AWXY*	MS.885 Rallye	ex Sandtoft, EI-AMG. CoA 1-2-97. Stored.	7-01
❏ G-BKAB	IS.28M2A	ex Sandtoft. Crashed 19-5-84. Wreck.	1-00
❏ G-BMOM	IS.28M2A	ex Rufforth. CoA 12-7-96.	1-00
❏ G-STAT	Cessna U206F	ex A6-MAM, N8732Q. Derelict.	3-00

HUMBERSIDE AIRPORT or Kirmington, on the A18 west of Grimsby
Global Aviation: Have a maintenance facility here. Their storage facility at Binbrook, Lincs, is believed closed. The 'serial' worn on the nose of Gnat XR541 derives from the Paint and Finishing course at St Athan, S Glam, that last dealt with it! ① Elster C G-LUFT moved to Rufforth, N Yorks, by November 2000.
By October 2000 at least 13 former Royal Saudi Air Force BAC Strikemaster Mk.80s and Mk.80As had arrived in dismantled form. These constituted 1102, 1104, 1105, 1107, 1108, 1112, 1114, 1115, 1120, 1121, 1125, 1129, 1130. The bulk of these seemed to flee the nest very quickly, with R J Everett of Ipswich, Suffolk, taking many of them, viz: 1102 (becoming G-BZWL and then to the USA as N399WH), 1105 (G-BZYF then to the USA) 1114 (G-BZYH and the USA), 1121 and 1125. Some of these may well settle in to *W&R* 'territory' in due course. Those that already have are: 1108 to Duxford, Cambs, 15-6-01; 1112 became G-FLYY in 9-01 and had moved to Chester Airport, Wales, the previous month; 1121 to North Weald, Essex, by 9-01.

❏ *	'PF179' Gnat T.1	XR541, ex Binbrook, Ipswich, Worksop, St Athan, 8602M, CFS, 4 FTS. Stored.	①	1-02

KIRTON-IN-LINDSEY on the B1398 north-east of Gainsborough
The *stored* Grasshopper is the frame of WZ757, the 'tail feathers' of WZ768 and the wings of XK820.

❏ WZ757	Grasshopper TX.1 ex Rufforth, Locking, Chichester.	4-01

LOUTH on the A16 south of Grimsby
The Stewart Ornithopter is believed to still be stored in the area.

❏ —	BAPC.161 Stewart Orni'	ex Cleethorpes, South Reston. *Coppelia*. Stored.	8-98

METHERINGHAM on the B1191 west of Woodhall Spa
Metheringham Airfield Visitor Centre: Established in what was the bomber base's rations store is an excellent display showing life at Metheringham and with 106 Squadron in particular.
◆ Open 9am to 5pm daily other than Xmas and New Year ✉ See under Cranwell, Lincs.

NEW WALTHAM on the A1098 west of Cleethorpes
NATO Aircraft Museum: By late 2000 the collection had to move from this site. After several different plans, by September 2001, all had moved to Grainthorpe, Lincs, about ten miles to the south. Making the move were the following: Lightning F.6 nose XR757 (moving 7th April 2001), Lightning F.6 XR770 (July 2001), Lightning T.5 XS416 (7th April 2001), Draken A-011 and F-104G 22+57 (both February 2001).

NORTH COATES AERODROME north of the A1031, south of Humberston
By September 2001, the nose of Lightning T.5 XS457 had arrived here. The stay was short and it settled upon Grainthorpe, Lincs. The nose of Canberra T.17 WJ565 arrived from Binbrook, Lincs, 30th December 1998. It moved to Coventry, W Mids, on 20th September 2001.

❏ G-MJSP*	Tiger Cub 440	ex Boston. CoA 31-1-86. Stored.	12-00
❏ BMU*	Slingsby T.21B	BGA.1085, ex East Kirkby, 9G-ABD,	
		BGA.1085.*Spruce Goose*. Powered version.	
		Crashed 22-9-97. Fuselage, spares.	2-02
❏ –	BAPC.61 Stewart	ex Louth, Tumby Woodside, East Kirkby, Tattershall,	
	Ornithopter	Wigan, Irlam, South Reston. *Bellbird II*.	2-02
❏ –	Rotec Rally 2B	ex Binbrook. Stored.	12-01

SANDTOFT AERODROME south of the M180, between Sandtoft and Westgate
Imperial Aviation (Sandtoft) Ltd: Several of the stored airframes have aspired to the UK civil register. Lincoln 2 G-29-1 is – to put it mildly – a fairly complex hybrid and this is a good time to retell its provenance. AWA-built at Baginton, RF342 was taken on charge at 10 MU, Hullavington, in June 1945. It was issued into the charge of CS(A) via Airwork at Langley in November 1948. During its days with the TFU at Defford, it became a 'Lincaster' or even a 'Lancoln' when the entire forward fuselage of AWA-built Lancaster I TW911 was grafted on. (TW911 served with Armstrong Siddeley from March 1946 as a test-bed, mostly on Python turboprop development. It was dismantled at Bitteswell in 1952 and officially struck off charge in January 1953.) RF342 went to Napiers at Luton for icing trails in January 1959 and became G-APRJ, later G-29-1 and in November 1952 it moved to Cranfield for further test work, where it became G-36-3. It was flown to Rochford for the Historic Aircraft Museum on 9th May 1967, as G-APRJ. With the wind-up of the museum it was sold at auction to Doug Arnold for £8,500 and it moved to Blackbushe on 11th November 1983. That year was the last that the aircraft was assembled, or wholly intact.

Beyond this, the Lincoln started a migration around Warbirds of Great Britain-associated sites, as charted in the history below. On 12th August 1987 the roof fell in on Lancaster X KB976 (G-BCOH) at Woodford where it was being rebuilt for Charles Church. To help get over this problem, the gutted fuselage of Lancaster X KB994 was acquired from Canada in 1988. Also acquired was the Lincoln – or elements thereof – then at North Weald. Charles Church was killed in the crash of Spitfire V G-MKVC on 1st July 1989 and the bulk of his restoration projects were disposed of.

In 1990 the badly damaged KB976, the hulk of KB994 and the Lincoln moved to Bedford for potential rebuild as a 'flyer'. By this time G-29-1 was certainly minus undercarriage and very probably *sans* engines. Doug Arnold died in November 1992 and a major diaspora of his collection commenced. G-BCOH was cancelled as sold in the USA in February 1993 and was freighted to Kermit Weeks later in the year. (This probably constituted the forward fuselage and wings. Elements of KB976 went to North Weald and certainly the very bashed extreme rear appeared at one time in a garden at Crowland, Lincs.) By April 1993 sections of KB994 had turned up at North Weald, although just how much has always remained an open question. (KB994 was registered as G-BVBP that August.) At the same time, G-29-1 also arrived again at 'Weald, although its nose section was never noted. In late September 1996 an intact Lancaster nose was reliably noted inside the former WoGB hangar at Bournemouth along with four large crates and T-34A Mentor N34AB.

In 1997 the noseless, engineless and undercarriage-less G-29-1 along with the cockpit section – minus framework and skinning – of KB994 and at least the rear fuselage (wing trailing edge to the join just forward of the crew door) of KB976 moved northwards to Sandtoft. (See under North Weald, Essex, for still more of KB994.) And the Lancaster nose of the Lincoln? It is a reasonable hypothesis to think this was exported, along with the majority of what was left of KB992. It is extremely unlikely a Lincoln nose will ever appear to complete this jig-saw puzzle. With G-29-1's hybrid past, it would be nice, and highly appropriate, to see it restored with a Lancaster nose, though this would seem to be a difficult, and expensive, task.

❑ G-29-1		Lincoln 2	RF342, ex North Coates, North Weald, Bournemouth, Bedford, North Weald, Bitteswell, Blackbushe, Southend, Cranfield, G-APRJ / G-36-3, Napier G-29-1, G-APRJ, RF342. Plus cockpit area of Lancaster X KB994 (G-BVBP) and section(s) of Lancaster X KB976 (G-BCOH) Dismantled. See epic above. 11-01
❑ WV499	'G'	Provost T.1	G-BZRF, ex North Weald, St Athan, Weeton 7698M, 6 FTS. 11-01
❑ WW421	'P-B'	Provost T.1	G-BZRE, ex Binbrook, Norwich, Lowestoft, East Kirkby, Tattershall, Lytham, St Athan 7688M, 3 FTS. 11-01
❑ WS776	'K'	Meteor NF.14	ex North Coates, North Luffenham, Lyneham, 7716M, 228 OCU, 85, 25. 11-01
❑ WZ584	'K'	Vampire T.11	G-BZRC, ex North Coates, St Albans, Hatfield, CATCS, 1 FTS, 2 CAACU, 32. 11-01
❑ XH313	'E'	Vampire T.11	G-BZRD, ex North Coates, St Albans, Hatfield, CATCS, Wattisham SF, 111. 11-01
❑ XL502		Gannet AEW.3	G-BMYP, ex Carlisle, Leuchars 8610M, 849, MinTech, Pershore, 849. CoA expired 29-9-89. 11-01
❑ '151632'		TB-25N-NC	G-BWGR, ex North Coates, North Weald, NL9494Z,Coventry, Blackbushe, 44-30925. *Gorgeous George-Ann*. Dismantled. 11-01

Others: Going back to *W&R17* (p140), the Hawker Tempests did *not* move on to Hibaldstow, Lincs, instead they settled on the Gainsborough, Lincs, area. The pod/centre-section of the Focke-Wulf Fw 189 project arrived at Sandown, Isle of Wight on 27th September 2001 with the eastern European nature of the rebuild apparently suspended. See under Sandown, for details of this incredible undertaking. Chipmunk 22 G-BCIW and T.10 WB732 are believed to have gone to Australia, perhaps via a Hereford-based owner. Commander 685 N9143C is thought to have been reduced to components. The anonymous Tiger Moth has moved on, destination/fate unknown.

❑ G-BHSA	Cessna F.152	ex N4889B. CoA 11-4-98. Dismantled. 11-01

SCAMPTON AIRFIELD on the A15 north of Lincoln
RAF Scampton: The 'Reds' moved in again during late December 2000. They were followed by their Gnat 'mascot' the following January.

❑ XR571*	Gnat T.1	8493M, ex Cranwell, Scampton, Cosford, Kemble, Brampton, Kemble, 4 FTS. Arrived 14-1-01. Outside 'Red Arrows' HQ. 1-01

Old Flying Machine Company: (See under Duxford, Cambs, for their main reference.) Have a store of jets for themselves and others here. Swift F.7 XF114 (G-SWIF) moved to Bicester, Oxfordshire, on 7th January 2002. Iskra 408 moved to Coventry, Warks, on 27th March 2001.

❑ 'WF714'*		Meteor F.8	WK914, ex Sandown, Duxford, Rochester, Manston, 85, CAW, 5 CAACU, 19. Arrived by 6-00. Fitted with FR.9 nose by 5-01. ® 1-02
❑ WV276*	'D'	Hunter F.4	ex Sandown, Duxford, Farnborough, Halton 7847M, Horsham St Faith, A&AEE, R-R. Arrived by 6-00. 1-02
❑ XF303		Hunter F.58A	G-BWOU, ex J-4105, Exeter, Swiss AF, G-9-315, XF303. 1-02
❑ XL587*	'Z'	Hunter T.7	G-HPUX, ex Duxford, Scampton, 8807M, 208, 237 OCU, 1 TWU, 229 OCU. Arrived 13-12-00. 1-02

❑ XX885*	Buccaneer S.2B	9225M, ex Lossiemouth, 12, 208, 12,	
		208, 216, 16. Arrived 30-6-00.	1-02
❑ J-4021	Hunter F.58	G-BWIU, ex Cambridge, Swiss AF.	1-02
❑ J-4031	Hunter F.58	G-BWFR, ex Exeter, Duxford, Swiss AF.	1-02
❑ J-4058	Hunter F.58	G-BWFS, ex 'XL741', Exeter, Duxford, Swiss AF.	1-02
❑ J-4066	Hunter F.58	G-BXNZ, ex Kemble, France, Swiss AF.	1-02
❑ J-4072	Hunter F.58	ex Speyer, Swiss AF. Dismantled.	1-02
❑ J-4081	Hunter F.58	G-BWKB, ex Bournemouth, Swiss AF.	1-02
❑ J-4090*	Hunter F.58	G-SIAL, ex Duxford, Exeter, Southend,	
		Swiss AF. Flew in 13-12-00.	1-02
❑ 98+14	Sukhoi Su-22M	ex WTD-61 Manching, Luftwaffe, East German AF. ®	1-02

SKEGNESS WATER LEISURE PARK or Ingoldmells, on the A52 north of Skegness
The Geronimo Apache conversion was noted in *W&R16* (p149) as having left its long-time haunt of Burgh-le-Marsh. It is assumed it came straight here. The Rallye fuselage is the original fitted with G-AZEE, which is thought still airworthy in North Lincolnshire ①.

❑ G-ARCW	Apache 160	ex N2187P. CoA 8-7-93.	®	7-01
❑ G-AZEE*	MS.880B Rallye	ex South Scarle, ?, Shipdham, F-BKKA. Stored.	①	7-01
❑ G-JENS*	MS.880B Rallye	ex G-BDEG, F-OCZU. Crashed 15-6-92. Stored.		7-01
❑ G-MJPV*	Quicksilver MX	CoA 1-2-95. Stored in rafters.	®	7-01
❑ PH-NLK*	Geronimo (PA-23)	ex Burgh-le-Marsh, Ipswich, OY-DCG,		
		SE-CKW. Fuselage. First noted 7-00.	®	7-01

SLEAFORD on the A15 south of Lincoln
David Needham: Acquired the late Dave 'Jim' Bean's Skyjeep and continues its restoration.

| ❑ G-AKVR | Chrislea Skyjeep | ex VH-OLD, VH-RCD, VH-BRP, G-AKVR. | ® | 11-01 |

SPALDING west of the A16, north of Peterborough
Skycraft: Established in the area is a thriving workshop, within which are some long-term inmates. A lot of light aircraft and gliders come through here for breaking, most being short-lived on site.

❑ G-ASML*	Luton Minor	ex Fenland. CoA 20-12-99. Stored.	11-01
❑ G-AWEN*	CEA DR.1050	ex Huddersfield, F-BIVD. Crashed 11-8-83. Stored.	11-01
❑ G-BASG*	AA-5 Traveler	ex Glenrothes, N5420L. CoA 20-1-00. Fuselage.	11-01
❑ G-BOBK*	Tomahawk 112	ex Biggin Hill, N2352G. Fuselage. Arr 5-11-01.	11-01

SPILSBY on the B1195 west of Skegness
Pat Miller: J/1N Alpha G-AHCK moved to Thwing, E Yorks, by July 2001. J/1N G-AJEI is a composite, including the fuselage frame of F-BFUT ①.

❑ G-AHAR	J/1 Autocrat	ex North Weald, F-BGRZ. Frame.		9-98
❑ G-AHSO	J/1N Alpha	CoA 6-4-95.	®	9-98
❑ G-AIGP	J/1 Autocrat	CoA 30-10-73. Lycoming O-320 conversion.	®	9-98
❑ G-AJDW	J/1 Autocrat	ex Luton area. CoA 17-1-77.	®	9-98
❑ G-AJEI	J/1N Alpha	ex Southampton, Bristol, Boston, Bodmin.	①	9-98
❑ G-AVOD	D5/180 Husky	crashed 31-7-92. Wreck.		9-98

STAMFORD
Robinson R-22B G-KENN migrated south from the former night-club here. By April 2001 it was to be found at Barkham, Berks. **Mike Doyle**'s Canberra T.4 nose WJ865 moved to Bromsgrove, H&W, in December 2000 and was replaced by a 'JP' nose.

| ❑ XS176* | 'N' Jet Provost T.4 | ex Luton, Solihull, Bruntingthorpe, Salford, Halton | |
| | | 8514M, CATCS, 3 FTS, 2 FTS. Nose. | 10-01 |

STURGATE AERODROME south-east of Gainsborough, near Heapham

❏ G-BISB	Cessna F.152 II	Crashed 6-11-95. Stored.	6-01
❏ G-BSOE	Silvaire 8A	ex N1604K, NC1604K. Fuselage, stored.	3-02

SUTTON BRIDGE on the A17 west of King's Lynn
Lindsey Walton: Two Pingouins are stored. Brother G-ASTG is at Duxford, Cambs.

❏ G-ASUA	Nord 1002	ex Elstree, F-BFDY. Crashed 30-7-64. Stored.	4-93
❏ 'NJ+C11'*	Nord 1002	G-ATBG, ex Duxford, F-BGVX, F-OTAN-5, FAF No.121. CoA 3-6-98. Luftwaffe colours. Stored.	6-97

TATTERSHALL THORPE on the B1192 south of Woodhall Spa
Lodge Road Flying Services: The insurance-bonded yard came to national significance in early February 2001 when the *Sunday Telegraph* published an air-to-ground shot of the contents. By that time the largest aeronautical content was the gruesome remains of the PanAm 747 blown-up over Lockerbie. Apparently, the material must be held in case there is any form of appeal. The shot did allow a glimpse at the otherwise seldom-recorded content, although it would appear that apart from the 747, the contents have not changed in several years. Only the former 32 Squadron Whirlwind HAR.10 could be confirmed from the newspaper image. Anonymous others were as follows: three Piper Tomahawk fuselages, two Cessna 172 cabins, two Cherokee fuselages, an American-registered Cherokee Arrow or similar and what very probably was a Navajo fuselage. Other than XP328, the others listed in *W&R17* – Enstrom F-28A G-BAWI, and Whirlwind HAR.10s XP329 and XP395 – are unaccounted for.

❏ XP328	Whirlwind HAR.10	G-BKHC, ex Northolt, 32, 21, 28, 110, 225, 110, 225. Crashed 22-8-88. Boomless.	2-01

WADDINGTON AIRFIELD on the A607 south of Lincoln
RAF Waddington: Gazelle AH.1 XX454 moved to Arborfield, Berks, by February 2001. Jet Provost T.4 XP638 left by road for St Athan, Wales, on 5th February 2002, moving again two days later for Ystrad Mynach, Wales.

❏ XM607	Vulcan B.2	8779M, ex 44, 101, 35. Display airframe.	11-01
❏ ZE356	'Q' F-4J(UK)	9060M, ex 74, USN 153850. ABDR.	11-01

WAINFLEET south-west of Skegness
Aerial Application Collection (AAC): The remains of Pawnee 235 G-AVDZ were scrapped on April 24, 2000. Extensive corrosion following fire damage suffered in an accident rendered this potential mobile cockpit exhibit beyond economical restoration.

◆ Dispersed store, visits are only possible by prior arrangement. ✉ Eastside, Eaudyke Road, Friskney, Boston, PE22 8NL **e-mail** bill@pawnee.demon.co.uk

❏ G-BFBP	Pawnee 235D	ex Rush Green. Crashed 11-5-78. Cockpit.	3-02
❏ G-BFEY	Pawnee 235D	ex Old Buckenham. CoA 19-1-87. Fuselage frame.	3-02

Elms Golf Centre: The Lightning T.5 acts as 'gate guardian' for the golf range here.

❏ XS456	'DX' Lightning T.5	ex Binbrook, LTF, 11, 56.	10-01

Others: Pawnee 235 G-BDPJ was sold and moved out in April 1999, it was flying again (from Bicester, Oxford) in July 2000.

❏ G-AWLX	J/2 Arrow	ex Gloucester, F-BGJQ, OO-ABZ. CoA 23-4-70.	® 4-98
❏ G-BENL	Pawnee 235D	ex Old Buckenham, Sutton Bank, N54893. Crashed 10-7-85. Stored.	2-96
❏ RAFGGA.502	L-Spatz 55	ex Brüggen. Identity subject to confirmation.	11-93

WOODHALL SPA on the B1192 south-east of Woodhall Spa
Thorpe Camp Visitor Centre: The former No.1 Communal Site (or 'Thorpe Camp') of RAF Woodhall Spa is now a superb visitor centre. Themes include life in Lincolnshire during the Second World War, the history of Woodhall Spa, including the histories of its resident units, including 617 and

627 Squadrons. A large array of models, artefacts, engines, photos are displayed, including elements of the Fordyce collection, previously at the Torbay Aircraft Museum. During March 2002 the centre took delivery of a Lancaster fuselage mock-up made for the TV drama *Night Flight*.

◆ On the B1192 south of the former Woodhall Spa. Open Sun and Bank Hols 2pm to 5pm, Easter to Sep plus Wed in Jul and Aug 2pm to 5pm. Other times by appointment. ✉ Lancaster Farm, Tumby Woodside, Mareham-le-Fen, Boston, Lincs, PE22 7SP ☎ 01526 342249 **fax** 01526 345249 **e-mail** mjhodgson@lancfile.demon.co.uk **web** www.thorpecamp.org.uk

❏   Argus REP   ex Southampton. Unfinished, stored.   3-02

GREATER LONDON

☛ Greater London constitutes the following boroughs: Barking and Dagenham, Barnet, Bexley, Brent, Bromley, Camden, City of Westminster, Croydon, Ealing, Enfield, Greenwich, Hackney, Hammersmith and Fulham, Haringey, Harrow, Havering, Hillingdon, Hounslow, Islington, Kensington and Chelsea, Kingston upon Thames, Lambeth, Lewisham, Merton, Newham, Redbridge, Richmond upon Thames, Southwark, Sutton, Tower Hamlets, Waltham Forest, Wandsworth. ...which leads us, of course, to Mornington Crescent.

BENTLEY PRIORY between the A409 and A4140 north of Harrow
RAF Bentley Priory, HQ 11/18 Groups: The display airframes should be unchanged.

❏	'K9926'	'JH-C' Spitfire FSM	BAPC.217, 317 Sqn colours.	2-02
❏	'BN230'	'FT-A' Hurricane FSM	BAPC.218, ex 'P3386', 43 Sqn colours.	2-02
❏	XM173	'A' Lightning F.1A	8414M, ex Binbrook, Binbrook TFF, Leuchars TFF, 226 OCU, 56.	2-02

BIGGIN HILL AIRPORT on the A233 north of Biggin Hill
Airport: DH.60G Moth G-ABYA took to the air again on 16th February 2002. It had been the 'victim' of the grim programme *Salvage Squad* who seemed to have been wholly responsible for its rebirth! Clearing up a reference here in *W&R17* (p144) Dove G-DDCD became G-OEWA and was ferried to Gloucestershire, Glos. Beagle 206-1 N181WW (formerly G-BCJF was up and flying again by mid-2001. Note that several of the entries listed here are very long-in-the-tooth date-wise, but avid readers will know that Biggin Hill *W&R* candidates can be very tenacious! Up and flying again are the following: Cherokee 140 G-ASSW by mid-2000; G-ATAS by mid-2000; Cherokee 140D G-AYRM by early 2000.

❏	G-AAOK	Travel Air	ex Yugoslavia, N370N, NC370N, NC352M. Damaged 21-10-83.	®	4-01
❏	G-AOGE	Proctor III	ex BV651, Halton SF, 2 GCS, FAA. CoA 21-5-84.		12-94
❏	G-AOKH	Prentice 1	ex VS251, 3 FTS, CFS, 2 FTS. CoA 2-8-73. Spares.		4-01
❏	G-APZR	Cessna 150	ex N6461T. Crashed 14-1-81. Engine test-bed.		5-01
❏	G-ARWC	Cessna 150B	ex Exeter, N1115Y. Crashed 28-4-84. Wreck.		2-95
❏	G-ASDA	Queen Air A80	CoA 8-11-79. Fuselage. Fire dump.		2-95
❏	G-ATTF*	Cherokee 140	ex N11C. Stored.		4-01
❏	G-AWCO	Cessna F.150H	CoA 29-8-75. Fuselage, poor state.		2-95
❏	G-AWGA	Airedale	ex Sevenoaks, Biggin, Bicester, EI-ATA, G-AWGA, D-ENRU. CoA 3-7-86. Spares for G-ATCC.		4-01
❏	G-BBNO	Aztec 250E	ex N964PA. CoA 18-1-92. Stored.		4-01
❏	G-BFAM	Navajo P	G-SASK, ex SE-GLV, OH-PNF. CoA 30-8-91.		12-01
❏	G-BFKG	Cessna F.152 II	ex Luton. Damaged 11-11-89. Wreck.		8-97
❏	G-BFZN	Cessna FA.152	crashed 4-10-80.	®	2-95
❏	G-BGFX	Cessna F.152 II	ex Nayland. CoA 23-6-91.	®	2-02
❏	G-BHCX	Cessna F.152 II	damaged 16-10-87. Stored.		4-01

❏ G-BHYS	Cherokee 181	ex N8218Y. Crashed 7-12-85. Wreck.	4-01
❏ G-BIFB	Cherokee 150C	ex Elstree, 4X-AEC. CoA 17-12-90. Fuselage.	4-01
❏ G-BIIF*	Fournier RF-4D	ex G-BVET, F-BOXG. CoA 18-3-93. Stored.	4-01
❏ G-BLDA	Rallye 110ST	ex F-GDGH. Damaged 16-10-87. Dumped.	6-92
❏ G-BMOP*	Turbo Arrow III	ex N38257. CoA 20-4-98. Stored.	4-01
❏ G-BMTI	Robin R3000	damaged 16-10-87. Dumped.	6-92
❏ G-BNJM	Warrior II	ex Carlisle, N8015V. Damaged 18-5-89.	8-99
❏ G-BNJV	Cessna 152 II	ex N5333B. Crashed 8-3-92. Fuselage.	4-01
❏ G-BTES*	Cessna 150H	ex N22575. CoA 20-8-00. Stored.	4-01
❏ G-BXPS	Aztec 250C	ex G-AYLY, N6258Y. CoA 16-10-97.	4-01
❏ G-KAFC	Cessna 152 II	ex Lutterworth. Damaged 16-10-87. Stored.	2-95
❏ G-OXTC	Aztec 250D	ex G-AZOD, N697RC, N6976Y. CoA 15-6-98. Stored.	4-01
❏ G-SARK	Strikemaster 84	ex N2146S, Sing ADC 311, G-5-12.	8-97
❏ G-UTSI*	Rand KR-2	Stored. First noted 11-98.	4-01
❏ G-YUGO*	HS.125-1B/522	ex Dunsfold, G-ATWH, HZ-BO1, G-ATWH. CoA 19-4-91. Dump. Arrived by 4-00.	4-01
❏	Civilian Coupe	Unfinished airframe, No.7. Stored.	10-95
❏ EI-BIB	Cessna 152 II	ex Galway. CoA 23-10-90. Stored.	2-95
❏ 'VT-EKG'*	Westland WG.30	VT-EKK. Stored.	4-01
❏ N6466*	Tiger Moth	G-BNKZ, ex F-BHIO, G-ANKZ, N6466, 2, GS, 1 GU, 14 RFS, Ox UAS, 8 RFS, 22 EFTS, Ox UAS, 3 EFTS, 16 EFTS, 10 EFTS, 17 ERFTS. CoA 15-4-99. Stored.	4-01

RAF Memorial Chapel: Continues to be guarded by full-size kits.

❏ 'L1710' 'AL-D' Hurricane FSM	BAPC.219, gate guardian.	3-00
❏ 'N3194' 'GR-Z' Spitfire FSM	BAPC.220, gate guardian. 2 Sqn colours.	3-00

CATFORD south of Greenwich, on the South Circular, A205

Catford Independent Air Force: As yet not rating a 'formal' listing, Alan has amassed a considerable number of parts from Spitfire Vb AR614 plus others. AR614 was the former G-BUWA, now in the USA. The 'Flea' carries a plaque saying 'Made at Capel' ①. The Harrier is thought to be an unused GR.1 cockpit section and may have come from Richmond Air Cadets originally ②. It has the fuselage number 41H/729048 which puts it between GR.1s XV810 and XW630.

✉ Alan Partington, 100 Culverley Road, Catford, London, SE6 2JY

❏	HM.14 'Flea'	unfinished.	①	3-02
❏	Spitfire V FSM	built by Feggans Brown for *Piece of Cake*. Cockpit.		3-02
❏	Harrier	nose section.	® ②	3-02
❏ XH783	Javelin FAW.7	ex Wycombe, Sibson, Aylesbury, Halton 7798M, 64, 25, GWTS, A&AEE. Nose.		3-02

CHESSINGTON on the A243 south of Surbiton

Light Aircraft Services: Geoff Masterton passed away at his desk on February 16, 2001. He had just been signed-up for the newly-established de Havilland Support Ltd as part-time chief inspector. He had also recently received an award from the Historic Aircraft Association for his tireless work in rethinking engineering and certification problems. Geoff had time for everyone's problems and often had fast and practical solutions to them. There can be no finer tribute to him than to call him by the nick-name that countless friends and colleagues knew him as – 'Mastermind'. LAS has been wound up although the strip continues to function. Some, or all, of the airframes listed below may well disperse.

Departures: Auster 5 G-ANHR had gone by late 2001, it is under restoration in Lincolnshire and was expected to fly by mid-2002. Pitts S-1D G-BKKZ was flying by July 2000. The frame of the Pitts long since stored here is *thought* to be the original fitted to G-AZPH – see under South Kensington, Gtr Lon ①.

❏ G-ASFD	L-200A Morava	ex OK-PHH (?), Bournemouth. CoA 12-7-84.	off site 10-92
❏ G-AWJX	Zlin Z.526	CoA 29-5-85. Stored.	5-01

❑ G-BIVW	Zlin Z.326	ex France, F-BPNQ. Burnt remains. Stored.	5-01
❑ G-BWDF*	Wilga 35A	CoA 30-11-98. Stored.	5-01
❑ G-ROVE*	Super Cub 135	ex PH-VLO, PH-DKF ntu, RNethAF R-156, 54-2446. CoA 21-7-98.	℗ 5-01
❑	Pitts S-1	fuselage frame. Stored.	① 1-95

CROYDON on the A23 in south London
Croydon Airport Visitor Centre: The superb visitor centre opened officially in October 2000. Much of the hard work behind the centre, and the guides to show visitors around, come from the **Croydon Airport Society** (CAS). In July 2001 the centre won the Innovation in Tourism Award for its efforts.
   Notes: The Tiger Moth 'flies' within the historic terminal building. The identity of this aircraft is open to debate, G-ANKV was not converted (at Croydon?) and was cancelled from the register in September 1956 ①. Heron 2D G-ANUO is painted as 'G-AOXL' of Morton Air Services. It was G-AOXL that made the last passenger flight from Croydon, on 30th September 1959 ②.
◆ At Airport House, Purley Way, Croydon. Open on the first Sunday of each month, 11am to 4pm. Group visits at other times by prior arrangement. ✉ CAS enquiries: Margaret White, 38 Long Walk, Tattenham Corner, Epsom, KT18 5TW. General enquiries: ☎ 020 8253 1009 **web** www.croydon. gov.uk/airport-soc/

❑ 'G-AOXL'	Heron 2D	G-ANUO, ex Biggin Hill, Exeter. CoA 12-9-86. Morton Air Services c/s. Pole-mounted.	① 3-02
❑ T7793	Tiger Moth	G-ANKV, ex Redhill. Displayed inside.	② 3-02

No.2157 Squadron Air Cadets: The Cessna 'does the rounds' of local events on behalf of 'Flightaid' – see also Dunkeswell, Devon.

❑ G-ATFX	Cessna F.172G	ex Eaglescott, Caterham. CoA 12-2-92.	1-00
❑ XN979	Buccaneer S.2	ex Popham, Stanbridge, Henlow, Cranfield, 801. Ditched 9-6-66. Nose.	12-97

DULWICH on the A205 South Circular, south of Peckham
Dulwich College:

❑ WB627	Chipmunk T.10	9248M, ex Cambridge, 5 AEF, 1 AEF, Lon UAS, Cam UAS, 2 SoTT, 22 GCF, Debden SF, Jurby SF, 8 RFS, 18 RFS.	10-96

GREENFORD on the A40 west of the city
Vanguard Haulage: The Hunter is occasionally displayed atop a tower in Vanguard's premises. XP745 is under restoration and will go on display in the grounds of the adjacent public house, 'The Lightning' (formerly the 'Nuffield Arms') which is also owned by Vanguard's principal.

❑ 'K9962'	Spitfire FSM	'JH-C', 317 Squadron colours. First noted 4-96.	4-96
❑ WT555	Hunter F.1	ex Cosford, Locking 7499M, A&AEE, Dunsfold.	6-95
❑ XP745	'H' Lightning F.3	ex Boulmer 8453M, Leconfield, 29, 56. Cockpit.	2-94

HANWELL on the A4020 east of Uxbridge

❑ G-AEXD	Aeronca 100	CoA 20-4-70. Including parts from G-AESP. Stored.	12-90

HENDON north-west London, near the end of the M1
Royal Air Force Museum (RAFM): In late November 2000 it was announced that the museum had been awarded a grant of £4.7 million by the Heritage Lottery Fund. This will allow the construction of a new building to house the 'Milestones of Flight' exhibition which will show the history of aviation and is due to open in December 2003 to mark the 100th anniversary of the Wright brothers' first foray into the air. The Grahame White hangar will be dismantled and moved onto the expanded RAF Museum site from the area that was previously RAF Hendon and is now scheduled for major redevelopment.

Additionally, the interactive 'Fun n Flight' gallery will be improved and expanded. Work started on 'Milestones of Flight' in February 2002 and with it came the first of a series of 'shuffles' of exhibits.

Notes: The Robinson was gifted from Cabair and used for travelling demos and within the 'Fun and Flight' area ①. The AA-5B was briefly at Cardington for turning into a 'hands-on' (bum-in, surely?) exhibit and is also in the 'Fun and Flight' area ②. Avro 504K 'E449' is a composite of G-EBJE and Type 548A G-EBKN, both of which used to ply their joy riding trade from Shoreham ③. The Battle restoration includes elements of P2183 ④. From February to November 2001, the Clark TWK was away at Wyton, Cambs, for recovering work ⑤. RAF Museum aircraft can also be found at the following locations: Brooklands, Surrey: Valiant nose; Cosford, Shrop: RAF Museum 'North' and the Conservation Centre; Coventry, Warks: Meteor and T-33A; Manchester, Gtr Man; Stafford, Staffs, 'deep' store; Tangmere, W Sussex: Hunter, Meteor, Swift. Wyton, Cambs, was the temporary home to the Conservation Centre.

Departures: to Cosford, Shrop: Cygnet G-EBMB 25-6-01; airship gondola *Nulli Secundus* during 2001; Camel F.1 F6314 30-10-01 (via Benson and Wyton briefly); Hind BAPC.82 14-6-01; MiG-15*bis* 01120 1-8-01; to Wyton, Cambs: Blériot XXVII 433 4-6-01; Vampire F.3 VT812 7-1-00; Proctor III Z7197 to Stafford, Staffs, 7-3-02; the anonymous Beaufighter II forward fuselage to East Fortune, Scotland, 11-12-00.

◆ On Grahame Park Way, signposted from the end of the M1 and A41. Open 10am to 6pm all week, except Christmas and New Year. More details of activities on receipt of an SAE, or via the 'hotline'. There is a very active **Friends of the RAF Museum** organisation with a variety of activities which also publishes a journal – *The Flying M* – details of membership from the address below. ✉ RAF Museum, Hendon, London, NW9 5LL ☎ 020 82052266 **event hotline** ☎ 020 8358 4964 **fax** 020 8200 1751 **web** www.rafmuseum.com

❑ 'G-RAFM'	Robinson R-22	G-OTHL, ex Redhill. CoA 2-3-00. 'Hands-on'.	①	3-02
❑ [G-ROWL]	AA-5B Tiger	ex Elstree, N28410 ntu. CoA 9-5-01. Cockpit.	②	3-02
❑ '168'	Tabloid REP	G-BFDE, ex Cardington, Hendon, Cardington. CoA 4-6-83.		3-02
❑ '687'	BE.2b REP	BAPC.181, ex Cardington.		3-02
❑ '2345'	FB.5 Gunbus REP	G-ATVP, ex Cardington, Hendon, Weybridge. CoA 6-5-69.		3-02
❑ '3066'	Caudron G.III	9203M, ex Henlow, Upavon, Heathrow, G-AETA, OO-ELA, O-BELA.		3-02
❑ 'A8226'	1½ Strutter REP	G-BIDW, ex Cardington, Land's End, '9382'. CoA 29-12-80.		3-02
❑ 'C4994'	Bristol M.1C REP	G-BLWM, ex Cardington, 'C4912', Hucknall. CoA 12-8-87.		3-02
❑ 'E449'	Avro 504K	9205M, ex Henlow.	③	3-02
❑ 'E2466' 'I'	Bristol F.2b	BAPC.165, ex Cardington, Weston-on-the-Green. Semi-skeletal.		3-02
❑ F938	RAF SE.5A	9208M, ex Henlow, Heathrow, Colerne, 'B4563', Brooklands, G-EBIC, F938 84 Sqn. CoA 3-9-30.		3-02
❑ F1010	Airco DH.9A	ex Cardington, Krakow, Berlin, 110.		3-02
❑ 'F8614'	Vimy REP	G-AWAU, ex 'H651', VAFA. CoA 4-8-69. *Triple First.*		3-02
❑ 'J9941'	Hawker Hart	G-ABMR, ex HSA, 'J9933'. CoA 11-6-57.		3-02
❑ 'K2227'	Bulldog IIA	ex Hatch, Cardington, Old Warden, Henlow, Filton, G-ABBB, Science Museum, R-11. Crashed 13-9-64. 56 Squadron colours.		3-02
❑ K4232	Rota I (C.30A)	ex Spain, Cardington, SE-AZB, K4232, SAC.		3-02
❑ K6035	Wallace II	ex Hatch, Henlow, Newark, Cranwell, 2361M, EWS, 502. Fuselage.		3-02
❑ K8042	Gladiator II	8372M, ex 61 OTU, 5 (P)AFU, A&AEE.		3-02
❑ K9942* 'SD-D'	Spitfire I	8383M, ex Rochester, Hendon, 71 MU Bicester, Fulbeck, Wroughton, Newark, Cardiff, 53 OTU, 57 OTU, 72. 72 Sqn colours. Arrived 7-12-00.		3-02
❑ L5343 'VO-S'	Fairey Battle I	ex St Athan, Cardington, Leeming, Iceland, 98, 266. Crashed 13-9-40. 98 Sqn colours.	④	3-02

❑	'L8756'		Bolingbroke IVT	ex Boscombe Down, RCAF 10001. 139 Sqn c/s as	
		'XD-E'		Blenheim IV.	3-02
❑	N1671	'EW-D'	BP Defiant I	8370M, ex Finningley, 285, 307. 307 Sqn c/s.	3-02
❑	'N5182'		Sopwith Pup	9213M, ex Blackbushe, Old Warden, G-APUP.	
			REP	CoA 28-6-78.	3-02
❑	N5628		Gladiator II	ex 263. Lost in Norway 4-40. Forward fuselage.	3-02
❑	N5912		Sopwith Triplane	8385M, ex Henlow, 49 MU, 5 MU, Cardington,	
				SAF Redcar, SAF Marske.	3-02
❑	N9899		Southampton I	ex Cardington, Henlow and Felixstowe. Fuselage.	3-02
❑	P2617	'AF-F'	Hurricane I	8373M, ex 71 MU, 9 FTS, 9 SFTS, 1, 607, 615.	
				607 Sqn colours.	3-02
❑	P3175		Hurricane I	ex 257. Shot down 31-8-40. Wreck.	3-02
❑	R5868	'PO-S'	Lancaster I	7325M, ex Scampton, 467, 83. 467 Sqn colours.	3-02
❑	R9125	'LX-L'	Lysander III	8377M, ex 161, 225. 225 Sqn colours.	3-02
❑	T6296		Tiger Moth II	8387M, ex Yeovilton SF, BRNC, RNEC, Stretton,	
				7 EFTS, 1 EFTS.	3-02
❑	W1048	'TL-S'	Halifax II	8465M, ex Henlow, Lake Hoklingen, Norway, 35,	
				102. Force-landed 27-4-42. 35 Sqn colours.	3-02
❑	'W2068'	'68'	Anson I	ex Duxford, Australia, VH-ASM, W2068, 4 SFTS,	
				3 SFTS. Fuselage only on 'Queen Mary' trailer.	3-02
❑	X4590		Spitfire I	8384M, ex Cosford, Finningley, 53 OTU, 303,	
		'PR-F'		57 OTU, 66, 609. 609 Sqn colours.	3-02
❑	'BE421'	'XP-G'	Hurricane FSM	BAPC.205, gate guard. 174 Sqn colours.	3-02
❑	BL614		Spitfire Vb	ex Rochester, Manchester, St Athan, 'AB871', Colerne,	
		'ZD-F'		Credenhill 4354M, 118, 64, 222, 242, 611. 222 Sqn c/s.	3-02
❑	'DD931'	'L'	Beaufort VIII	9131M, ex Cardington, Chino, New Guinea.	
				Composite. 42 Sqn colours.	3-02
❑	FE905		Harvard IIB	ex Cardington, Winthorpe, Cardington, Royston,	
				London Bridge, Southend, LN-BNM, Danish AF	
				31-329, RCAF, 41 SFTS, FE905, 42-12392.	3-02
❑	KK995	'E'	Hoverfly I	ex Cranfield, 43 OTU, R-4B 43-46558.	3-02
❑	MF628		Wellington T.10	9210M, ex Abingdon, St Athan, Biggin Hill, Hendon,	
				Heathrow, Wisley, Vickers, *Dambusters*, 1 ANS.	3-02
❑	'MH486'	'FF-A'	Spitfire FSM	BAPC.206, gate guard. 132 Sqn colours.	3-02
❑	ML824	'NS-Z'	Sunderland V	ex Pembroke Dock, Aéronavale, 330, 201. 201 Sqn c/s.	3-02
❑	MN235		Typhoon Ib	ex Shawbury, Smithsonian, USAAF FE-491.	3-02
❑	MP425		Oxford I	ex Cardington, Winthorpe, Cardington, G-AITB,	
				Shawbury, Perth, MP425, 7 FTS, 18 (P)AFU, 1536	
				(BAT) Flt. CoA 24-5-61. 1536 Flt colours.	3-02
❑	PK724		Spitfire F.24	7288M, ex Finningley, Gaydon, Norton, Lyneham.	3-02
❑	'PR536'		Tempest II	ex Duxford, Cardington, Chichester, Indian AF	
		'OQ-H'		HA457, RAF. 5 Sqn colours.	3-02
❑	RD253		Beaufighter TF.X	7931M, ex St Athan, Portuguese AF BF-13.	3-02
❑	TJ138	'VO-L'	Mosquito TT.35	7607M, ex St Athan, Swinderby, Finningley, Colerne,	
				Bicester, Shawbury, 5 CAACU, 98. 98 Sqn colours.	3-02
❑	WE139		Canberra PR.3	8369M, ex Henlow, 231 OCU, 39, 69, 540.	3-02
❑	WH301		Meteor F.8	7930M, ex Henlow, Kemble, 85, CAW, 609, DFLS.	3-02
❑	WP962*	'C'	Chipmunk T.10	ex Newton, 3 AEF, Bri UAS, AAC, Lon UAS, 61	
				GCF, 662. Arrived 5-5-00, on three-year loan.	3-02
❑	WZ791		Grasshopper TX.1	8944M, ex Syerston, Halton, High Wycombe, Hove.	3-02
❑	XB812	'U'	Sabre F.4	9227M, ex Duxford, Rome, Italian AF MM19666,	
				XB812, 93, 112, RCAF (no service) 19666.	3-02
❑	XD818		Valiant BK.1	7894M, ex Marham, 49 'A' Flt.	3-02
❑	XG154		Hunter FGA.9	8863M, ex St Athan, 1 TWU, 229 OCU, 54, 43, 54.	3-02
❑	XG474	'O'	Belvedere HC.1	8367M, ex 66, 26, 66. 66 Sqn colours.	3-02
❑	XL318		Vulcan B.2	8733M, ex Scampton, 617, 230 OCU, Wadd Wing,	
				617, 230 OCU, Scamp Wing, 617.	3-02

❑ XM463 '38' Jet Provost T.3A ex 1 FTS, RAFC. Fuselage. 'Hands-on' exhibit. 3-02
❑ XM717 Victor K.2 ex Cardington, Marham, 55, 57, 55, 543, Witt W,
100. *Lucky Lou*. Nose. 3-02
❑ XN962 Buccaneer S.1 8183M, ex Cosford, St Athan, 'XN972', Abingdon. Nose. 3-02
❑ XS925 'BA' Lightning F.6 8961M, ex Binbrook, 11, 5-11 pool. 3-02
❑ XV424 'I' Phantom FGR.2 9152M, ex St Athan, Wattisham, 56, 228 OCU, 29,
92, 228 OCU, 29, 228 OCU, 111, 29. 3-02
❑ XV732* Wessex HCC.4 ex Shawbury, Queen's Flight. Due 4-02. due
❑ XW323 '86' Jet Provost T.5A 9166M, ex 1 FTS, RAFC. 3-02
❑ XX946 'WT' Tornado P.02 8883M, ex Honington, Laarbruch, Honington, Warton. 3-02
❑ XZ997 'V' Harrier GR.3 9122M, ex 233 OCU, 1453F, 4, 1, 4. 4 Sqn c/s. 3-02
❑ ZJ116* EH-101 PP8 ex Yeovil, G-IOIO. Due 4/5-02. due
❑ A2-4 Seagull V ex Cardington, Wyton, VH-ALB, RAAF A2-4. 3-02
❑ A16-199 Hudson IIIA G-BEOX, ex Strathallan, VH-AGJ, VH-SMM,
'SF-R' A16-199, FH174, 41-36975. 3-02
❑ HD-75 Hanriot HD.1 ex Cardington, N75, G-AFDX, OO-APJ, Belgian AF. 3-02
❑ 920 'QN' Stranraer ex CF-BXO Queen Charlotte AL, RCAF 920. 3-02
❑ 8417/18 Fokker D.VII 9207M, ex Cardington, Hendon, Cardington, Hendon,
Cardington, Heathrow, Brooklands, R G Nash,
Versailles, OO- ?, Belgian AF (?), Jasta 71. 3-02
❑ 4101 '12' Bf 109E-3 8477M, ex St Athan, Henlow, Biggin, Fulbeck,
Wroughton, Stanmore, DG200, 1426 (EA) Flt, A&AEE,
DH, Hucknall, RAE. Force-landed 27-11-40. 3-02
❑ 10639* '6' Bf 109G-2 G-USTV, ex Duxford, Benson, Northolt, Lyneham
8478M, Henlow, Wattisham, Stanmore Park, Sealand,
CFE-EAF, 1426 Flt, RN228, Lydda, 3 Sqn Gambut,
III-JG77. Crashed 12-10-97. Arrived 10-3-02. 3-02
❑ 120227 He 162A-2 8472M, ex St Athan, Colerne, Leconfield, VH513,
AM.65, Farnborough, Leck, JG1. JG1 c/s. 3-02
❑ 360043 Ju 88R-1 8475M, ex St Athan, Henlow, St Athan, Biggin Hill,
'D5+EV' Fulbeck, Wroughton, Stanmore, PJ876, 47 MU, CFE,
1426 (EA) Flt, RAE. Defected 9-5-43. 3-02
❑ 494083 Ju 87D-3 8474M, ex St Athan, Henlow, St Athan, Fulbeck,
'RI+JK' Wroughton, Stanmore, Eggebek. 3-02
❑ 584219 '38' Fw 190F-8-U1 8470M, ex St Athan, Gaydon, Henlow, Fulbeck,
Wroughton, Stanmore, Wroughton, Brize Norton,
AM.29, Farnborough, Karup. 3-02
❑ 701152 He 111H-23 8471M, ex St Athan, Henlow, Biggin Hill, Fulbeck,
'NT+SL' Stanmore Park, RAE, 56th FG USAAF. 3-02
❑ 730301 Bf 110G-4-R6 8479M, ex St Athan, Biggin Hill, Stanmore Park,
'D5+RL' 76 MU, RAE, AM.34, Karup, I/NJG3. 3-02
❑ MM5701 Fiat CR-42 8468M, ex St Athan, Biggin Hill, Fulbeck, Wroughton,
'13-95' Stanmore Park, AFDU, RAE, BT474, 95 SCT.
Force-landed Orfordness 11-11-40. 3-02
❑ E3B-521 CASA Jungmann ex Spain, Spanish AF. 11-01
❑ '34037' TB-25N-20-NC 8838M, ex Blackbushe, N9115Z, *Hanover Street*,
Catch 22, USAAF 44-29366. 3-02
❑ '413573' P-51D-25-NA 9133M, ex Halton, N6526D, RCAF 9289, 44-73415.
'B6-K' Composite. 363rd FS c/s, *Little Friend*. 3-02
❑ 44-83868 'N' B-17G-95-DL ex Stansted, N5237V, Andrews AFB, TBM Inc,
Aero Union, USN PB-1W 77233. 94th BG c/s. 3-02
❑ — BAPC.92 Fi 103 (V-1) ex Cardington. 3-99
❑ — BAPC.100 Clarke TWK ex Wyton, Cardington, Hayes, South Kensington.
Science Museum loan. ⑤ 3-02

Locally: A private collector in the area has taken delivery of a Canberra cockpit.
❑ WD954* Canberra B.2 ex Rayleigh, East Kirkby, Tattershall, Bicester,
76, Upwood, Hemswell. Cockpit. 5-01

KENLEY on the A22 south of Croydon
No.450 Squadron Air Cadets:
❑ XK822   Grasshopper TX.1 ex Wimbledon, West Malling, Wimbledon. Stored.   10-00

KEW on the A307 north of Richmond
August 1994 was the last time that C-47A nose 42-93510 (6W-SAE) was noted. It has moved to LOST!

LONDON
'Planet Hollywood': In Coventry Street, Leicester Square. 'Flying' from the ceiling is *Little Nellie*, the famous autogyro from *You Only Live Twice*. This is *not* the original, but has been assembled by Ken Wallis (see under Reymerston Hall, Norfolk) so is doubtless based on one of his 'spares'.
❑ 'G-ARZB'   Wallis WA-116   ex Reymerston Hall. *Little Nellie*.   12-98

Queen Mary College: Mile End Road. An Islander fuselage is in use with the Engineering Dept.
❑ –*   BN-2 Islander   primered fuselage.   2-02

'The Roadhouse': Nothing new on either the R-22 or the venue.
❑ 'C-RASH'   Robinson R-22   arrived 1-96.   1-96

Trocadero: In Piccadilly Circus. In a sacrifice beyond words, the Editor ventured in to check on the Harrier. In the leisure-play complex upstairs within this midden through endless horrific galleries full of sad so-and-sos playing electronic games – many of these people do not know what daylight is – can be found the tiger-striped and shark-mouthed Harrier. A chronic waste of a now-rare airframe.
❑ ZD670   Harrier GR.3   ex Bruntingthorpe, Wittering, 233 OCU.   12-01

LONDON AIRPORT or Heathrow, on the A4 west of Hounslow
Trident Preservation Society (TPS): The Trident still earns its keep teaching towing and de-icing training with BA's Service Delivery Training unit, but is maintained as a living museum. So much so that it emerged from the BA paint bay on 23rd August 2001 in the BEA livery that it entered service in during October 1971.
◆ Visits on prior arrangement *only* basis – send SAE. ✉ Kevin Bowen, TPS, Flat 4, Royal Free Court, Bachelor's Acre, Windsor, SL4 1ER e-mail g-awzk@msn.com, web www.hs121.org.uk
❑ G-AWZK   Trident 3B-101   ex BA, BEA. 14-10-86. BEA colours.   11-01

British Airways Archives and Museum Collection: Established in buildings in Viscount Way, Hatton Cross. The archive has been consolidated and expanded.
◆ Visits are possible on a prior arrangement *only* – open Wed and Fri 9.30am to 2.30pm. ✉ Archives and Museum Collection, Building 387 (E.121), British Airways plc, PO Box 10, Heathrow Airport, Hounslow, TW6 2JA. ☎ / fax 020 8562 3124

NORTHOLT AIRFIELD on the A4180 north-west of Northolt
RAF Northolt:
❑ 'MH777' 'RF-N' Spitfire FSM   BAPC.221, gate guardian. 303 Sqn colours.   11-01

SIDCUP south-east London, on the A211
Russell Carpenter: Lightning F.2 XN769 cockpit went to the Malta Aviation Museum in late 2000.

SOUTH KENSINGTON on the A4 west of Westminster
Science Museum (ScM): The Avro 504, Lockheed 10A, 'Flying Bedstead' and SC.1 are part of the museum's 'Making the Modern World' (MMW) gallery on the ground floor. The Cessna is in the 'hands-on' 'Flight Laboratory' on the third floor, close to the main 'Flight' gallery ①. The original fuselage frame from Pitts G-AZPH is *thought* to be the one stored at Chessington, Gtr Lon ①.

ScM's 'large object' store is at Wroughton, Wilts. The gondola of the Piccard Gas balloon OO-BFH, last noted here in March 2000, is now at Wroughton, Wilts.
◆ Daily 10am to 6pm. In Exhibition Road, off the Cromwell Road. Nearest tube, South Kensington. ✉ South Kensington, London SW7 2DD ☎ 020 7942 4455 or '4454 fax 020 7942 4421 web www. sciencemuseum.org.uk

❑ G-EBIB	RAE SE.5A	ex 'F939', Hendon, G-EBIB, F937, 85 Sqn. CoA 6-6-35.		3-02
❑ G-AAAH	DH.60G Moth	CoA 23-12-30. *Jason*. Amy Johnson's machine.		3-02
❑ G-ASSM	HS.125-1-522	ex Wroughton, Chester, Southampton, 5N-AMK, G-ASSM.		3-02
❑ G-AWAW	Cessna F.150F	ex OY-DKJ. CoA 8-6-92.	①	3-02
❑ G-AZPH	Pitts S-1S	ex Meppershall, Chessington, N11CB. *Neil Williams*. Damaged 10-5-91.	②	3-02
❑ DFY	S-Hirth Cirrus	BGA.2097, ex Army GA.		3-02
❑ NC5171N	Lockheed 10A	G-LIOA, ex Wroughton, Orlando, N5171N, NC243 Boston-Maine AW, NC14959 Eastern.	MMW	3-02
❑ 304	Cody Type V	BAPC.62, with the museum since 1913.		3-02
❑ D7560	Avro 504K	ex Middle Wallop, South Kensington, Hull, Waddon, 3 TDS.	MMW	3-02
❑ J8067	Pterodactyl I	ex Yeovil, Farnborough.		3-02
❑ L1592 'KW-Z'	Hurricane I	ex 9 PAFU, 5 PAFU, 9 AOS, SDF, 615, 43, 152, 17, 43, 87, 17, 56. 615 Sqn colours		3-02
❑ P9444 'RN-D'	Spitfire IA	ex Sydenham, 53 OTU, 61 OTU, 58 OTU, 72. 72 c/s.		3-02
❑ S1595 '1'	Supermarine S.6B	ex RAFHSF. Schneider winner 1931.		3-02
❑ W4041/G	Gloster E.28/39	ex Farnborough.		3-02
❑ AP507 'KX-P'	Cierva C.30A	ex Halton, Sydenham, 76 MU, 5 MU, 529, 1448 Flt, Duxford Calibration Flt, RAE, G-ACWP. 529 Sqn c/s.		3-02
❑ XG900	Short SC.1	ex Wroughton, Yeovilton, Wroughton, Hayes, South Kensington, RAE Bedford.	MMW	3-02
❑ XJ314	R-R Thrust Rig	ex Wroughton, Yeovilton, East Fortune, Strathallan, Hayes, South Kensington, RAE.	MMW	3-02
❑ XN344	Skeeter AOP.12	ex Middle Wallop 8018M, 654, 652.		3-02
❑ XP831	Hawker P.1127	ex Hendon 8406M, RAE Bedford, Dunsfold.		3-02
❑ —	Short Bros Gas	balloon basket, 1910.		3-02
❑ —	Airship No.17	*Beta II*. Gondola, 1910.		3-02
❑ — '448'	Dakota IV	ex Ottawa, RCAF, KN448, 436, 10, 44-76586. Nose.		3-02
❑ 210/16	Fokker E.III	BAPC.56, captured 8-4-16. Stripped airframe.		3-02
❑ 191316	Me 163B-1a	ex Halton, 6 MU, Farnborough, Husum, II/JG.400.		3-02
❑ 442795	Fi 103 (V-1)	BAPC.199. Sectioned.		3-02
❑ — BAPC.50	Roe Triplane	Roe's second, first flown 13-7-09.		3-02
❑ — BAPC.51	Vickers Vimy IV	Alcock and Brown's machine, 1919.		3-02
❑ — BAPC.53	Wright Flyer REP	Hatfield-built.		3-02
❑ — BAPC.54	JAP-Harding	Blériot-based.		3-02
❑ — BAPC.55	Antoinette	ex Robert Blackburn, Colwyn Bay. 1909 model.		3-02
❑ — BAPC.124	Lilienthal REP	built for the Museum.		3-02

SOUTH LAMBETH on the A3203 east of Lambeth Palace
Imperial War Museum (IWM): The gallery in which the large exhibits (tanks to a bus, Polaris to Camel) are displayed is most impressive.
◆ Open 10am to 6pm daily. Closed 24-26th December.✉ Lambeth Road, London SE1 6HZ. ☎ 020 74165320 fax 020 74165374 web www.iwm.org.uk

❑ 2699	RAF BE.2c	ex Duxford, South Lambeth, 192, 51, 50.	11-01
❑ N6812	Camel 2F1	ex 'F4043', Yeovilton, Lambeth, 212, Martlesham, Felixstowe. Culley's aircraft.	11-01

❑	R6915	Spitfire I	ex Cardiff, RNDU, 57 OTU, 61 OTU, 609.	11-01
❑	DV372	Lancaster I	ex 1651 CU, 467. SOC 4-1-45. *Old Fred.* Nose.	11-01
❑	PN323	Halifax A.VII	ex Duxford, South Lambeth, Duxford, Staverton, Radlett, HP. SOC 28-5-48. Walk-through nose.	11-01
❑	120235	He 162A-1	ex Duxford, South Lambeth, Cranwell, Brize Norton, Farnborough AM.68, JG.1, Leck.	11-01
❑	733682	Fw 190A-8	9211M, ex Duxford, South Lambeth, Biggin Hill, Cranwell, Brize Norton, Farnborough AM.75.	11-01
❑	'472218' 'WZ-I'	P-51D-25-NA	ex Duxford, RCAF 9246, USAAF 44-73979. 'WZ-I', *Big, Beautiful Doll*, 78th FG colours.	11-01
❑	–	A6M5 *Zeke*	ex Duxford, South Lambeth, ATIAU-SEA. Cockpit.	11-01
❑	–	BAPC.198 Fi 103 (V-1)	–	11-01

SUTTON on the A232 west of Croydon
No.219 Squadron, Air Training Corps: Noted languishing in the undergrowth at their HQ during October 2000 was the fuselage of long forgotten Duchess G-BOJT. (One time at Halfpenny Green, crashed 13th February 1992). However by mid-December 2000 it had gone. Two questions: how long had it been there and what of its fate?

UXBRIDGE on the A4020 south of the town
RAF Uxbridge: Still displays its Spitfire-on-a-stick.
| ❑ | 'BR600' 'SH-V' | Spitfire FSM | BAPC.222, gate guardian. 64 Sqn colours. | 11-01 |

WALLINGTON GREEN at the junction of the A232 and A237 west of Croydon
| ❑ | G-ASMO | Apache 160G | ex Bournemouth, 5N-AAU, 5N-ADB, N4473P. CoA 2-9-81. Stored. | 7-96 |

WOOLWICH near the A205 South Circular, south-east London
FirePower: Under this title the Royal Regiment of Artillery's international collection of 800 artillery pieces – from bronze guns to missile systems – is now displayed. The science and technology of gunnery is demonstrated using interactives. Within the 'Field of Fire' theme can be found experiences of 20th century warfare with the Auster AOP.9 dramatically suspended above.
◆ Open daily except 25th Dec, 10am to 5pm. Close to Woolwich ferry and Woolwich Arsenal station.
✉ Royal Arsenal, Woolwich, SE18 6ST ☎ 020 8855 7755 **fax** 020 8855 7100 **e-mail** info@firepower.org.uk **web** www.firepower.org.uk
| ❑ | XR271 | Auster AOP.9 | ex Larkhill, St Athan, Middle Wallop. | 3-02 |

GREATER MANCHESTER

☛ Within the administrative regional county boundaries can be found the unitary authorities of Bolton, Bury, Manchester, Oldham, Rochdale, Salford, Stockport, Tameside, Trafford and Wigan.

BARTON AERODROME on the A57 south of the M62/M63 junction at Eccles
Barton Visitor Centre: Run by the Barton Aviation Heritage Society .
◆ Open Sun 10am to 4pm. ✉ Barton Aviation Heritage Society, Barton Aerodrome, Eccles, M30 7SA
| ❑ | WH850 | Canberra T.4 | ex Chelford, Samlesbury, St Athan, Laarbruch SF, Wildenrath SF, 14, 88, Marham SF. Nose. | 1-01 |

❑ XD534   '41' Vampire T.11   ex Chelford, Hadfield, Wythenshawe, Cheadle
Hulme, Woodford, Chester, Shawbury, 7 FTS,
CFS, 9 FTS, 10 FTS. Wings from XD535.   3-00

❑ 333   Vampire T.55   ex Chelford, Hadfield, Dukinfield, New Brighton,
Chester, Iraqi AF. Pod.   7-98

Allan Witt: Vampire T.11 pod XE921 went to Stoke-on-Trent, Staffs, by July 2001. See also under Bruntingthorpe, Leics. Both of the complete Vampires are reported up for sale, with XE849 said to be going to a Northamptonshire-based collector. The SF-25A is kept in a trailer.

❑ G-BECF*   Scheibe SF-25A   ex OO-WIZ, D-KARA ntu. CoA 1-3-94.   12-01

❑ XE849   'V3' Vampire T.11   ex Shobdon, Mildenhall, Long Marston, Yatesbury,
Monkton Farleigh, Conington, Ware, St Athan,
7928M, CNCS, 5 FTS, 7 FTS, 1 FTS, 4 FTS.   12-01

❑ XK627   Vampire T.11   ex Bacup, Hazel Grove, Woodford, Chester,
St Athan, 8 FTS, CFS.   12-01

Aerodrome:

❑ G-AFIU   Luton Minor   ex Wigan, Stoke, Hooton Park, Wigan, Peel Green,
Pembroke. Stored in rafters.   6-01

❑ G-APUY   Turbulent   CoA 10-6-86.   ® 6-01

❑ G-ASXR   Cessna 210   ex 5Y-KPW, VP-KPW, N6532X. CoA 3-1-93.   9-01

❑ G-BEVO*   Fournier RF-5   ex 5N-AIX, D-KAAZ. CoA 20-8-96. Stored.   11-01

❑ G-BFWL*   Cessna F.150L   ex Caernarfon, PH-KDC. CoA 27-3-00.   1-02

❑ G-MMEP*   Tiger Cub 440   Canx 4-2-92. Stored. First noted 1-01.   6-01

❑ G-TERY*   Archer II   ex G-BOXZ, N22402. CoA 26-6-98. Stored.   1-02

❑ N33528   SNCAN SV-4C   G-BRXP, ex F-BGGU, Fr mil 678, F-BDNX ntu.   ® 1-01

CHADDERTON on the A663 north-east of Manchester
BAE Systems: (British Aerospace as was.) An ATP cockpit section is used by the apprentices.

❑ –   ATP   cockpit. *Possibly* c/n 2074 or 2076.   3-00

LEVENSHULME on the A6 south-east of Manchester
No.1940 Squadron Air Cadets: Located in St Oswald's Road.

❑ WG418   Chipmunk T.10   8209M, ex Woodvale, Hamble, Jever SF, Lon UAS,
61 GCF, QUB UAS, Lon UAS, 3 BFTS, 16 RFS.   2-02

❑ XM474*   Jet Provost T.3   8121M, ex Firbeck, Heaton Chapel, Warrington,
Shrewsbury, Shawbury, MinTech, 6 FTS, MoA,
6 FTS, CFS. Nose. Arrived by 7-00.   2-02

MANCHESTER
Imperial War Museum North: Due to open in July 2002, IWM North took delivery of the former Fleet Air Arm Museum AV-8A and installed it within what is best described as a 'memorable' building. This museum will be very different from the norms to be experienced at South Lambeth or Duxford.

◆ Opens July 2002, enquiries for now via IWM South Lambeth or Duxford – *qv*.

❑ 159233*   '03' AV-8A-MC   ex Yeovilton, VMA-231, USMC. Arrived 21-11-01.   11-01

Museum of Science and Industry in Manchester, Air and Space Gallery: Several airframes are on loan from The Aeroplane Collection, marked TAC. TAC have centred their activities on Hooton Park, Cheshire – *qv*. Kieran Medd is building an HM.14 at the museum ①. The Easy-Riser is in store awaiting collection by the Griffin Trust, see under Hotton Park, Cheshire ②. TAC's J/1N Alpha G-AJEB moved to Hooton Park, Cheshire, by July 2000.

◆ Open daily from 10am to 5pm, including Bank Holidays but excluding December 23-25. There is an active **Friends of the Museum**, membership enquiries to the address below.✉ Liverpool Road, Castlefield, Manchester M3 4JP ☎ 0161 832 2244 or **24-hour info** line 0161 6060 121 **fax** 0161 6060 186 **e-mail** n.forder@msim.org.uk **web** www.msim.org.uk

❑ G-EBZM	Avian IIIA	ex Higher Blagdon, Peel Green, Lymm, Liverpool, Huyton, Manchester, Hesketh Park. CoA 20-1-38.	TAC	3-02
❑ G-ABAA	Avro 504K	9244M, ex 'H2311', Henlow, Nash. CoA 11-4-39.		3-02
❑ G-ADAH	Dragon Rapide	ex East Fortune, Peel Green, Booker. CoA 9-6-47. *Pioneer.*	TAC	3-02
❑ G-APUD	Bensen B.7M	ex Firbeck, Nostell Priory, Wigan, Biggin Hill. CoA 27-9-60.	TAC	3-02
❑ G-AWZP	Trident 3B-101	ex Heathrow, BA, BEA. CoA 14-3-86. Nose.		3-02
❑ G-AYTA	MS.880B Rallye	ex Moston, Wickenby. CoA 7-11-88. 'Hands on'.		3-02
❑ G-MJXE*	Mainair Tri-Flyer	ex Droylesdon, Blackpool. Last flew 1995.	TAC	3-02
❑ MT847 'AX-H'	Spitfire XIV	ex Cosford, Weeton, Middleton St George, Freckleton, Warton, 6960M, 226 OCU, A&AEE.		3-02
❑ WG763	EE P.1A	ex Henlow, 7816M, RAE, A&AEE, EE.		3-02
❑ WP270	Eton.TX.1	ex Henlow, Hendon, 8598M, 27 MU, 61 GCF. Dism.		3-02
❑ WR960	Shack'ton AEW.2	ex Cosford, 8772M, 8, 205, A&AEE, 210, 42, 228.		3-02
❑ WT619	Hunter F.1	ex Henlow, St Athan, 7525M, 233 OCU, 222, 43.		3-02
❑ WZ736	Avro 707A	ex Waddington, Cosford, Finningley, 7868M, RAE Bedford, A&AEE, Avro.		3-02
❑ XG454	Belvedere HC.1	ex Henlow, 8366M, Abingdon, A&AEE, Bristol, Old Sarum, Belvedere Trials Unit.		3-02
❑ XL824	Sycamore HR.14	ex Henlow, 8021M, Wr'ton, CFS, 1564 Flt, 103, 284.		3-02
❑ 997	Ohka 11	BAPC.98. Ex 8485M, Henlow, Cottesmore, Cranwell.		3-02
❑ BQT	EoN 460 Srs 1	BGA.1156, ex Seighford, Staffs GC, EGC / BGA.2666, BGA.6, BGA.1156. Last flown 13-1-97.		3-02
❑	BAPC.6 Roe Triplane REP '14'	ex London, Southend, Irlam, Peel Green, Old Warden, Woodford. *Bullseye Avroplane.*	TAC	3-02
❑	BAPC.12 HM.14 'Flea'	ex East Fortune, Chester-le-Street, Newcastle, Wigan, Stockport, Rishworth.	TAC	3-02
❑ —	BAPC.175 Volmer VJ-23	ex Old Warden. David Cook, cross-channel flight.		3-02
❑ —	BAPC.182 Wood Ornithopter	ex Hale. Stored.	off-site	3-02
❑ —	BAPC.251 Hiway Spectrum	ex Lytham. Built c 1980. Stored.		3-02
❑ —	BAPC.252 Flexiform h-g	ex Lancaster. Built Macclesfield c 1982. Stored.		3-02
❑ —	HM.14 'Flea'.	under construction.	①	3-02
❑ —	Skyhook Safari	stored. From Len Gabriel, London-Paris flight.		3-02
❑ —	Easy-Riser	stored.	②	3-02

Granada Studios Experience: Within the 'US Street' is a Rotorway Exec, visible from Water Street!

❑	Rotorway Exec	—	10-97

MANCHESTER AIRPORT or Ringway, junction 5, M56
Amid the seeminlgly constantly-chaning landscape here, by mid-2001 HS.748-1A/101 G-ARMX and
Aztec 250C G-ATJR had given up the ghost on the dump.

❑ 'G-SMOKE'	Trident 1C	G-ARPK, ex BA, BEA. CoA 17-5-82. Fire. Green c/s.	7-01
❑	c/n 2072 ATP	ex Chadderton. Fuselage. Fire.	7-01

MOSTON on the B6393 north of Manchester

❑ G-AXYX	Ekin Airbuggy	damaged 30-7-83.	7-94

RADCLIFFE on the A665 south-west of Bury
No.1005 Squadron Air Cadets: The 'JP' nose is 'parented' by RAF Sealand.

❑ XN466	Jet Provost T.3A	ex 1 FTS, 7 FTS, 1 FTS. Nose.	4-97

ROYTON on the A671 north of Oldham
No.1855 Squadron Air Cadets: 'Parent' is Sealand, the HQ is located in Park Lane.

❏ WS726   'G' Meteor NF.14   7960M, ex Kemble, 1 ANS, 2 ANS, 25.   5-99

SALFORD south-west of Manchester
University of Salford:
❏   VJ-23 hang-glider donated by Peter Barlow.   7-99
❏ [XS179] '20' Jet Provost T.4   ex Halton '8237M' (8337M), Kemble, Shawbury,
CAW, RAFC.   2-01

STOCKPORT on the A6 south-east of Manchester
No news on the Sea Venom pod.
❏ XG692   Sea Venom   ex Baxterley, Hatton, Alcester, Wellesbourne Mountford,
FAW.22   Sydenham, Castlereagh, Sydenham, 750. Pod.   6-99

WIGAN north-west of Manchester
Ponsford Collection: See Breighton, E Yorks, and Selby, N Yorks, for the bulk of Nigel's 'fleet'.
As predicted in *W&R17*, Cadet TX.1 RA854 moved to Elvington, Yorks, on 6th April 2000.
❏ G-ARIF   OH-7 Coupe   —   3-02
❏ CHQ   T.31B   BGA.1559, ex Bury St Edmunds, Leeds, XN247.   3-02
❏ RA848   Cadet TX.1   ex Harrogate, Wigan, Handforth. Cockpit.   3-02
❏ —   BAPC.15 Addyman STG   ex Warmingham, Wigan, Harrogate.   3-02

WOODFORD AIRFIELD on the A5102 east of Wilmslow
Avro Heritage Centre / The '603 Club: After almost 20 years of restoration Avro XIX G-AHKX
flew again on 8th March 2001. Avro XIX G-AGPG moved to Hooton Park, Cheshire, for restoration by
June 2000. By late 2001 the nose of Hunter FGA.9 XE584 had also moved to Hooton Park.
◆ Visits to the Heritage Centre by prior permission *only*. ✉ Avro Heritage Society, BAE Systems,
Woodford, Stockport, SK7 1QR.
❏ G-AHKX   Avro XIX Srs 2   ex Strathallan, Kemps, Treffield, Meridian,
Smiths. First flown 8-3-01.   3-01
❏ WB491   Ashton 2   ex Cardiff-Wales, Dunsfold, Farnborough, RAE.
Nose. BOAC colours. Stored.   ® 1-01
❏ XM602   Vulcan B.2   ex St Athan 8771M, 101, Wadd Wing, 35,
230 OCU, Wadd W, Cott W, 12. Nose.   2-00
❏ XM603   Vulcan B.2   ex 44, 101, Wadd Wing, Scampton Wing, 9.   9-01

Avro International Aerospace / BAE Systems: The number of ATPs (aka 'Jetstream 61') in store
has swollen, but they face a future as freighters. The anonymous HS.748 fuselage used for ATP trials
has not been noted since July 1996 and has been deleted.
❏ G-BTZH*   ATP   ex Merpati PK-MTW, G-BTZH. Stored. Arr 3-4-01.   2-02
❏ G-BTZK*   ATP   ex Merpati PK-MTZ, G-BTZK. Stored. Arr 25-4-00.   2-02
❏ G-BUWM   ATP   ex CS-TGB, G-BUWM, CS-TGB, G-11-9.
CoA 12-6-93. Stored.   2-02
❏ G-GCJL*   Jetstream 4100   ex Prestwick. CoA 29-4-95. Stored.   9-01
❏ G-JMAC*   Jetstream 4100   ex Prestwick, G-JAMD, G-JXLI.
CoA 6-10-97. Stored.   1-01
❏ G-MANU*   ATP   ex Manx, N378AE ntu, G-11-8, CS-TGA,
G-BUUP. Stored. Arrived 31-1-01.   2-02
❏ G-PLXI   ATP   ex G-MATP, G-OATP ntu. CoA 2-12-92. Stored.   2-02
❏ PK-MTV*   ATP   ex Merpati, G-BTZG, PK-MTV, G-BTZG.
Stored. First noted 1-01.   12-01
❏   c/n 2071 ATP   ex Chadderton. Fuselage.   1-01

MERSEYSIDE

☛Within the administrative regional county boundaries can be found the unitary authorities of Knowsley, Liverpool, St Helens, Sefton and Wirral.

ALTCAR south of Formby, west of the A565
The gunnery ranges *should* still have their Wessex.
| ❑ XT486 | Wessex HU.5 | ex Brize Norton 8919M, Wroughton, 845. | 10-99 |

BIRKDALE on the A565 south-west of Southport
No.281 Squadron Air Cadets: In Upper Aughton Road, keep a 'Chippax'. 'Parent' is Sealand.
❑ WG477	Chipmunk T.10	8362M, ex Hamble G-ATDP, G-ATDI ntu, Marham	
	PAX	SF, MECS, 114, Bri UAS, Abn UAS, 11 RFS,	
		2 BFTS, 25 RFS, Liv UAS, 25 RFS.	10-01

BIRKENHEAD DOCKS
Historic Warship Preservation Trust: HMS *Plymouth* plays host to a Wasp. Also on public view is the submarine HMS *Onyx* and, at weekends and school holidays, the Mersey Bar Lightship.
◆ Open daily Apr to Sep 10am to 5pm, Oct to Mr 10am to 4pm. Well signed.✉ Corn Warehouse Quay, East Float, Dock Road, Birkenhead L41 1DJ ☎ 0151 650 1573 **fax** 0151 650 1473 **e-mail** manager@warships.freeserve. co.uk **web** www.warships.freeserve.co.uk
| ❑ XS570 | '445' Wasp HAS.1 | ex Glasgow, Plymouth, Lee-on-Solent, A2699. | 3-02 |

HAYDOCK on the A580 north of Newton-le-Willows
A collector here acquired a 'JP' nose during 2001.
| ❑ XN492* | Jet Provost T.3 | 8079M, ex Levenshulme, Firbeck, Stock, Odiham, | |
| | | Cosford, Halton, 6 FTS, RAFC. Cockpit. | 10-01 |

HESWALL on the A540, south Wirral
Barry Jones: By November 2001 Canberra B.2 WJ676 nose had moved to <u>Hooton Park</u>, Cheshire.

LIVERPOOL
Auster J/5Fs G-AMUI and G-BGKZ were up for sale and thought to have moved to the Bedford area.

LIVERPOOL AIRPORT or Speke, south of the A561
(The airport was renamed in July 2001 in honour of the planet's greatest musician – John Winston Lennon.) The Yankee fuselage is used as a travelling recruiting aid for Liverpool Flying Club. Last noted in June 1998, the hulk of Tomahawk 112 G-BTJJ is thought to have moved on.
| ❑ G-SEXY | AA-1 Yankee | ex G-AYLM. Damaged 11-2-94. Dismantled. | 1-01 |

Liverpool Marriott Hotel South: The 'north site' airfield closed for flying on 29th August 2000.On 29th June 2001 the tastefully-refurbished former airport terminal was opened. Due to be unveiled at that time was a full-size model Dragon Rapide. The FSM was built by Mike Davey and friends in a workshp at Hooton Park, Cheshire. This was eventually put into place on 4th September 2001.
| ❑ 'G-AEAJ' | Rapide FSM | Railway Air Service colours, *Neptune*. | |
| | | 'Unveiled' 4-9-01. | 3-02 |

NEWTON-LE-WILLOWS on the A572 north of Warrington
Colin Waterworth:
| ❑ WB440 | Firefly AS.6 | ex Manchester, Heaton Chapel, Newton, Salford, | |
| | | Failsworth, Anthorn, 812. Cockpit. | 1-00 |

WOODVALE AIRFIELD on the A565 north of Formby
RAF **Woodvale**: On 16th July 2001 Phantom FGR.2 XV468 was reduced to scrap in double-quick time. Always a huge 'hole' in the 'relevant gate guardians' policy, it was nevertheless sad to see it go.

WEST MIDLANDS

☛ Within the administrative regional county boundaries can be found the unitary authorities of Birmingham, Coventry, Dudley, Sandwell, Solihull, Walsall and Wolverhampton.

BERKSWELL between the A452 and the A45 west of Coventry
Ken Woolley: The Dingbat still slumbers...
❑ G-AFJA	Dingbat	ex Headcorn. Crashed 19-5-75. Stored.	1-02

BIRMINGHAM
Millennium Point Discovery Centre: The £114 million centre opened officially on 29th September 2001. Within is 'Thinktank' a museum of science and discovery and it is here that the Spitfire and Hurricane can be found 'flying'. The huge complex includes an IMAX theatre.
♦ Open Sat to Thu 10am to 5pm, ie *not* open Fri. ✉ Curzon Street, Birmingham. ☎ 0121 20222222

❑ 'P3395'	Hurricane IV	KX829, ex Loughborough, 631, 1606 Flt,	
'JX-B'		137. 1 Sqn, F/L Arthur Clowes DFM colours.	9-01
❑ ML427	Spitfire IX	ex Castle Bromwich, St Athan, South Marston,	
'HL-A'		Millfield, Hucknall, 6457M, FLS, 3501 SU. FLS c/s.	9-01

BIRMINGHAM AIRPORT or Elmdon, on the A45 east of Birmingham
The Jetstream 31 prototype lives behind the extensive fire station.
❑ G-WMCC	Jetstream 3102	ex G-31-601, G-TALL, G-31-601. Fire crews.	2-02

BRIERLEY HILL on the A461 south-west of Dudley
No.2156 Squadron Air Cadets: 'Parented' by Cosford.
❑ XZ131	Harrier GR.3	9174M, ex St Athan, 1417 Flt, 233 OCU, 4, 1, 4. Nose.	11-95

COVENTRY
There are three restoration projects in the area. **Roy Nerou**'s Chilton makes progress. Established by David Kingshott and Annette Bowden, the **Mustang Restoration Group** acquired what they estimate to be a ten-year project in April 2001. It was imported into the UK in 1996 by another owner. **Maurice** and **Peter Bayliss'** Hurricane, most likely a former Canadian example, is believed underway locally – though the report is now long-in-the-tooth. See Coventry Airport, Warks, for their Spitfire Tr.IX. The Canberra nose is with a local collector.
❑ G-AFSV	Chilton DW.1A	CoA 12-7-72.	® 7-00
❑ WJ565*	Canberra T.17	ex North Coates, Binbrook, Bruntingthorpe, Cosford 8871M, St Athan, 360, CA. Nose. Arrived 20-9-01.	9-01
❑ 413954*	P-51D-5-NA	ex Norwich, Ailes Anciennes Le Bourget, Bordeaux, 338th FS, 55th FG. *Da'Quake*. Arr 17-4-01.	® 4-01
❑	Hurricane		® 12-93

HOCKLEY HEATH south of Solihull, near the M42-M40 interchange
Much camouflaged, the Aztec *should* still serve on the paintball range.
❑ G-SHIP	Aztec 250F	ex Coventry, Birmingham, N62490. Cr 4-12-83.	11-99

SOLIHULL south-east of Birmingham centre
Alan Bleetman: Jet Provost T.4 nose XS176 moved initially to Luton, Beds, then settled upon Stamford, Lincs. **Julian Lamb** has acquired the former Wells ATC Chipmunk for restoration. **Keith Williams** and **Mike Thorn** continue to work on the Bristol Scout. Refer to *W&R16* for the background to **John Fawke**'s Spitfire I K9851 'starter' project. **Solihull College**: Cessna 150J G-BPCJ moved to Binfield, Berks, by July 2001. Canberra PR.7 nose WT534 which had been at the **Haslucks Green Barracks**, Shirley, moved to Boscombe Down, Wilts by September 2001.

❑ 'A1742'	Bristol Scout REP	BAPC.38, ex Norwich, Lowestoft, Duxford, Avon area, St Mawgan, St Athan, Colerne, Weeton.	®	1-02
❑ WD335*	Chipmunk T.10	G-CBAJ, ex Wells, Dur UAS, Ox UAS, Gla UAS, Nott UAS, Lon UAS, Gla UAS, Aber UAS, St A UAS, Gla UAS, 11 RFS, 23 RFS.	®	8-01

SUTTON COLDFIELD north of Birmingham centre
Bob Mitchell: The PT Flight lives in storage at Cosford, Shrop – *qv*. Bob has two potential restoration projects, held in this general area.

❑ G-AEUJ	Whitney Straight	ex Marple, E Midlands, Bournemouth. CoA 4-6-70. Stored.	6-92
❑ G-AFRZ	Monarch	ex Shipdham, G-AIDE, W6463, Kemble, 10 GCF, FTCCF, 13 EFTS, G-AFRZ. CoA 29-6-70. Stored.	6-92

WOLVERHAMPTON
Boulton Paul Association (BPA) / **Boulton Paul Aircraft Heritage Project**: The museum and workshop, courtesy of Smiths Aerospace Wolverhampton (a rename of Dowty Aerospace), continues to flourish. An extensive exhibition of BP's history has been created and this is also home to the **West Midland Aviation Archive**.
    Notes: Several of the airframes are on loan and are marked ±: Goevier 3 from Bob Arnold; ANEC Missel Thrush REP from Bob Trickett of King's Lynn, Norfolk - *qv*; Anson nose from TAC – see under Manchester, Gtr Man; the Cadet TX.3 from Vaughan Mears; the 'JP' from Peter Alcock and Vaughan Mears and will become a 'hands-on' exhibit; the Danish Hunter nose is on loan from Classic Jet of Exeter, Devon. The An-2 and Canberra T.17 cockpits arrived here as noted and did not move on to Madeley, Shrop, as noted on p158 of *W&R17*. Both are on loan from Alec Brew's Black Country Aircraft Collection (BCAC). The P.6 was an early Boulton & Paul aircraft, filling a substantial 'gap' in the line-up. It has been completed and is a shining example of how to beat 'extinction' ①. The Defiant project uses an original turret, and some parts from salvaged remains, but is more accurately assessed as a full-scale model than a restoration with the airframe being created around a wooden frame. The rear fuselage of N3378 and other parts are displayed in a diorama depicting the Bleaklow Moor crash site ②. Also part of BCAC is the Cadet TX.1, this has been restored to represent an example that served from Walsall with 43 Gliding School ③.
◆ Within the Smiths Aerospace complex, in Wobaston Road, off the A449 Wolverhampton to Stafford road, west of Ford Houses/Oxley. (Site partially the former Pendeford aerodrome and astride the West Midlands/Staffordshire border.) Open Fri 2pm to 5pm and first Sun of the month 10am to 5pm, May to Oct. ✉ Cyril Plimmer, 25D Bilbrook Road, Bilbrook, Wolverhampton, WV8 1EU.

❑ [CRZ]*	T.8 Tutor	BGA.1759, ex Chipping, RAFGSA.178. F/n 6-01.		3-02
❑ DBU	Goevier 3	BGA.1992, ex D-5233. Stored.	±	3-02
❑ [G-FBPI]	Missel Thrush REP	ex Stoke-on-Trent. Unfinished fuselage.	±	3-02
❑ 'X-25'	B&P P.6 FSM	BAPC.274. Complete by 6-01.	①	3-02
❑ RA-01641* '3'	An-2 *Colt*	forward fuselage. Crashed 9-99. Arr 2-11-99.	BCAC	3-02
❑ 'L7005'	Defiant FSM	using some parts from originals.	②	3-02
❑ 'PD685'	Cadet TX.1	ex Stoke-on-Trent, Dowty GC, Pershore, CG, ATC. Fuselage. Arrived 8-01.	BCAC ③	3-02
❑ VP519	Anson C.19/2	G-AVVR, ex 'Manchester', Dukinfield, Hadfield, Stockport, Peel Green, Cosford, Wigan, Irlam, Shawbury, FCCS, 11 GCF, MCS, 31, Malta CF, TCDU. Nose.	±	3-02
❑ WJ576*	Canberra T.17	ex Bruntingthorpe, Cardiff, St Athan, 360, MoA, *Swifter* Flight, 231 OCU. Nose. Arr 9-11-99.	BCAC	3-02

❏	WN149		Balliol T.2	ex Bacup, Salford, Failsworth, RAFC.		
				Mock-up rear fuselage.	®	3-02
❏	WN534		Balliol T.2	ex Bacup, Salford, Failsworth, 22 MU, RAFC.	®	3-02
❏	WT877*		Cadet TX.3	ex St Athan GC, Syerston, 621 GS. F/n 10-00.	±	3-02
❏	XR662	'25'	Jet Provost T.4	ex Bicester, Kemble, Finningley, Halton 8410M,		
				SoRF, CAW, CATCS, RAFC, CAW, 6 FTS, CAW.	±	3-02
❏	ET-272*		Hunter T.7	ex North Weald, Bruntingthorpe, Bournemouth,		
				Bruntingthorpe, Bitteswell, Hatfield, RDanAF,		
				Esk.724, G-9-430. Nose. Arrived 19-12-00.	±	3-02

Michael Boulanger: Keeps his 'JP' in the area.
◆ Viewable by prior arrangement only. ☎ 01902 820371 e-mail gfc66@dial.pipex.com

| ❏ | XW315 | Jet Provost T.5 | ex Long Marston, 'Lincolnshire', CFS, | |
| | | | 3 FTS, CFS. Nose. | 6-01 |

NORFOLK

BODNEY CAMP on the B1108 west of Watton
Army Training Estate (ATE) **East**: Formerly Stanford Training Area (STANTA). South of the camp is an extensive training area, centred upon Stanford Water. The two airframes are located within the 'drop zone' and are thought to be 'passive' targets (ie they do not get shot at) but as the whole area is totally restricted access, it is not easy to confirm. This is a huge training area. See also its 'southern' end, listed as East Wretham, Norfolk.

| ❏ | WJ775 | Canberra B.6RC | ex St Athan, Swanton Morley 8581M, 51, 192. | 5-96 |
| ❏ | | Wessex | — | 5-96 |

COLTISHALL AIRFIELD east of the B1150, north of Coltishall
RAF Coltishall: The two Lightnings and the Phantom noses are looked after by a volunteer team led by W/O Mick Jennings MBE. The F.3 is on loan from the Lightning PG from Bruntingthorpe, Leics ①; the F.6 from Charles Ross of Binbrook, Lincs ②. The newly-arrived Jaguar GR.1 XZ375 is to be returned to its Gulf War status as *The Guardian Reader* ③. The former Brüggen Jaguar 'guardian' is a composite, based upon the nose and forward fuselage of S.07 XW563 ④. Hunter FGA.9 XG254 was offered for tender during mid-2000 and moved to Clacton, Essex, on 10th October 2000. The hulk of Jaguar GR.1B XX733 was tendered during mid-2000 moving to Faygate, W Sussex, in October 2000.

❏	'V7467'	'LE-D'	Hurricane FSM	BAPC.223, 242 Sqn colours. Gate.		2-02
❏	XP703		Lightning F.3	ex Bruntingthorpe, Warton, MoD(PE), 29,		
				56, 74. Cockpit.	® ①	5-01
❏	XS899	'BL'	Lightning F.6	ex Bruntingthorpe, Cranfield, Binbrook,		
				11, 5-11 pool, 23, 5. Nose.	® ②	5-01
❏	XV426	'P'	Phantom FGR.2	ex Coningsby, 56, 23, 228 OCU, 111, 31. Nose.		6-01
❏	XX109	'US'	Jaguar GR.1	8918M, ex Warton, A&AEE. WLT.		6-00
❏	XX744	'DJ'	Jaguar GR.1	9251M, ex Cosford, Shawbury, 31, 17, A&AEE. Fuse.		6-00
❏	'XX822'*		Jaguar GR.1	8563M. ex Brüggen. Arr 10-8-01. Gate 31-8-01.	④	2-02
❏	XX830*		Jaguar T.2	ex Warton, Shawbury, St Athan, ETPS. Fuse. Arr 6-7-00.		7-00
❏	XX979*		Jaguar GR.1	ex St Athan, DTEO, A&AEE. GIA. Arr 19-2-02.		2-02
❏	XZ375*	'GR'	Jaguar GR.1	ex St Athan, 9255M, 54, 14, 20. Fuse.Arr 19-2-02.	③	2-02

DEOPHAM GREEN north of the A11, north of Attleborough
Chris Jefferson:

❏	G-ARRZ	Turbulent	ex Tonbridge. Crashed 21-7-90. *Tarzan.*	®	2-99
❏	G-ASSV*	Kensinger KF	ex Brenchley, Deopham Green, Tonbridge,		
			Bobbington, N23S. Crashed 2-7-69. Stored.		2-99

EAST DEREHAM on the A47 west of Norwich
Russel Dagless: Wasp XT793 moved to Thruxton, Hants, during 2001, as G-BZPP and airworthy.

❏ 5X-UUX	Scout Srs 1	G-BKLJ, ex Tattershall Thorpe, Heysham, Panshanger, Uganda Police Air Wing.	8-99
❏ XP166	Scout AH.1	ex Farnborough, RAE, G-APVL.	8-99
❏ XP849	Scout AH.1	ex Boscombe Down, ETPS. Damaged 3-4-97.	8-99
❏ XT420	Wasp HAS.1	ex Fleetlands, Wroughton.	8-99
❏ XV134	'P' Scout AH.1	G-BWLX, ex Ipswich, Fleetlands, Middle Wallop.	8-99
❏ XV138	Scout AH.1	ex Almondbank, Wroughton, 658. Arrived by 12-97.	8-99

EAST WINCH AERODROME on the A47 east of King's Lynn

❏ G-BEXK	Pawnee 235D	ex N82424 ntu. Crashed 4-10-92.Frame.	8-97

EAST WRETHAM east of the A1075 north of Thetford
Thorpe Camp: See also the 'northern' end of this area, listed under Bodney Camp, Norfolk.

❏ XM386	'08' Jet Provost T.3	ex St Athan 8076M, Halton, Shawbury, 2 FTS, CFS	6-00
❏ [XT643]	Scout AH.1	ex Waterbeach, Wroughton, 660, 661. Pink scheme.	6-00

FELTHORPE AERODROME south of the B1149, north-west of Norwich

❏ G-ARBG	Nipper II	crashed 16-5-84.	® 5-91

GREAT YARMOUTH
Dick Melton Aviation (DMA): This magnificent project is reported to be up for sale.

❏ W2718	Walrus I	G-RNLI, ex Winchester, Southampton, 276, 751, 764.	5-00

Sea-Front Crazee Golf: The hulk of a Cessna Centurion adorns part of the course.

❏ G-MANT	Cessna 210L II	ex Oxford, G-MAXY, N550SV. Crashed 16-2-92.	7-01

KING'S LYNN
Bob Trickett: The Bristol F.2b is making good progress, off-site. The BAC Drone project, based around a centre-section and other parts, also progresses but it is in too early a stage to formally list. Auster J/1N G-AJAC was passed on to a Peterborough-based owner. The anonymous Skylark 3B was broken up for spares. Tiger Moth T5595 (G-BYLB) was sold is due to move 'overseas'. Bob's Missel Thrush REP is at Wolverhampton, W Mids.

❏ G-AIUA	Hawk Trainer III	ex West Chiltington, Benington, Bushey, Old Warden, Duxford, Felthorpe, T9768, 10 AGS, 7 FIS, 15 EFTS, Wyton SF. CoA 13-7-67. Fuselage.	3-02
❏ 'C850'*	'Salmson' FSM	ex Doncaster, Barton, Chelford, Coventry.	12-01
❏ –*	Bristol F.2b	ex Weston-on-the-Green. Fuselage.	off-site ® 2-02

Others: A Terrier is under restoration in the area.

❏ G-AYDW*	Terrier 2	ex Little Gransden, King's Lynn, Camberley, Cranfield, Bushey, G-ARLM, AOP.6 TW568, LAS, AOPS, 227 OCU, 43 OTU. CoA 1-7-73.	® 10-01

LITTLE SNORING AERODROME north of the A148, north of the village

❏ G-BPMU	Nord 3202B	ex High Ham, N22546, G-BIZJ ntu, Liverpool, USA, ALAT No.70 'AIX'. CoA 19-10-90.	7-96

LUDHAM north-east of the village, north of the A1062
Adding to *W&R17*, the nose of B-26K 417657 moved to <u>Norwich</u>, Norfolk.

MARHAM AIRFIELD south of the A47 west of Swaffham

RAF Marham: It has been confirmed that the Victor is owned privately and on 'extended' loan to the station. It is due to be replaced by a Tornado GR.1, reported to be ZA407 'AJ-N'. By February 2001, Canberra PR.7 WH779 had moved to Shawbury, Shropshire. Between 17th-23rd July 2001 Buccaneer S.2B XV332 was scrapped, with the cockpit section being saved. Buccaneer S.2B XZ431 was acquired by a Belgian enthusiast for donation to the Brussels Museum. The logistics of moving it defeated him and the aircraft's fate now hangs in the balance.

❏ WT509	'BR' Canberra PR.7	ex 100, 13, MoS, 58, 80, 17, 31. Stored.	8-01
❏ XH673	Victor K.2	8911M, ex 57, Witt Wing, 139, MoA. Outside SHQ. Joint 55 and 57 Sqn colours. Hemp scheme.	6-00
❏ XZ431	Buccaneer S.2B	9233M, ex 12, 208, 12, 208.	8-01
❏ ZA267	Tornado F.2	9284M, ex Boscombe Down. Inst..	1-00

MARTHAM on the B1152 north of Great Yarmouth

Jeremy Moore: Has established a workshop in the area, with at least two major projects in hand. The Focke-Wulf has been registered to an owner in Seattle, USA; the Seafire is registered to Wizzard Investments, see under North Weald, Essex.

❏ PP972*	Seafire III	G-BUAR, ex Earls Colne, Audley End, East Midlands, Biggin Hill, Thruxton, Biggin Hill, Vannes-Meucon, Gavres, Aéronavale 12F, Bien Hoa, 1F, PP972, FAA, 767, 809.	® 2-02
❏ 1227*	Fw 190A-5	N19027, ex North Weald, G-FOKW, Biggin Hill, Wycombe Air Park, Russia, 'DG+HO'. Crashed 19-7-43.	® 2-02

NARBOROUGH on the A47 north-west of Swaffham

Wellesley Aviation: Shackleton WR971 nose moved to West Walton Highway, Norfolk.

NEATISHEAD east of the A1151, north of Hoveton

RAF Neatishead: The Phantom guards the gate. The base awaits closure.

❏ XV420	'BT' Phantom FGR.2	9247M, ex Wattisham, 92, 23, 29, 23, 19, 56, 29.	10-00

Air Defence Radar Museum: Opened in October 1994 by AM Sir John Allison the museum is dedicated to every aspect of the history of radar, air defence and battle management. Housed in the original 1942 Operations Building, exhibits include a Battle of Britain 'Ops' Filter Room, a 'Cold War' era 'Ops' Room, ROC Field Post and much more.
◆ Open 10am to 5pm (last entry 3pm) on the second Saturday of each month, Bank Holiday Mondays and every Tuesday and Thursday, early April to end of September. Group visits by prior arrangement. 'Brown signed' off the A149. ✉ Museum Manager, RAF Air Defence Radar Museum, RAF Neatishead, Norwich, NR12 8YB. ☎ 01692 633309 web www.neatishead.raf.mod.uk

NORWICH

Hull Aero: Ralph Hull is working on a Spitfire that will return to Canada when completed. Work is also reported underway on the former OFMC Sea Fury, for Kermit Weeks.

❏ D-CACY	Sea Fury FB.11	G-BWOL, ex Wycombe (!), Duxford, Uetersen, DLB ES3617, G-9-66, WG599.	® 2-00
❏ TD314	Spitfire IX	ex Canada, 'N601DA', South Africa, SAAF, 234, 183.	® 3-96
❏ 417657*	B-26K Invader	N99218, ex Ludham, Booker, Canterbury, Southend, Chino, USAF. Nose. Arrived 1999.	5-00

Ted Sinclair: Has two Tempest cockpits. The former Ludham example is the most complete and has been used as a pattern for the Tempest Too project – see under Gainsborough, Lincs.

❏	Tempest V	ex Spanhoe. Cockpit.	® 2-02
❏ *	Tempest V	ex Ludham, Norwich. Cockpit.	® 4-95

Others: A former Russian Spitfire IX is believed stored in the area, awaiting restoration. P-51D 44-14291 moved to Coventry, Warks.

❏ SM639   Spitfire IX   ex Russia, USSR. Stored.   3-96

NORWICH AIRPORT or Horsham St Faith, east of the A140, north of the city
City of Norwich Aviation Museum (CNAM): Indoor exhibitions recall the local presence of the US 8th Air Force. The RAF 100 Group Association collection is in a special section devoted to Bomber Command. Other displays show the history of RAF Horsham St Faith, the role of women in aviation and local aviation pioneers. Hunter F.6A XG172 is on loan from Mick Jennings (he of Coltishall, Norfolk, fame) ①. Javelin FAW.9 XH767 moved to Elvington, N Yorks on 4th February 2001.
◆ Access from the A140, north of the airport, follow 'brown signs'. Open Jan to Mar, Nov and Dec Sun noon to 4pm, Wed and 10am to 4pm. Apr to Oct Sun noon to 5pm, Tue to Sat 10am to 5pm. Also Bank Holidays. Closed 21st Dec to 2nd Jan. Evening on Tue and Thu by prior arrangement. ✉ Old Norwich Road, Horsham St Faith, Norwich, NR10 3JE. ☎ 01603 625309

❏ G-ASKK		Herald 211	ex Air UK, PP-ASU, G-ASKK, PI-C910, CF-MCK. CoA 19-5-85.	3-02
❏ G-BHMY*		Friendship 200	ex KLM uk, Air UK, F-GBDK, F-GBRV ntu, PK-PFS, JA8606, PH-FDL. Arrived 10-8-00.	3-02
❏ WK654		Meteor F.8	ex Neatishead 8092M, Kemble, 85, CFE, Odiham SF, AWFCS, 247.	3-02
❏ 'XF383'		Hunter F.51	E-409, ex Cardiff-Wales, 'WV309', 'XF383', Dunsfold, G-9-437, DanAF Esk.724.	3-02
❏ XG172*	'A'	Hunter F.6A	ex North Weald, Ipswich, Scampton 8832M, 1 TWU, 229 OCU, 263, 19. Arrived 2-2-01. ①	3-02
❏ XM612		Vulcan B.2	ex 44, Wadd Wing, Scampton Wing, 9.	3-02
❏ XP355	'A'	W'wind HAR.10	ex G-BEBC, Faygate, 8463M, 38 GCF, 21, CFS.	3-02
❏ XP458		Grasshopper TX.1	ex Fakenham area. On loan. Stored.	6-00
❏ ZF592*		Lightning F.53	ex Portsmouth, Luxembourg, *Wing Commander*, Stretton, Warton, RSAF 223, 53-686, G-AWON, G-27-56. On loan. Arrived 6-2-02.	3-02
❏		Scimitar CIM	—	3-02
❏ 121		Mystère IVA	ex Sculthorpe, FAF. '8-MY'. *Patrouille de France* c/s.	3-02
❏ 16718		T-33A-5-LO	16718, ex Sculthorpe, Turkish AF ntu, FAF.	3-02

Airport: Jet Provost T.5A XW423 (G-BWUW) was flying by late 1999 while by April 2001 T.4 XP558 had moved to Ipswich, Suffolk. Friendship 200 G-BHMY was donated to the City of Norwich Aviation Museum by KLM uk and trundled to the museum site on 10th August 2000.

❏ G-APWH	Herald 201	ex Air UK, BIA, BUA. wfu 11-7-80. Dump, poor.	8-97
❏ G-ATIG	Herald 214	ex BAC Express, PP-SDI, G-ATIG. Dump.	8-00
❏ G-AVEZ	Herald 210	ex Museum, Air UK, BIA, BUA, PP-ASW, G-AVEZ, HB-AAH. CoA 5-1-81. Fire.	8-00
❏ G-BCDN	Friendship 200	ex Air UK, PH-OGA, JA8615, LV-PMR ntu, PH-FDP. CoA 19-7-96. Training airframe.	6-99
❏ G-BCDO	Friendship 200	ex Air UK, PH-OGB, JA8621, PH-FEZ. *Lord Butler*. Fuselage. Damaged 19-7-90. Air UK Tech College.	10-96
❏ G-BTOM	Tomahawk 112	ex Tattershall Thorpe. Crashed 26-9-92.	6-99
❏ EI-CAZ	FH.227D	ex Iona, SE-KBR, EI-CAZ, SE-KBR, C-FNAK, CF-NAK, N2735R. Dump by 9-95.	8-97

Offshore Fire and Survival Training Centre: Run by the Petroleum Training Association, North Sea (PETANS), have a 'helicopter' mounted on a landing deck. Bright red and wearing the 'reggie' 'G-DRNT', this is largely based upon a Ford Transit! Also within the site is another fuselage, again synthetic and simulating an S-61, used for evacuation drills. In March 2002, they received the real thing.

❏ [N5880T]*	WG.30-100	ex Weston-super-Mare, Yeovil, Air Spur, G-17-31. Arrived 3-02.	3-02

REYMERSTON near East Dereham
Wallis Autogiros: See under London, Gtr Lon, for another 'G-ARZB'. WA-116-T G-AXAS was
flying again by July 2001.Please note the location is *not* open to public inspection.

❑ G-ARRT	WA-116/McC	CoA 26-5-83.	7-01
❑ G-ARZB	WA-116 Srs 1	ex XR943, G-ARZB. CoA 29-6-93. *Little Nellie.*	7-01
❑ G-ASDY	WA-116/F	CoA 30-4-90.	7-01
❑ G-ATHM	WA-116/F	ex 4R-ACK, G-ATHM. CoA 23-5-93.	7-01
❑ G-AVDG	WA-116 Srs 1	CoA 23-5-92.	7-01
❑ G-AVJV	WA-117	CoA 21-4-89.	7-01
❑ G-AVJW	WA-118/M	CoA 21-4-83.	7-01
❑ G-AXAS	WA-116-T/Mc	CoA 23-5-92.	5-00
❑ G-AYVO	WA-120 Srs 1	ex South Kensington. CoA 31-12-78.	5-00
❑ G-BAHH	WA-121/Mc	CoA 26-10-93.	7-01
❑ G-BGGU	WA-116	—	7-01
❑ G-BGGW	WA-122/RR	CoA 26-10-93.	7-01
❑ G-BLIK	WA-116/F-S	CoA 24-4-98.	7-01
❑ G-BMJX	WA-116/X	CoA 1-4-89.	7-01
❑ G-BNDG	WA-201/R	CoA 3-3-88.	7-01
❑ G-SCAN	WA-116-100	CoA 10-7-91.	7-01
❑ G-VIEW	WA-116/L	CoA 6-10-85.	7-01
❑ (G-VTEN)	WA-117	CoA 3-12-85.	7-01
❑ XR944	WA-116/F	G-ATTB, ex XR944, G-ARZC. CoA 23-5-92.	7-01

SEETHING AERODROME east of the B1332, north of Bungay
Station 146 Control Tower Museum: The original control tower has been restored and contains a
museum dedicated to the history of the aerodrome and the surrounding area. The tower is a living
memorial to the Liberator-equipped 448th BG. There is a shop and refreshments are available.
◆ Access from the Thwaite St Mary road to the south. Open the first Sunday of the month May to Oct,
10am to 5pm. ✉ 'The Beeches', Brooke Road, Seething, Norwich, NR15 1DJ ☎ 01508 550288

SHIPDHAM AERODROME off the A1075 south-west of East Dereham
By July 2000 Aircoupe G-ARHF and Cherokee 140 G-ATTG had moved to Swanton Morley, Norfolk.

❑ G-AYAF	Twin Com' 160C	ex N8842Y. CoA 8-5-77. Stored.	4-96
❑ G-JDIX*	Mooney M.20B	ex G-ARTB. CoA 16-1-00. Stored.	5-01
❑ G-MJUC*	Tiger Cub 440	CoA 20-1-92. Stored.	5-01

SWANTON MORLEY AERODROME east of the B1110, north of East Dereham
Tiger Moth G-AMCK was up and flying by mid-1999 and by August 2000 Apache 160H G-ASMY was
also back in the air. By March 2000 PT-13 G-BRTK had moved to Old Sarum, Wilts. By September
2001 PT-13D N5345N had moved on to Tibenham, Norfolk, for completion by Black Barn Aviation
and was ready for air test. Thanks to Andy Marden, the Grasshopper listed here has been identified. It
was XP490 latterly with Ipswich School (*W&R16* p218) and moved to Watton, Norfolk.

❑ G-ARHF*	Aircoupe	ex Shipdham. CoA 10-5-94. Stored. F/n 7-00.	7-01
❑ G-ATTG*	Cherokee 140	ex Shipdham. CoA 3-10-92. Stored. F/n 7-00.	7-00
❑ G-BBXZ*	Evans VP-1	CoA 8-3-96. Stored. F/n 7-01.	7-01
❑ G-BGRC*	Cherokee 140B	ex SE-FHF. CoA 26-10-97. Stored. F/n 5-00.	7-01
❑ G-HRVD	Harvard IV	ex Wellesbourne, Thruxton G-BSBC, Mozambique, Port AF 1741, WGAF BF+055, AA+055, 53-4629. ®	7-99
❑ G-MJSU	Tiger Cub 440	CoA 31-1-86. Stored.	7-01
❑ N39132*	Tomahawk 112	ex G-NCFD ntu, N39132. Stored. F/n 7-01.	7-01
❑ N53091	PT-17 Kaydet	ex USA, 41-25306. Stored. ®	7-98
❑ N65200	A75N1	ex USA, Canada, FJ767. Frame. Stored.	2-02
❑ N73410	N2S-3 Kaydet	ex Tibenham, USA, BuNo 38140. ®	2-01
❑ 40-1766	PT-17 Kaydet	ex Old Buckenham, USA. ®	12-93

TERRINGTON ST CLEMENT north of the A17, west of King's Lynn
Terrington Aviation Collection: The collection continues to be trimmed down. As predicted in W&R17, Buccaneer S.2B XN983 cockpit moved to West Walton Highway, Norfolk, in late 2000. The nose of Lightning F.6 XS933 moved to Langport, Somerset, by November 2001.
♦ Visits by prior arrangement *only.* ✉ Haydn Block, Seagull Cottage, Long Road, Terrington St Clement, King's Lynn, PE34 4JW e-mail nigel.claxton@btinternet.com
❏ XM468   Jet Provost T.3   ex King's Lynn, Stock, St Athan, Halton 8081M, Shawbury, 6 FTS, RAFC. Stored.   3-00

THORPE ABBOTTS north of the A143, east of Diss
100th Bomb Group Memorial Museum: Contents of the tower museum are exceptional, offering poignant insights into the life and times of the men and machines of the 'Bloody Hundredth'.
♦ 'Brown signed'. Open 10am to 5pm weekends and Bank Hols. Also Wed 10am to 5pm May to Sep. *Closed* November to end of January. Other times by appointment. Regular special events are staged.
✉ 100th BG Memorial Museum, Common Road, Dickleburgh, Diss, IP21 4PH ☎ 01379 740708, or Sam Hurry on 01553 766089

TIBENHAM north of the B1134, north of Diss
Black Barn Aviation:
❏ G-AYPP   Super Cub 95   ex ALAT 18-1626, 51-15626. Frame.   6-96
❏ N1325M   N2S-5 Kaydet   ex USA, BuNo 43390.   7-98
❏ N1328   Fairchild F.24KS   ex USA, NC1328.   11-01
❏ N16676   Fairchild F.24CBF   ex USA, NC16676.   11-01
❏ N62840   PT-17D   ex USA.   4-00
❏ N68427   N2S-4 Kaydet   ex USA, BuNo 55771   7-98

TUNSTEAD east of the B1150, north of Hoveton
❏ G-BARD   Cessna 337C   ex North Coates, SE-FBU, N2557S. Cr 12-6-94. 9-99

WALPOLE ST ANDREW south of the A17, south-east of Sutton Bridge
Murray Flint: Murray's Lightning T.5 continues its restoration.
❏ XS420   Lightning T.5   ex West Walton Highway, Narborough, Binbrook, LTF, 5, LTF, 226 OCU.   ℝ 9-01

WATTON on the A1075, south of East Dereham
No.611 Volunteer Gliding School: Have a Grasshopper to remind them of times gone by!
❏ XP490*   Grasshopper TX.1 ex Swanton Morley, Ipswich, Syerston, Grantham.   5-00

Wartime Watton Exhibition: Housed in the former Officers' Mess of the equally former RAF station, the displays are dedicated to the RAF and USAAF units and personnel that served 1939-1945.
♦ *Normally* open Sundays 2pm to 5pm, May to September. Parties by appointment at other times. ☎ 01953 881440.

WEST WALTON HIGHWAY on the A47 north-east of Wisbech
Fenland and West Norfolk Aviation Museum: Run by the Fenland and West Norfolk Aircraft Preservation Society. The museum has a close association with the Terrington Aviation Collection (TAC – see also under Terrington St Clement, Norfolk) and among the latter's artefacts on loan are the Buccaneer and MiG-29 cockpit sections. Two airframes are not available for public inspection – §.
♦ At Bamber's Garden Centre, Old Lynn Road, West Walton Highway, – signed off the A47/B198 junction. Weekends and Bank Hols, Mar and Oct 9.30am to 5pm. Other times by appointment.✉ F&WNAM, Old Lynn Road, West Walton, Wisbech, PE14 7DA ☎ 01945 584440 e-mail petewinning@btinternet.com web www.fawnaps.freeserve.co.uk

❑	G-ARNH		Colt 108	ex Chatteris, Elstree. Damaged 1-9-72. Off-site.	§ ®	3-02
❑	WR971*	'Q'	Shackleton MR.3/3	ex Narborough, Cosford 8119M, 120, Kinloss Wing, 201, 120, Kinloss Wing, CA. Fuselage.		3-02
❑	XD434	'25'	Vampire T.11	ex Marham, Barton, Woodford, Chester, St Athan, 5 FTS, 7 FTS.		3-02
❑	XM402	'J'	Jet Provost T.3	ex Narborough, West Raynham, Halton, Newton 8055AM, Shawbury, 6 FTS, 2 FTS.		3-02
❑	XN983*		Buccaneer S.2B	ex Terrington St Clement, 12, 208, 15, 12. Nose.	TAC	3-02
❑	XP488		Grasshopper TX.1	ex Long Sutton, Halton, West Malling. Stored.	§	3-02
❑	XS459	'AW'	Lightning T.5	ex Narborough, Binbrook, 5, LTF, 56, 29, 226 OCU.		3-02
❑	—		Jet Provost	Procedure trainer. On loan from March Air Cadets.		3-02
❑	526		MiG-29 *Fulcrum*	25887, ex Fairford. Crashed 21-7-93. Cockpit.	TAC	3-02

WEYBOURNE on the A149 west of Cromer
Muckleburgh Collection: Bannered as Britain's largest working military collection, there is much to fascinate here, including 'live' tank demonstrations every Sunday and daily during the summer season. The *Saving Private Ryan* CG-4 Hadrian '43-241170' moved to Elvington, Yorks, by July 2001.
◆ Open mid-Feb to Oct 10am to 5pm daily. ✉ Weybourne Military Camp, Weybourne, NR25 7EG ☎ 01263 588210 fax 01263 588425 e-mail info@muckleburgh.co.uk web www.muckleburgh.co.uk

❑	WD686	'S'	Meteor NF.11	ex Duxford, RAE Bedford, Wroughton, TRE Defford. 141 Squadron colours.	3-02
❑	XN967	'103'	Buccaneer S.1	ex Fleckney, Helston, Culdrose A2627 / SAH-20, Lossiemouth. Cockpit.	3-02
❑	XZ968	'3G'	Harrier GR.3	ex Marham 9222M, St Athan, 233 OCU, 1417F, 1, 4.	3-02
❑	—*		Fi 103 V-1 REP	first noted 6-01.	3-02

WYMONDHAM on the A11 south-west of Norwich
Wymondham College Aircraft Restoration Group: Restoration of the Vampire is thought to continue. It is on loan from the IWM, Duxford, Cambs.

❑	XG743	'597'	Sea Vampire T.22 ex Duxford, Brawdy SF, 736, 764.	®	1-94

NORTHAMPTONSHIRE

CORBY
Frank Millar: Took delivery of the nose of former Stock, Essex, Canberra PR.9 XH177 during 2000. Frank presented it on loan to Winthorpe, Notts, on 2nd November 2000.

'The Works': The 112A 'flies' from the ceiling and billed as a 'Rockwell World War Two Fighter'!

❑	G-TCSL	Commander 112A ex Spanhoe, N506CA, N1322J. Crashed 5-12-94.	12-95

CROUGHTON on the B4031 south-west of Brackley
USAF Croughton: Midland Air Museum repainted and refurbished the base's two 'guardians' during August 2001, in readiness for its 50th anniversary.

❑	24428	'WW'	F-105G-RE	ex Upper Heyford, Davis-Monthan 'FK095', 128 TFS, Georgia ANG. 561 TFS, Korat, colours.	8-01
❑	'63000'	'000'	F-100D-11-NA	42212, ex Upper Heyford, Sculthorpe, FAF.	8-01

HARRINGTON south-east of Market Harborough
'Carpetbagger' Aviation Museum: This museum is centred upon the hardened group operations building of what was once USAAF Station 179, home of the clandestine 492nd and 801st BGs. This

building, restored to its wartime state, houses exhibitions describing the covert operations carried out by the US from Harrington and by the RAF from Tempsford, Beds.

Notes: Working in support of the museum is the **Harrington Aviation Museum Society** (Ron Clarke, 43 Greenhill Road, Kettering, NN15 7LP). In the former Paymaster's building, is the **Northants Aviation Museum** run by the Northamptonshire Aviation Society. This benefits from the NAS's extensive 'dig' activity in the county. (✉ Membership enquiries for NAS to 53 Palmerston Road, Northampton, NN1 5EU.) The Harvard is on loan from Gordon King ①. The Widgeon's construction number could be WA(H)/51/152 - make any sense? ②

◆ Take the minor road south out of Harrington village, towards Lamport, and turn right after the A14 underpass – follow the signs. Open from Easter to October weekends and Bank Holidays, 10am to 5pm. Other times by prior appointment – min 15 people – to the address and number below. ✉ Sunny Vale Farm Nursery, off Lamport Road, Harrington, Northampton, NN6 9PF ☎ 01604 686608 e-mail cbaggermuseum@aol.com web www.harringtonmuseum.org.uk

❑ 42-12417	Harvard IIB	ex East Tilbury, Windsor, North Weald, Amsterdam, Dutch AF B-163, RCAF FE930, 42-12417. US Navy SNJ-2 colours.	①	3-02
❑ —	Widgeon	ex Corby (?), Sywell, *Eye of the Needle*. Forward fuselage.	②	3-02

HINTON-IN-THE-HEDGES just west of Brackley
The smashed hulk of a blue wooden glider was noted in a dump of bits and pieces close to the threshold of Runway 15 in July 2001 – was this the Eagle ①? The hulk that was Cessna F.172H G-BAKK (last noted in July 1995) has moved on.

❑ G-AZKN	Robin HR.100	ex East Midlands. Crashed 1-9-95. Wreck.		10-01
❑ G-AZLL*	Cessna FRA.150L	crashed 4-2-99. Wreck. First noted 8-00.		10-01
❑	T.42 Eagle	Wreck.	①	6-01

KINGSCLIFFE south of the A47, west of Peterborough
John Tempest: About 90% of the parts from the *original* Cosmic Wind G-ARUL are held plus other components. (G-ARUL, as *Ballerina II* is airworthy.)

❑ G-ARUL	Cosmic Wind	ex Halfpenny Green, N22C. Crashed 29-8-66.	®	7-00

NORTHAMPTON AERODROME or Sywell, north-east of Northampton, off the A43
Sywell Aviation Museum: Adjacent to the lovely art-deco 'terminal' building – now 'The Aviator Hotel' – three former USAAF Nissen huts, retrieved from Bentwaters, Suffolk, have been erected to form the new museum. The museum is run in partnership with SAM and the Northamptonshire Airfields and Aircraft Research Group. Officially opened on 21st July 2001 by Alex Henshaw, larger display will be launched for the 2002 'season'. The Grasshopper is on loan from the Visitor Centre and Archive, Shoreham, W Sussex.

◆ Open weekends and Bank Hols 10am to 4.30pm, Easter to end of Oct. Other times by appointment. ✉ Sywell Aerodrome, Sywell, Northants, NN6 0BN ☎ 01604 890925, or '811582 e-mail bbrown@sherwooddunham.com web www.sywellaerodrome.co.uk/aviation

❑ WZ820*	Grasshopper TX.1	ex Shoreham, Lancing College.	®	3-02

Aerodrome: Fordaire's Dragon Rapide G-AKRP made its first post restoration flight on 6th April 2000. Next project is the wonderful Q6. Widgeon G-ANLW was due to move to Flixton, Suffolk, as W&R closed for press ①. Sloane's have a travelling airframe, which is used at fetes and other events – R-22 'G-BEAR' ②.

Hiller UH-12B G-APKY, last noted in March 2000, was cancelled as sold in the USA during January 2002. Skeeter AOP.10 XK482 (G-BJWC) was auctioned in the Phillips sale of 16th March 2000, reaching £2,300. By August 2000 it had moved to Fyfield, Essex.

❑ G-AFFD*	Percival Q6	ex Isle of Man, Sutton Coldfield, Duxford, Redhill, G-AIEY ntu, X9407, MCS, 510, Old Sarum SF, Halton SF, Heston SF, Northolt SF, 6 AACU, G-AFFD. CoA 31-8-56. Arrived 9-01 onwards.	®	9-01

❏	G-ANLW	Widgeon 2	ex Blackpool, 'MD497', Wellingborough, Little Staughton, Tattershall Thorpe, *Eye of the Needle*, Southend. CoA 27-5-81.	①	4-02
❏	G-APTU	Auster Alpha 5	CoA 8-6-98. Stored.		10-98
❏	G-AVGU*	Cessna F.150G	ex Little Staughton, Cranfield. Cr 25-5-83. F/n 4-00.		4-00
❏	G-AYIA	Hughes 369HS	damaged 1-6-88. Spares.		2-98
❏	G-BAUK	Hughes 269C	CoA 20-9-93. Stored.		2-98
❏	'G-BEAR'	Robinson R-22	G-HOVR, ex N2647M. Crashed 9-1-89.	②	7-97
❏	G-BIVF*	Emeraude	ex F-BJVN. CoA 17-6-92. Stored.		4-00
❏	G-BWEC	Colson Cassutt	ex Little Gransden. CoA 11-9-91.	®	10-98
❏	G-MNUL*	SX130/Firefly	Cancelled 12-9-94. Stored.		4-00
❏		Enstrom F-28A	cabin shell. Fire dump.		11-97
❏	NL985	Tiger Moth	G-BWIK, ex Cranfield, Leighton Buzzard, Bushey, Leamington Spa, Finningley 7015M. Frame.		2-90

ROTHWELL on the A6 west of Kettering
Cadet TX.3 WT901 and the anonymous Sedbergh TX.1 are believed to have moved on.

SPANHOE LODGE AERODROME south-east of Harringworth
Windmill Aviation: A trio of Airedales from Abbeyshrule arrived on 15th March 2001. One will be restored, the others will be used for spares.

❏	G-AYZI	SNCAN SV-4C	ex Abbeyshrule, F-BBAA, Fr military.	®	1-02
❏	EI-AYL*	Airedale	ex Abbeyshrule, G-ARRO, EI-AVP ntu, G-ARRO. CoA 1-2-86. Arrived 15-3-01.		9-01
❏	EI-BAL*	Airedale	ex Abbeyshrule, G-ARZS. Cancelled 29-6-79. Arrived 15-3-01.		9-01
❏	EI-BBK*	Airedale	ex Abbeyshrule, G-ARXB, EI-ATE ntu, G-ARXB. CoA 11-11-83. Arrived 15-3-01.		9-01

WELLINGBOROUGH
Wellingborough School: The Grasshopper is kept by the school but *may* be moving soon.

❏	XP454	G'hopper TX.1	ex Kimbolton, Holt.	2-02

NORTHUMBERLAND and TYNESIDE

☛ The five unitary authorities of Gateshead, Newcastle-upon-Tyne, Sunderland, North Tyneside and South Tyneside comprise the 'counties'.

BAMBURGH on the B4130 east of Belford and north-west of Seahouses
Bamburgh Castle Aviation Artefacts Museum: As the name might imply, this small museum is located within the castle. Run by Derek Walton, the two rooms cover a wide sweep of local aviation history, including wreckage from local 'digs'.
◆ 'Brown signed' off the A1. Open daily Mar to Oct 11am to 5pm – last entry 4.30pm. ✉ Administrator, Bamburgh Castle, Bamburgh, NE69 7DF ☎ 01668 214515 **fax** 01668 214060 **web** www.bamburghcastle.com/

BIRTLEY on the A6127 south of Gateshead
Birtley Car Co: The nose Buccaneer S.2B XV161 left for Dundonald, Scotland on 9th July 2001. By September 2001 a visit to the yard showed that compatriot nose XX893 had also moved on, perhaps to a collector in the Newcastle area.

BOULMER AIRFIELD east of Alnwick
RAF Boulmer: The SAR base continues to be guarded by the Phantom.
❑ XV415   'E' Phantom FGR.2   9163M, ex 56, 74, 228 OCU, 23, 56, 92, 29,
                                   228 OCU, 56, 228 OCU, 31, 228 OCU, 41,
                                   228 OCU, 41, 54, A&AEE. Gate   2-02

BRUNTON AERODROME west of the B1340, south-west of Beadnell
All three of the inmates listed in *W&R17* (p167) have returned to the skies: SF-25A G-AVIZ, Motor
Cadet III G-AYAN and Cadet III G-BUAC.

ESHOTT south of the B6345 north of Morpeth
Condor G-AXGU left the site "several years ago", Hiller UH-12B G-ATKG moved on in 2001.

FELTON on the B6345 south of Alnwick
David Thompson: During the weekend of 9th/10th February 2002, Vampire T.11 XH278 moved to
Elvington, Yorks.

NEWCASTLE AIRPORT or Woolsington, on the A696 north-west of Newcastle
Robin DR.400/160 G-BAPV was flying again by March 2002. The hulk of Short 330-200 N331L had
either perished or had been scrapped during 2000.

NEWCASTLE UPON TYNE
Military Vehicle Museum: Created by the North East Military Vehicle Club, the museum is centred
upon the last remaining pavilion of the 1929 North East Coast Exhibition. A wide array of vehicles and
other exhibits are on show. John Stelling's Auster composite is stored here, for eventual display. It
comprises G-ANFU's forward fuselage, attached to a 'spare' AOP.6 frame, the starboard wing of G-
AKPH and the port from an AOP.6 ①. Please note the Auster is not available for public viewing.
◆ Off the A167(M) at the junction with the B1318. Open 10am to 4pm daily, Nov to March 10am to
   dusk on weekends and school holidays only. Other times by appointment.✉ Military Vehicle
   Museum, Exhibition Park Pavilion, Newcastle upon Tyne, NE2 4PZ ☎ 0191 281 7222 **web**
   www.military-museum.org.uk/
❑ 'NJ719'   Auster 5   G-ANFU, ex NEAM, Bristol, TW385,
                                 663, 227 OCU, 13 OTU. Stored.   ①   3-02

SOUTH SHIELDS on the A1018 north of Sunderland.
A collector in the area took on the former Dundonald Vampire T.11 during mid-2001.
❑ XD602*   Vampire T.11   ex Dundonald, Firbeck, Crowland, ?, Brands Hatch,
                                Birmingham, 7737M, Sutton Coldfield, Smethwick,
                                RAFC, 125. Arrived by 7-01.   7-01

SUNDERLAND site of the former Usworth aerodrome, west of Sunderland
North East Aircraft Museum (NEAM): Work to consolidate the main display hall and other
buildings continues.
   Notes: Flea 'G-ADVU' (BAPC.207) incorporates parts from an original, built in Congleton, Ches
①. Work is underway to turn the Short 330 into a 'hands-on' exhibit, including access for wheelchair-
users ②. The exotically-registered Bö 105 pod (c/n S.863) was donated by Rotortech and is being
converted into a 'hands-on' cockpit and travelling exhibit by a NEAM member in Surrey ③. Chipmunk
T.10 WB685 is a composite, including the rear fuselage of WP969 (G-ATHC) ④. The rear fuselage of
Firefly AS.5 VT409 is stored, ready for fitment to WD889 in due course ⑤. Vampire T.11 WZ518 is
fitted with the wings of WZ608, the 'pod' of which can be found at Rayleigh, Essex ⑥. 'JP4' XP627 is
fitted with the wings of Mk.3 XN584, the fuselage of which can be found at Bruntingthorpe, Leics ⑦.

Departures: Whippet repro 'K-158' (BAPC.207) to Doncaster, S Yorks, 1-00; Dove 8 G-ARHX to Doncaster by 3-00; Brigand TF.1 fuselage RH746 to Kemble, Glos, on loan 19-4-01; Gazelle 03 XW276 to Winthorpe, Notts 26-4-99; anonymous HP C-10A nose to Doncaster, S Yorks, 1-00.

◆ East of Washington on the Old Washington Road between the A1290 and A1231. Signed off the A1290 and the A19. Daily 10am to 5pm (or dusk in winter). Group visits welcome with prior notice.

✉ Old Washington Road, Sunderland, SR5 3HZ ☎ 0191 519 0662 e-mail neam_uk@yahoo.com

❑ 'G-ADVU'	HM.14 'Flea'	BAPC.211, ex Stoke-on-Trent.		①	3-02
❑ 'G-AFUG'	Luton Minor	BAPC.97, ex Stoke-on-Trent, Sunderland, Sibson, Sunderland, Stanley.			3-02
❑ G-APTW	Widgeon	ex Helston, Southend, Westlands. CoA 26-9-75.			3-02
❑ G-ARAD*	Luton Major	ex local, Borgue. Unflown, started 1959. Arr 4-6-01.			3-02
❑ G-ASOL*	Bell 47D-1	ex Weston-super-Mare, Panshanger, N146B. CoA 6-9-71. Arrived 2001.			3-02
❑ G-AWRS	Anson C.19	ex Strathallan, Kemps, Junex, Hewitts, TX213, WCS, 22 GCF, OCTU, 18 GCF, 2 TAF CS, 527, CSE, RCCF. CoA 10-8-73. On loan.		®	3-02
❑ G-BEEX	Comet 4C	ex East Kirkby, Tattershall, Woodford, Lasham, Dan-Air, SU-ALM. Nose.			3-02
❑ G-MBDL	Lone Ranger	microlight. Stored.			3-02
❑ G-OGIL	Short 330-100	ex Gill, G-BITV, G-14-3068. Damaged 1-7-92.		②	3-02
❑ 'G-BAGJ'	Gazelle 1	ex Carlisle, G-SFTA, HB-XIL, G-BAGJ, XW858 ntu. Crashed 7-3-84.		®	3-02
❑ LQ-BLT	MBB Bö 105CBS	ex Bourn, Brazil. Cr 8-6-96. Original pod. off-site ® ③			3-02
❑ VV217	Vampire FB.5	ex Barnham, Bury St Edmunds, 'VV271', 7323M, Oakington, DH. Stored.			3-02
❑ WA577	Sycamore 3	ex King's Heath, Shirley, St Athan 7718M, A&AEE, G-ALST ntu.			3-02
❑ WB685	Chipmunk T.10	ex Leeds, Irlam, Edn UAS, Lyneham SF, 8 RFS, 1 RFS.		④	3-02
❑ WD790	Meteor NF.11	ex Darlington, Leeming, 8743M, RAE Llanbedr, RS&RE, RRE, TRE. Nose, travelling exhibit.			3-02
❑ WD889	Firefly AS.5	ex Failsworth. Cockpit section.		⑤	3-02
❑ WG724	Dragonfly HR.5	ex Chester-le-Street, Moor Monkton, Blackbushe, Lossiemouth SF, Ford SF.		®	3-02
❑ WJ639	Canberra TT.18	ex Samlesbury, 7, 57.			3-02
❑ WK198	Swift F.4	ex Failsworth, Kirkham, 7428M, Aldergrove, MoS. Fuselage.		®	3-02
❑ WL181	'X' Meteor F.8	ex Chester-le-Street, Acklington, Kemble, CAW, Tangmere SF, 34.			3-02
❑ WN516	Balliol T.2	ex Failsworth, RAFC. Cockpit, stored.			3-02
❑ WZ518	Vampire T.11	ex Chester-le-Street, Handforth, Pomona Dock, 5 FTS, Oldenburg SF, 2 TAF CF, 14.		⑥	3-02
❑ WZ767	Grasshopper TX.1	ex Halton. Stored. On loan.			3-02
❑ XG680	'438' S' Venom '22	ex Sydenham, ADS, 891, Yeovilton SF.			3-02
❑ XL319	Vulcan B.2	ex 44, Wadd Wing, 35, 230 OCU, 617, 230 OCU, Scampton Wing, 617.			3-02
❑ XN258	'589' Whirlwind HAR.9	ex Helston, Culdrose SF, *Endurance* Flt, Culdrose SF, *Hermes* Flt.			3-02
❑ XP627	Jet Provost T.4	ex London Colney, Hatfield, Shawbury, 6 FTS, 3 FTS, 1 FTS.		⑦	3-02
❑ XT236	Sioux AH.1	ex Middle Wallop, MoAF, Sek Kong. Stored.			3-02
❑ ZF594	Lightning F.53	ex Warton, RSAF 53-696, G-27-66.			3-02
❑ A-522	FMA Pucará	ex Yeovilton, St Athan 8768M, Stanley, Argentine AF. FAA Museum loan.			3-02
❑ E-419	Hunter F.51	ex Dunsfold, G-9-441, Dan AF Esk.724.			3-02
❑ 146	'8-MG' Mystère IVA	ex Sculthorpe, French AF.			3-02

❏ 42157 '11-ML'	F-100D-16-NA	ex Sculthorpe, French AF.		3-02
❏ 54439 'WI'	T-33A-1-LO	ex Sculthorpe, French AF.		3-02
❏ 6171	F-86D-35-NA	ex Hellenikon, Greek AF, USAF 51-6171.	®	3-02
❏ 26541	F-84F-40-RE	ex Hellenikon, Greek AF, USAF 52-6541.		3-02
❏ BAPC.96	Brown Helicopter	ex Stanley.		3-02
❏ BAPC.119	Bensen B.7	ex Stanley.		3-02
❏ — BAPC.228	Olympus	hang glider. Stored, in its bag!		3-02

No.2214 Squadron Air Cadets: Vampire and newly-arrived Phantom are 'parented' by Leeming.

❏ XD622	Vampire T.11	ex Leeming, Barkston Ash 8160M, Shawbury, 118, RAFC.	9-01
❏ XV460*	'R' Phantom FGR.2	ex Coningsby, 74, 92, 228 OCU, 29, 228 OCU, 92, 19, 56, 31. Nose. Arrived 7-3-00.	9-01

NOTTINGHAMSHIRE

☛ Within the administrative county of Nottinghamshire is the unitary authority of Nottingham.

BALDERTON on the A1 south-east of Newark-on-Trent
Former **A1 Commercials**:

❏ XN728	'V' Lightning F.2A	ex Coningsby, 8546M, 92. Poor state.	4-02

BEESTON on the A6005 south-west of Nottingham
A more precise location for this is Toton, Notts, see below.

FARNSFIELD south of the A617, east of Mansfield
Wonderland Pleasure Park: A Hurricane FSM has arrived while the anonymous Spitfire FSM is reported to have moved to the Isle of Man by December 2000.

❏ XS919	Lightning F.6	ex Devonport, Lower Tremar, Binbrook, 11, 5, 11, 5, 56, 11.	11-01
❏ —*	Hurricane FSM	—	11-01

HUCKNALL AERODROME south of the town
The former Russavia Drone is under restoration. It is a composite with the wings of G-AEJH and tail of G-AEEN. Within Rolls-Royce buildings on the site, the hulk of Spitfire XIV RM689 is stored.

❏ G-AEDB	BAC Drone 2	ex Tadlow, Bishop's Stortford, Duxford, BGA 2731.CoA 26-5-87.	® 8-01
❏ G-ARXN	Nipper 2	CoA 19-8-80. Stored.	8-01
❏ RM689	Spitfire XIV	G-ALGT, ex East Midlands, 'RM619', Hucknall, 443, 350. Crashed 27-6-92. Stored.	8-01

LANGAR AERODROME east of the A46, south of Whatton
The para-club *should* still have its exit-trainer.

❏ G-BATD	Cessna U.206F	ex Isle of Man, Sibson, Shobdon, N60204. Cr 5-4-80.	4-98

MANSFIELD on the A60 north of Nottingham
No.384 Squadron Air Cadets: Should still have their Canberra nose. 'Parent' is Newton.

❏ WT507	Canberra PR.7	8548M, ex Halton 8131M, St Athan, 31, 17, 58, A&AEE, 58, 527, 58. Nose.	7-97

NEWARK-ON-TRENT
Cliff Baker: As *W&R* closed for press Auster B.8 Agricola ZK-BXO cleared the docks and was due to arrive in the area for restoration to flying condition. Along with a huge raft of spares, this represents (to the compiler, if nobody else!) a fantastic import. ZK-BXO was technically airworthy when it was crated, so it may well be that its return to the air will not take long, hence the lack of a 'formal' entry below. Auster 6A G-ARGI moved to <u>Doncaster</u>, S Yorks, during January 2000. J/5F Aiglet Trainer G-AMUJ has been reduced to produce.
◆ The workshop/store is *not* open to the public and visits are *strictly* by prior permission.

❑ G-AIGR	J/1N Alpha	ex Northampton Airport, fuselage frame.		4-00
❑ G-AIJI	J/1N Alpha	ex East Midlands, Elsham Hall, Goxhill,		
		Kirmington. Damaged 12-1-75. Frame, spares.		4-00
❑ G-AIKE	Auster 5	ex Portsmouth, NJ728, 661. Crashed 1-9-65.		4-00
❑ G-AJAS	J/1N Alpha	CoA 11-4-90.		4-00
❑ G-AJPZ*	J/1 Autocrat	ex Bournemouth, Stoke, Sopley, Bournemouth,		
		Wimborne, New Milton, Thruxton, F-BFPE,		
		G-AJPZ. Damaged 2-3-84. Frame, f/n 10-01.		10-01
❑ G-AKWT	Auster 5	ex East Midlands, Elsham Hall, Goxhill, Stroxton		
		Lodge, Tollerton, MT360, 26, 175, 121 Wing,		
		181, 80, 486, 56, 19. Crashed 7-8-48. Frame.		4-00
❑ G-ALNV	Auster 5	ex Nottingham, Leicester, RT578, 341, 329.		
		CoA 4-7-50.		4-00
❑ G-ANHU	Auster 4	ex Shoreham, EC-AXR, G-ANHU, MT255, 659.	®	4-00
❑ G-ANHW	Auster 5D	ex Shipdham, TJ320, 664. CoA 9-3-70.	®	4-00
❑ G-ANHX	Auster 5D	ex Leicester, TW519, 661, A&AEE. Cr 28-3-70.		4-00
❑ G-AOCP	Auster 5	ex TW462, 666. Damaged 4-70. Composite.	®	4-00
❑ G-APKM	J/1N Alpha	CoA 9-1-89.		4-00
❑ G-APTR	J/1N Alpha	CoA 11-4-87.		4-00
❑ G-ARGB	Auster 6A	ex Waddington, VF635, 662, 1901F. CoA 21-6-74.		4-00
❑ G-AROJ	Airedale	ex Leicester, Thorney, HB-EUC, G-AROJ. CoA 8-1-76.		4-00
❑ G-ARTM	Terrier 1	ex Chirk, Auster T.7 WE536, 655, 657,		
		Schwechat SF. Crashed 28-5-70.		4-00
❑ G-ARXC	Airedale	ex Kirton-in-Lindsey, EI-ATD, G-ARXC. CoA 27-6-76.		4-00
❑ G-ASWF	Airedale	ex Leicester. CoA 27-4-83.		4-00
❑ EI-AMF	Taylorcraft	ex Abbeyshrule, G-ARRK, G-AHUM, LB286, Coltishall		
	Plus D	SF, 309, 70 GCF, 84 GCF, 22 EFTS, 43 OTU, 653.		4-00
❑ F-BBSO	Auster 5	ex Taunton, G-AMJM, TW452, 62 GCF. Frame.		1-98
❑	c/no 3705 Auster D.6-180	ex White Waltham, Rearsby. Frame.		4-00
❑	c/no 648 Terrier 3	ex White Waltham, Rearsby. Frame.	≠	4-00
❑ WZ729	Auster AOP.9	G-BXON, ex Singapore.	®	4-00

Others: Gnat T.1 XR534 moved to <u>Winthorpe</u>, Notts, on 2nd December 2000.

NEWTON AIRFIELD on the A46 east of Nottingham
RAF Newton: Departures: Chipmunk T.10 WP962 moved to <u>Hendon</u>, Gtr Lon, on 5-5-00. Bulldog T.1s: XX623 and XX657 to <u>Andover</u>, Hants, by 3-01; XX657 sold in the USA 7-00; XX665 to <u>Halton</u>, Bucks, by 11-01; XX702 sold during 8-01, becoming G-CBCR; XX710 to <u>St Athan</u>, Wales, 20-3-01. Chipmunk T.10 PAX WG362 moved to <u>Ely</u>, Cambs, during 5-01.

NOTTINGHAM
Malcolm and **Sarah Bent**: The nose of Canberra B.15 WH960 moved to <u>Derby</u>, Derbyshire.

NOTTINGHAM AERODROME or Tollerton, south of the A52, east of the city
RC-3 Seabee G-SEAB was cancelled as sold in the USA during January 2002, it reverted to N6210K.

❑ G-AJIW*	J/1N Alpha	ex Cranfield, Panshanger. CoA 16-10-82.	®	8-01

❏ G-BGGF*	Tomahawk 112	ex N9674N. CoA 15-10-<u>94</u>. Stored.	4-01
❏ G-GRAY	Cessna 172N	ex N4859D. Ditched 2-4-93. Stored.	9-01

RADCLIFFE ON TRENT on the A52, east of Nottingham
Don Cashmore: Having completed the rebuild of the ANEC G-EBJO, Don Cashmore has taken on the restoration of Shuttleworth's Granger Archaeopteryx.

❏ G-ABXL*	Archaeopteryx	ex Old Warden, Chilwell. CoA 22-9-82. Arrived 13-12-00.	℗ 12-00

RETFORD AERODROME or Gamston, off the B6387 south of East Retford
The hulk of King Air A90 5N-ATU has expired by mid-2001 at the latest.

SOUTH SCARLE in between the A46 and the A1133 south-west of Lincoln
South Scarie Aviation: The original fuselage of Rallye G-AZEE departed some time back, only to 'surface' at <u>Skegness</u>, Lincs, by July 2001.

❏ G-AYJD	Fournier RF-3	ex F-BLXA. CoA 19-5-95. Stored.	2-97

SYERSTON AIRFIELD off the A46 south-west of Newark-on-Trent
RAF Syerston / Air Cadets Central Gliding School: The status of the unofficial 'Air Cadets Vintage Glider Flight' formed under the wing of the RAFGSA's Four Counties Gliding Club needs updating, their listings being somewhat long-in-the-tooth. Both of the Viking T.1s previously listed returned to service, ZE611 in April 2000 and ZE636 in September 2001.

❏ XA302	Cadet TX.3	HAK/BGA.3786. CoA 5-96.	℗ 3-97
❏ XE799	Cadet TX.3	ex 8943M, CGS.	℗ 2-96
❏ XN185	Sedbergh TX.1	HNS/BGA.4077, ex 8942M, CGS, 643 VGS,	
	✈	4 MGSP, 633 VGS, 635 VGS.	4-98

TOTON on the A6005 south-west of Nottingham
No.350 Field Squadron Headquarters, Chetwynd Barracks: More precisely listed under this heading and not the previous Beeston – in Swiney Way, which links the B6003 and the A6005.

❏ XW267	'SA' Harrier T.4	ex 'Chilwell', Boscombe Down, SAOEU, RAE, A&AEE, RAE, 233 OCU.	1-02

WINTHORPE SHOW GROUND
Newark Air Museum (NAM): Over the weekend of 16th/17th June 2001, the museum staged the second *CockpitFest* – a gathering of cockpit collectors from all over the country. The 2001 event was supported by *FlyPast* and was a resounding success. No less than 15 cockpits (two resident with NAM) were on view, plus some superb instrument panels. It all looks set to become a regular gathering and compulsive for *W&R* readers! NAM's refreshing policy of collecting civilian airframes continues.
Notes: Several airframes are on loan from outside bodies: the Autocrat from Leicestershire Museum, Arts and Records Service; the Chipmunk and McBroom from TAC (see under Manchester, Gtr Man); the Canberra PR.7 from the 81 Squadron Associates; the Canberra T.17 nose from Aaron Braid; the Gazelle from the Museum of Army Flying, Middle Wallop, Hants; the Canberra PR.9 nose from Frank Millar. These are marked ±.
Canberra T.19 WH904 was built by Shorts Brothers and Harland as a B.2 and therefore the forward fuselage *should* have a plate reading SHB-0-2388. Inspection found the nose to have the plate EEP71123, which would make it WH651. The logic works out like this. WH651 was issued to English Electric for conversion from a B.2 to a T.4 on 5th July 1956 and in this process it would have been fitted with a new-build T.4 cockpit. It looks as though the old cockpit passed on to Boulton Paul for use in the B.2 to T.11 conversions. WH904 was issued to BP on 17th October 1957 for T.11 fit, it received the cockpit of WH651. (And, later was further converted to T.19 status.) ① Monospar ST-12 VH-UTH is at Innsworth, Glos.

◆ Signposted from the A1, on Newark Showground, off the A46 Lincoln Road. Open daily Mar to Oct 10am to 5pm, Nov to Feb daily 10am to 4pm. Closed Xmas period. Buildings suitable for the disabled. Special events staged – SAE for details. ✉ The Airfield, Winthorpe, Newark, NG24 2NY ☎ / fax 01636 707170 e-mail newarkair@lineone.net web www.newarkairmuseum.co.uk

❑ G-AGOH	J/1 Autocrat	ex Leicester. CoA 24-8-95. On loan.	±	3-02
❑ G-AHRI	Dove 1	ex Long Marston, East Kirkby, Tattershall, Little Staughton, 4X-ARI, G-AHRI. 'Newark Air Museum'.		3-02
❑ G-ANXB	Heron 1	ex Biggin Hill, Fairflight, BEA, G-5-14. CoA 25-3-79. BEA Scottish colours. *Sir James Young Simpson*.		3-02
❑ G-APVV	Mooney M.20A	ex Skelmersdale, Barton, N8164E. Crashed 11-1-81.		3-02
❑ G-BFTZ	Rallye Club	ex Firbeck, Hooton Park, Warmingham, Fownhope, Cardiff-Wales, F-BPAX. CoA 19-9-81.		3-02
❑ G-BJAD*	FRED Srs 2	ex Retford. Uncompleted project. Arrived 9-1-02.		3-02
❑ G-BKPG*	Rattler Strike	ex Egginton, Tatenhill. Stored. Arrived 12-00.		3-02
❑ 'G-MAZY'	Tiger Moth	ex Innsworth, Staverton, Newark area. Composite, mostly G-AMBB/T6801, ex Scampton SF, 6 FTS, 18 EFTS. Partially uncovered.		3-02
❑ G-MBBZ*	Volmer VJ-24W	ex Old Sarum. CoA 3-9-93. First noted 7-00.		3-02
❑ G-MBUE	Tiger Cub 440	ex Retford, Worksop. *The Dormouse Zeitgeist*.		3-02
❑ KF532	Harvard IIB	ex 781, 799, 727, 799, 758. Cockpit section.		3-02
❑ RA897*	Cadet TX.1	fuselage in workshop. First noted 7-01.		3-02
❑ TG517	Hastings T.5	ex 230 OCU, SCBS, BCBS, 202, 53, 47.		3-02
❑ VL348	Anson C.19	G-AVVO, ex Southend, Shawbury, 22 GCF, 24 GCF, Colerne SF, 62 GCF, HCMSU, RCCF.		3-02
❑ VR249 'FA-EL'	Prentice T.1	G-APIY, ex 1 ASS, RAFC. CoA 18-3-67.		3-02
❑ VZ608	Meteor FR.9	ex Hucknall, Shoreham, MoS, RR. RB.108 test-bed.		3-02
❑ VZ634	Meteor T.7	ex Wattisham 8657M, 5 MU, MoA, Leeming SF, Stradishall SF, 41, 141, 609, 247.		3-02
❑ WB624	Chipmunk T.10	ex Hooton Park, Firbeck, Long Marston, Warmingham, East Midlands, Wigan, Dur UAS, Abn UAS, Henlow, St Athan, 22 GCF, Debden, Jurby SF, 8 FTS, 18 RFS. Stored.	±	3-02
❑ WF369 'F'	Varsity T.1	ex 6 FTS, AE&AEOS, AES, 2 ANS, 201 AFS.		3-02
❑ WH791	Canberra PR.7	8187M, ex Cottesmore, St Athan 8165M, 8176M, 81, 58, 82, 542.	±	3-02
❑ WH863	Canberra T.17	ex Marham 8693M, 360, RAE, IAM. Nose.	±	3-02
❑ WH904 '04'	Canberra T.19	ex Cambridge, 7, 85, West Raynham TFF, 228 OCU, 35, 207.	①	3-02
❑ WK277 'N'	Swift FR.5	ex Cosford, Leconfield 7719M, 2. 2 Sqn colours.		3-02
❑ WM913 '456'	Sea Hawk FB.3	ex Fleetwood, Sealand 8162M, Culdrose A2510, Abbotsinch, 736.		3-02
❑ WR977 'B'	Shackleton MR.3/3	ex Finningley, 8186M 203, 42, 206, 203, 42, 201, 206, 201, 220.		3-02
❑ WS692 'C'	Meteor NF.12	ex Cranwell, Henlow 7605M, 72, 46.		3-02
❑ WS739	Meteor NF.14	ex Misson, Church Fenton 7961M, Kemble, 1 ANS, 2 ANS, 25.		3-02
❑ WT651 'C'	Hunter F.1	ex Lawford Heath, Halton, Credenhill 7532M, 229 OCU, 233 OCU, 229 OCU, 222.		3-02
❑ WT933	Sycamore 3	ex Sutton, Strensall, Halton 7709M, G-ALSW ntu.		3-02
❑ WV606 'P-B'	Provost T.1	ex Halton 7622M, 1 FTS.		3-02
❑ WV787	Canberra B.2/8	ex Abingdon 8799M, A&AEE. Heffner 'bunny' logo.		3-02
❑ WW217 '351'	Sea Ven FAW.21	ex Cardiff, Ottershaw, Culdrose, Yeovilton, ADS, 891, 890.		3-02
❑ WX905	Venom NF.3	ex Henlow, Hendon, Yatesbury 7458M, 27 MU, 23.		3-02
❑ XD593 '50'	Vampire T.11	ex Woodford, Chester, St Athan, 8 FTS, CFS, FWS, 5 FTS, 4 FTS. CFS colours.		3-02

❏	XH177*		Canberra PR.9	ex Corby, Stock, Cardiff-Wales, Boscombe, 13, 58. Nose. Arrived 4-11-00.	±	3-02
❏	XH992	'P'	Javelin FAW.8	ex Cosford 7829M, Shawbury, 85. 85 Sqn colours.		3-02
❏	XJ560	'243'	Sea Vixen FAW.2	ex RAE Bedford, Farnborough, Halton 8142M, 893, 899, 892, 890.		3-02
❏	XL149		Beverley C.1	ex Finningley 7988M, 84, 30, 84, 242 OCU. Cockpit.		3-02
❏	XL764	'J'	Skeeter AOP.12	ex Nostell Priory, Rotherham, Middle Wallop, Arborfield 7940M, Hayes, A&AEE, MoA, AAC, Saro, AAC.		3-02
❏	XM383	'90'	Jet Provost T.3A	ex Crowland, Scampton, 7 FTS, 1 FTS, RAFC, 6 FTS, BSE, 2 FTS, A&AEE, 2 FTS.		3-02
❏	XM594		Vulcan B.2	ex 44, Scampton Wing, 617, 27.		3-02
❏	XM685	'513'	Whirlwind HAS.7	ex Panshanger area, Elstree, Luton, G-AYZJ ntu, Fleetlands, Lee-o-S, 771, *Ark* Ship's Flt, 847, 848.		3-02
❏	XN412*		Auster AOP.9	ex Metlon Mowbray, Innsworth, Swindon, Dorchester, Middle Wallop, 6 Flt, C(A). Stored.		3-02
❏	XN573		Jet Provost T.3	ex Blackpool Airport, Kemble, 1 FTS, CFS. Nose.		3-02
❏	XN819		Argosy C.1	ex Finningley 8205M, Shawbury, Benson Wing, 105, MoA. Cockpit section. In small display hall.		3-02
❏	XN964	'613'	Buccaneer S.1	ex Bruntingthorpe, East Midlands, Brough, Pershore, 807.		3-02
❏	XP226	'073'	Gannet AEW.3	ex Lee-on-Solent, Southwick, Lee-on-Solent, A2667, Lossiemouth, Ilchester, 849.		3-02
❏	XR534*	'65'	Gnat T.1	ex Newark, Valley 8578M, 4 FTS, CFS. Arr 2-12-00.		3-02
❏	XS417	'DZ'	Lightning T.5	ex Binbrook, LTF, 5, 11, 5, 11, LTF, 56, 23, 11, 23, 226 OCU.		3-02
❏	XT200	'F'	Sioux AH.1	ex Middle Wallop.		3-02
❏	XV728	'A'	Wessex HC.2	ex Fleetlands, 72, 2 FTS, CFS, 18. *Argonaut*.		3-02
❏	XW276		Gazelle 03	ex Sunderland, Wroughton, Southampton, Middle Wallop, Farnborough, Leatherhead, F-ZWRI.	±	3-02
❏	AR-107		S.35XD Draken	ex Scampton, Esk.729, RDanAF.		3-02
❏	83	'8-MS'	Mystère IVA	ex Sculthorpe, French AF.		3-02
❏	56321		SAAB Safir	G-BKPY, ex Norwegian AF.		3-02
❏	42223		F-100D-16-NA	ex Sculthorpe, French AF.		3-02
❏	51-9036		T-33A-1-LO	19036, ex '5547', Sculthorpe, Fr AF. 48th FIS c/s.		3-02
❏	—	BAPC.43	HM.14 'Flea'	ex East Kirkby, Tattershall, Wellingore.		3-02
❏	—	BAPC.101	HM.14 'Flea'	ex Tumby Woodside, East Kirkby, Tattershall, Sleaford. Fuselage. (Also G-AFUL's rudder.)		3-02
❏	—	BAPC.183	Zurowski ZP.1	ex Burton-on-Trent. Homebuilt helicopter, unflown. Polish AF colours.		3-02
❏	—	BAPC.204	McBroom hang-g	ex Hooton Park, Warmingham.	±	3-02
❏	*		Hiway Demon	first noted 7-00.		3-02
❏			Jet Provost CIM	Procedures trainer.		3-02
❏			Gnat T.1 CIM	ex Melton Mowbray. Procedures trainer.		3-02
❏			Lynx EMU	ex Firbeck, Cardiff-Wales, Bedford. *Lenny the Lynx*		3-02

Newark Gliding Club: An SF-27MB is under slow restoration in the hangar.

| ❏ | G-BSUM | Scheibe SF-27MB | ex D-KIBE. | ® | 9-97 |

OXFORDSHIRE

ARNCOTT south of the A41 south-east of Bicester

| ❏ | G-ASEF | Auster 6A | ex Somerton, Bicester, RAFGSA, VW985, 664. CoA 19-12-66. Stored, poor state.. | 10-96 |

BANBURY
John Horton: At this *private* location, the Cessna plaything may still be found.
❑ G-ARRF*   Cessna 150A   ex Perranporth, N7197X. Crashed 11-3-88.
                                  Fuselage. Arrived 28-7-88.   3-00

BENSON AIRFIELD east of the A4074, east of Wallingford
RAF Benson:
❑ 'EN343'   Spitfire FSM   BAPC.226, gate.   3-02
❑ [XT681]   'U' Wessex HC.2   9279M, ex Shawbury, 72, WTF, 18. ABDR   7-01

BICESTER AERODROME on the A421 north-east of Bicester
RAF Gliding and Soaring Association (RAFGSA) Centre: The Grasshopper 'fuselage' noted
here in previous editions, is thought to have been the rear 'bridge' structure only and has been deleted.

❑ G-AYUP   T-61A Falke   ex XW983, G-AYUP. CoA 15-7-96. Stored.   8-99
❑ CLJ   EoN Primary   BGA.1625, ex WP267. CoA 2-72. Stored.   ®   1-02
❑ EVU   Doppleraab   BGA.2944. Stored.   1-02
❑ WB556   Chipmunk T.10   ex Oxf UAS. SOC 12-9-73. Fuselage.   8-99
❑ WB645   Chipmunk T.10   8218M, ex Little Rissington, Cottesmore SF, Edn UAS,
                                  8 FTS, 1 CAACU, 17 RFS, 1 RFS. Fuselage. Spares   8-99
❑ WG303   Chipmunk T.10   8208M, ex Shawbury, Kemble, Ox UAS, Gatow SF,
                                  Wittering SF, Marham SF, Bir UAS, 5 RFS, 2 BFTS.   7-97
❑ ZE589   Viking T.1   EXT/BGA.3045, ex 634 VGS, Shawbury, Syerston.
                                  Crashed 9-7-92. Stored.   11-99
❑   Chipmunk T.10   cockpit section. Hulk.   3-95

Locally: The Swift is stored in this general area.
❑ XF114*   Swift F.7   G-SWIF, ex Scampton, Bournemouth, Connah's Quay,
                                  Aston Down, CS(A), Cranfield. Stored. Arr 7-1-02.   1-02

BRIZE NORTON AIRFIELD on the A4095 south-west of Witney
RAF Brize Norton: The nose of VC-10 ZD234 *should* still serve as a procedures simulator ①.
❑ XR806   VC-10 C.1K   9285M, ex 10. Ground accident 18-12-97.
                                  Forward fuselage. ABDR   1-00
❑ ZD234   Super VC-10   8700M, ex Heathrow, G-ASGF, BA, BOAC. Nose.   ①   4-92

Air Movements School: As noted in *W&R17*, Sioux XT141 *did* go to Moreton-in-Marsh, Glos.
❑ XV118   'T' Scout AH.1   9141M, ex Wroughton, 657, 658, 652, 651, 660.   6-01
❑ XZ994   'O' Harrier GR.3   9170M, ex St A', 1417F, 233 OCU, 1417F, 233'.   6-01

CHALGROVE AIRFIELD on the B480 north-west of Watlington
Martin Baker: Meteor T.7 WL419 *Asterix* continues to act as a flying test-bed for MB. By June 2001
it had been joined in the air by T.7(mod) WA638. The cockpit and centre section of Meteor T.7 WL405
moved to Yatesbury, Wilts, on 30th October 2001. The contents of the scrap dump were recently
inspected, with interesting results.
❑ EE416   Meteor III   ex Wroughton, South Kensington, MB. Nose.   2-01
❑ –*   Northrop F-5A   ex Greek AF, 63-8418. Nose. Dump.   2-01
❑ –*   MiG-19 *Farmer*   ex Pakistan? Nose. Dump.   2-01

CULHAM on the A415 south-east of Abingdon
UKAEA, Lightning Studies Unit: Still have their Hunter in an upstairs lab.
❑ WV381   '732' Hunter GA.11   ex Kemble, FRADU, FRU, FWS, 222. Fuselage.   6-01

ENSTONE AERODROME on the B4030 east of Chipping Norton
By June 2000 Seneca 200-2 G-BBNH was flying again. By the same time the glider store had been
cleaned out: T.21Bs ATL and ELH, and Blaniks CAW and DCL.

❏ G-AVGJ	SAN DR.1050	ex F-BJYJ. CoA 22-4-85.	® off-site	10-01
❏ G-AWSP*	Condor	CoA 23-1-<u>95</u>. Stored.		10-01
❏ G-AZTD	Cherokee Six 300	ex N8611N. CoA 16-8-98. Stored.		10-01
❏ G-BBRY	Cessna 210	ex Cranfield, Blackbushe, Chessington, 5Y-KRZ, VP-KRZ, N7391E. Crashed 2-4-78. Stored.		10-99

HENLEY-ON-THAMES on the A4155 north of Reading
No.447 Squadron Air Cadets: 'Parented' by Benson.

❏ XS218	Jet Provost T.4	ex Woodley, Halton 8508M, Shawbury, 3 FTS. Nose.	12-97

KIDLINGTON on the A423 north of Oxford
Julian Mitchell: Should still have his Hunter nose.

❏ XF383	Hunter F.6	ex North Scarle, Wittering 8706M, Kemble, 12, 216, 237 OCU, 4 FTS, 229 OCU, 65, 111, 263. Nose.	12-00

NORTH MORETON south of the A4130, west of Wallingford

❏ G-ARET	Tri-Pacer 160	CoA 20-5-83.	®	5-96

OXFORD
C W Engineering: Spitfire IX SM520 (G-BXHZ) moved to <u>Ramsbottom</u>, Lancs.

OXFORD AIRPORT or Kidlington, on the A4260, north of Oxford
Oxford Air Training School:

❏ G-ARJR	Apache 160G	ex N4447P. CoA 24-10-78.	6-97
❏ G-RING	FR.182RG	ex D-EFGP. Crashed 23-2-91. Dump.	7-98
❏ [XN500]	Jet Provost T.3A	ex 1 FTS, 7 FTS, RAFC, 3 FTS, RAFC.	2-02

SHRIVENHAM east of Swindon, south of the A420
Royal Military College of Science: The Gnat is painted in Red Arrows colours on one side and air
defence grey on the other! ① A Harrier and Scout are displayed within the grounds ② all others are
within the Aviation Hall.

❏ XP542	'42'	Gnat T.1	8575M, ex St Athan, 4 FTS.	① 10-01
❏ XT621		Scout AH.1	ex Wroughton, 655, 656, 666, 664, 666.	10-01
❏ XV122	'A'	Scout AH.1	ex Almondbank, Wroughton.	② 10-01
❏ XV744	'3K'	Harrier GR.3	9167M, ex St Athan, 233 OCU, 1, 233 OCU.	② 10-01
❏ XW919	'W'	Harrier GR.3	A2610 [3], ex A2609, Culdrose, Cosford, 4, 1, 233 OCU.	10-01
❏ 69-16445		AH-1F Cobra	ex US Army, 1/1CAV, Budingen. 'IFOR' markings. Last flight 2-7-96.	10-01
❏ 70-15154		OH-58CR Kiowa	ex Lyneham (transit), US Army.	10-01

WITNEY north of the A40 west of Oxford
Witney Technical College: By mid-1998 the hulk of Aztec 250B G-ASRI had gone. However, a
local farm was seen to have the cockpit area of an 'Apache', marked as 'G-IRIS' during June 2000. This
was last heard of at Faringdon, Oxfordshire – see *W&R16* (p195). As G-ASRI is a short-nose Aztec,
could this be one and the same?

❏ 'G-IRIS'	Aztec/Apache	ex Faringdon? See above.	6-00

SHROPSHIRE

ASTLEY east of the A49 north of Shrewsbury

☐ G-AWGM   Kittiwake II   ex Hanworth, Halton. Damaged 18-1-86.   ®   9-95

BRIDGNORTH on the A442 south of Telford
Derek Leek: The Canberra cockpit *may* have moved on...

☐ WD935   Canberra B.2   ex Ottershaw, Egham, 8440M, St Athan, 360, 97,   151, CSE, EE, BCDU, RAAF A84-1 ntu. Nose.   5-95

CHETWYND AERODROME on the A41 north-west of Newport
Staffordshire Sports Skydiving Club: Should still have the Cessna hulk.

☐ G-ATIE   Cessna 150F   ex Market Drayton, N6291R. Crashed 28-7-79.   5-97

COSFORD AIRFIELD south of Junction 3 of the M54
Royal Air Force Museum: The main focus of attention is the Michael Beetham Conservation Centre, a major achievement for the museum – this is treated separately, see below. With the major 'Milestones of Flight' project underway and due to open in 2003, there will be a series of movements down the M54, M6 and M1 to Hendon, Gtr Lon, these aircraft are marked ➡. Several airframes are in deep store and not available for inspection – marked ❖. Bristol 173 XF785 moved to Kemble, Glos, on 3rd January 2002.
     Notes: The Canberra B.2 nose carries the c/n EEP.71038 which should make it WD956 (which had no service life, undertaking 'Red Dean' missile trials), comments? ①. The T-tail rear fuselage of the Short SB.5 is displayed alongside WG768 ②. The Blériot is suspended inside the visitor centre ③. Airframes marked § are in deep store and not generally available for public inspection. Airframes out on loan: Coventry, Warks, Meteor WS838, T-33A 51-7473. Kemble, Glos, Bristol 173 G-ALBN; Manchester, Gtr Man, Shackleton WR960; Tangmere, W Sussex, Meteor EE549, Hunter WB188; Woodley, Berks, Jet Gyrodyne XJ389.

◆   Open daily 10am to 6pm (last admission 4pm) with the exception of Xmas and New Year. Annual airshow in which several museum aircraft (and others from the SoTT) that are not normally outside are displayed - extra charges apply. Near to Junction 3 of the M54 and well signposted. The **Aerospace Museum Society** provides a vital link in both the restoration of exhibits and the running of the museum and special events. ✉ Cosford, Shifnal, TF11 8UP ☎ 01902 376200 **fax** 01902 376211 **e-mail** cosford@rafmuseum.com **web** www.rafmuseum.com

☐ G-AAMX	DH.60GM Moth	ex Shoreham, NC926M. CoA 7-5-94.	3-02
☐ G-AEEH	HM.14 'Flea'	ex St Athan, Colerne, Bath, Whitchurch.	3-02
☐ 'G-AFAP'	CASA 352L	ex Spanish AF T2B-272. British Airways c/s.	3-02
☐ 'G-AJOV'	Dragonfly HR.3	WP495, ex Biggin Hill, Banstead, Warnham, Wimbledon. BEA colours.	3-02
☐ G-AMOG	Viscount 701	ex Cardiff-Wales, BOAC, Cambrian, BEA *Robert Falcon Scott*, G-AMNZ ntu. CoA 14-6-77. BEA c/s.	3-02
☐ G-AOVF	Britannia 312F	ex Southend, 9Q-CAZ, G-AOVF, Stansted, Donaldson, British Eagle, BOAC. BOAC c/s.	3-02
☐ G-APAS	Comet 1XB	ex Shawbury 8351M, XM823, G-APAS, G-5-23, Air France, F-BGNZ. BOAC c/s.	3-02
☐ G-APFJ	Boeing 707-436	ex British Airtours, BOAC. CoA 16-2-82. Airtours c/s.	3-02
☐ G-ARPH	Trident 1C	ex BA, BEA. CoA 8-9-82. BA colours.	3-02
☐ G-ARVM	VC-10 Srs 1101	ex BA, BOAC. CoA 5-8-80. BA colours.	3-02
☐ G-AVMO	BAC 111-510ED	ex Bournemouth, BA, BEA. *Lothian Region.*	3-02
☐ G-BBYM*	Jetstream 200	ex Cranfield, BAe, G-AYWR, G-8-13. CoA 20-9-98. Arrived 23-5-00.	3-02
☐ 'B5577'	'W' Camel REP	BAPC.59, ex St Athan 'D3419', St Mawgan, 'F1921', St Athan, Colerne. Stored. ❖	3-02
☐ F6314*	'B' Camel F.1	9206M, ex Wyton, Hendon, Heathrow, Colerne, Hendon, Tring, Waddon. Arrived 30-10-01.	3-02

❑	K4972		Hart Trainer	ex Cardington, Hendon, St Athan,		
				Carlisle 1764M, 2 FTS. Stored.	❖ ➠	3-02
❑	DG202/G		F.9/40 Meteor	ex Yatesbury, Locking 5758M, Moreton Valance.		3-02
❑	'FS628'		Argus II	ex Rochester, G-AIZE, Cosford, Henlow, Hanwell,		
				N9996F, 43-14601. CoA 6-8-66. SEAC colours.		3-02
❑	'KG374'	'YS'	Dakota IV	KN645, 8355M, ex Colerne, AFN CF, MinTech,		
				AFN CF, MinTech, AFN HQ, SHAPE CF,		
				Malta CF, BAFO CS, 2nd TAF CS, 44-77003.		3-02
❑	'KL216'		P-47D-40-RA	9212M, ex Duxford, Cardington, Bitteswell,		
		'RS-L'		Yugoslavia 13064, USAAF 45-49295. 30 Sqn c/s.	➠	3-02
❑	KN751		B-24L-20-FO	ex Colerne, Ind AF 6 Sqn HE807, RAF KN751, 99.		3-02
❑	LF738		Hurricane II	ex Rochester, Biggin Hill, Wellesbourne Mountford,		
		'UH-A'		5405M, 22 OTU, 1682 BDTF. 682 BDTF colours.		3-02
❑	RF398		Lincoln B.2	8376M, ex Henlow, Abingdon, CSE, BCBS.		3-02
❑	RW393		Spitfire XVI	ex St Athan, Turnhouse 7293M, 602, 3		
		'XT-A'		CAACU, 31, FCCS, 203 AFS. 603 Sqn c/s.		3-02
❑	TA639	'AZ-E'	Mosquito TT.35	7806M, ex CFS, 3 CAACU, Aldergrove TT Flt.		3-02
❑	TG511		Hastings T.5	8554M, ex 230 OCU, SCBS, BCBS, 202, 47.		3-02
❑	[TS798]		York C.1	ex 'MW100', Shawbury, Brize Norton,		
				Staverton, 'LV633', G-AGNV, Skyways,		
				BOAC, TS798. CoA 6-3-65.		3-02
❑	TX214		Anson C.19	ex Henlow 7817M, HCCS, MCS, RCCF,		
				Staff College CF, 1 FU, 16 FU.		3-02
❑	VP952		Devon C.2/2	8820M, ex St Athan, 207, 21, WCS, SCS,		
				Upavon SF, TCCF, MCS, BCCS, HCCS,		
				A&AEE, MCCF, AAFCE, TCCF, Hendon SF, HS.		3-02
❑	'VX461'		Vampire FB.5	ex Cardington, Cosford, Henlow, Hendon,		
				3/4 CAACU, 1 FTS, 7 FTS, 130, 98, 102 FRS.		
				Booms of VX461. Identity confirmed. Stored.	❖	3-02
❑	VX573		Valetta C.2	8389M, ex Henlow, Wildenrath CF,		
				Buckeburg CF. *Lorelei*. Stored.	❖	3-02
❑	WA634		Meteor T.7(mod)	ex St Athan, Martin Baker.		3-02
❑	WD931		Canberra B.2	ex Aldridge, Pershore, RRE, RAE. Nose. Stored.	❖	3-02
❑	WE600		Auster C4	ex St Athan, Swinderby, Finningley 7602M,		
			(T.7 mod)	Trans-Antarctic Expedition, 663. Skis.		3-02
❑	WE982		Prefect TX.1	8781M, ex Cardington, Henlow, Syerston,		
				Manston, ACCGS, CGS, 1 GC, 621 GS, 612 GS,		
				644 GS, 643 GS, 166 GS, 143 GS. Stored.	❖	3-02
❑	WG760		EE P.1A	ex Binbrook, Henlow, Bicester 7755M,		
				St Athan, Warton, A&AEE.		3-02
❑	WG768		Short SB.5	ex Topcliffe, Finningley 8005M, ETPS, RAE		
				Bedford, RAE Farnborough, A&AEE, RAE		
				Bedford, A&AEE. With 'T'-tail alongside.		3-02
❑	WG777		Fairey FD-2	ex Topcliffe, Finningley 7986M, RAE Bedford.		3-02
❑	WK935		Meteor F.8(mod)	ex St Athan, Colerne 7869M, RAE. Prone-pilot .		3-02
❑	WL679		Varsity T.1	9155M, ex Farnborough, RAE, BLEU.		3-02
❑	WL732		Sea Balliol T.21	ex Henlow, A&AEE, Lossiemouth, Anthorn.		3-02
❑	WP912		Chipmunk T.10	8467M, ex Hendon, Man UAS, RAFC, ITS,		
				Cam UAS, CFS, 2 FTS, Lon UAS,		
				FTCCS, HCCS, 8 FTS.		3-02
❑	WS843	'Y'	Meteor NF.14	ex Hendon, St Athan, Henlow 7937M,		
				St Athan, Kemble, 1 ANS, MoA, 228 OCU.		3-02
❑	WV562	'P-C'	Provost T.1	ex Cranwell 7606M, Henlow, 22 FTS.		3-02
❑	WV746		Pembroke C.1	8938M, ex 60, 207, 21, WCS, TCCF,		
				FTCCS, BCCS, HS, 2 TAF CF.		3-02
❑	WZ744		Avro 707C	ex Topcliffe, Finningley 7932M, RAE, Avro.		3-02
❑	XA564		Javelin FAW.1	ex 2 SoTT, Locking 7464M, Filton.		3-02

☐ XA893		Vulcan B.1	ex Abingdon, Bicester 8591M, A&AEE, Avro. Nose.	3-02
☐ XD145		SARO SR.53	ex Brize Norton, Henlow, Westcott, A&AEE.	3-02
☐ XD674		Jet Provost T.1	ex St Athan, Swinderby, Finningley 7570M, 71 MU, Hunting. Stored. ❖	3-02
☐ XE670		Hunter F.4	8585M / 7762M, ex St Athan, Abingdon, Bicester, 93, 26. Nose.	3-02
☐ XF926		Bristol 188	8368M, ex Foulness Island, RAE.	3-02
☐ XG337		Lightning F.1	ex 2 SoTT 8056M, Warton, A&AEE, Warton.	3-02
☐ XH171	'U'	Canberra PR.9	ex 2 SoTT 8746M, 39, 13, 39 MoA, 58.	3-02
☐ XH672		Victor K.2	9242M, ex Shawbury, 55, 57, 543, MoA. *Maid Marion*.	3-02
☐ XJ918		Sycamore HR.14	ex 2 SoTT 8190M, 32, MCS, Kemble, Wroughton, 110, Seletar, A&AEE, 275.	3-02
☐ XK724		Gnat F.1	ex Cranwell, Bicester, Henlow 7715M, Folland.	3-02
☐ XL568*	'C'	Hunter T.7A	9224M, ex Cranwell, Lossiemouth, 12, 74, MoA, 74, HS. Arrived 28-2-02.	3-02
☐ XL703		Pioneer CC.1	8034M, ex Manchester, Henlow, 209, 230.	3-02
☐ XL993	'T'	Pioneer CC.1	8388M, ex Henlow, Shawbury, 21, 78.	3-02
☐ XM351	'Y'	Jet Provost T.3	8078M, ex 1 SoTT, Halton, Shawbury, 3 FTS, 7 FTS, 2 FTS.	3-02
☐ XM555		Skeeter AOP.12	ex Shawbury 8027M, Ternhill, CFS, HQ BAOR, 654.➡	3-02
☐ XM598		Vulcan B.2	8778M, ex 44, Wadd Wing, Cott Wing, 12.	3-02
☐ XN714		Hunting 126/50	ex RAE Bedford, NASA Ames and Moffett, Holme-on-Spalding Moor, RAE.	3-02
☐ XP299		W'wind HAR.10	8726M, ex 22, 230, 1563F, Queen's Flt, 230, CFS. ➡	3-02
☐ XP411		Argosy C.1	ex 2 SoTT 8442M, 6 FTS, Kemble, 70.	3-02
☐ XR220		TSR-2 XO-2	ex Henlow 7933M, A&AEE. Never flown.	3-02
☐ XR371		Belfast C.1	ex Hucknall, Kemble, 53. *Enceladus*.	3-02
☐ XR977		Gnat T.1	ex 2 SoTT 8640M, Red Arrows, 4 FTS. 'Reds' c/s.	3-02
☐ XS639		Andover E.3A	9241M, ex Northolt, 32, 115, 32, 46.	3-02
☐ XV591		Phantom FG.1	ex St Athan, 111, 43, 892. Trans-Atlantic c/s. Nose.	3-02
☐ XW547		Buccaneer S.2B	9169M, ex Shawbury, 9095M, Gulf Det, 12, 237 OCU, 208, 12, 216, 12, 237 OCU, 12. *Guinness Girl / Pauline / The Macallan*. Pink c/s. ➡	3-02
☐ XX765		Jaguar GR.1 (mod)	ex Loughborough, Warton, BAe, RAE, A&AEE, 226 OCU, 14. ACT 'fly-by-wire' test-bed.	3-02
☐ '164'		Blériot XI	9209M, BAPC.106, ex Cardington, Hendon, Heathrow, Colerne, Hendon. ➡	3-02
☐ –		P.1121	ex Henlow, Cranfield. Sections, stored. ❖	3-02
☐ A-515		FMA Pucará	9245M, ex ZD485, A&AEE, Yeovilton, Stanley, Arg AF A-515.	3-02
☐ L-866		PBY-6A Catalina	8466M, ex Colerne, Danish AF Esk.721, 82-866, BuNo 63993.	3-02
☐ 112372		Me 262A-2a	8482M, ex St Athan, Cosford, Finningley, Gaydon, Cranwell, Farnborough, VK893/AM.51, I/KG51. ➡	3-02
☐ 191614		Me 163B-1a	8481M, ex Biggin Hill, Westcott, Brize Norton, Farnborough, Hussum, II/JG400. ®	3-02
☐ 420430	'3U+CC'	Me 410A-1-U2	8483M, ex St Athan, Cosford, Fulbeck, Wroughton, Stanmore Park, Brize Norton, Farnborough, AM.72, Vaerlose.	3-02
☐ 475081		Fi 156C-7	ex St Athan, Coltishall, Bircham Newton, Finningley 7362M, Fulbeck, VP546, AM.101, Farnborough.	3-02
☐ –		Fa 330A-1	8469M, ex Henlow, Farnborough.	3-02
☐ –		Fi 103 (V-1)	8583M / BAPC.94.	3-02
☐ 5439		Ki 46 *Dinah*	8484M / BAPC.84, ex St Athan, Biggin Hill, Fulbeck, Wroughton, Stanmore Park, Sealand, ATAIU-SEA.	3-02
☐ –	'24'	Ki 100-1b	8476M / BAPC.83, ex St Athan, Cosford, Henlow, Biggin Hill, Fulbeck, Wroughton, Stanmore, Sealand.	3-02

❏	—	Ohka 11	8486M / BAPC.99, ex St Athan, Cosford, Westcott.	3-02
❏	204	SP-2H Neptune	ex Dutch Navy, 320 Sqn, Valkenburg, 5 Sqn, 321 Sqn.	3-02
❏	01120*	MiG-15*bis* (Lim-2)	ex Hendon, Cardington, South Lambeth, Hendon, Middlesborough, Polish AF. Arrived 1-8-01.	3-02
❏	6130	Ventura II	ex SAAF Museum, SAAF, RAF AJ469. Stored. ❖	3-02
❏	J-1704	Venom FB.54	ex Greenham Common and Swiss Air Force.	3-02
❏	'6771'	F-84F-51-RE	ex Rochester, Southend, Belgian AF FU-6, USAF 52-7133. Stored. ❖	2-00

Michael Beetham Conservation Centre: The first turf was cut on the new £2.8 million centre in mid-March 2001. The keys were handed over in mid-December 2001 with most of the airframes making the move from Wyton, Cambs, in the previous month. The centre was due to be officially opened in May 2002. A public gallery allows visitors to the museum 'proper' to glimpse the restoration work going on.

❏	G-EBMB*		Hawker Cygnet	ex Hendon, Cardington, Henlow, Lympne No.14. CoA 30-11-61. Arrived 25-6-01.	11-01
❏	G-AHED*		Dragon Rapide	ex Wyton, Cardington, Henlow, RL962, Witney. CoA 17-4-68.	11-01
❏	F-HMFI*		Farman F.141	9204M, ex Wyton, Cardington, Henlow, Nash Colln.	11-01
❏	433*		Blériot XXVII	9202M / BAPC.107, ex Wyton, Hendon, Cardington, Nash collection. Arrived 9-11-01.	11-01
❏	D5329*		5F1 Dolphin REP	ex Wyton, Cardington. Using original parts. ®	11-01
❏	P1344*	'PL-K'	Hampden I	9175M, ex Wyton, Cardington, Hatch, Petsamo, USSR, 144, 14 OTU. Forced down 6-9-42 ®	11-01
❏	DG590*		Hawk Major	ex Wyton, Cardington, Middle Wallop, Henlow, Ternhill, G-ADMW, Swanton Morley SF, Wyton SF, G-ADMW. CoA 4-6-83.	11-01
❏	'FX760'* 'GA-?'		Kittyhawk IV	9150M, ex Wyton, Cardington, Hendon, USA. Composite. 112 Sqn c/s.	11-01
❏	HS503*		Swordfish IV	BAPC.108, ex Wyton, Cardington, Cosford, Henlow, Canada. Arrived 7-11-01.	11-01
❏	LA226*		Spitfire F.21	ex Wyton, Cardington, St Athan, Shawbury, Abingdon, Biggin Hill, South Marston, London, South Marston, Little Rissington, 7119M, 3 CAACU, 122.	11-01
❏	NV778*		Tempest TT.5	ex Wyton, Cardington, Hendon, 8386M, Leeming, Middleton St George, North Weald, Foulness, 233 OCU, Napier. Arrived 13-11-01. ®	11-01
❏	PK664* 'V6-B'		Spitfire F.22	ex Wyton, Cardington, St Athan, Binbrook, Waterbeach, 7759M, 615.	11-01
❏	PM651* 'X'		Spitfire PR.XIX	ex Wyton, Cardington, St Athan, Hendon, Benson, Bicester, Andover, Hucknall, Leconfield, Church Fenton, 7758M, C&RS, 3 CAACU, 604.	11-01
❏	SL674* 'RAS-H'		Spitfire XVI	ex Wyton, Cardington, St Athan, 8392M, Biggin Hill, Little Rissington, 501, 17 OTU.	11-01
❏	VT812* 'N'		Vampire F.3	7200M, ex Wyton, Hendon, Cosford, Shawbury, Colerne, Cardington, 602, 601, 614, 32. Arr 19-11-01. ®	11-01
❏	VX275*		Sedbergh TX.1	BGA.572, ex Wyton, Cardington, St Athan, 8884M, 612 GS, 613 GS, 623 GS, 123 GS.	11-01
❏	XS695*		Kestrel FGA.1	ex Wyton, Cardington, Yeovilton, Culdrose, SAH A2619, Manadon, Tri-Partite Evaluation Sqn, A&AEE, RAE.	11-01
❏	XT903* 'X'		Phantom FGR.2	ex Wyton, Leuchars, 56, 92, 228 OCU, 23, 228 OCU. Nose.	11-01
❏	15195*		PT-19A Cornell	ex Wyton, Cardington, Henlow, Canada.	11-01
❏	J-1172*		Vampire FB.6	ex Wyton, Cardington, Manchester, Cosford, 8487M, Colerne, Swiss AF.	11-01
❏	—*		*Nulli Secundus*	ex Hendon. Airship gondola, 1907. Arrived -01.	3-02
❏	—*	BAPC.82	Afghan Hind	ex Hendon, Kabul, RAfghan AF, RAF. Arr 14-6-01.	6-01

No.1 School of Technical Training (SoTT): The passage of time continues to terrify... A Tornado F.3 has joined the SoTT, seems like only yesterday they were coming on stream! The School is split into a series of squadrons and flights, each teaching specialist elements: Airframe Training Squadron; Electrical Trade Training Flight; Engineering Standards Training Squadron; Hangar Training Flight; Propulsion and Weapons Training Squadron; and the Line Training Flight. While airframes are allocated to each, and generally remain quite 'faithful', no attempt is made to delineate each airframe's custodian. Going back to *W&R17* (p179) Jet Provost T.3A XM471 went to the USA as N471XN in July 1999.

❏ XM362		Jet Provost T.3	8230M, ex Halton, Kemble, Shawbury, 3 FTS,	
			2 FTS. 'Cutaway' and camouflaged.	7-00
❏ XR574	'72'	Gnat T.1	8631M, ex Halton, Cosford, Kemble, 4 FTS.	3-00
❏ XS641	'Z'	Andover C.1(PR)	9198M, ex Shawbury, 60, 115, 46, 84, SAR Flt, 84.	6-01
❏ XS710	'O'	Dominie T.1	9259M, ex Cranwell, 3 FTS, 6 FTS, CAW.	6-01
❏ XS726	'T'	Dominie T.1	9273M, ex Cranwell, 3 FTS, 6 FTS, CAW.	6-01
❏ XS729	'G'	Dominie T.1	9275M, ex Cranwell, 3 FTS, 6 FTS.	11-00
❏ XS733	'Q'	Dominie T.1	9276M, ex Cranwell, 3 FTS, 6 FTS, RAFC, CAW.	11-00
❏ XS734	'N'	Dominie T.1	ex Cranwell, 3 FTS, 6 FTS.	6-01
❏ XS738	'U'	Dominie T.1	9274M, ex Cranwell, 3 FTS, 6 FTS.	11-00
❏ XV752	'B'	Harrier GR.3	9078M, ex 4, 3, 1, 233 OCU, 1, 233 OCU.	3-00
❏ XW265	'W'	Harrier T.4	9258M, ex Shawbury, 20, 233 OCU, A&AEE.	6-01
❏ XW290	'MA'	Jet Provost T.5A	9199M, ex Shawbury, 3 FTS, RAFC, CFS.	6-01
❏ XW292	'MA'	Jet Provost T.5A	9128M, ex Halton, Shawbury, 3 FTS, RAFC, CFS.	7-00
❏ XW294	'45'	Jet Provost T.5A	9129M, ex Halton, Shawbury, 3 FTS,	
			RAFC, Leeming SF, 3 FTS, CFS.	3-00
❏ XW299	'MB'	Jet Provost T.5A	9146M, ex Halton, 1 FTS, RAFC, 1 FTS.	7-00
❏ XW301	'MC'	Jet Provost T.5A	9147M, ex Halton, 1 FTS.	2-02
❏ XW303	'127'	Jet Provost T.5A	9119M, ex Halton, 7 FTS, 1 FTS.	3-00
❏ XW304	'MD'	Jet Provost T.5	9172M, ex 6 FTS, CFS, 1 FTS.	6-01
❏ XW309	'ME'	Jet Provost T.5	9179M, ex Shawbury, 6 FTS, 1 FTS.	6-01
❏ XW311	'MF'	Jet Provost T.5	9180M, ex Shawbury 6 FTS.	6-01
❏ XW312	'64'	Jet Provost T.5A	9109M, ex Halton, 1 FTS.	2-02
❏ XW318	'MG'	Jet Provost T.5A	9190M, ex 1 FTS, RAFC, CFS, RAFC, CFS, 3 FTS.	2-02
❏ XW320	'71'	Jet Provost T.5A	'9018MA', ex Halton, 9015M, 1 FTS, Leeming	
			'hack', 3 FTS, RAFC. Really 9016M.	3-00
❏ XW321	'MH'	Jet Provost T.5A	9154M, ex Shawbury, 1 FTS, 7 FTS, RAFC, 3 FTS.	7-00
❏ XW327	'62'	Jet Provost T.5A	9130M, ex Halton, CFS, 7 FTS, 6 FTS,	
			7 FTS, 1 FTS, CFS, RAFC.	3-00
❏ XW328	'MI'	Jet Provost T.5A	9177M, ex 1 FTS, RAFC, CFS, RAFC.	7-00
❏ XW330	'MJ'	Jet Provost T.5A	9195M, ex 1 FTS, 7 FTS, 3 FTS, Leeming SF,	
			CFS, RAFC, 3 FTS.	2-02
❏ XW335	'74'	Jet Provost T.5A	9061M, ex Halton, Kemble, 3 FTS, RAFC,	
			CFS, RAFC.	7-00
❏ XW351	'31'	Jet Provost T.5A	9062M, ex Halton, Kemble, 3 FTS, RAFC,	
			1 FTS, RAFC.	3-00
❏ XW358	'MK'	Jet Provost T.5A	9181M, ex Shawbury, 1 FTS, RAFC.	2-02
❏ XW360	'ML'	Jet Provost T.5A	9153M, ex Shawbury, 1 FTS, RAFC, 7 FTS.	6-01
❏ XW361	'MM'	Jet Provost T.5A	9192M, ex 1 FTS, RAFC, 7 FTS, RAFC.	7-00
❏ XW364	'MO'	Jet Provost T.5A	9188M, ex Shawbury, 3 FTS, RAFC, CFS, 1 FTS.	2-02
❏ XW365	'73'	Jet Provost T.5A	'9015M', ex Halton, 1 FTS, RAFC. Really 9018M.	3-00
❏ XW366	'75'	Jet Provost T.5A	9097M, ex Halton, 1 FTS, 3 FTS, RAFC.	3-00
❏ XW367	'MO'	Jet Provost T.5A	9193M, ex 1 FTS, RAFC.	2-02
❏ XW370	'MP'	Jet Provost T.5A	9196M, ex 1 FTS, 3 FTS.	2-02
❏ XW375	'52'	Jet Provost T.5A	9149M, ex Halton, CFS, 6 FTS, RAFC.	3-00
❏ XW405	'MQ'	Jet Provost T.5A	9187M, ex Shawbury, 6 FTS, 1 FTS, 7 FTS,	
			6 FTS, 1 FTS, RAFC.	2-02
❏ XW410	'MR'	Jet Provost T.5A	9125M, ex Shawbury, 1 FTS, RAFC, 3 FTS.	2-02
❏ XW413	'69'	Jet Provost T.5A	9126M, ex Halton, 1 FTS, RAFC.	3-00

❑ XW416	'MS'	Jet Provost T.5A	9191M, ex 1 FTS, RAFC.	7-00
❑ XW418	'MT'	Jet Provost T.5A	9173M, ex Shawbury, 1 FTS, 7 FTS, CFS, 3 FTS, Leeming SF, 3 FTS.	2-02
❑ XW419	'125'	Jet Provost T.5A	9120M, ex Halton, 7 FTS, 1 FTS, RAFC.	3-00
❑ XW420	'MU'	Jet Provost T.5A	9194M, ex 1 FTS, RAFC.	2-02
❑ XW421	'60'	Jet Provost T.5A	9111M, ex PWTS, Halton, Shawbury, CFS, 3 FTS, Leeming SF, 3 FTS.	3-00
❑ XW425	'MV'	Jet Provost T.5A	9200M, ex CFS, 6 FTS, CFS, 3 FTS, Leeming SF, CFS.	2-02
❑ XW427	'67'	Jet Provost T.5A	9124M, ex Halton, 1 FTS, CFS, 3 FTS, CFS, 3 FTS.	3-00
❑ XW430	'MW'	Jet Provost T.5A	9176M, ex 1 FTS, CFS, 3 FTS, Leeming SF, 3 FTS.	2-02
❑ XW432	'MX'	Jet Provost T.5A	9127M, ex Shawbury, 1 FTS, Leeming SF, 3 FTS.	7-00
❑ XW434	'MY'	Jet Provost T.5A	9091M, ex Halton, 1 FTS, 7 FTS, 3 FTS, CFS.	2-02
❑ XW436	'68'	Jet Provost T.5A	9148M, ex Halton, 1 FTS, CFS, 3 FTS, Leeming SF, 3 FTS, RAFC.	3-00
❑ XW768	'N'	Harrier GR.3	9072M, ex Halton, 4, 1, 4, 20.	3-00
❑ XX110	'EP'	Jaguar GR.1	8955M, ex Shawbury, 6, A&AEE, BAC.	6-01
❑ 'XX110'		Jaguar GR.1 rig	BAPC.169, engine systems rig.	7-99
❑ XX726	'EB'	Jaguar GR.1	8947M, ex Halton, Shawbury, 6, 54, 14, 54, 6, JOCU.	3-00
❑ XX727	'ER'	Jaguar GR.1	8951M, ex PWTS, Shawbury, 6, 54, 6, JOCU.	2-00
❑ XX730	'EC'	Jaguar GR.1	8952M, ex Shawbury, 6, JOCU.	3-00
❑ XX739	'I'	Jaguar GR.1	8902M, ex Halton, Shawbury, Gibraltar Det, 6.	3-00
❑ XX743	'EG'	Jaguar GR.1	8949M, ex Halton, Shawbury, 6.	3-00
❑ XX746	'09'	Jaguar GR.1A	8895M, ex Halton, 226 OCU, 14, 17, 6, 31, 226 OCU.	6-01
❑ XX751	'10'	Jaguar GR.1	8937M, ex 226 OCU, 14.	6-01
❑ XX756	'AM'	Jaguar GR.1	8899M, ex 14, 41, 14, 20, 226 OCU, 14.	6-00
❑ XX757	'CU'	Jaguar GR.1	8948M, ex Halton, Shawbury, 20, 226 OCU, 14.	3-00
❑ XX818	'DE'	Jaguar GR.1	8945M, ex Halton, Shawbury, 31, 20, 17.	6-01
❑ XX819	'CE'	Jaguar GR.1	8923M, ex Shawbury, 20, 17.	6-01
❑ XX824	'AD'	Jaguar GR.1	9019M, ex Halton, Shawbury, 14, 17, 14.	3-00
❑ XX825	'BN'	Jaguar GR.1	9020M, ex Halton, Shawbury, 17, 31, 14.	3-00
❑ XX826	'JH'	Jaguar GR.1	9021M, ex Shawbury, 2, 20, 14.	3-00
❑ XX837	'Z'	Jaguar T.2	8978M, ex Halton, Shawbury, 226 OCU.	7-00
❑ XX947		Tornado P.03	8979M, ex St Athan, Marham, Warton.	3-00
❑ XX948	'P'	Tornado P.06	8878M, ex Warton. 617 Sqn colours.	3-00
❑ XX956	'BE'	Jaguar GR.1	8950M, ex Halton, Shawbury, 17, 31, 14, 17.	3-00
❑ XX958	'BK'	Jaguar GR.1	9022M, ex Shawbury, 17, 14.	6-01
❑ XX959	'CJ'	Jaguar GR.1	8953M, ex Shawbury, 20, 14.	6-01
❑ XX966		Jaguar GR.1A	8904M, ex Halton, Shawbury, 6, 54, 20, A&AEE, 20, 17.	7-00
❑ XX967	'AC'	Jaguar GR.1	9006M, ex Shawbury, 14, 31.	6-01
❑ XX968	'AJ'	Jaguar GR.1	9007M, ex Shawbury, 14, 31.	6-01
❑ XX969	'01'	Jaguar GR.1	8897M, ex 226 OCU, 3, 17, 31, 14, 31.	6-01
❑ XX975	'07'	Jaguar GR.1A	8905M, ex Halton, 226 OCU, 31, 17, 226 OCU.	3-00
❑ XX976	'BD'	Jaguar GR.1	8906M, ex Halton, Shawbury, 17, 31.	3-00
❑ XZ130	'A'	Harrier GR.3	9079M, ex 4, 3, 233 OCU, 3, 1453F, 1, 4, 20.	3-00
❑ XZ368	'AG'	Jaguar GR.1	8900M, ex Coltishall, 14, 41, 14, 6, 14.	6-01
❑ XZ370	'JB'	Jaguar GR.1	9004M, ex Shawbury, 17.	6-01
❑ XZ371	'AP'	Jaguar GR.1	8907M, ex Shawbury, 14, 17.	6-01
❑ XZ374	'JC'	Jaguar GR.1	9005M, ex Shawbury, 14, 20.	6-01
❑ XZ383	'AF'	Jaguar GR.1	8901M, ex Colt', 14, 41, 54, 14, 226 OCU, 14, 17.	6-01
❑ XZ384	'BC'	Jaguar GR.1	8954M, ex Shawbury, 17, 31, 20.	3-00
❑ XZ389	'BL'	Jaguar GR.1	8946M, ex Halton, Shawbury, 17, 31, 20.	3-00
❑ XZ390	'DM'	Jaguar GR.1	9003M, ex Shawbury, 2, 20, 31.	6-01
❑ ZD462*		Harrier GR.7	9302M, ex St Athan, 1. Ditched 25-1-97. Arr 22-10-01.	10-01
❑ ZD939*	'AS'	Tornado F.2	ex St Athan, Warton, St Athan, 229 OCU. Forward fuselage. Arrived 18-2-02.	2-02

❑ ZE340* 'GO' Tornado F.3   9298M, ex Coningsby, 56. With rear fuselage
of ZE758. Arrived by road 10-9-01.   9-01

PT Flight: Care of the CO of RAF Cosford, Bob Mitchell's PT Flight and other airframes are kept here. (See also Sutton Coldfield, W Mids.) They are *not* available for inspection.

❑ G-AWIW		SNCAN SV-4B	ex museum, F-BDCC. CoA 6-5-73.	®	8-99
❑ G-AYKZ		SAI KZ-VIII	ex Coventry, HB-EPB, OY-ACB. CoA 17-7-81. Stored.		8-99
❑ G-BADW		Pitts S-2A	ex museum. CoA 6-9-95.		8-99
❑ G-RIDE		Stephens Akro	ex N81AC, N55NM. CoA 13-8-92.		8-99
❑ N1344		PT-22 Recruit	ex 41-20877.		8-99
❑ N49272	'23'	PT-23-HO	ex USAAF.		8-99
❑ N56421	'855'	PT-22 Recruit	ex 41-15510.		8-99
❑ N58566		BT-15 Valiant	ex USAAF.		8-99

Others:

❑ XG225   'S' Hunter F.6A   8713M, ex Weapons School, 2 SoTT, Kemble,
229 OCU, 92, 74, 20. Parade ground.   7-99

Locally: In a field near Junction 3 of the M54 is a Vampire, used by a war-gaming group.

❑ XE993   Vampire T.11   ex Cosford 8161M, 8, 73. Poor state.   1-02

LUDLOW on the A49 north of Leominster

❑ G-ABUS	Comper Swift	ex Heathfield. CoA 19-6-79.	® 2-91
❑ G-BADV	MB.50 Pipistrelle	ex Dunkeswell, F-PBRJ. CoA 9-5-79.	® 2-91

MADELEY west of the A442, south of Telford

Black Country Aircraft Collection: Following restoration off-site to camouflaged wartime Air Training Corps status Alec Brew's anonymous Cadet TX.1 moved to <u>Wolverhampton</u>, West Midlands, during August 2001. His An-2 and Canberra T.17 cockpits did *not* come here, despite what p182 of *W&R17* might say! (See also Wolverhampton, W Mids.)

MARKET DRAYTON on the A53 north of Telford

Roger Marley: Is a leading light with the new museum at <u>Sleap</u>, Shropshire. The Hunter FGA.9 nose moved to the museum as did Hawker Fury II REP 'K7271' (BAPC.148) previously at Cosford, Shropshire and a Typhoon cockpit section.

SHAWBURY on the A53 north-east of Shrewsbury

Parry's Haulage: The Buccaneer has been acquired on long-term loan by the Buccaneer Supporters Club (see under Kemble, Glos, for details) and is being prepared for the move to Bruntingthorpe, Leics. It is hoped that this will have take place during the summer of 2002.

❑ XW544   'Y' Buccaneer S.2C   8857M, ex Cosford, Shawbury, 16, 15.   11-01

SHAWBURY AIRFIELD on the B5063 north of Shawbury

Defence Aviation Repair Agency (DARA): The Bulldogs went through store like a knife through butter. Sales of Gazelles are stepping up likewise, with Wessex HC.2s looking to be the next 'movers'. Because of the newly-established 'hot sales' policy, there is every chance that 'new' Gazelles and former 72 Squadron Wessex added to the store will not become 'long-termers' – thus *W&R19* (!) may well have to retract some of the additions given below. (The Bulldogs were a classic example of 'hot sales'. Received ex-unit, perhaps some avionics or other equipment removed then offered for sale via auction or tender within months of arrival. The aim is to almost have airframes sold as they come off-line, perhaps avoiding a specialised maintenance unit at all and going direct to purchaser.) Bulldog XX654 is stored for the RAF Museum ①. More Jaguars have joined the store, but in general the fast jet side is stable. A reminder that the Tucano store here is largely 'rotated' on flying hours and as such the airframes are not long-term enough to list. No.72 Squadron disbanded in March 2002, marking the end of the UK operation of Wessex and they will all come here for disposal. (The handful operating in Cyprus are destined to be replaced by contractorised Eurocopters. The Wessex there may not return to the UK.)

Phillips staged a sale on behalf of the Defence Disposal Sales Agency on 29th November 2000 in London. Bulldogs, Gazelles and Hunters were involved from here. The Bulldogs were effectively 'hot sales' and were not in store long enough to merit a listing here – see Appendix A. Aircraft are given in lot order as follows: type, serial, date last flown, airframe flying hours, high bid, departure:

Gazelle HT.3	XZ932	29-9-97	7,955	£62,000	became 3D-HGW, then G-CBJZ
Gazelle HT.2	XW868	21-5-97	7,599	£62,000	became G-CBKD
Gazelle HT.2	XW907	7-7-97	7,324	£62,000	became G-BZOT
Gazelle HT.2	XW894	21-5-97	6,118	£80,000	became G-BZOS
Hunter GA.11	XF368	25-4-95	8,439	£10,200	to Exeter, Devon 12-2-01 as G-BZRH
Hunter GA.11	WV256	24-4-95	7,686	£10,200	to Exeter, Devon 13-2-01 as G-BZPB
Hunter GA.11	XF300	12-6-95	5,877	£12,000	to Exeter, Devon 14-2-01 as G-BZPC

Phillips staged another sale on 24th May 2001 in London. Bulldogs, Gazelles and Wessex were involved from here. Comments on the Bulldogs as before – see Appendix A. Aircraft are given in lot order as follows: type, serial, date last flown, airframe flying hours, high bid, departure:

Gazelle AH.1	XW903	15-12-97	9,382	£35,000	became G-BZYC
Gazelle AH.1	XZ329	30-1-98	9,340	£48,000	became G-BZYD
Gazelle AH.1	XW885	4-2-98	9,800	£36,000	left 7-6-01
Gazelle AH.1	XW911	11-12-97	9,283	£35,000	became N911XW
Gazelle AH.1	XZ317	30-1-98	9,289	£42,000	became 3D-HGZ
Gazelle HT.3	XX382	26-9-97	9,866	£32,000	became G-BZYB
Gazelle HT.3	XW862	26-9-97	9,916	£42,000	became G-CBKC
Gazelle HT.3	XW858	23-7-97	8,518	£58,000	became G-DMSS
Gazelle HT.3	XW898	28-1-97	9,514	£60,000	left 15-6-01
Gazelle HT.3	ZA803	24-6-97	8,231	£56,000	left 4-6-01
Wessex HC.2	XT606	1-6-97	11,390	£25,000	to New Zealand
Wessex HC.2	XS677	1-6-97	10,703	£25,000	became ZK-HBE

Phillips squeezed in another sale on 25th October 2001, this time dealing with the remaining Bulldogs - see Appendix A. Highlighting the sale was Wessex HCC.4 XV733. Flown into Shawbury on 13th March 1998, the airframe flying hours were not quoted. It was 'hammered' for £50,000 to The Helicopter Museum and departed as noted below.

Departures: Gazelle AH.1s XW885 auctioned 24-5-01, see above; XW903 auctioned 24-5-01, see above; XW911 auctioned 24-5-01, see above; XX388 left 10-1-01, perhaps for the Hungerford, Berks, area; XZ317 auctioned 24-5-01, see above; XX413 to Poole, Somerset, 8-01; XX433 pod left 10-1-01, perhaps for the Hungerford, Berks, area; XZ329 auctioned 24-5-01, see above; **Gazelle HT.2s** XW853 left 18-9-01 to 'Somerset' (Poole?); XW856 sold as G-CBBY; XW868 auctioned 29-11-00, XW887 sold as G-CBFD; XW894 auctioned 29-11-00, see above; XW907 auctioned 29-11-00, see above; XX391 sold as ZK-HTB 7-01; XX441 sold as ZK-HBH 7-01; XX446 sold as ZK-HTF 7-01; XZ938 to St Athan, Wales, 27-2-02; XZ940 sold as G-CBBV; XZ941 to St Athan, Wales, 10-10-01; ZB646 sold as G-CBGZ, left 6-11-01; **Gazelle HT.3s** XW858 auctioned 24-5-01, see above; XW862 auctioned 24-5-01, see above; XW870 to Manston, Kent, 29-11-01; XW898 auctioned 24-5-01, see above; XW902 to Boscombe Down, Wilts, 23-11-01; XX382 auctioned 24-5-01, see above; XZ930 to Gosport, Hants, late 2000; XZ931 sold as N931XZ; XZ932 auctioned 29-11-00, see above; XZ933 to Boscombe Down, Wilts, by 3-01; ZA803 auctioned 24-5-01, see above; ZA804 to Boscombe Down, Wilts, 29-11-01; **Hunter F.6** XG164 to Poole, Somerset, 3-01; **Hunter GA.11s** WV256, XF300 and XF368 auctioned 29-11-00, see above; **Wessex HC.2** XR508 to Gosport, Hants, 12-9-00; XR518 arrived from Fleetlands, Hants, 9-00 for spares recovery, it had gone by 11-01; XR523 from Fleetlands, Hants, by 4-01 for spares recovery, to Gosport, Hants, 15-1-02; XR524 wreck scrapped and burnt (and as reported by one source, *buried* on site!) by 11-00; XR525 was on extended overhaul, it rejoined 72 Squadron; XS677 auctioned 24-5-01, see above; XT606 auctioned 24-5-01, see above; XV724 arrived from Fleetlands, Hants, 2-4-01, to Gosport, Hants, 15-1-02; **Wessex HCC.4** XV732 due to move to Hendon, Gtr Lon, 4-02; XV733 to Weston-super-Mare, Somerset, 15-11-01.

❑ WH779*	Canberra PR.7	ex Marham, RAE, 100, 13, 31, 80, 13, 542. Arrived by 2-01. Stored.		2-02
❑ WT480	'AT' Canberra T.4	ex Marham, 1 PRU/39 Sqn, 231 OCU, 360, 7, 231 OCU, 13, 7, 231 OCU, CFS, 102.		2-02

❑ XH174		Canberra PR.9	ex 1 PRU, 39, 13, 39, MoS, 39, 58. Nose.	2-02
❑ XR506	'V'	Wessex HC.2	ex 72, 18.	3-00
❑ XT607*	'P'	Wessex HC.2	ex Fleetlands, 72. Arrived 2-4-01.	2-02
❑ XW200*		Puma HC.1	ex 33, 240 OCU, HOCF. Crashed 9-4-01. .	2-02
❑ XW845	'47'	Gazelle HT.2	ex 705, A&AEE.	2-02
❑ XW852*		Gazelle HT.3	ex Fleetlands, 32. First noted 4-01.	2-02
❑ XW854	'46'	Gazelle HT.2	ex 705.	2-02
❑ XW855*		Gazelle HCC.4	ex Fleetlands, 32. First noted 4-01.	2-02
❑ XW857	'55'	Gazelle HT.2	ex FONA, 705.	2-02
❑ XW864	'54'	Gazelle HT.2	ex 705, Wroughton.	2-02
❑ XW871	'44'	Gazelle HT.2	ex 705, Weston-super-Mare, 705.	2-02
❑ XW892		Gazelle AH.1	ex 666, 658, 662, 663, 662, 653, 663, 660.	2-02
❑ XX144*	'U'	Jaguar T.2A	ex 16, 226 OCU, 6, 54, 226 OCU, JOCU. F/n 3-00.	2-02
❑ XX304*		Hawk T.1A	ex Shawbury, St Athan, 'Reds'. Cat 4 24-6-88.	
			Nose held as FRP spare. Arrived 25-9-01.	2-02
❑ XX431	'43'	Gazelle HT.2	9300M, ex 705, FONA, 705. Inst airframe.	11-01
❑ XX436	'39'	Gazelle HT.2	ex 705, Wroughton.	2-02
❑ XX654*	'3'	Bulldog T.1	ex Newton, CFS, 3 FTS, CFS, 3 FTS,	
			Bri UAS, 2 FTS. Arrived by 5-00.	2-02
❑ XX724	'GA'	Jaguar GR.1A	ex 54, 14, 54, JOCU.	9-99
❑ XX741	'04'	Jaguar GR.1A	ex 16, 6, 54.	2-02
❑ XX745*	'GV'	Jaguar GR.1A	ex St Athan, 54, 16, 6, 16, 226 OCU, 6, 226 OCU, 6,	
			54, 6, 20, 226 OCU. Damaged 31-5-00. Arr by 2-01.	2-02
❑ XX829*	'GZ'	Jaguar T.2A	ex St Athan, 54, 16, 6, A&AEE, 226 OCU, 6,	
			54, 6, 54, 6, 54, 41, 54. Arrived 6-3-01.	2-02
❑ XX832*	'EZ'	Jaguar T.2A	ex 6, 16, 226 OCU, ETPS, 226 OCU. Arr 10-10-01.	2-02
❑ XX836	'ER'	Jaguar T.2A	ex 6, 17, 14, 226 OCU, 14. Spares.	2-02
❑ XX955	'GK'	Jaguar GR.1A	ex 54, 14, 17, 14.	2-02
❑ XZ114	'FB'	Jaguar GR.1A	ex 41.	2-02
❑ XZ367*	'GP'	Jaguar GR.3	ex 54, 2, 226 OCU, 2, 14. Overstressed. Arr 29-9-00.	2-02
❑ XZ378	'EP'	Jaguar GR.1A	ex 6, 41, 17, 41, 20.	2-02
❑ XZ392	'GQ'	Jaguar GR.1A	ex 54, 20, 31.	3-00
❑ XZ934	'U'	Gazelle HT.3	ex 2 FTS, CFS.	2-02
❑ XZ935*		Gazelle HT.3	ex Fleetlands, 32, CFS. Arrived 28-3-01.	2-02
❑ XZ942	'42'	Gazelle HT.2	ex 705, Fleetlands.	2-02
❑ XZ971	'U'	Harrier GR.3	9219M, ex Shawbury, Benson, HOCU,	
			1417F, 233 OCU.	2-02
❑ ZA802	'W'	Gazelle HT.3	ex 2 FTS, CFS.	2-02
❑ ZB627	'A'	Gazelle HT.3	ex 2 FTS, 7, 2 FTS, CFS.	2-02
❑ ZB647	'40'	Gazelle HT.2	ex 705, FONA, 705.	2-02
❑ ZB649		Gazelle HT.2	ex 705, FONA, 705. .	2-02
❑ ZD935*		Tornado F.2	ex St Athan, Warton, Coningsby, St Athan, 229 OCU,	
			ETPS, 229 OCU. Hybrid. Arrived 22-3-00.	2-02
❑ ZD938	'AR'	Tornado F.2	ex St Athan, 229 OCU. F'ward fuse. Arrived 1-3-00.	2-02
❑ ZD789*		Tornado GR.1	ex St Athan. Arrived 27-3-00.	2-02

Others: The Whirlwind on the gate is reported to be being replaced by a Gazelle. Within the base a full-size reproduction of an Airspeed Horsa is underway. A fuselage section of TL659 and other parts have been loaned by the Museum of Army Flying at Middle Wallop, Hants, to act as patterns. The aim is to display the finished product somewhere in the Midlands as a tribute to airborne forces. In its early stages, the project does not yet merit a 'formal' listing.

❑ XM927	'60'	Wessex HAS.3	8814M, ex Wroughton. Dump.	11-01
❑ XN549		Jet Provost T.3	'8235M' / 8225M, ex Halton, Shawbury,	
			1 FTS, CFS. Dump.	11-01
❑ XP351	'Z'	W'wind HAR.10	8672M, ex ABDR, 2 FTS, SAR Wing, 22. Gate.	11-01

SLEAP AERODROME south-west of Wem
Wartime Aircraft Recovery Group Aviation Museum: A delightful museum has developed at this equally delightful aerodrome. Quietly beavering away here, this museum is now in its fourth year. As well as the airframes there are plenty of aero engines and artefacts recovered from 'digs' – including WAG's 'founder', 61 OTU Spitfire IIa P7304 involved in a mid-air collision near High Ercall on 22nd August 1943 and recovered in 1977. The Fury, Hunter and Typhoon are on loan from chairman Roger Marley. The Spitfire FSM with *original* instrumentation etc is on loan from Keith Jones. This is now complete with wings etc. The nose of Hunter FGA.9 XG195 came from Seighford, Staffs, but moved out via Bruntingthorpe, Leics, 8-9-01, ending up at Lewes, E Sussex.
◆ Open the second and fourth Sun in summer, also often open Sat afternoons. Please 'phone to check. Otherwise by prior arrangement. ☎ 01630 672969 web www.wargroup.homestead.come

❏ 'K7271'*	Fury II REP	BAPC.148, ex Market Drayton, Cosford.		3-02
❏ 'EN398'* 'JE-J'	Spitfire IX FSM	ex Cannock. Arrived 29-6-01.		3-02
❏ 'GBH-7'*	'Gunbus' REP	BAPC.234, ex High Halden, Hawkinge, Manston, Chelford, Coventry, Old Warden, White Waltham. Based on modified DH.2 frame.	®	3-02
❏ –*	Typhoon	ex Market Drayton. Cockpit.	off-site	3-02

Aerodrome:

❏ G-BLLO*	Super Cub 95	ex D-EAUB, Belg AF OL-L25, 53-4699. CoA 12-10-96. Fuselage.	10-01

TILSTOCK AERODROME on the A41 south of Whitchurch
The para-trainer may well have moved on.

❏ G-ASNN	Cessna 182F	ex N3612U. Crashed 5-1-85. Para-trainer.	1-98

SOMERSET

☛ Within the administrative county boundaries of Somerset can be found the unitary authorities of North West Somerset and Bath and North East Somerset.

AXBRIDGE on the A38 west of Cheddar
An anonymous Robin HR.100 is the fifth to be built, it is reported to have been the personal aircraft of Pierre Robin - that should tie an identity down! (How about G-BLAY?)

❏ –	HR.100-200B	ex Keynsham. Dismantled, spares.	12-00

BATH
No.93 Squadron Air Cadets: Still have their Wessex.

❏ XS486*	'F' Wessex HU.5	9292M, ex Wroughton, Lee-on-Solent.	1-00

BRISTOL AIRPORT or Lulsgate, on the A38 south-west of Bristol
A convincing helicopter mock-up in the fire pits has been joined by a pseudo-Boeing 767. The Varsity has been removed from the 'burning' area as a health-risk (!) and awaits its fate. Brunel Technical College airframes are marked ☆ – see also Bristol, Glos (!).

❏ G-ANAP	Dove 6	ex CAFU Stansted. CoA 6-9-73. Dump.		2-02
❏ G-AVFM	Trident 2E	ex BA and BEA. CoA 2-6-84. Orange/yellow c/s.	☆	2-02
❏ G-AVPK*	Rallye Comm	CoA 10-1-92. Stored.		2-00
❏ G-BAUI	Aztec 250D	ex LN-RTS. CoA 15-12-88.	☆	2-00
❏ G-BFRL	Cessna F.152 II	Crashed 24-8-92. Stored.		2-00
❏ G-BIUO	Commander 112A	ex Staverton, OY-PRH, N1281J. Cr 12-5-84.		2-00

| ❏ G-NERI* | Archer II | ex G-BMKO, N31880. Wreck. | 2-00 |
| ❏ WF410 | 'F' Varsity T.1 | ex 6 FTS, 2 ANS, 5 FTS, 2 ANS, RAFC, CNCS, 201 AFS. Dump | 2-02 |

Paintball Adventure West: Located on the edge of the airport, now have two 'choppers'.

| ❏ G-AWOX | Wessex 60 | ex Weston-super-Mare, Bournemouth, Weston, G-17-2, G-AWOX, 5N-AJO, G-AWOX, 9Y-TFB, G-AWOX, VH-BHE, G-AWOX, VR-BCV, G-AWOX, G-17-1. CoA 13-1-83. | 2-02 |
| ❏ (S-882)* | S-55C | ex Weston-super-Mare, Panshanger, Elstree, Dan AF Esk.722. Spares. | 2-02 |

CLEVEDON west of Junction 20, M5
'Boz' Robinson: And friends are restoring a former Kennet Aviation Provost in the area.

| ❏ WW453* | Provost T.1 | G-TMKI, ex Cranfield, Thatcham, Strathallan, Perth, Hunting, 1 FTS, 2 FTS. | ® 11-01 |

HENSTRIDGE AERODROME south of the A30, east of Henstridge Marsh

❏ G-ALYG	Auster 5D	ex Charlton Mackrell, Heathrow, Irby-on-Humber, MS968, 661, 653. CoA 19-1-70. Frame. Stored.	3-98
❏ G-ANEW	Tiger Moth	ex NM138, Oxf UAS, 8 RFS, 29 EFTS. CoA 18-6-62.	3-98
❏ G-ARJD	Colt 108	crashed 17-11-71. Frame. Stored.	4-97
❏ G-AWYX	Rallye Club	ex Compton Abbas. CoA 27-6-86. Stored.	8-97
❏ NC2612	Stinson Junior R	stored, dismantled.	3-98

KEW STOKE north of Weston-super-Mare
Mark Templeman: Mark and his anonymous Hunter F.4 moved here during December 2001. Mark would appreciate any details that would help to tie down its history. In red colour scheme as per the famed 'WB188' it carries the autograph of Neville Duke on the starboard side.

| ❏ —* | Hunter F.4 | ex Portishead, Boscombe Down, Salisbury, Cove, Farnborough. Nose. Red c/s. Arrived 12-01. | 12-01 |

LANGPORT on the A372 west of Somerton
A collector took on Lightning F.6 nose XS933 in 2001. It moved to Farnham, Surrey, early in 2002.

MARKSBURY on the A39 west of Bath
Hamburger Hill: The paintball wargaming park should still have its S-55 to keep the testosterone levels of kickers and movers trending upwards, year-on-year.

| ❏ S-887 | S-55C | ex Weston-super-Mare, Panshanger, Elstree, RDanAF | 2-02 |

NORTON FITZWARREN on the B3227 west of Taunton
Military Aircraft Spares Ltd: MASL relocated to Poole, Somerset, by late 2000. The three Wessex HC.2s listed in *W&R17* (XR501, XS677, XT606) did *not* come here – see Shawbury, Shropshire.

OAKHILL on the A37 north of Shepton Mallet

| ❏ FFZ* | T.21B | BGA.3238, ex Aston Down, WB981. Stored. | 10-00 |

POOLE on minor road north of Wellington
Military Aircraft Spares Ltd (MASL): Relocated to the Poole Industrial Estate from Norton Fitzwarren, Somerset, by late 2001 – see under than location. They acquired a new gate guardian by

March 2001. Note that their last 'guardian' (Harrier GR.3 XZ967) was flogged off fairly quickly, so the Hunter may well be more correctly regarded as 'stock' although it is in a rockery-cum-shrubbery that would do Alan Titchmarsh justice! XG164 has the starboard wing of T.7 XL623. The port wing, dear reader, is at Beck Row, Suffolk, the fuselage – with *altogether* different wings – at Woking, Surrey!

MASL very probably have another yard nearby (in Wellington itself?) in which it is believed spares reclamation takes place. In August 2001, MASL acquired four Bulldog T.1s from Shawbury, Shropshire: XX539, XX634, XX656 and XX671. Of these, XX634 and XX671 are listed under Wellesbourne Mountford, Warks. By August 2001 MASL had been allocated the following Gazelle AH.1s via Shawbury, Shropshire: XW893, XX388, XX413, XX418, XX450 and ZA730. They may – or may not – have come here.

❏ XG164*   Hunter F.6   ex Shawbury, Halton 8681M, Kemble, West Raynham
                                  SF, 74, 111. Composite. Arrived 20-3-01.   5-01

PORTISHEAD on the A369 west of Bristol
Mark Templeman: Mark and his anonymous Hunter F.4 came here during September 2000. They moved on to Kewstoke, Somerset during December 2001.

WELLS east of Shepton Mallett
No.1955 Squadron Air Cadets: Chipmunk PAX 'WD355' (WD335) moved to Solihull, W Mids.

WESTON-SUPER-MARE AERODROME on the A371 east of Weston-super-Mare
The Helicopter Museum (THM): A 'fast-track' bid to the Heritage Lottery Fund secured the former Queen's Flight Wessex for THM at the Phillips auction staged on 25th October 2001. THM's superb new display building and the associated Hafner Restoration Building has transformed the site with the core collection under cover. THM has also purchased the land it 'sits' on, giving it assured longevity.

Readers well used to *W&R* will know that THM acquire not just exhibits, but potential exchange items. In the past, these items have been listed within the main content. With the continued development and maturity of the museum, the opportunity has been taken to list these separately below as they are not generally available for public inspection.

Notes: The Frelon started life as SA.321 c/n 116. It is in Olympic Airways colours and the scheme it wore at the 1969 Paris Salon ①. The Devon and Cornwall Police Bö 105 pod and boom is *thought* to be the original from G-PASA. That would make it the former G-BGWP, F-ODMZ, G-BGWP, HB-XFD, N153BB and D-HDAS. The helicopter was rebuilt in 1993, discarding the original pod (and much else) going on to become G-BUXS which is currently operational in Scotland ②. Airframes on loan from Elfan ap Rees are marked ➨. For Fairey Ultra-Light G-AOUJ see Innsworth, Glos. In 'the pipeline' awaiting funding or sponsorship to cover transport costs are the following a Kaman HH-43F Huskie 62-4552 ex Pakistan Air Force and a Sikorsky CH-37C 145872 (N7393) ex US Marines.

Departures: WG.30-100 G-BIWY to Italy for Agusta 11-00; Wasp HAS.1 'XS463' (XT431) and Scout AH.1 XV123 were part of the exchange for Whirlwinds XK940 and XR486 and moved to Ipswich, Suffolk, by 4-01.

◆ Nov to Mar, Wed-Sun 10am to 4pm, Apr to Oct Wed to Sun 10am to 6pm. Daily during Easter and Summer holidays. 'Open Cockpit' days are held every second Sunday in the month, March to October and the annual 'HeliDays' fly-in is held on the Weston Sea Front on the last weekend of each July. There are also regular 'Family Flight' days. SAE brings leaflet. THM run an excellent gift shop, with a splendid array of helicopter kits and other items on offer and the 'Choppers' cafeteria. There is also a **Friends of the Helicopter Museum** – which produces the house magazine *Straight Up!* – enquiries to the address below. ✉ The Heliport, Locking Moor Road, Weston-super-Mare, BS24 8PP ☎ 01934 635227 **fax** 01934 645230 **e-mail** helimuseum@fsnet.co.uk **web** www.helicoptermuseum.co.uk

❏ [G-ACWM]   Cierva C.30A   ex Staverton, Tewkesbury, AP506, 529, 1448 Flt,
                                 74 Wing, 5 RSS, G-ACWM. Frame.   ➨ 3-02
❏ G-ALSX   Sycamore 3   ex Duxford, Staverton, G-48/1, G-ALSX,
                                 VR-TBS ntu, G-ALSX. CoA 24-9-65.   ➨ 3-02
❏ [G-ANFH]   Whirlwind Srs 1   ex Redhill, Gt Yarmouth, Bristow, BEAH.
                                 CoA 17-7-71.   ➨ 3-02

❏ G-AODA		Whirlwind Srs 3	ex Redhill, Bristow, 9Y-TDA, EP-HAC, G-AODA. *Dorado*. CoA 23-8-91.	3-02
❏ G-AOZE		Widgeon 2	ex Cuckfield, Shoreham, 5N-ABW, G-AOZE. ➟ ®	3-02
❏ G-ARVN		Grasshopper 1	ex Shoreham, Redhill. CoA 18-5-63.	3-02
❏ G-ASTP		Hiller UH-12C	ex Biggin Hill, Thornicombe, 'Wales', Thornicombe, Redhill, N9750C. CoA 3-7-82.	3-02
❏ G-AVKE		Gadfly HDW-1	ex Southend, Thruxton. Stored. ➟	3-02
❏ G-AVNE and G-17-3		Wessex 60 Srs 1	ex Bournemouth, Weston-super-Mare, G-17-3, 5N-AJL, G-AVNE, 9M-ASS, VH-BHC, PK-HBQ, G-AVNE. CoA 7-2-83.	3-02
❏ G-AWRP		Grasshopper III	ex Blackpool, Heysham, Shoreham, Redhill. CoA 12-5-72.	3-02
❏ G-BAPS		Campbell Cougar	ex Weston-super-Mare. CoA 20-5-74.	3-02
❏ G-BGHF		WG.30-100	ex Yeovil, Westlands. CoA 1-8-86.	3-02
❏ G-BKGD		WG.30-100	ex Yeovil, Penzance, G-BKBJ ntu. CoA 6-7-93.	3-02
❏ G-EHIL		EH-101 PP3	ex Yeovil, ZH647.	3-02
❏ G-ELEC*		WG.30-200	ex Westland W-s-M, Yeovil, G-BKNV. CoA 28-6-85. 'Rescue' and 'Helicopter Museum' titles. Arr 7-12-01.	3-02
❏ G-HAUL		WG.30-TT300	ex G-17-22, Yeovil. CoA 27-10-86.	3-02
❏ G-LYNX		Lynx 800 ✈	ZB500 ex Yeovil, ZA500 ntu, G-LYNX.	3-02
❏ G-OAPR		Brantly B.2B ✈	ex G-BPST ntu, N2280U. ➟	3-02
❏ G-OTED*		Robinson R-22 ✈	ex Elstree, G-BMYR, ZS-HLG. Arrived 2-02.	3-02
❏ G-PASB		MBB Bö 105D	ex Bourn, VH-LSA, G-BDMC, D-HDEC.	3-02
❏ [D-HMQV]		Bö 102 Helitrainer	ground trainer. (c/n 6216) ➟	3-02
❏ [D-HOAY]		Ka-26 *Hoodlum*	ex Germany, Interflug DD-SPY. ®	3-02
❏ 'F-OCMF'	'335'	SA.321F Frelon	ex Aérospatiale, Olympic, F-BTRP, F-WKQC, F-OCZV, F-RAFR, F-BMHC, F-WMHC. Olympic c/s, *Hermes*. ①	3-02
❏ OO-SHW		Bell 47H-1	ex Thruxton, G-AZYB, LN-OQG, SE-HBE, OO-SHW. Crashed 21-4-84. ➟	3-02
❏ SP-SAY		Mil Mi-2	ex PZL-Swidnik, Hiscso, ZEUS, PZL.	3-02
❏ N114WG		WG.30-160	ex Yeovil, Westland Inc, G-EFIS, G-17-8. Boomless.	3-02
❏ WG719		Dragonfly HR.5	G-BRMA, ex 'WG718', Shawbury, Weston, Yeovilton, Yeovilton SF, 705. ➟	3-02
❏ XD163	'X'	Whirlwind HAR.10	ex Wroughton, 8645M, CFS, Akrotiri SAR Flt, MoA, 228, 275, 155, MoA. ➟	3-02
❏ –	XE521	Rotodyne Y	ex Cranfield, White Waltham. Large sections. ➟	3-02
❏ XG452		Belvedere HC.1	G-BRMB, ex Ternhill, 2 SoTT 7997M, Westlands. ➟ ®	3-02
❏ XG547	'S-T'	Sycamore HR.14	G-HAPR, ex St Athan 8010M, Kemble, CFS. ➟	3-02
❏ XK940*	'911'	Whirlwind HAS.7	G-AYXT, ex Tibenham, Redhill, Northampton, Heysham, Carnforth, Panshanger, Elstree, Luton, Blackpool, Fleetlands, 771, Culdrose SF, 705, 825, 824, 845. CoA 4-2-99. Arrived 6-6-00.	3-02
❏ XL811		Skeeter AOP.12	ex Stoke-on-Trent, Warmingham, Southend, 9/12 Lancers, 17F, 652, 651. ➟	3-02
❏ XM330		Wessex HAS.1	ex Farnborough, RAE.	3-02
❏ XP165		Scout AH.1	ex Yeovilton, Weston, HAM Southend, RAE.	3-02
❏ XR486*		Whirlwind HCC.12	G-RWWW, ex Redhill, Tattershall Thorpe, 32, QF, 32, QF. CoA 25-8-96. Arrived 8-6-00. ➟	3-02
❏ XT190		Sioux AH.1	ex Wattisham, Soest, Middle Wallop, UNFICYP.	3-02
❏ XT443	'422'	Wasp HAS.1	ex Oldmixon, Sherborne, *Aurora* Flt.	3-02
❏ [XT472]	'XC'	Wessex HU.5	ex Hullavington, Netheravon, Wroughton, 845.	3-02
❏ XV733*		Wessex HCC.4	ex Shawbury, Queen's Flight. Arrived 15-11-01.	3-02
❏ XW839		Lynx 00-05	ex Yeovilton, A2624 [2], A2657, A2710, Manadon, BS Engines.	3-02
❏ XX910*		Lynx HAS.2	ex DERA/RAE Farnborough, Aberporth, A&AEE. Boomless. Arrived 5-12-00.	3-02

☐	ZE477		Lynx 3	ex G-17-24, Yeovil, Westlands.		3-02
☐	622		HUP-3 Retriever	ex N6699D, RCN, 51-16622.		3-02
☐	09147		Mil Mi-4 *Hound*	ex Prague, Sechov, Tabor, Czech AF.		3-02
☐	[S-886]		S-55C	ex Panshanger, Elstree, Dan AF Esk.722.	→	3-02
☐	FR-108	'CDL'	Djinn	ex France, ALAT F-MCDL.		3-02
☐	96+26		Mi-24 *Hind-D*	ex Basepohl, Luftwaffe, E German 421.		3-02
☐	1005	'05'	WSK SM-2	ex Poland.		3-02
☐	2007		Mil Mi-1 (SM-1)	ex Poland. Soviet colours.		3-02
☐	16506		OH-6A Cayuse	ex US Army. (FY67)		3-02
☐	[66-16579]		UH-1H-BF	ex US Army.		3-02
☐			Lynx 3 EMU	ex Yeovil. Built 1984 using Lynx and WG.30 parts.		3-02
☐	–		Bö 105	ex Middlemoor.	②	3-02
☐	–	BAPC.10	Hafner R-II	ex Middle Wallop, Locking, Weston-super-M, Old Warden, Yeovil.		3-02
☐	–	BAPC.60	Murray Helicopter	ex Wigan, Salford.		3-02
☐	–	BAPC.128	Watkinson CG-4	ex Horley, Bexhill. Man powered rotorcraft.		3-02
☐	–	BAPC.153	WG.33 EMU	ex Yeovil. Ultra-light helicopter. Restored 2001.		3-02
☐	–	BAPC.213	Cranfield Vertigo	ex Yeovil, Cardington, Yeovil. Man-powered helo.		3-02
☐	–	BAPC.264	Bensen B.8M	ex Westbury-on-Trym. Built 1984. Unflown.		3-02

THM 'Reserve Collection': As noted above, the airframes in deep store, used for spares or held for potential exchange have been separated for the first time in this edition. As they are not generally available for public inspection, their listing above might well frustrate the visitor. (Depending on staffing levels, THM are happy to show visitors these airframes, with prior application.) Wessex HAS.3 XS149 is fitted with the rear fuselage of Srs 60 G-17-6 ①.

Departures: Bell 47D-1 G-ASOL to Sunderland, N&T, 2001; WG.30-160 N116WG moved to Montrose, Scotland, 27-7-01; WG.30-100 N5880T to Norwich, Norfolk, 3-02; S-55C S-882 to Bristol Airport, Somerset 2-02.

☐	[G-ANJV]		Whirlwind Srs 3	ex Redhill, Bristow and VR-BET.		3-02
☐	G-ASCT		Bensen B.8M	ex Hungerford. CoA 11-11-66.		3-02
☐	G-ASHD		Brantly B.2A	ex Oxford and area. Crashed 19-2-67. Spares.		3-02
☐	G-ATBZ		Wessex 60 Srs 1	ex Bournemouth, G-17-4, Weston. CoA 15-12-81.		3-02
☐	G-AXFM		Grasshopper III	ex Blackpool, Heysham, Shoreham, Redhill. Rig.		3-02
☐	G-AZAU		Grasshopper III	ex Blackpool, Heysham, Shoreham, Redhill. Rig.		3-02
☐	[N112WG]		WG.30-100	ex Yeovil, Midway.		3-02
☐	[N118WG]		WG.30-160	ex Yeovil, PanAm.		3-02
☐	[N5820T]		WG.30-100	ex Yeovil, Air Spur, G-BKFD.		3-02
☐	[N5840T]		WG.30-100	ex Yeovil, Air Spur, G-BKFF.		3-02
☐	[VR-BEU]		Whirlwind Srs 3	ex Redhill, VR-BEU, G-ATKV, EP-HAN, G-ATKV.		3-02
☐	VZ962		Dragonfly HR.1	ex Helston, BRNC Dartmouth.		3-02
☐	[XA862]		Whirlwind HAS.1	ex Coventry, Wroughton, Lee-on-Solent A2542, Seafield Park, Haslar, Lee-on-Solent, Fleetlands, 781, 771, 700, *Protector* Flt, 700, *Protector* Flt, 705, G-AMJT ntu.		3-02
☐	XG462		Belvedere HC.1	ex Henlow, Weston-super-Mare, 72, 66. Crashed 5-10-63. Nose. ®	®	3-02
☐	[XG596]	'66'	Whirlwind HAS.7	ex Wroughton, A2651, 705, 829, 771, 705, 737. Returned from off-site 8-99.	→	3-02
☐	[XP404]		Whirlwind HAR.10	ex Finningley, Benson 8682M, 22, SAR Wing, 202, 228. Boomless.		3-02
☐	XR526		Wessex HC.2	ex Yeovil, Sherborne, Farnborough, Odiham 8147M, 72. Damaged 27-5-70. Hydraulics rig.		3-02
☐	XS149	'61'	Wessex HAS.3	ex Templecombe, Wroughton, 737.	①	3-02
☐	XT148		Sioux AH.1	ex Halton, Panshanger, Wroughton, ARWF. Spares.		3-02
☐			WG.30-300 EMU	ex Yeovil. Transmission rig, using parts from c/n 022.		3-02
☐	(S-881)		S-55C	ex Panshanger, Elstree, Dan AF Esk.722. Spares.		3-02
☐	–	BAPC.212	Bensen B.6	gyroglider.		3-02

GKN-Westland Industrial Plastics Ltd (Agusta-Westland): (Also known as the Old Mixon plant.) A case of a clear-out: WG.30-200 G-ELEC was painted up in yellow/red 'Rescue' markings with 'Helicopter Museum' titles and delivered to the museum, above, 7-12-01; Gazelle AH.1 XZ318 to Fleetlands, Hants, by 8-00; SA.330L Puma ZE449 to 33 Squadron at Benson on 7-3-01; Wasp HAS.1 NZ3905 to Cranfield, Beds, 23-5-00.

WESTON ZOYLAND AERODROME ton the A372 east of Bridgwater
Pegasus XL-R G-MTAW and Quasar G-MWPU were flying again by 2000
❑ G-MNSN	Pegasus Flash 2	CoA 19-4-97. Stored.	5-98
❑ G-MVMA	Pegasus XL-Q	CoA 28-2-98. Damaged. Stored.	5-98

YEOVIL AIRFIELD to the west of Yeovil
Agusta Westland: (Another name change...) The hulks of WG.30-100s G-BKKI and G-OGAS had been cleared by May 2001.
❑ XZ181	Lynx AH.7	ex Arborfield, Fleetlands, 656, 663, 653, 654. Spares.	10-99
❑ XZ671	Lynx AH.7	ex Fleetlands, Yeovil, Wroughton. Crashed 24-1-85.	
		With boom of ZE377. Systems trials.	10-99
❑ *	'961' EH.101 EMU	static test airframe. Stored.	3-02

Yeovil Technical College:
❑ [XP886]	Scout AH.1	ex Arborfield, Wroughton, 652, 660, 651.	2-02
❑ 'XV137'	Scout AH.1	XV139, ex Arborfield, Wroughton, 657,	
		656, 662, 653.	2-02

YEOVILTON AIRFIELD on the B5131, south of the A303, north of Yeovil
Fleet Air Arm Museum (FAAM): The 'Leading Edge' hall was officially opened on 10th July 2000. Funded by part of the museum's £3.7 million Heritage Lottery Fund grant, the display includes many interactive displays and 'stations' showing the development of aviation from biplanes to Concorde. Also 'on stream' at the same time was the Lockheed Martin sponsored 'Merlin Experience' showing the roles that the up-coming EHI Merlin will play with the Fleet Air Arm of the future. Aircraft on view inside 'Leading Edge' are marked ➤. The exceptional Cobham Hall storage facility is listed separately, below.
Notes: Several aircraft are on loan and are marked as follows ±. These are: Concorde, Sea Vampire LZ551 and Ohka from the Science Museum; the Short 184 from the Imperial War Museum; the Bristol Scout D REP from Sir George White. Its 'serial' number is actually its US civil registration. Sopwith Baby 'N2078' is a composite, using parts from the sequential 8214 and 8215. Both of these machines, ordered in 1915, were passed on to the Italian government to act as pattern aircraft in July 1916, for production by Macchi. This would go a long way to explaining the Italian tricolour on the rudder of the components acquired by R G J Nash ①. The long-term restoration of Barracuda II DP872 took a major step forward in late 2000 with the arrival of the substantial wreckage of Mk.II LS931 from its crash site on the Scottish Isle of Jura ②. Wessex XP142 *Humphrey* returned to the museum from Cobham Hall in March 2002 for a new exhibition to mark the 20th anniversary of the Falklands conflict which runs until October 2002 ③. Visitors to the incredible 'Carrier' exhibition travel to the flight deck 'on board' Wessex XT769 and disembark from XT482 ④!
After many, many years on the 'gate' of the museum, Buccaneer S.1 XK488 moved to Cobham Hall – below – on 27th March 2001. Tiger Moth 'G-ABUL' made the move to Cobham Hall on 5th March 2002. FAAM aircraft can be found at the following locations: Coventry, Warks, Gannet XA508; East Fortune, Scotland, Whirlwind XG594, F-4S 155848; Mickleover, Derby, MB.339 0767; Montrose, Scotland, Sea Hawk XE340; Sunderland, Tyneside, Pucará A-522; Weston-super-Mare, Som, Dragonfly VZ962; Woodley, Berks, Gannet XG883. And, a little further away, Scimitar F.1 XD220 on the USS *Intrepid* in New York!
◆ Open every day (other than Xmas) Apr to Oct 10am to 5.30pm and Nov to Mar 10am to 4.30pm. There is a very active **Friends of the FAAM**. Membership enquiries via the museum. ✉ RNAS Yeovilton, Ilchester, BA22 8HT ☎ 01935 840565 **fax** 01935 842630 **e-mail** info@fleetairarm.co **web** www.fleetairarm.com

❑ G-BSST	Concorde 002	UK prototype, ff 9-4-69. CoA 30-10-74.	± ➤	3-02

❏	8359		Short 184	ex Duxford, South Lambeth, Buncrana, Rosyth, Dundee, Killingholme. Forward fuselage.	± 3-02
❏	'B6401'		Camel REP	G-AWYY, ex 'C1701', N1917H, G-AWYY. CoA 1-9-85.	3-02
❏	L2301		Walrus I	ex Arbroath, Thame, G-AIZG, EI-ACC, IAAC N18, Supermarine N18, L2301.	3-02
❏	L2940		Skua I	ex Lake Grotli, Norway, 800. Crashed 27-4-40.	3-02
❏	N1854		Fulmar II	ex Lossie', Fairey G-AIBE, A&AEE. CoA 6-7-59.	3-02
❏	'N2078'		Sopwith Baby	ex Fleetlands, Heathrow, Nash. *The Jabberwock*. ①	3-02
❏	'N4389'	'4M'	Albacore	N4172, ex Land's End, Yeovilton.	3-02
❏	N5419		Bristol Scout REP	ex Kemble, Banwell, Cardington, USA. ± ➤	3-02
❏	'N5492'		Sopwith Triplane REP	BAPC.111, ex Chertsey. *Black Maria*. 10 (Naval) Sqn, 'B' Flight colours.	3-02
❏	'N6452'		Pup REP	G-BIAU, ex Whitehall. CoA 13-9-89.	3-02
❏	'P4139'		Swordfish II	HS618, ex 'W5984', Manadon A2001, Donibristle.	3-02
❏	'S1287'		Flycatcher REP	G-BEYB, ex Andover, Middle Wallop, Duxford, Middle Wallop, Yeovilton. 405 Flt colours.	3-02
❏	Z2033*	'275'	Firefly TT.1	G-ASTL, ex Duxford, Staverton, G-ASTL, SE-BRD, Z2033. 1771 Sqn c/s, *Evelyn Tentions*. Arr 25-7-00.	3-02
❏	AL246		Martlet I	ex Loughborough, 768, 802.	3-02
❏	DP872		Barracuda II	ex Andover area, Yeovilton, Enagh Lough, 769. Cr 18-1-44. Forward fuselage. Remainder stored. ②	3-02
❏	EX976		Harvard IIA	ex Portuguese AF 1657, EX976, 41-33959.	3-02
❏	KD431	'E2-M'	Corsair IV	ex Cranfield, 768, 1835, BuNo 14862. 768 Sqn c/s. ⑧	3-02
❏	KE209		Hellcat II	ex Lossie, Stretton, Anthorn, BuNo 79779.	3-02
❏	LZ551/G		Sea Vampire I	ex CS(A), DH, A&AEE, RAE. ±	3-02
❏	SX137		Seafire F.17	ex Culdrose, 'W9132', Stretton, 759, 1831, Culham.	3-02
❏	VH127	'200'	Firefly TT.4	ex Wroughton, Y'ton, Culdrose, FRU, 700, 737, 812.	3-02
❏	VR137		Wyvern TF.1	ex Cranfield. Eagle-powered proto, not flown. ➤	3-02
❏	WA473	'102'	Attacker F.1	ex Abbotsinch, 736, 702, 800.	3-02
❏	WG774		BAC 221	ex East Fortune, RAE Bedford, Filton. ➤	3-02
❏	WJ231	'115'	Sea Fury FB.11	ex Wroughton, Yeovilton 'WE726', Yeovilton SF, FRU.	3-02
❏	WN493		Dragonfly HR.5	ex Culdrose, 705, 701, A&AEE.	3-02
❏	WV856		Sea Hawk FGA.6	ex RAE, 781, 806.	3-02
❏	WW138	'227'	Sea Ven FAW.22	ex AWS, 831, 809. Suez stripes.	3-02
❏	XA127		Sea Vampire T.22	ex CIFE, 736. Pod. ➤	3-02
❏	XB446		Avenger ECM.6B	ex Culdrose SF, 831, 751, 820, USN 69502. D-Day stripes and camouflage.	3-02
❏	XD317	'112'	Scimitar F.1	ex FRU, RAE, 800, 736, 807.	3-02
❏	XG574	'752'	Whirlwind HAR.3	ex Portland, Wroughton, Yeovilton, Wroughton, Lee-on-Solent, A2575, 771.	3-02
❏	XL503	'070'	Gannet AEW.3	ex RRE, 849 'D', 'A' Flts, A&AEE, 849 HQ Flt, C(A), 849 'A' Flt.	3-02
❏	XL580	'723'	Hunter T.8M	ex FRADU, FOFT, 764. ➤	3-02
❏	XN332	'759'	SARO P.531	ex Portland, Wroughton, Yeovilton, Wroughton, Yeovilton, Manadon, A2579, G-APNV.	3-02
❏	XN957	'630'	Buccaneer S.1	ex 736, 809.	3-02
❏	XP142*		Wessex HAS.3	ex Cobham, Wroughton, Yeovilton, 737. *Humphrey*. Arrived 19-3-02. ③	3-02
❏	XP841		HP.115	ex Cosford, Colerne, RAE Bedford. ➤	3-02
❏	XP980		P.1127	A2700, ex Culdrose, Tarrant Rushton, RAE Bedford, Cranwell, A&AEE. ➤	3-02
❏	XS590	'131'	Sea Vixen FAW.2	ex 899, 892.	3-02
❏	XT482	'ZM'	Wessex HU.5	A2656 [2], ex A2745, Lee-on-Solent, Wroughton, 848. ④	3-02
❏	XT596		Phantom FG.1	ex BAe Scampton, Holme-on-Spalding Moor, RAE Thurleigh, Holme, Filton, Hucknall, Patuxent River, Edwards. Dbr 11-10-74.	3-02

❑ XT769	'823'	Wessex HU.5	ex Lee-on-Solent, Wroughton, Culdrose, 771, 846, 848.	③	3-02
❑ XV333	'234'	Buccaneer S.2B	ex 208, 12, 15, 16, FAA, 237 OCU, 12. 801 Sqn c/s.		3-02
❑ XZ493*	'001'	Sea Harrier FRS.1	ex Dunsfold, Yeovilton, Lee-on-Solent, 899, 801. Ditched 15-12-94. Arrived 22-3-00.	➤	3-02
❑		Fairey IIIF	fuselage frame.	®	3-02
❑ 'D.5397'		Albatros D.Va REP	G-BFXL, ex Leisure Sport, Land's End, Chertsey, D-EGKO. CoA 5-11-91.		3-02
❑ '102 /17'		Fokker Dr I REP	BAPC.88, scale REP, based on a Lawrence Parasol.		3-02
❑ 15-1585		Ohka 11	BAPC.58, ex Hayes, South Kensington.	±	3-02
❑ 01420		MiG-15bis / Lim-2	G-BMZF, ex North Weald, Gamston, Retford, Polish AF. North Korean colours.		3-02

FAAM Cobham Hall: Home of the FAAM's reserve collection, workshop, archive and much more. Dragonfly HR.1 VX595 is on loan from the RAF Museum ①. The Jet Provost might seem an odd choice. It was donated by a former RN pilot who earned his wings on this very aircraft while with 1 FTS – where a large number of Navy pilots received their training ②.
Wessex HAS.3 XP142 moved back to the museum proper on 19th March 2002 for the new Falklands exhibition. AV-8A 159233 moved to <u>Manchester</u>, Gtr Man, on 21st November 2001.
◆ *Not* open to the public. A series of special open days are planned.

❑ 'G-ABUL'*		Tiger Moth	XL717, ex G-AOXG, T7291, 24 EFTS, 19 EFTS. Arrived 5-3-02.		3-02
❑ G-AZAZ		Bensen B.8M	ex Wroughton, Houndstone, Yeovilton, Manadon.		3-02
❑ [G-BGWZ]		Super Eagle h/g	ex Wroughton, Houndstone, Yeovilton.		3-02
❑ VV106		Supermarine 510	ex Wroughton, Lee-on-Solent, Cosford, St Athan, Colerne, Cardington, Halton, Melksham, 7175M.		3-02
❑ VX272		Hawker P.1052	ex Wroughton, Lee-on-Solent, Cosford, St Athan, Colerne 7174M.		3-02
❑ VX595		Dragonfly HR.1	ex Portland, Gosport, Fleetlands, Henlow, Fleetlands. ①		3-02
❑ WM292	'841'	Meteor TT.20	ex B'thorpe, Cardiff, Yeovilton, FRU, Kemble, 527.		3-02
❑ WP313	'568'	Sea Prince T.1	ex Wroughton, Kemble, 750, Sydenham SF, 750, Lossiemouth SF, 750.		3-02
❑ WS103		Meteor T.7	ex Wroughton, Crawley, Wroughton, Lee-on-Solent, FRU, Kemble, Yeovilton Standards Sqn, Anthorn.		3-02
❑ WT121	'415'	Skyraider AEW.1	WT983, ex Culdrose, 849, USN 124121.		3-02
❑ WV106*	'427'	Skyraider AEW.1	ex Culdrose, Helston, Culdrose, 849, Donibristle, Abbotsinch, 124086. 849 Sqn c/s. Arr 6-12-00.		3-02
❑ XA129		Sea Vampire T.22	ex Wroughton, Yeovilton, CIFE, 736.		3-02
❑ XA466	'777'	Gannet COD.4	ex Wroughton, Yeovilton, Lee-on-Solent, Lossie', 849.		3-02
❑ XA864		Whirlwind HAR.1	ex Wroughton, Yeovilton, RAE, A&AEE, RAE, CA, G-17-1.		3-02
❑ XB480	'537'	Hiller HT.1	ex Wroughton, Yeovilton, Manadon, A2577, 705.		3-02
❑ XJ481*		Sea Vixen FAW.1	ex Fleetlands, Southampton, Ilkeston, Yeovilton, Portland, Yeovilton, Boscombe Down, LRWE. Arrived 29-11-01.		3-02
❑ XK488*		Buccaneer S.1	ex museum, BSE Filton and Blackburns. Arr 27-3-01.		3-02
❑ XL853		Whirlwind HAS.7	ex Portland, Fleetlands, Southampton, Middle Wallop, Lee-on-Solent, A2630, Wroughton, Y'ton SF, 824.		3-02
❑ XN334		SARO P.531	ex Wroughton, Crawley, Weston-super-Mare, Yeovilton, Arbroath, Lee-on-Solent A2525.		3-02
❑ XN462	'17'	Jet Provost T.3A	ex Wroughton, Sharnford, Shawbury, 1 FTS, 2 FTS, CFS, 3 FTS, 7 FTS, 1 FTS.	②	3-02
❑ XS508		Wessex HU.5	A2677 [2], ex A2766, Lee-on-Solent, Wroughton.		3-02
❑ XS527		Wasp HAS.1	ex Wroughton, *Endurance* Flt.		3-02
❑ XT176	'U'	Sioux AH.1	ex Wroughton, 3 CBAS.		3-02
❑ XT427	'606'	Wasp HAS.1	ex Helston, Yeovilton, Wroughton.		3-02

❑ XT778	'430'	Wasp HAS.1	A2642 [2], ex A2722, ex Portland, West Moors,	
			Lee-on-Solent. *Achilles* Flt c/s.	3-02
❑ –	BAPC.149	Short S.27 REP	ex Lee-on-Solent. Stored.	3-02
❑		Sea Vixen CIM	ex Wroughton, Yeovilton. Cockpit.	3-02
❑ AE-422		UH-1H Iroquois	ex Wroughton, Yeovilton, Stanley, Argentine	
			Army, 74-22520.	3-02
❑ 0729	'411'	T-34C-1	ex Wroughton, Yeovilton, Stanley, Pebble Island,	
		Turbo Mentor	Arg Navy.	3-02
❑ 100545		Fa 330A-1	ex Wroughton, Yeovilton, Higher Blagdon,	
			Cranfield, Farnborough.	3-02

Royal Navy Historic Flight (RNHF) / **The Swordfish Trust**: The Trust is a charitable concern designed to support RNHF – and, by definition, particularly the 'Stringbags'. Sea Fury FB.11 VR930 took to the air again on 1st March 2001. Its flying days were strictly limited. Following a flight on 21st August 2001, inspection of the rough-running engine found substantial damage to the Centaurus. The massive costs involved in repairing the engine cannot, at this time, be met and the Fury has been 'mothballed'. Firefly WB271 made its first post-restoration ground-runs on 27th February 2002 with first flight not far off ①. Swordfish NF389 is at Brough, E Yorks, under restoration to flying condition.
♦ Not available for public inspection at Yeovilton, but are frequent attendees at airshows. ✉ RNHF Support Group, RNAS Yeovilton, BA22 8HT ☎ 01935 456279 **web** www.flynavyheritage.org/uk

❑ W5856	'A2A'	Swordfish II ✈	G-BMGC, ex Brough, Strathallan, Alabama, RCN,	
			Wroughton, Manston. 810 Sqn c/s. *City of Leeds*.	3-02
❑ LS326	'L2'	Swordfish II ✈	ex Westlands, G-AJVH, Worthy Down, 836.	
			City of Liverpool .	® 3-02
❑ VR930		Sea Fury FB.11	ex Brough, Yeovilton, Boscombe Down,	
	'110'		Lee-on-Solent, Wroughton, Yeovilton, 8382M,	
			Colerne, Dunsfold, FRU, Lossiemouth, Anthorn,	
			801, Anthorn, 802. First flown 1-3-01.	
			Grounded 21-8-01. Stored.	3-02
❑ VZ345		Sea Fury T.20S	ex Brough, Yeovilton, Boscombe Down, DLB D-CATA,	
			D-FATA, ES.8503, G-9-30, Hawkers, Dunsfold,	
			VZ345, 1832. Accident 19-4-85.	11-97
❑ WB271*	'204'	Firefly AS.5	ex Dunsfold, Yeovilton, RAN Nowra, 723,	
		✈	725, 816/817, 814. 812 Sqn colours.	① 3-02
❑ WB657	'908'	Chipmunk T.10	ex BRNC, Leeds UAS, 16 RFS, 25 RFS,	
		✈	Leeds UAS, 25 RFS. 'Hack'.	3-02
❑ WK608		Chipmunk T.10	ex BRNC, Bri UAS, 7 FTS, 3 FTS,	
			Edin UAS,11 RFS. 'Hack'.	3-02
❑ WV908*		Sea Hawk	ex Dunsfold, Yeovilton, Dunsfold, Yeovilton,	
	'188'	FGA.6	Culdrose SF, Halton 8154M, Sydenham A2660,	
			738, 806, 898, 807. Arrived by 3-01.	3-02
❑ WV911*	'115'	Sea Hawk	A2622 [2], ex Dunsfold, Lee-on-Solent A2626,	
		FGA.6	Fleetlands, Lee-on-Solent A2526. Arrived 10-7-00.	3-02

Others: Airframes dealt with by the **Flight Safety and Accident Investigation Unit** (FSAIU) tend to be transitory. Two airframes are used by the **Engineering Training School** (ETS). The **Heron Gliding Club** (HGC) also operate from here. Gazelle XW890 (with the boom of AH.1 ZB668) is displayed outside the DHSA building ①.
    Departures: The hulk of Starduster Too G-BPOD has gone; Cadet TX.3 XE807 to Keevil, Wilts, and sold abroad; hulks of Wessex HAS.1s XP157 and XS128 left 13-7-00 and 31-8-00 respectively for a scrap dealer reported to be at Hartley Witney, Hants; Lynx 1-06 XW837 had gone by 10-00.

❑ WV903	'128'	Sea Hawk FGA.4	ex Dunsfold, Lee-on-Solent, Culdrose A2632,	
			Halton 8153M, Sydenham. Dump.	11-01
❑ XE339	'149'	Sea Hawk FGA.6	ex Dunsfold, Lee-on-Solent, Culdrose A2635,	
			Halton 8156M. Dump.	11-01
❑ XT653		Swallow TX.1	FUW/BGA.3545, ex Halesland, Syerston, CGS.	
			Stored.	HGC 5-98

❑ [XV280]   Harrier GR.1   A2700 [2], ex Foulness, Boscombe Down, A&AEE,
                               HSA. Nose, Sea Harrier style, trailer-mounted.   3-02
❑ XV755   'M' Harrier GR.3   A2606 [3], ex A2604, 233 OCU, 3, 233 OCU, 3,
                               233 OCU, 1, 233 OCU, 1, 233 OCU. Dump.   3-02
❑ XW630*   Harrier GR.3   A2671 [2], ex Gosport, A2759 Lee-on-Solent, 3, 4,
                               3, 20. FAA colours. Dump. Arrived 17-5-00.   3-02
❑ XW890   Gazelle HT.2   ex Fleetlands, Wroughton, 705. Displayed.   ①   3-02
❑ XZ129   'ETS' Harrier GR.3   A2604 [3], ex A2602, Cranfield, 233 OCU, 1,
                               233 OCU, 1, 233 OCU.   ETS 11-01
❑ ZB601*   Harrier T.4   ex Dunsfold, St Athan, ETS Yeovilton, 899,
                               233 OCU. BDRT. Arrived 5-6-00.   3-02
❑ —   RG-05 Lynx static rig   ex Weston-super-Mare, Blackpool, Coventry,
                               Yeovil. Fire training, poor state.   11-01
❑   Sea Harrier F/A.2 EMU, built by Ogle Designs.   ETS 7-97

STAFFORDSHIRE

☞ Includes within its boundaries the unitary authority of the City of Stoke-on-Trent.

BURSLEM on the A50 north-west of Stoke-on-Trent
Supermarine Aero Engineering: Work is undertaken on SL611 on a time available basis, in between work on purpose-built components for Spitfire projects worldwide.
❑ SL611   Spitfire XVI   ex Scafell, 603, 111 OTU. Crashed 20-11-47.   6-01

BURTON-UPON-TRENT
No.351 Squadron Air Cadets: Located on the northern edge of the town, near a railway yard.
❑ XP735   Lightning F.3   ex Stafford, Pendine, Leconfield, 29 Wattisham
                               TFF, 23. Nose.   3-01

CANNOCK on the A34 north of Walsall
Keith Jones: Moved his Spitfire FSM to Sleap, Shropshire, on loan on 29th June 2001.

ECCLESHALL on the A5013 north-west of Stafford
Malcolm Goosey: Tiger Moth G-OOSY moved to Stoke-on-Trent, Staffs, during 2001. Taking its place was another example.
❑ G-ANNN*   Tiger Moth   ex Hatch, T5968, Wattisham SF, 61 GCF, 3 RFS,
                               28 EFTS, 57 OTU.   ®   1-02

HALFPENNY GREEN AERODROME
Adopted the name Wolverhampton Business Airport in March 2000 — who are we to argue? See below.

HEDNESFORD on the A460 northeast of Cannock
Martyn Jones: *Should* still have his 'JP' nose.
❑ XM417   'D' Jet Provost T.3   ex Fownhope, Halton 8054BM, Shawbury,
                               6 FTS, 7 FTS, 2 FTS. Nose.   8-94

HIXON west of the A51, east of Stafford
Air and Ground Aviation: Located on the former airfield, have tendered for a series of helicopters.
❏ XT463*   'D' Wessex HU.5C   ex Predannack, Gosport A2624 [3], Shawbury,
Akrotiri, 84, FAA. Tail of XR503. Arrived 5-12-00.   12-00

LICHFIELD north-west of Tamworth
No.1206 Squadron Air Cadets: Cherry Orchard, near the city railway station. 'Parent' is Stafford.
❏ WK576   Chipmunk T.10   8357M, ex AOTS, 3/4 CAACU, Cam UAS, Oxf UAS,
          PAX   Lon UAS, Cam UAS, Lon UAS, Cam UAS, Hull
                               UAS, Cam UAS, Bir UAS, Cam UAS, 22 RFS.   6-00

Others: The Bensen *should* still be in the area.
❏ G-AXCI   Bensen B.8M   ex Lutterworth, East Midlands. Stored.   9-93

LONGTON on the A50 south of Stoke-on-Trent
Motor Clinic: On the Trentham Road, have a 'JP'.
❏ XM425   Jet Provost T.3A   ex King's Lynn, Bruntingthorpe, Halton 8995M,
                               7 FTS, 1 FTS, RAFC, 3 FTS, CFS. '88'.   3-01

RUGELEY on the A51 east of Stafford
❏ WW444   'D' Provost T.1   ex Sibson, Coventry, Bitteswell, Shawbury,
                             CAW, 5 AEF, 6 FTS, 3 FTS, 22 FTS.   ® 2-96
❏ XD515   Vampire T.11   ex Winthorpe, Misson, Linton-on-Ouse 7998M,
                             3 FTS, 7 FTS, 1 FTS, 5 FTS, 206 AFS.   ® 6-99

SEIGHFORD AERODROME south of the B5405, west of Stafford
Staffordshire Gliding Club: Rallye G-AXIT was disposed of via a reclaims operation in southern
Lincolnshire and likely reduced to produce.

STAFFORD (Beaconside, west of the city)
Royal Air Force Museum Reserve Collection: This is the new 'deep store' for the RAF Museum
(see under Cosford, Shropshire). It is very probable that more airframes will come here.
◆ Viewing is *not* possible.
❏ A301*   Morane BB   ex Wyton, Cardington, Hendon. Fuselage.   11-01
❏ Z7197*   Proctor III   8380M, ex Hendon, St Athan, Swinderby,
                           Finningley, G-AKZN, AST, 18 EFTS, 1 RS, 2 SS.
                           CoA 29-11-63. Arrived 7-3-02.   3-02
❏ –*   FE.2b   ex Wyton, Cardington. Cockpit nacelle.   11-01
❏ –*   BAPC.194 Demoiselle REP   ex Wyton, Cardington, Brooklands, Henlow, Gatow.   11-01
❏ –*   BAPC.237 Fi 103 (V-1)   ex Wyton, Cardington, St Athan.   11-01

Defence Storage and Distribution Centre (DSDC) / Tactical Supply Wing (TSW).
❏ XT469   Wessex HU.5   8920M, ex Wroughton.   TSW 2-99
❏ XZ287   Nimrod AEW.3   9140M, ex Abingdon, Waddington, JTU,
                             Woodford. Fuselage. *Fly Suki Airways*.   TSW 3-01
❏ XZ987   'C' Harrier GR.3   9185M, ex St Athan, 1417 Flt, 3, 4. Gate.   12-01

STOKE-ON-TRENT
The Potteries Museum and Art Gallery: The Spitfire is being restored – with visitors able to
watch progress – by volunteers from the local company, Supermarine Aero Engineering.

◆ Open Mar to Oct Mon to Sat 10am to 5pm, Sun 2pm to 5pm; Nov to Feb Mon to Sat 10am to 4pm, Sun 1pm to 4pm. ✉ Bethesda Street, Hanley, Stoke ST1 3DE ☎ 01782 232323 fax 01782 232500 e-mail museums@stoke.gov.uk web www.stoke.gov.uk/museums

❑ RW388   Spitfire XVI   ex Kemble, 'AB917', 71 MU 6946M, 19 MU, 5 MU,
     'U4-U'   Andover, Benson, FC&RS, 612, 667. 667 Sqn c/s.   ® 3-02

Ken Fern: Contrary to *W&R17*, Auster G-AJPZ did not come here — see under Bournemouth, Dorset. What *did* come here was the pod of Vampire T.11 XE921 but it quickly moved on to Welshpool, Wales. T-6G 114700 moved to a syndicate at Bruntingthorpe, Leics. DH.88 Comet project G-ACSP moved to Derby Aerodrome, Derbyshire, where work continues. Ken was due to move his workshop to Derbyshire to be closer to this project as *W&R* closed for press.

❑ G-OOSY*   Tiger Moth   ex Eccleshall, F-BGFI, FAF, DE971.   ® 3-02

STONE on the A34 north of Stafford
Alan Simpson: XG629 was at Fownhope, H&W, October 2000 to August 2001.

❑ XG629   Sea Venom   ex Long Marston, Fleetlands, Higher Blagdon,
     '668'   FAW.22   Culdrose, ADS, 831, 893.   4-02

TATENHILL AERODROME south of the B5234, west of Burton-on-Trent
By August 2000, Luscombe P3 Rattler Strike G-BKPG had moved to Egginton, Derby. By mid-2001 Globe Swift G-BFNM had moved to Oakham, Leics.

❑ G-ARNN   GC-1B Swift   ex Leicester, VP-YMJ, VP-RDA, ZS-BMX,
                              NC3279K. Crashed 1-9-73.   ® 7-91
❑ G-AZHE   Slingsby T.61B   ex N61TB, G-AZHE. Damaged 17-6-88.   ® 7-91
❑ G-BUPJ   Fournier RF-4D   ex N7752.   ® 6-95
❑ G-BUXM   Quickie TriQ   ex N4435Y. CoA 10-8-95. Stored.   7-98
❑ G-BXGE*   Cessna 152 II   ex N89283. CoA 16-7-00. Fuselage, stored.   4-01

WESTON-ON-TRENT on the A51 north-east of Stafford
Chell Air: Have a yard in Salt Works Lane. Processing is swift but they do keep the cockpit of a former Shawbury Jetstream.

❑ XX483*   '562' Jetstream T.1   ex Shawbury, 750, CFS, 5 FTS. Cockpit   12-01

WOLVERHAMPTON BUSINESS AIRPORT, or Halfpenny Green, south of the B4176,
                                                   east of Bridgnorth
Note the new and imposing name, adopted on 28th March 2000.

❑ G-BSYK   Tomahawk 112   ex N23449. Stored. First noted 9-97.   10-01
❑ G-BSYL   Tomahawk 112   ex N91333. Stored.   10-01
❑ G-BUJN   Cessna 172N II   ex Wellesbourne, N6315D. Damaged 18-1-95.   ® 8-00
❑ G-OBEY   Aztec 250C   ex G-BAAJ, SE-EIU. CoA 4-8-86.   12-97
❑   T.31   BGA.1346, ex Bidford, RAFGSA.297. Air Scouts.   2-00

SUFFOLK

BECCLES AERODROME south of the A146 west of Lowestoft
The cockpit of Carvair CF-EPV had moved on to Halesworth, Suffolk, by November 1999. By March 2000 Apache 160G had arrived here from Southend. It had moved on to Sibson, Cambs, by 2001.

❑ G-AVPH*   Cessna F.150G   ex Blackpool, Woodvale. CoA 9-4-86. F/n 3-00.   3-00

BECK ROW on the A1101 north of Mildenhall
The Hunter (with the starboard wing of XL572 and XL623 to port) is kept on a farm in the area. (See under Poole, Somerset, for the saga of XL623.)

☐ XG210   Hunter F.6   ex DRA Bedford, BAe Hatfield, CFE, 19, 14.   1-01

BURY ST EDMUNDS on the A14 east of Newmarket
Nigel Hamlin-Wright: Has taken on the Chrislea FC.1 Airguard for restoration. Only original components are being used, the reproduction elements having been discarded.

☐ G-AFIN*   Chrislea Airguard   ex Wigan, Stoke-on-Trent, Warmingham, Wigan, Finningley.   ® 1-00

No.863 Squadron Air Cadets: (Thurston Upper School) By March 2002 Chipmunk T.10 PAX WG471 had moved to East Tilbury, Essex.

FELIXSTOWE at the end of the A14, south-east of Ipswich
Glenn Cattermole: Restoration of the Buccaneer cockpit is well in hand.

☐ XT284   'T' Buccaneer S.2A   ex Stock, St Athan, Abingdon 8855M, St Athan, 237 OCU, 15, 208. Nose.   ® 2-02

FLIXTON on the B1062 west of Bungay
Norfolk and Suffolk Aviation Museum (N&SAM): The museum remains as vibrant as ever with yet another 'new' display hall going up. This one is the 1937 Boulton & Paul hangar from the former Ipswich Airport. Once up and ready, some more aircraft exhibits are planned. The Air-Sea Rescue/Coastal Command building is being extended and the 446th BG buildings may get the same treatment. During 2001, the museum opened a raised boardwalk through the rear couple of acres of their land down to the River Waveney, offering a pleasant stroll. See under Northampton Aerodrome, Northants, for an exhibit due to arrive.

Notes: The Striker microlight was the last aircraft to fly from Flixton before the runways were broken up ①. The EoN Primary is on loan from the Norfolk Gliding Club ②. Newly-arrived Canberra nose WG789 is on loan from Steve Pickup. The extreme nose section of a Felixstowe flying-boat, once used as a potting shed, amounts to some 10ft, and while not fitting our criteria totally, does represent a singular survivor. Another section of Felixstowe, about 8ft long, is on hand from the RAF Museum ④.

Ian Hancock owns several of the airframes - IH. An interesting exhibit of Ian's in the main hangar is a Spitfire XVI fuselage centred around the original skin of TD248 acquired from Historic Flying (HF). The skin, coupled with an original frame No.19, and a fibreglass tail section has created a fuselage that will, ultimately, contain as many original fittings as possible. The fuselage is due to be painted in the colours of 695 Squadron as '8Q-T'. (See under Duxford, Cambs, for the airworthy TD248.) ⑤

♦ Open Apr to Oct, Sun to Thu 10am to 5pm (last admission 4pm); Nov to Mar, Tue, Wed and Sun 10am to 4pm (last admission 3pm). Important note from N&SAM Secretary Huby Fairhead, the adjoining 'Flixton Buck' pub is now so popular – rightly so – that it is well advisable to book reservations for lunch, get them on ☎ 01986 892382! ✉ The Street, Flixton, near Bungay, NR35 1NZ. ☎ 01986 896644 during opening hours e-mail nsam.flixton@virgin.net web www. aviationmuseum.net

☐ G-AZLM	Cessna F.172L	ex Badminton. Cr 23-3-91. Fuselage.		3-02
☐ G-BDVS	Friendship 200	ex Norwich, Air UK, S2-ABK, PH-FEX, PH-EXC, 9M-AMM, PH-EXC, PH-FEX.		
		Eric Gander Dower. Nose, on loan.		3-02
☐ — G-BFIP	Wallbro Mono REP	ex Shipdham, Swanton Morley. CoA 22-4-82.		3-02
☐ G-MTFK	Flexiform Striker	On loan.	①	3-02
☐ CDN	EoN Primary	BGA.1461, ex Tibenham area. CoA 5-69.	②	3-02
☐ 'P8140'	Spitfire FSM	BAPC.71, ex Chilham Castle, 'P9390' and		
'ZP-K'		'N3317', *Battle of Britain*. *Nuflier*. 74 Sqn c/s.		3-02
☐ 'TD248'	Spitfire XVI	see above.	⑤	3-02
☐ VL349	Anson C.19	ex Norwich, N5054, G-AWSA, SCS, NCS, North Coates		
'V7-Q'		SF, WSF, FCCS, HCCS, HCEU, 116, CSE, 1 FU.		3-02

❑ VX580		Valetta C.2	ex Norwich, MCS, MEAFCS, 114, HS. Loan.	3-02
❑ WF128		Sea Prince T.1	ex Honington 8611M, Kemble, Sydenham SF, A&AEE, 750.	3-02
❑ WF643	'X'	Meteor F(TT).8	ex Coltishall, Kemble, 29, Nicosia SF, 611, 1, 56.	3-02
❑ WG789*		Canberra B.2/6	ex Mendlesham, Wycombe, Kew, Burgess Hill, Bedford, 231 OCU. Nose. Arrived 6-3-02. ③	3-02
❑ WH840		Canberra T.4	ex Seighford, Locking 8350M, St Athan, Geilenkirchen SF, A&AEE, 97, 151, 245, 88, 231 OCU, CFS. IH	3-02
❑ WV605	'T-B'	Provost T.1	ex Henlow, Higher Blagdon, 6 FTS, 3 FTS, 22 FTS.	3-02
❑ XG254*		Hunter FGA.9	8881M, ex Clacton, Coltishall, Weybourne, Coltishall, St Athan, 1 TWU, 2 TWU, TWU, 229 OCU, 54, HS, 54. Arrived 19-2-02. IH	3-02
❑ XG329		Lightning F.1	ex Swinderby, Cranwell 8050M, A&AEE, Warton. IH	3-02
❑ XG518		Sycamore HR.14	ex Sunderland, Balloch, Halton 8009M, Wroughton, Khormaksar SF, El Adem SF, Habbiniya SF, CFS, Amman SF. IH	3-02
❑ XG523	'K'	Sycamore HR.14	ex Sunderland, Hayes, Middle Wallop, Ternhill 7793M, CFS, JEHU. Damaged 25-9-62. Nose. IH	3-02
❑ XH892	'J'	Javelin FAW.9R	ex Duxford, Colerne 7982M, Shawbury, 29, 64, 23.	3-02
❑ XJ482	'713'	Sea Vixen FAW.1	ex Wimborne Minster, A2598, 766, 700Y.	3-02
❑ XK624	'32'	Vampire T.11	ex Lytham St Annes, Blackpool, CFS, 3 FTS, 7 FTS, 1 FTS, 23 GCF, CFS, 7 FTS.	3-02
❑ XM279		Canberra B(I).8	ex Firbeck, Nostell Priory, Cambridge, 16, 3. Nose. IH	3-02
❑ XN304	'W'	Whirlwind HAS.7	ex Bedford, Henlow, Wroughton, Shrivenham, Wroughton, 705, Old Sarum, 848. 848 Sqn c/s.	3-02
❑ XR485	'Q'	W'wind HAR.10	ex Wroughton, 2 FTS, CFS.	3-02
❑ A-528		FMA Pucará	ex Sunderland, Middle Wallop, Cosford, Abingdon 8769M, Stanley, Argentine AF, 9th AB, 3rd AB.	3-02
❑ 79	'2-EG'	Mystère IVA	ex Sculthorpe, FAF, ET.2/8, 314 GE, EC.1/5.	3-02
❑ 42196		F-100D-11-NA	ex Sculthorpe, French AF. EC.4/11, EC.2/11, USAF 48th FBW, 45th FS. 'Skyblazers' colours.	3-02
❑ 54433 'TR-433'		T-33A-5-LO	ex Sculthorpe, French AF, 328 CIFAS, 338 CEVSV, USAF 803rd ABG. 20th FBG c/s.	3-02
❑ 146289		T-28C Trojan	ex East Ham, France, N99153, Zaire AF FG-289, Congolese FA-289, USN VT-3, VT-5, NABTC 146289. Crashed 14-12-77. Fuselage.	3-02
❑		Felixstowe F.5	ex Felixstowe. Nose section. ④	3-02
❑ —	'LHS-1'	Bensen B.7	BAPC.147, ex Loddon, Marham, Coltishall. .	3-02
❑	BAPC.115	HM.14 'Flea'	ex Earls Colne, Andrewsfield, Balham, South Wales. IH	3-02
❑ —	BAPC.239	Fokker D.VIII	ex Lowestoft. ⁵⁄₈th scale reproduction.	3-02

FRAMLINGHAM AERODROME or Parham, on the B1116 north of Woodbridge
No.390th Bomb Group Memorial Air Museum and **British Resistance Museum**: The tower here houses a superb museum dedicated to the 390th and Parham, USAAF Station No.153. Within can be found a wide array of engines and many other artefacts. The Resistance Museum is dedicated to the work of the Auxiliary Units. The Dakota is under long term restoration and will eventually be placed in a blister hangar. Planning permission for this was granted by early 2000 and construction has started.
◆ Open 11am to 6pm on Sun and Bank Hols Mar to Oct. Also Wed 11am to 4pm in Jun, Jul, Aug. Other times by prior arrangement. ✉ Colin Durrant, 101 Avondale Road, Ipswich, IP3 9LA ☎ 01473 711275

❑ N4565L		DC-3-201A	ex Ipswich, Dublin, LV-GYP, LV-PCV, N129H, N512, N51D, N80C, NC21744. *Aisling*. ®	3-02

Aerodrome: The references to the wrecks of Cherokee 140C G-BFPE (last noted April 1992) and Cessna 150M N11824 (March 1994) are long-in-the-tooth and have been confined to LOST!

HALESWORTH on the A144 south of Bungay
No.56th Fighter Group Museum: Established on the former 8th Air Force airfield, this small museum includes a wide range of small exhibits, including items from crash sites.

John Flanagan: Keeps his Carvair cockpit section nearby.

❑ CF-EPV*	Carvair	ex Beccles, Thorpe Abbotts, Fritton Lake, Woodbridge, Southend, EI-AMR, N88819, 42-72343. Cockpit.	1-00

HONINGTON AIRFIELD on the A1088 south-east of Thetford
RAF Honington: F-4J(UK) ZE361 was scrapped in mid-2001.

❑ XK526	Buccaneer S.2	8648M, ex RAE Bedford, RRE. Gate.	5-99

HORHAM on the B1117 east of Eye
Horham Airfield Heritage Association: Founded in 2000, the association is seeking to preserve, research and promote the heritage of the former USAAF Station 119, once home to the B-17s of the 95th Bomb Group. Main project at the moment is the restoration of the 'Red Feather' club on the former airfield site, in association with the Friends of the 95th.
◆ Occasional open days. Otherwise, viewing *only* by prior application.✉ Park Farm, Hoxne, Eye, IP21 5BS. ☎ 01379 678471 e-mail frank.sherman @bushinternet.com

IPSWICH
Bolenda Engineering: No news on the store here.

❑ XP890	'G' Scout AH.1	ex Almondbank, Wroughton, ARWF. Cr 6-10-81.	12-97
❑ XR628	Scout AH.1	ex Almondbank, Wroughton, 656, 657, 666. Crashed 8-6-82.	12-97
❑ XR629	Scout AH.1	ex Almondbank, Wroughton, Garrison Air Sqn, 657, 665, 653, 666.	12-97
❑ XT631	'D' Scout AH.1	ex Boscombe Down, 658, 655.	12-97
❑ XT645	Scout AH.1	ex Almondbank, Wroughton, 656, 663, 653.	12-97
❑ XW284	'A' Scout AH.1	ex Almondbank, Wroughton, ARWF.	12-97

Francis Chamberlain: Sadly Skeeter zealot Francis died in 2000. Flyable Skeeter AOP.12 G-SARO (XL812) was joined by Mk.8 G-APOI during 1999. There are reports that three, perhaps four, Skeeters were imported from Germany 1999-2000.

❑ XN351	Skeeter AOP.12	G-BKSC, ex Lossiemouth, Inverness, Shobdon, Cardiff, Higher Blagdon, Old Warden, Wroughton, 3 RTR, 652, 651. CoA 8-11-84.	10-96

Everett Aero: The former Royal Saudi Air Force Strikemasters were largely handled by this company – see under Humberside Airport, Lincs, for more details. Examination of much-travelled Scout 'XR625' reveals the build number F.8618, which would make it XR633, written off 7th September 1966. The *real*XR625, also crashed in Malaysia (3rd January 1968) and both airframes were reportedly reduced to scrap during 1967-68. Is this a case of the boom of XR625 and the pod of XR633? ①.
    Departures: Hulk of Cherokee G-AXSG and the anonymous ARV 2 fuselage last noted 12-95 and best deleted; Hunter GA.11 WT806 to Shoreham, W Sussex 3-7-01; Hunter F.6 XG274 to Newmarket, Suffolk, in 2001; Hunter F.6A XJ639 to Exeter, Devon, 7-2-01; Gnat T.1 XP502 arrived from St Athan, Wales, 3-5-00 but by 2-01 had moved to Kemble, Glos; Wessex HC.2 XR517 to Shoreham, W Sussex, 7-12-01; Jet Provost T.5 XS231 to Barnstaple, Devon, 9-6-01; SBLim-2 09008 (G-BZMN) sold in the USA 6-01. Scout AH.1 XV123 arrived by 4-01, but moved to Thruxton, Hants, late 2001.

❑ G-TORE* '42'	Jet Provost T.3A	ex Cranfield, XM405, 1 FTS, RAFC, 1 FTS, 2 FTS. CoA 5-5-95. Arrived 8-12-00.	4-01
❑ —	DEZ ICA IS.29D	BGA.2068. Stored. Since 12-95 at least.	3-00
❑ WZ792	G'hopper TX.1	ex Falgunzeon, Dishforth, Barnard Castle.	9-01
❑ XK788	Grasshopper TX.1	ex Hamois (Belgium), Halton, West Malling, Sevenoaks, Godalming.	9-01

❏ XM412	'41'	Jet Provost T.3A	ex North Weald, Binbrook, Colsterworth, Halton 9011M, 1 FTS, 3 FTS, 2 FTS. '	9-01
❏ XN510*	'40'	Jet Provost T.3A	G-BXBI, ex Binbrook, Shawbury, Linton-on-Ouse, 1 FTS, 3 FTS, RAFC, 7 FTS, 1 FTS. Arr 24-2-00.	4-01
❏ XN634	'53'	Jet Provost T.3	ex Scampton, 1 FTS, 7 FTS, RAFC, 6 FTS. Fuselage.	9-01
❏ XP558*	'20'	Jet Provost T.4	ex Norwich, Honington 8648M, St Athan, Culdrose A2628, CAW, 3 CAACU, RAFC. F/n 1-01.	9-01
❏ XP563	'C'	Jet Provost T.4	ex Bicester, Witney, Bruntingthorpe, Halton 9028M, Shawbury, CATCS, SoRF, 6 FTS, CATCS, RAFC.	9-01
❏ XP854*		Scout AH.1	TAD.043 / 7898M, ex Wattisham, Middle Wallop. Crashed 15-5-65. Arrived 6-01.	6-01
❏ XP888*		Scout AH.1	ex Arborfield, Middle Wallop, Wroughton, 651, 652, 14 Flt. Arrived 6-01.	6-01
❏ XP905*		Scout AH.1	ex Arborfield, Middle Wallop, Wroughton, 656, 655, 652, 654, 652. Arrived 6-01.	6-01
❏ XR597*		Scout AH.1	ex Wattisham, Arborfield, Middle Wallop, Wroughton, 654, 655, 653, 665, 653. Arrived 6-01.	6-01
❏ 'XR625'		Scout AH.1	XT625, ex Almondbank, 'XR777', Middle Wallop, Sutton Coldfield, M' Wallop, TAD625. ①	3-00
❏ XR627*		Scout AH.1	ex Wattisham, Arborfield, Dishforth, Middle Wallop, Wroughton, Garrison Air Sqn, 3 CBAS. Arr 6-01.	6-01
❏ XR635*		Scout AH.1	ex Arborfield, Yeovilton, Middle Wallop, 653, 660.	6-01
❏ XS463*		Wasp HAS.1	XT431, ex Weston-super-Mare, Fleetlands, Lee-on-Solent. Boom of XT431. First noted 1-01.	9-01
❏ XS674	'R'	Wessex HC.2	ex Fleetlands, 60, 72, 18, 78, 72.	4-01
❏ XT640*		Scout AH.1	ex Arborfield, Lee-on-Solent, Middle Wallop, 654, 666, 663. Arrived 6-01.	6-01
❏ XW796*	'X'	Scout AH.1	ex Wattisham, Middle Wallop, Wroughton, 660, 659. Arrived 6-01.	6-01

KESGRAVE on the A12 east of Ipswich
The Super Cub is still to be found in Monument Farm Lane, near Foxhall.

❏ MM54-2372	Piper L-21B	ex Embry-Riddle, Woodbridge, Italian Army 'EI-184', I-EIXM, USAF 54-2372. Derelict.	3-02

LAKENHEATH AIRFIELD on the A1065 south of Brandon
USAF Lakenheath: The aircraft in the **Wings of Liberty Memorial Park** (MEM) are dramatically – and substantially – plinth-mounted.
◆ Visitor centre and memorial park are viewable *only* by prior permission.

❏ 'BM631'	Spitfire V FSM	BAPC.269, 71 'Eagle' Sqn, Chesley Peterson			
	'XR-C'	colours.		MEM	7-99
❏ '65-777'	'SA' F-4C-15-MC	37419, ex Alconbury, Texas ANG. 48th TFW c/s.	MEM	3-00
❏ 30091	F-15A-8-MC	ex Soesterberg. ABDR. 'ABDR'.			10-96
❏ '92-048'	'LN' F-15A-12-MC	40131, ex 122 TFS / Louisiana ANG.		MEM	3-00
❏ 60029	F-15A-15-MC	ABDR.			10-96
❏ 60124	F-15B-15-MC	ABDR.			2-00
❏ '63319'	'FW-319' F-100D-16-NA	42269, ex '54048', French AF. Main gate.			3-00
❏ '72-448'	'LN' F-111E-CF	68011, ex U' Heyford, 20 TFW. *Miss Liberty*.		MEM	3-00

MENDLESHAM west of the A140 north-east of Stowmarket
Steve Pickup: Moved his Canberra B.2/6 nose WG789 to <u>Flixton</u>, Suffolk, on 6th March 2002.

MONEWDEN south of the A1120, north of Ipswich

❏ G-ARDZ	SAN D.140A	CoA 29-11-91. Stored.	5-01

❏ G-AVTT	Ercoupe 415D	ex SE-BFZ, NC3774H. CoA 20-1-86. Stored.	5-01
❏ G-BENF	Cessna T.210L	ex Ipswich, N732AE, D-EIPY, N732AE. Cr 29-5-81.	5-01

NAYLAND on the B1087 north-west of Colchester
Cessna 182G G-ASRR was up and flying, in Austria no less, by mid-2000.

❏ G-AHTE	Proctor V	ex Llanelli, Cardiff, Swansea, Llanelli. CoA 10-8-61. ®	5-98
❏ G-BMWV	Putzer Elster B	ex D-EEKB, 97+14, D-EBGI. Stored.	9-99

NEW MARKET on the A1304 east of Cambridge
A private collector has taken on a Hunter in the area.

❏ XG274*	'71' Hunter F.6	ex Ipswich, Halton 8710M, 4 FTS, 229 OCU, 66, 14. Arrived 2001.	12-01

RATTLESDEN west of Stowmarket

❏ XP494	Grasshopper TX.1	ex Breighton, Stoke-on-Trent, Syerston, Stamford, Cosford, Ratcliffe College, Syerston. ®	12-96

STOW MARKET on the A14 east of Bury St Edmunds
Giles Howell: Have the famed EE P.1B in this general area for restoration and eventual display.

❏ XA847	EE P.1B	ex Portsmouth, Southampton, Hendon 8371M, Farnborough, A&AEE, EE.	7-99

SUDBURY on the A134 north-west of Colchester
AJD Engineering / Hawker Restorations Ltd (HRL): By the middle of 2001, AJD/HRL had closed their 'flight test centre' at Earls Colne. Hurricane XII AE977 (G-TWTD) moved to HRL's flying base at Earls Colne, Essex, by June 2000 for flight test and export. The JN4 'Jenny' is stored for Aero Vintage (see under St Leonards-on-Sea, East Sussex) ① The BE.2 is being restored for a New Zealand collector ②. The Yak-1 is under restoration for the Historic Aircraft Collection of Jersey (see under Duxford, Cambs) Some work on it is being carried on off-site ③. The Yak-3 is held for Eddie Coventry ④. Spitfire FSM 'BR600' was exported to the Canadian Fighter Association.

❏ G-ROBT	Hurricane I	ex Dunkirk, P2902, 245. Crashed 3-5-40.	®	10-94
❏ S-AHAA	Avro 504L	G-EASD, ex Sweden, S-AAP, G-EASD. Stored.		3-95
❏	JN4 'Jenny'	ex USA, *Great Waldo Pepper*. Stored.	①	4-94
❏ A1325*	RAF BE.2e	G-BVGR, ex Hatch, London Colney, Norway, RNorAF '37' and '133'.	® ②	10-99
❏ Z5053*	Hurricane II	G-BWHA, ex Cam, Russia, 151 Wing, 402. Composite. Under restoration as 'Z5252'.	®	5-01
❏ BW853	Hurricane XIIA	ex G-BRKE, Canada, RCAF. Project.		7-99
❏ BW881	Hurricane XIIA	G-KAMM, ex Canada, RCAF.	®	10-99
❏ 1342	Yakovlev Yak-1	G-BTZD, ex Audley End, Paddock Wood, USSR.	® ③	10-99
❏	Yakovlev Yak-3	ex Russia. Stored, for Eddie Coventry.		9-94

WALPOLE on the B1117 south-east of Halesworth
Blyth Valley Aviation Collection: The collection is in the process of being trimmed down. Among the many artefacts held is an airborne lifeboat from an SB-29. The nose of Hunter F.2 WN907 moved to Robertsbridge, East Sussex, 17th March 2002.

The Victor nose, or Project XL160, is owned by the **HP Victor Association**, who are working to restore it ①. The association serves to link all those who flew, worked on, or just love, the Victor. (Ken McGill, 'Home Run', 191 Yarmouth Road, Thorpe St Andrew, Norwich, Norfolk, NR7 0SQ.)

◆ By prior permission *only*. ✉ Cliff Aldred, 'Vulcan's End', Mells Road, Walpole, Halesworth, IP19 0PL ☎ 019867 84436

❏ WE122	'845'	Canberra TT.18	ex North Weald, Stock, St Athan, FRADU, 7, 98, 245, 231 OCU. Nose.	3-02
❏ WE192		Canberra T.4	ex Long Marston, Firbeck, Winsford, Samlesbury, St Athan, 231 OCU, 360, 231 OCU, 39, 231 OCU, 3, 231 OCU. Cockpit.	3-02
❏ WH953		Canberra B.6(M)	ex Lowestoft, Stock, Farnborough, RAE. Nose.	3-02
❏ WM267		Meteor NF.11	ex Firbeck, Hemswell, Misson, 151, 256, 11. Nose.	3-02
❏ XH165		Canberra PR.9	ex Stock, St Athan, 1 PRU, 39, 13, 58. Nose.	3-02
❏ XL160		Victor K.2	ex Marham 8910M, 57, 55, 57, 55, Witt Wing, 100, MoA. Nose.	① 3-02
❏ XL388		Vulcan B.2	ex Honington 8750M, 50, Wadd Wing, Scampton Wing,9. Nose.	3-02
❏ XL445		Vulcan K.2	ex Lyneham 8811M, 50, 44, 35, 230 OCU, Wadd Wing, Akrotiri Wing, Wadd Wing, 27. Nose.	3-02
❏ XN696	'751'	Sea Vixen FAW.2	ex Farnborough, Tarrant Rushton, ADS, 899. Nose.	3-02
❏ XP919	'706'	Sea Vixen FAW.2	ex Norwich, Chertsey, Halton 8163M, 766, 899, A&AEE.	3-02
❏ XR718	'DA'	Lightning F.3	ex Wattisham 8932M, ABDR, LTF, 11, LTF, 11, 5, LTF, 5, 11, LTF, 5, LTF, 5, 226 OCU, 29, 56.	3-02

WATTISHAM AIRFIELD north of the B1078, south of Stowmarket
No.3 Regiment, Army Air Corps / 24 Air Mobile Brigade / 7 Battalion, REME: The Chinook is for Air Mobility Training – AMT.
   Departures: Whirlwind HAR.10 XD165 to Elvington, N Yorks, 12-00; Wessex HU.5 XS488 (last noted 2-98) to Gosport, Hants, by 4-01; CH-47C ZH257 to Fleetlands, Hants, 6-00. During June 2001 four Scout AH.1s were put up for tender, all going to Ipswich, Suffolk: XP854 from Middle Wallop; XR597 from Arborfield, both first noted in 11-00; XR627; XW796.

❏ XL739		Skeeter AOP.12	ex Detmold, 15/19 Hussars, 1 Wing, 651, A&AEE, BATUS, A&AEE. Displayed, pole-mounted	2-01
❏ XP852		Scout AH.1	ex Hildesheim, Wroughton, ARWF, 651. Cabin only.	2-98
❏ XT550	'D'	Sioux AH.1	ex Detmold, Middle Wallop, Wroughton, 651. Gate.	11-94
❏ XT617		Scout AH.1	ex Almondbank, Wroughton, 653, 660. Displayed	2-01
❏ XW835		Lynx 1-02	ex Dishforth, Middle Wallop, Yeovil, G-BEAD. Boomless. AMT	2-98
❏ XX153		Lynx AH.1	ex Foulness, Westlands.	2-01
❏ ZA676*	'FG'	Chinook HC.1	9230M, ex Odiham, Manston, Fleetlands, N37023. Crashed 15-11-84. First noted 6-00. AMT	6-00

SURREY

BROOKLANDS or Weybridge, on the B374 south of Weybridge
Brooklands Museum: In November 2000 large tracts of the UK were hit by terrible flooding. One of the victims was the museum with considerable damage being done to buildings, artefacts and records. Damage was estimated at £1.7 million. The museum fully re-opened on 17th July 2001. On a much brighter note, the Heritage Lottery Fund came up with £994,000 of the £1.4 million needed to restore and transform the 'Wellington' hangar on 10th October 2001. The hangar – Grade II listed – will be refurbished and new displays will be created within.
   Notes: Several airframes are on loan, as follows: the Ladybird from the estate of the late Bill Manuel; the Harrier and Hunter F.51 from BAE Systems; the Valiant nose from the RAF Museum; the Chipmunk PAX from Peter Smith (see under Hawkinge, Kent); the P.1127 from the RAF Museum and BAE Systems jointly; the Sea Vixen and Hunter XL621 from John Hallett. These are marked ±. See also under Bournemouth, Dorset, for another K5673 ①. Note that the Hunter is marked as 'G-BCNX' on the

starboard side ②. The Demoiselle was built by Julian Aubert and friends and uses the original method of construction, employing bamboo and using wing-warping ③. See under Kemble, Glos, for Beagle 206 G-ARRM which is on loan to BAC.

Departures: Tiger Moth F-BGEQ was being restored at Hungerford, Berks, by 9-00; Supermarine 544 nose WT859 left 9-8-01 initially for Wycombe Air Park, Bucks, but on 4-9-01 left for Long Marston, Warks; Vampire T.11 'U-1215' (XE998) left during 2000 for Farnborough, Hants.

◆ On the B374 south of Weybridge, access from Junctions 10 or 11 of the M25 - well signed. Open Tuesday to Sunday 10am to 5pm (last entry 4pm), Easter to October. Winter months, 10am to 4pm, last entry is 3pm. Note: *closed* on Mondays. Normally closed Good Friday, Xmas. Pre-arranged guided tours available Tuesdays to Fridays, contact 01932 857381. There is a very active **Association of Friends of Brooklands**, membership details from the address below. The **Brooklands Hurricane Fund** has been set up. Those who wish to support Z2389 – born and bred at Brooklands – can do so by donation; details from the address below. ✉ Brooklands Museum, Brooklands Road, Weybridge, KT13 0QN ☎ 01932 857381 **fax** 01932 855465 **e-mail** brooklands @dial.pipex.com **web** www.motor-software.co.uk/brooklands

❑ 'G-EBED'	Viking REP	BAPC.114, ex 'R4', Chertsey, *The Land Time Forgot*.		3-02
❑ 'G-AACA'	Avro 504K REP	BAPC.177, ex 'G1381', Henlow.	®	3-02
❑ 'G-ADRY'	HM.14 'Flea'	BAPC.29, ex Aberdare, Swansea.		3-02
❑ G-AEKV	Kronfeld Drone	BGA.2510/DZQ. CoA 6-10-60.		3-02
❑ G-AGRU	Viking 1	ex Cosford, Soesterberg, Channel, Kuwait Oil, BWIA, VP-TAX, G-AGRU, BEA. *Vagrant*. CoA 9-1-64.	®	3-02
❑ G-APEJ	Merchantman	ex Hunting Cargo, ABC, BEA. *Ajax*. Nose.		3-02
❑ G-APEP	Merchantman	ex Hunting Cargo, ABC, BEA. *Superb*.		3-02
❑ G-APIM	Viscount 806	ex Southend, BAF, BA, BEA. Damaged 11-1-88. *Viscount Stephen Piercey*.	®	3-02
❑ G-ASYD	BAC 111-475AM	ex Filton, BAe, BAC. 'Fly By Light Technology'.		3-02
❑ G-LOTI	'2' Blériot XI REP	CoA 19-7-82.		3-02
❑ G-MJPB	Ladybird	microlight	±	3-02
❑ G-VTOL	Harrier T.52	ex ZA250, Dunsfold. CoA 2-11-86.	±	3-02
❑ –	ATH Slingsby Gull 3	BGA.643, (Hawkridge Kittiwake).		3-02
❑ –	HFZ Scud I REP	BGA.3922.		3-02
❑ –	Willow Wren	BGA.162, ex Bishop's Stortford. *Yellow Wren*.		3-02
❑ –	Voisin scale REP	G-BJHV, ex Old Warden.		3-02
❑ –	Vimy repro	cockpit section.		3-02
❑ –	VC-10 EMU	test shell, nose section. BOAC colours.		3-02
❑ –	Rogallo hang glider	*Aerial*. On loan.		3-02
❑ A40-AB	VC-10 1103	ex Sultan of Oman, G-ASIX.		3-02
❑ 'B7270'	Camel REP	G-BFCZ, ex Land's End, Duxford, Thorpe Park. CoA 23-2-89. Ground-runs.		3-02
❑ 'F5475'	'A' SE.5A REP	BAPC.250, built on site. *1st Battalion Honourable Artillery Company*.		3-02
❑ 'K5673'	Fury I FSM	BAPC.249, built on site. 1 Sqn 'A' Flt colours.	①	3-02
❑ N2980	'R' Wellington Ia	ex Loch Ness, 20 OTU, 37, 149. Ditched 31-12-40.		3-02
❑ Z2389	Hurricane II	ex St Petersburg, Siberia, Sov AF, RAF 253, 136, 247, 71, 249.	®	3-02
❑ WF372	'A' Varsity T.1	ex Sibson, 6 FTS, 1 ANS, RAFC, 201 AFS.		3-02
❑ WP921	Chipmunk T.10 PAX	ex Croydon, Henley-on-Thames, Benson, G-ATJJ, Colerne SF, Ox UAS, HCMSU, 10 RFS.	±	3-02
❑ XD816	Valiant BK.1	ex Henlow, BAC, 214, 148. Stratosphere chamber.	±	3-02
❑ XJ571	'242' Sea Vixen FAW.2	ex Dunsfold, Southampton, Cosford 8140M, Halton, Sydenham, 893, 892, 899.	±	3-02
❑ XL621	Hunter T.7	ex Bournemouth, G-BNCX, RAE Bedford, 238 OCU, RAE. ETPS colours.	± ②	3-02
❑ XP984*	Hawker P.1127	ex Dunsfold, Lee-on-Solent, Manadon A2658, RAE. Arrived 28-9-00.	±	3-02

❑	XT575		Viscount 837	ex Bruntingthorpe, DRA Bedford, OE-LAG. Nose.		3-02
❑			TSR-2 EMU	ex Farnborough. Nose.		3-02
❑	E-421		Hunter F.51	ex Brooklands Tech, Kingston, Dunsfold,		
				G-9-443, Aalborg, Esk.724, RDanAF.	±	3-02
❑	—	BAPC.187	Roe I Biplane REP	displayed in reproduction of Roe's shed.		3-02
❑	—	BAPC.256	Demoiselle REP	Taxiable.	③	3-02

CAMBERLEY on the M3 south of Bracknell
Parkhouse Aviation: (See also Wycombe Air Park, Bucks.)

❑	XH330	'76'	Vampire T.11	ex Bridgnorth, Bushey, London Colney, Chester,	
				Woodford, Chester, Shawbury, RAFC. Pod.	8-01
❑	XL449	'044'	Gannet AEW.3	ex Wycombe Air Park, Camberley, Cardiff,	
				Lossiemouth, 849. Cockpit.	8-01

Others: No news on Keith Attfield's and Paul Raymond's Eagle or 'JP'.

❑	G-MBTY		American Eagle	ex Ottershaw, Southall.	2-96
❑	'XN493'		Jet Provost T.3	XN137, ex Ottershaw, Camberley, Abingdon,	
				3 FTS, CFS, Huntings. Nose.	9-93

CATERHAM west of the A22, north-east of Redhill
A yard in the general area seems to deal in insurance write-off hulks. This is almost certainly the yard last mentioned in *W&R13*. In those days turnover was swift, but going by the dates on some of those listed below, these may well be long-termers. It was from this yard that Rallye Commodore G-AYET gained fame of sorts in the dire programme *ScrapheapChallenge*. Its fate beyond this is unknown.

❑	G-ASSE*	Colt 108	ex N5961Z. CoA 12-6-00.	1-01
❑	G-BADL*	Seneca 200 II	ex N5307T. Crashed 21-10-<u>95</u>.	1-01
❑	G-BBEW*	Aztec 250E	ex EI-BYK, G-BBEW, N40262. Crashed 20-4-99.	1-01
❑	G-BCCP*	Robin HR.200	Crashed 9-4-89.	1-01
❑	G-BGTP*	Robin HR.200	ex G-BGTN ntu, F-BVCP. Canx 25-1-00.	1-01
❑	G-BIAB*	TB-9 Tampico	Crashed 6-8-93.	1-01
❑	G-BSIB*	Warrior II	ex N8182C. Canx 22-11-99.	1-01
❑	G-WIGL*	Robinson R-22	Damaged 21-11-97.	1-01

CHARLWOOD west of the A23/A217 junction, north of Gatwick Airport,
Gatwick Aviation Museum: (Formerly the Peter Vallance Collection.) The planning dispute with Mole Valley District Council is still in a period of grace. Alan Allen has solved the 'identity crisis' on the Canberra nose here and it is as given ①. Harrier GR.3 XV751 was removed in February 2001 to take part in a TV advert. From this 'stardom', it moved to <u>Bruntingthorpe</u>, Leics, on 14th February 2001.
◆ Occasional open weekends throughout the year – SAE for details. Otherwise by prior appointment.
✉ Lowfield Heath Road, Charlwood, RH6 0BT ☎ / fax 01293 862915 e-mail gpvgat@aol.com web www.gatwick-aviation-museum.co.uk

❑	[G-TURP]		Gazelle 1	ex Redhill, G-BKLS, N17MT, N14MT, N49549.	
				Crashed 9-9-91. Original pod.	3-02
❑	VZ638		Meteor T.7	G-JETM, ex North Weald, Bournemouth,	
				Southampton, Southend, Kemble, CAW, RAFC,	
				237 OCU, 501, Biggin Hill SF, FCCS, 85, 54, 25, 500.	3-02
❑	WF118	'569'	Sea Prince T.1	G-DACA, ex Gloucester-Cheltenham, Kemble,	
				750, A&AEE, 727, A&AEE, RAE.	3-02
❑	WH773		Canberra PR.7	ex Wyton, 8696M, 13, 58, 80, 31, 82, 540.	3-02
❑	WK146		Canberra B.2	ex Hull, Wr'ton, Abingdon, Bicester, 59, 102. Nose. ①	3-02
❑	WP308	'572'	Sea Prince T.1	G-GACA, ex Staverton, Kemble, 750.	3-02
❑	WR974	'K'	Shackleton	ex Cosford 8117M, Kinloss Wing, 203, 42,	
			MR.3/3	203, SWDU, MinTech, ASWDU, CA.	3-02
❑	WR982	'J'	Shack' MR.3/3	ex Cosford 8106M, 201, 206, MoA, 205, 203, 206.	3-02

❑ WW442	'N'	Provost T.1	ex Kings Langley, Leverstock Green, Cranfield, Booker, St Merryn, Houghton-on-the-Hill, Kidlington, Halton 7618M, CNCS, 3 FTS.	3-02
❑ (XE489)		Sea Hawk FB.5	G-JETH, ex Bournemouth, Southend, 'XE364', XE489, FRU, 899. 'Gate'.	3-02
❑ XK885		Pembroke C.1	N46EA, ex Staverton, St Athan, 8452M, 60, 21, WCS, Seletar SF, B&TTF, Seletar SF, S&TFF, 209, 267.	3-02
❑ XL164		Victor K.2	ex Brize Norton 9215M, 55, 57, 55, 57, MoA. Nose.	3-02
❑ XL472	'044'	Gannet AEW.3	ex Boscombe Down, 849 'B', HQ, 'A' Flts.	3-02
❑ XN923		Buccaneer S.1	ex Boscombe Down, West Freugh.	3-02
❑ XP398		Whirlwind HAR.10	ex Peckham Rye, Shawbury, 8794M, 22, 1563 Flt, 202, 103, 110, 225.	3-02
❑ XS587		Sea Vixen FAW.2	G-VIXN, ex Bournemouth, TT mod, FRL, RAE, 8828M, FRL, ADS, 899.	3-02
❑ XX734		Jaguar GR.1	ex Park Aviation, Coltishall, Abingdon, 8816M, Indian AF JI014, XX734, 6, JOCU. Damaged hulk.	3-02
❑ ZF579*		Lightning F.53	ex Portsmouth, Luxembourg, *Wing Commander*, Stretton, Warton, RSAF 203, 53-671, G-27-40. Arrived 18-4-00.	3-02
❑ (E-430)		Hunter F.51	ex Faygate, Chertsey, Dunsfold, G-9-448, Esk.724, Dan AF. FAA colours, GA.11-style.	3-02
❑ J-1605		Venom FB.50	G-BLID, ex Duxford, Swiss AF.	3-02

Park Aviation Supply / Aerospace Logistics:

❑ XX121	'EQ'	Jaguar GR.1	ex Cosford, Shawbury, 6, 54, 226 OCU, JOCU.	8-01
❑ XX140*		Jaguar T.2	ex Faygate, 226 OCU, 54, JOCU, JCT. Cockpit.	8-01
❑ XX223		Hawk T.1	ex Henlow, 4 FTS. Crashed 7-7-86. Cockpit.	8-01
❑ XX252*		Hawk T.1A	ex St Athan, Red Arrows. Crashed 17-11-98.	8-01

DUNSFOLD AIRFIELD on the A281 south of Guildford
BAE Systems: The airfield closed on 29th September, 2000, and an era ended. Trident 1C G-ARPZ was hacked to death by a determined JCB nine days earlier. Harrier T.2 XW272 nose *may* have moved to either Warton or Samlesbury, Lancs. The following airframes have all gone, most likely scrapped – last noted dates in brackets: HS.125-403B G-TACE (3-00); HS.125-600B HZ-AA1 (3-00); Harrier GR.3 XV760 (11-97); Harrier GR.5 ZD412 (12-95). **Departures:** HS.125-1B/522 gone by 4-00, to Biggin Hill, Gtr Lon; Firefly AS.5 WB271 to Yeovilton, Somerset, late 2000; Sea Hawk FGA.6 WV908 to Yeovilton, Som, by 3-01; Sea Hawk FGA.6 WV911 to Yeovilton, Som, 10-7-00; P.1127 XP984 to Brooklands, Surrey, 28-9-00; Sea Harrier FRS.1 XZ493 to Yeovilton, Somerset, 22-3-00; Harrier T.4 ZB601 to Yeovilton, Somerset, 5-6-00; Harrier GR.5 ZD353 to Brough, E Yorks.

EGHAM on the A30 west of Staines
Jeremy Hall: Using as many original parts as possible, Jeremy has created the forward fuselage (all 21ft of it) of a Lancaster. It 'does the rounds' of shows and events.
❑ –	Lancaster REP	*Hi Ho!, Hi Ho!* Forward fuselage.	6-98

FAIROAKS AERODROME on the A319 east of Chobham
A.109 Mk.II G-GBCA, used as a ground-travelling demonstrator, was disposed of several years ago. The dump was inspected in August 2001 and found lacking of anything to do with aviation. JetRangers G-BIZB and G-JGFF have been deleted.

FARNHAM on the A31 south-west of Aldershot
A collector in the general area took on a Lightning nose early in 2002.
❑ XS933*	Lightning F.6	ex Langport, Terrington St Clement, Narborough, Binbrook, 5, 11, BAC, 5, 56, 11. Nose.	3-02

GODALMING on the A3100 south of Guildford
No.1254 Squadron Air Cadets: In Hallam Road at the TAVR Centre, keep a Hunter nose.
❑ WV332 Hunter F.4 7673M, ex Dunsfold G-9-406, Halton,
234, 112, 67. Nose. 7-01

GUILDFORD
Martin Painter: Should still have the Nimrod cockpit.
❑ XV148 Nimrod proto ex Woodford, A&AEE, HSA. Cockpit. 10-99

HASLEMERE on the A286 south-west of Godalming
Sea Vixen Preservation Group: Located in Weyhill, just off the B2131, this is the preservation 'arm' of **1268 Squadron Air Cadets.**
✉ Kevin Burchett, 48 Hibiscus Grove, Bordon, GU35 0XA **e-mail** KEVIN@ seavixen.fsnet.co.uk
❑ XP925 Sea Vixen FAW.2 ex Farnborough, Tarrant Rushton, ADS, 899. Nose. ® 3-00
❑ Lightning CIM ex Farnborough. Cockpit. ® 3-00

HORLEY on the A23 south of Reigate
❑ G-AFZE Heath Parasol CoA 10-5-64. Stored. 11-93
❑ Bensen gyroplane Stored. 11-93

LINGFIELD on the B2028 north of East Grinstead
Gary Brown: Work should continue on the Bf 109.
❑ 'FM+BB' Bf 109G FSM ex Germany. ® 6-99

MYTCHETT on the B3411 south of Camberley
Defence Medical Services Training Centre: Is guarded by a Hunter.
❑ XG196 '31' Hunter F.6A 8702M, ex Bracknell, Kemble, 1 TWU, TWU,
229 OCU, 19. Gate. 2-01

REDHILL on the A23 east of Reigate
East Surrey Technical College: In Gatton Hill. Pressures of space forced the college to give up its Sea Devon C.2/2 'G-DOVE' (G-KOOL) and it was donated to the East Surrey Aviation Group who in turn loaned it to the local ATC unit. 'G-DOVE' made the move (down the page!) on 29th August 2000.

Turbine World: Located on a *private* site in this general area.
❑ G-AZBY Wessex 60 Srs 1 ex Weston-super-Mare, Bournemouth, W-s-M,
Full Metal Jacket 'EM-16', 5N-ALR,
G-AZBY. CoA 14-12-82. 10-99
❑ 9G-DAN Wessex 60 ex Bournemouth, *Full Metal Jacket* '150225',
G-17-1, Thruxton, Bournemouth, Weston-super-Mare,
Bristows, VH-SJD, G-AYNC. CoA 17-8-87. 10-99
❑ XT671 Wessex HC.2 G-BYRC, ex 72. 10-99
❑ XV729 Wessex HC.2 G-HANA, ex Fleetlands, 60, 22, SARTS, 72, 103, 78. 10-99
❑ XV731 Wessex HC.2 ex Fleetlands, 72, WTF, 240 OCU, 18, 78. 10-99

No.135 Squadron Air Training Corps: At the TAVR Centre, Batts Hill. Took delivery of a Sea Devon C.2/2 during August 2000. It will be returned to military markings. The aircraft is on loan from the **East Surrey Aviation Group** (Daniel Hunt, 28 Windmill Way, Reigate, Surrey RH2 0JA.).
❑ 'G-DOVE'* Sea Devon C.2/2 G-KOOL, ex East Surrey Tech, Biggin Hill, VP967,
Kemble, 781, 21, 207, SCCS, SCS, WCS, SCS,
NCS, SCS, MCS, MoA, MCS, CCCF, 38 GCF,
TTCCF, FCCS, 2 TAF CS, MCCS, RAFG CS,
2 TAF CS, Wahn SF, RCCF. Arr 29-8-00. 8-00

REDHILL AERODROME south of South Nutfield, south-east of Redhill
Taylorcraft F.22 G-BVOX was flying by mid-2000. The Scion is owned by the Historic Aircraft Society
of Southend, Essex ①. Of two long term ex-Nigerian wrecked 212s stored, one was moved to the dump
in March 2000, but as yet, it is not clear which is which! ② Fuji FA.200 G-FUJI had moved to
'Wiltshire' by mid-2001.

❑ G-AEZF	Scion II	ex East Tilbury, Southend. CoA 5-5-54. Frame.	⑬ ①	5-00
❑ G-BOSC	Cessna U.206F	F-GHEN (ntu?). ex 5N-ASU, N7256N. Fuselage.		9-99
❑ G-BOVY*	Hughes 269C	ex EI-CIL, G-BOVY, N1096K. Crashed 17-3-99.		5-00
❑ G-BXVC	Turbo Arrow IV	ex D-ELIV, N2152V. Crashed 22-8-98. Wreck.		9-99
❑ G-FISS	Robinson R-22	ex N40833. Crashed 31-3-96. Pod		9-99
❑ G-OROB	Robinson R-22	ex G-TBFC, N80287. CoA 25-6-95. Pod		9-99
❑ 5N-ALQ	Bell 212	ex Nigeria. Crashed 11-9-95. Stored.	②	3-00
❑ 5N-AQW	Bell 212	ex Nigeria. Crashed 14-1-93. Stored.	②	3-00
❑ *	G'hopper TX.1	'fuselage' frame. Stored. First noted 7-00.		7-00

REIGATE on the A217 west of Redhill
Surrey Fire and Rescue Service Headquarters: The Trident *should* still be with the firemen.
❑ G-AWZI	Trident 3B-101	ex Heathrow, BA, BEA. CoA 5-8-85. Fuselage.	12-98

Others: Inspection of the Vulcan nose here establishes it as an 'unplumbed' B.1 with a B.2 'hood'.
❑ –	Vulcan B.1 EMU	ex East Kirkby, Tattershall, Waddington. Nose.	⑬	6-01

SUNBURY-ON-THAMES south of J1 of the M3
J and C Motor Spares: (Note name change – in Fordbridge Road, the B375)
❑ –	Hobbycopter	—	2-01

WALTON ON THAMES
Adrian Windsor: Still has his Hunter cockpit.
❑ E-420	Hunter F.51	ex Marlow, Ascot, Dunsfold G-9-442, RDanAF. Cockpit.	3-02

WEYBRIDGE on the B374 south of the town
Brooklands Technical College: The airframes are believed unchanged.
❑ G-ASSB	Twin Comanche	ex Bournemouth. CoA 6-5-88.	3-00
❑ XN586	'91' Jet Provost T.3A	ex Cosford 9039M, 7 FTS, 1 FTS, CFS, 2 FTS, RAFC.	3-00

WOKING on the A320 north of Guildford
Big Apple: The Hunter-on-a-stick is still outside and the Hunter nose can still be found in the 'assault
course' in the crèche! (See under Poole, Somerset, for the saga of XL623.) The nose of Hunter fGA.78
QA-12 was sold off during 2000, going to 'Wales'.
❑ XL623	Hunter T.7	8770M, ex Newton, Cosford, 1 TWU, 74, 19, 1,	
		43, 92, 208, 65. Pole-mounted.	12-01

EAST SUSSEX

☛ Within the administrative boundaries can be found the unitary authority of Brighton and Hove.

BEXHILL on the A259 west of Hastings
❑ G-ACXE	L25cl Swallow	ex 'Hastings', Bagshot, Birmingham. CoA 7-4-40.	⑬	10-98

BRIGHTON
No.225 Squadron Air Cadets: There are reports that this PAX trainer has been sold off.
❑ WD370	Chipmunk T.10 PAX	ex Hove, 3 AEF, 2 SoTT, 1 AEF, Hull UAS, 2 BTFS. SOC 12-3-75.	7-98

Others: A balloon, previously held by the BPG, is stored in the area.
❑ G-AZBT	Western O-65	ex Lancing. *Hermes*. CoA 9-4-76. Stored.	3-98

DEANLAND south of the B2124, west of Hailsham
At the strip a Dragonfly is stored.
❑ G-BRKY*	Dragonfly II	CoA 8-6-<u>94</u>. Fuselage. Stored.	8-01

HAILSHAM on the A22 north of Eastbourne
Grenville Helicopters: The helipad at the Boship Manor Hotel still has its 'guardian' which carries the tail stabiliser of G-AXKW – to confuse all and sundry! The main aim of this composite is to act as a recognition aid for those who are rotor-bound and trying to find the 'pad'!
❑ 'G-AXKW'	Bell 47G	G-AYOE, ex F-OCBF, F-BKQZ, D-HEBO. Cr 16-7-77. Composite, including Sioux parts.	10-00

Others: A local strip has two long-term *W&R* inmates.
❑ G-BARN*	Taylor Titch	CoA 2-10-<u>92</u>. Stored.	8-00
❑ 'K3731'*	Isaacs Fury	G-RODI. CoA 17-8-<u>95</u>. Stored.	8-00

HOLLINGTON on the B2159 west of Hastings
St Leonard's Motors: In Church Wood Drive, is the pole-mounted former Hastings Meteor.
❑ WL345	Meteor T.7	ex Hastings, Kemble, CAW, 8 FTS, 5 FTS, CFE, 229 OCU.	1-02

LEWES on the A27 north-east of Brighton
Two more long-term residents to record here.
❑ G-AMYL*	PA-17 Vagabond	ex N4613H, NC4613H. CoA 20-6-<u>89</u>. *Yankee Lady*.	8-00
❑ G-APNS	Fairtravel Linnet	ex Chessington. CoA 6-10-78.	8-00
❑ G-AYMU*	Wassmer D.112	ex F-BJPB. Damaged 7-1-<u>92</u>.	8-00
❑ G-BKCZ	Wassmer D.120	ex F-BKCZ. Stored.	8-00

A collector her has taken delivery of a Hunter nose.
❑ XG195*	Hunter FGA.9	ex Sleap, Seighford, Macclesfield, Bitteswell, G-9-453, 208, 1, 19. Nose. Arrived 16-10-01.	10-01

NEWHAVEN east of Brighton on the A259
Newhaven Fort: Robertsbridge Aviation Society (see below) have an on-going display here. Also within the Fort (but not RAS originated) is a feature on the much-missed Royal Observer Corps.
◆ Apr to Oct, daily 10.30am to 6.00pm. Weekends in Mar and Oct and Half Terms. ✉ Newhaven Fort, Fort Road, Newhaven, BN9 9DL ☎ 01273 517622 **fax** 01273 512059

No.1216 Sqn Air Cadets: By March 2002 the nose of Jet Provost T.4 XR681 had moved to Robertsbridge, East Sussex.

ROBERTSBRIDGE on the A21 north-west of Hastings
Robertsbridge Aviation Centre: Operated by the Robertsbridge Aviation Society, the museum is a barrage of artefacts covering many aspects of aviation. RAS has a close relationship with Newhaven Fort, E Sussex, with a series of displays there. The Tornado nose moved to Welshpool, Wales.

♦ Open by appointment *only*. ✉ Philip Baldock, 53 Wannock Avenue, Willingdon, BN20 9RH ☎ 01323 483845

❑ WA630	Meteor T.7	ex Newhaven, Robertsbridge, Oakington SF, 4 FTS, 205 AFS, RAFC. Nose.	3-02
❑ WE173	Canberra PR.3	ex Stock, Coltishall, Farnborough, 231 OCU, 39, RAE, 39, 69, 82. Nose.	3-02
❑ WN907*	Hunter F.2	ex Walpole, Ascot, St Athan, Colerne 7416M, 257. Nose. Arrived 17-3-02.	3-02
❑ XJ488	Sea Vixen FAW.1	ex Nottingham, New Milton, Portsmouth, Boscombe Down, 22 JSTU, A&AEE. Nose.	3-02
❑ XP701	Lightning F.3	ex High Halden, Hawkinge, Binbrook 8924M, LTF, 5, 11, 56, 29, 111, 29, A&AEE. Nose.	3-02
❑ XR681*	Jet Provost T.4	ex Newhaven, Odiham, Abingdon 8588M, RAFEF, CATCS, 6 FTS, RAFC. Nose.	3-02
❑ 7907	Su-7 *Fitter*	ex Farnborough, Egyptian AF. Nose.	3-02

ST LEONARDS-ON-SEA west of Hastings

Aero Vintage: Nimrod I S1581 (G-BWWK) moved to Henlow, Beds, for flight test by June 2000. It made its first flight there on 11th July 2000 and shortly afterwards flew to Duxford, Cambs, where it joined The Fighter Collection. As explained in *W&R17*, the Nimrod was exchanged for Hurricane XII 'Z7381' (G-HURI), which is based at Duxford as part of the closely-associated **Historic Aircraft Collection of Jersey** – and see under the ARCo heading within Duxford for more details. Bristol F.2b 'D7889' (G-AANM) moved to Old Warden, Beds, in March 2001. Aero Vintage's latest find – an Airco DH.9 – can be found at Hatch, Beds. See also under Sudbury, Suffolk, for their 'Jenny'.

❑ VT-DPE	Tiger Moth	G-BUJY, ex Shipdham, Indian AF HU858. Stored.		3-94
❑ K3661	Nimrod II	G-BURZ, ex 802 Sqn. Other history obscure.	®	8-95
❑ K5600	Audax I	G-BVVI, ex 2015M, Kirkham, SAC, 226.	®	8-95
❑	Fury II	Fuselage frame.	®	8-95
❑	Fury REP	—	®	8-95

SEDLESCOMBE AERODROME on the B2244 north of Hastings

W&R16 wrote out HM.293 G-AXPG as flying again. Not so, it remains stored.

❑ G-AXPG*	Mignet HM.293	CoA 20-1-77. Stored.	11-01
❑ G-BLUL	CEA DR.1051M	ex F-BMPJ. CoA 24-10-91. Stored.	11-01
❑ G-BUNS	Cessna F.150K	ex F-BSIL. Stored.	11-01

UCKFIELD east of the A22, south of Crowborough

A former LOST! inmate was been traced to this area. MS.317 G-BPLG, last noted at Fenland, Lincs, appeared here by January 2000. It was offered for sale in mid-2000 and moved to France.

WANNOCK east of the A22, north of Eastbourne

Foulkes-Halbard Collection: At Filching Manor is a staggering collection of vintage cars, easily going into three figures. A pre-war hangar once at Gatwick has been acquired and is being erected to house the aircraft exhibits.

♦ Easter to Oct 1st Thu to Sun, 10.30am to 4.30pm, plus Bank Holidays. Other times by appointment.
✉ Filching Manor, Wannock, BN26 5QA ☎ 01323 487838 or '487124 **fax** 01323 486331

❑ G-BHNG	Aztec 250E	ex Seaford, Shoreham, N54125. Cr 19-12-81. Fuse.		2-00
❑ —	BAPC.127 Halton Jupiter	ex Old Warden, Cranwell, Halton. Stored.		2-00
❑ —	IAHC.2 Aldritt Mono REP	ex Portlaoise.	®	2-00

ASHINGTON west of the A24, at the junction of the A283, north of Worthing
Paul Whelland:

❑	'XN594' '19'	Jet Provost T.3	XN458, ex WAM Cardiff, St Athan 8334M, Halton, Shawbury, 1 FTS.	2-02

BOSHAM south of the A259, south-west of Chichester
Mike Jelley: Keeps the Whirlwind in his garden in the area.

❑	XN263	'H' Whirlwind HAS.7	ex Wroughton, Shrivenham, Wroughton, Middle Wallop, Wroughton, 771, Brawdy SF, 705, 848.	4-01

CRAWLEY
Crawley Technical College:

❑	XN494* '43'	Jet Provost T.3A	ex Bruntingthorpe, Middle Wallop, Halton 9012M, 1 FTS, RAFC.	6-99

EAST GRINSTEAD on the A264 east of Crawley
Sabrewatch: Lingfield Road.

❑	WF408	Varsity T.1	ex Northolt, 8395M Cosford, 2 SoTT, 6 SS, 2 ANS, 1 RS, 11 FTS, 201 AFS.	5-99
❑	XT257	Wessex HAS.3	ex Cosford 8719M, Halton, A&AEE. Yellow c/s.	5-99

No.1343 Squadron Air Cadets: Morton Road, close to Sunnyside Post Office. 'Parent' is Odiham.

❑	XP677	Jet Provost T.4	8587M, ex Headley, Abingdon, RAFEF, 2 FTS. Nose.		8-01
❑		Jaguar GR.1	cockpit.	®	9-96

FAYGATE on the A264 between Horsham and Crawley
Park Aviation Supply / Sheet Metal Products: The forward fuselage of Jaguar T.2 XX140 had appeared here by July 2000, but by August 2001 has moved to Charlwood, Surrey. The yard and the surrounding area are due to become a housing estate.

❑	XW268 '720'	Harrier T.4N	ex Yeovilton, 899, 233 OCU.	8-01
❑	XX163*	Hawk T.1	ex Bruntingthorpe, St Athan, Valley 9243M, CFS, 4 FTS, CFS. Crashed 1-7-93. Nose. F/n 7-00.	8-01
❑	XX733* 'ER'	Jaguar GR.1B	ex Coltishall, 6, 54, A&AEE, 6, JOCU. Crashed 23-1-95. Wreck. Arrived 10-00.	8-01
❑	XZ492*	Sea Harrier FA.2	ex 800, 801, 899, 800. Ditched 10-12-96. F/n 7-00.	8-01
❑	ZD400	Harrier GR.7	ex Wittering, 1, Dunsfold, Shawbury, 1. Cr 19-5-97.	8-01
❑		Jaguar GR.1	forward fuselage.	7-00

FORD north of the A259 west of Littlehampton
Peter Hague: Perched atop a lofty plinth on the appropriately-named Hunterford site on the periphery of the former entrance of what was HMS *Peregrine*, the famed FAA station, is Peter's Hunter.

❑	WW654 '834'	Hunter GA.11	ex Oving, Portsmouth, Culdrose A2664, A2753, SAH, FRADU, 738, 229 OCU, 98, 4, 98.	7-01

GATWICK AIRPORT junction 9 of the M23 north of Crawley
Airport: The Comet and Trident serve on as ground trainers.

❑	G-APMB	Comet 4B	ex Dan-Air, Channel, BEA. CoA 18-5-79.	3-02
❑	G-AWZX	Trident 3B-101	ex Heathrow, BA, BEA. CoA 30-4-84.	2-02

Skyview Visitors Centre: Located in the South Terminal, much of what is on offer is inter-active and 'virtual', but the Comet nose and the Herald perched atop the northern corner of the terminal are well worth admiring and there is a spectators' gallery.

◆ Daily, summer 7am to 7pm and winter 9am to 4pm. Parking in South Terminal ☎ 01293 502244

❏ 'G-AMXA'	Comet C.2R	XK655, ex Hatch, Carlisle, Maryport, Carlisle, Lutterworth, Strathallan, 51, BOAC, G-AMXA ntu. Nose. BOAC colours.	2-02
❏ G-CEXP	Herald 209	ex ChanEx, I-ZERC, G-BFRJ, 4X-AHO. Skyview c/s.	3-02

Gatwick Hilton: Massive extensions to the hotel were underway during early 2002. The Moth reproduction used to 'fly' in the lobby but may well have moved on.

❏ 'G-AAAH'	DH.60G REP	BAPC.168, *Jason*.	10-00

GOODWOOD AERODROME or Westhampnett, north of Chichester

ARV Super 2 G-BNGX had left by October 2000, possibly for Manston, Kent, or the area. Enstrom F.28A-UK G-BAAU was flying again by 2000.

❏ G-BGRN*	Tomahawk 112	ex N9684N. CoA 12-2-00. Dump by 9-01.	9-01
❏ G-COUP*	Ercoupe 415C	ex N99280, NC99280. CoA 17-7-99. *Jenny Lin*. Dismantled.	9-01
❏ N281Q	Enstrom 280C	Hulk. Spares recovery.	11-96

HAYWARD'S HEATH on the A272 north of Brighton

No.172 Squadron, Air Training Corps: Have a Bulldog *allocated* to them.

❏ XX520*	Bulldog T.1	9288M, ex Newton, EM UAS, CFS, RNEFTS, 2 FTS.	due

---

KIRDFORD north of the A272, west of Billingshurst

Sailplane Preservation Group (SPG): Established by Bob Kent, SPG aims to save a few of the many gliders that are rotting away across the land. SPG did hold Grunau Baby III DUD (BGA.2384) but it moved to the Bristol area during 3rd March 2002 for restoration to flying condition.

◆ Viewing by appointment *only*. Organisations interested in gliders for exhibits should contact SRG.✉ 44 Shadwells Road, Lancing, BN15 9EW ☎ 01903 533835 **e-mail** avsearch@eidosnet.co.uk

❏ CWU*	Schleicher Ka-4	BGA.1872, ex D-5427.	®	2-02

LANCING on the A27 east of Worthing

Balloon Preservation Group (BPG): Formed in 1993, BPG is now the world's largest balloon collection. The majority of the balloons are held in a storage facility in the county. From April to October many are distributed to regional storage sites for ease of transportation for participation at events. Cameron DG-19 G-BKIK and Cameron Zero 25 OO-JAT are on loan at Farnborough, Hants. The envelope of Cameron N-56 OO-ARK has been reduced to spares and can be deleted. Cameron A-210 was placed on loan to an orphanage in Austria, it will return in 2003 ①. Colting 77A G-BLUE and Colt 56A G-CFBI can be deleted.

◆ *Not* available to casual visitors. BPG are willing to attend events with balloons on request. BPG have equipment available for long-term loan to museums etc, contact the address below for details. ✉ 44 Shadwells Road, Lancing, BN15 9EW ☎ 01903 533835 **e-mail** bpg@balloons.flyer.co.uk **web** www.balloons.flyer.co.uk/bpg1.htm

☞ From this edition, a two-column layout has been adopted. This means that some of the details previously given have been omitted, but for those with a specific interest in balloons and airships, this will be readily available elsewhere. Letters are used to denote the 'extent' of the artefact: -B Basket; -C complete (including burner), -E Envelope; -G Gondola and combinations thereof.

❏ G-AYVA	Cameron O-84 -C	3-02		❏ G-BAST	Cameron O-84 -E	3-02
❏ G-BAKO	Cameron O-84 -C	3-02		❏ G-BBDJ	Thunder Ax7-56 -C	3-02
❏ G-BAND	Cameron O-84 -E	3-02		❏ G-BBYR	Cameron O-65 -E	3-02
❏ G-BAOW	Cameron O-65 -E	3-02		❏ G-BCAS	Thunder Ax7-77 -C	3-02

❑ G-BCCH	Thunder Ax6-56A -E	3-02	
❑ G-BCRE	Cameron O-77 -C	3-02	
❑ G-BDGO*	Thunder Ax7-77 -E	3-02	
❑ G-BDMO	Thunder Ax7-77 -E	3-02	
❑ G-BEIF	Cameron O-56 -E	3-02	
❑ G-BEJB*	Thunder Ax6-56 -E	3-02	
❑ G-BGST*	Thunder Ax7-65 -C	3-02	
❑ G-BHAT*	Thunder Ax7-77 -E	3-02	
❑ G-BJZC	Thunder Ax7-65 -C	3-02	
❑ G-BKIY	Thunder Ax3 -C	3-02	
❑ G-BKOW	Colt 77A -C	3-02	
❑ G-BLDL	Cameron 56SS -E	3-02	
❑ G-BLIP	Cameron N-77 -E	3-02	
❑ G-BLKJ	Thunder Ax7-65 -C	3-02	
❑ G-BLSH	Cameron V-77 -E	3-02	
❑ G-BLZB	Cameron N-65 -E	3-02	
❑ G-BMKX	Cameron 77SS -E	3-02	
❑ G-BMST	Cameron N-31 -E	3-02	
❑ G-BMWU	Cameron N-42 -C	3-02	
❑ G-BNHL	Colt Beer Glass 90 -C	3-02	
❑ G-BOGT	Colt 77A -E	3-02	
❑ G-BONK*	Colt 180A -E	3-02	
❑ G-BONV	Colt 17A -E	3-02	
❑ G-BOOP	Cameron N-90 -E	3-02	
❑ G-BORA	Colt 77A -E	3-02	
❑ G-BOTE	Thunder Ax8-90 -E	3-02	
❑ G-BPAH*	Colt 69A -E	3-02	
❑ G-BPFJ	Cameron 90SS -E	3-02	
❑ G-BPFX*	Colt 21A -E	3-02	
❑ G-BPSZ*	Cameron N-180 -E	3-02	
❑ G-BPZO*	Cameron N-90 -E	3-02	
❑ G-BRFR	Cameron N-105 -E	3-02	
❑ G-BRLX*	Cameron N-77 -E	3-02	
❑ G-BSBM	Cameron N-77 -C	3-02	
❑ G-BSWZ*	Cameron A-180 -E	3-02	
❑ G-BTML	Cameron SS -E	3-02	
❑ G-BTPV*	Colt 90A -E	3-02	
❑ G-BUET	Cameron SS -E	3-02	
❑ G-BUEU	Colt 21A -E	3-02	
❑ G-BUIZ*	Cameron N-90 -E	3-02	
❑ G-BUKC*	Cameron A-180 -E	3-02	
❑ G-BUXA*	Colt 210A -E	3-02	
❑ G-BVBJ*	Colt SS -E	3-02	
❑ G-BVBK	Colt Coffee Jar SS -E	3-02	
❑ G-BVFY*	Colt 210A -E	3-02	
❑ G-BVIO*	Colt SS Can -E	3-02	
❑ G-BVWH*	Cameron N-90 -E	3-02	
❑ G-BVWI*	Colt 65SS -E	3-02	
❑ G-BWAN*	Cameron N-77 -E	3-02	
❑ G-BWGA*	Lindstrand 105A -E	3-02	
❑ G-BWUR*	Thunder Ax10-210 -E	3-02	
❑ G-BXAL*	Cameron SS -E	3-02	
❑ G-BXHM*	Lindstrand 25A -E	3-02	
❑ G-BXHN*	Lindstrand SS -E	3-02	
❑ G-BZIH*	Lindstrand 31A -E	3-02	
❑ G-COLR	Colt 69A -E	3-02	
❑ G-COOP	Cameron N-31 -E	3-02	
❑ G-CURE	Colt 77A -E	3-02	
❑ G-DHLI*	Colt 90SS -E	3-02	
❑ G-DHLZ*	Colt 31A -E	3-02	
❑ G-ETFT*	Colt SS -E	3-02	
❑ G-FZZY	Colt 69A -E	3-02	
❑ G-GEUP*	Cameron N-77 -E	3-02	
❑ G-GURL	Cameron A-210 -E	① 3-02	
❑ G-HELP*	Colt 17A -E	3-02	
❑ G-HENS	Cameron N-65 -E	3-02	
❑ G-HLIX	Cameron SS -E	3-02	
❑ G-IAMP*	Cameron H-34 -E	3-02	
❑ G-IGEL*	Cameron N-90 -E	3-02	
❑ G-IMAG*	Colt 77A -E	3-02	
❑ G-JANB*	Colt SS -E	3-02	
❑ G-KORN	Cameron 70SS -E	3-02	
❑ G-LLAI*	Colt 21A -E	3-02	
❑ G-MAPS*	Thunder Ax7-77 -E	3-02	
❑ G-MOLI*	Cameron A-250 -E	3-02	
❑ G-NPNP*	Cameron N-105 -E	3-02	
❑ G-NPWR	Sky SS -E	3-02	
❑ G-NWPB*	Thunder Ax7-77Z -E	3-02	
❑ G-OAFC	Airtour AH-56 -E	3-02	
❑ G-OCND	Cameron O-77 -E	3-02	
❑ G-OHDC*	Colt SS -E	3-02	
❑ G-OLDV*	Colt 90A -E	3-02	
❑ G-OSVY*	Sky 31-24 -E	3-02	
❑ G-OXRG*	Colt SS -E	3-02	
❑ G-PONY*	Colt 31A -E	3-02	
❑ G-POPP*	Colt 105A -E	3-02	
❑ G-PSON*	Colt SS -E	3-02	
❑ G-PURE*	Colt 70SS -E	3-02	
❑ G-PYLN*	Colt 80SS -E	3-02	
❑ G-RARE*	Thunder Ax5-42 -E	3-02	
❑ G-RIPS*	Colt 110SS -E	3-02	
❑ G-SCAH	Cameron V-77 -E	3-02	
❑ G-SCFO	Cameron O-77 -E	3-02	
❑ G-SEGA*	Cameron SS -E	3-02	
❑ G-SEUK*	Cameron TV-80SS -E	3-02	
❑ G-TTWO	Colt 56A -E	3-02	
❑ G-UNIP	Cameron SS -E	3-02	
❑ G-VOLT*	Cameron N-77 -E	3-02	
❑ G-WATT*	Cameron SS -E	3-02	
❑ G-WCAT	Colt SS -E	3-02	
❑ G-WINE	Thunder Ax7-77 -E	3-02	
❑ C-GYZI	Cameron O-77 -E	3-02	
❑ D-OPHA	Fire Balloons 3000 -E	3-02	
❑ D-PAMGAS	Cameron N-90 -E	3-02	
❑ DQ-PBF*	Thunder Ax10-180 -E	3-02	
❑ N413JB	Cameron O-84 -E	3-02	
❑ N4519U	Head Ax-09-118 -E	3-02	
❑ N5023U	Avian Magnum IX -E	3-02	
❑ N9045C*	Barnes SS -E	3-02	
❑ OO-BDO	Cameron N-90 -E	3-02	
❑ VH-AYY*	Kavanagh D-77 -E	3-02	

Jim Pearce: The three Ilyushin Il-2 hulks moved on by late 2000, to Gainsborough, Lincs.

LITTLEHAMPTON on the A259 west of Worthing
Frank Matthews: The Islander forward fuselage will eventually be trailer-mounted.
❑ VQ-SAC   BN-2A Islander   ex Shoreham. Crashed 4-9-76. Forward fuselage.   ℗   3-94

PULBOROUGH on the A29 south-west of Horsham
Miles Aircraft Collection (MAC): Because the entire MAC collection is dispersed across several sites, to avoid confusion it has been decided to move their entry – previously listed under Woodley, Berks – to this 'stand-alone' heading. Several MAC artefacts can be found under the Woodley listing. Large 'chunks' of Messengers and Geminis are held as well as those listed below plus components and sections from a variety of Masters.
◆ Airframes in store at several locations and *not* available for inspection. ✉ Peter Amos, 4 Castle Bungalows, Storrington, near Pulborough, RH20 4LB **e-mail** tkhome@ndirect.co.uk

❑ G-AKGD	Gemini 1A	ex Henley, Cranfield, Bushey, 'Sussex', Southend. CoA 14-11-66. Cockpit. Poor condition.	3-02
❑ G-AKHZ	Gemini 1A	ex Henley, Cranfield, Bushey, Elsham Hall, Handforth. CoA 6-1-64.	3-02
❑ VP-KJL	Messenger 4A	ex Stoke-on-Trent, Coventry Airport, G-ALAR, RH371, BAFO CW, AEAF CS.	3-02

SHOREHAM AIRPORT west of the River Adur, south of the A27
Visitor Centre and Archive: Located near the entrance to the 1930s terminal building, a wide array of archives and artefacts are on show. The 'Flea' was built during 2001 by archivist Tim Hogben and friends and largely complete by August.
The cockpit of Herald 214 G-ASVO moved to Perth, Scotland, in early October 2000. Grasshopper TX.1 moved to Northampton, Northants, on loan, by March 2002.
◆ Open daily 10am to 5pm. Guided tours are organised on a regular basis - booking *essential*. An increasing archive of documents and photographs is maintained and a quarterly journal, *The Archive*, produced for the **Friends of the Archive**.✉ 14J Cecil Pashley Way, Shoreham Airport, Shoreham-by-Sea, BN43 5FF. ☎ 01273 441061 **e-mail** bhrg@ukonline.co.uk **web** www. thearchiveshoreham.co.uk

❑ —	BAPC.20	Lee-Richards Annular REP	ex Winthorpe, *Those Magnificent Men...* 350cc Douglas for ground-running.	3-02
❑ —*	BAPC.277	HM.14 'Flea'	see above.	3-02

Museum of D-Day Aviation: Set inside a World War Two blister hangar, the interior of the museum contains artefacts from all aspects of the Allied invasion, including an Airspeed Horsa 'half-fuselage' using many original parts. There is a compound that allows good views of the light aircraft park.
◆ Open 11am to 5pm daily Apr to Oct. Weekends, 11am to 5pm in Mar and Nov. ✉ Shoreham Aerodrome, Shoreham-by-Sea, BN43 5FJ ☎ 01903 851447

❑ 'MJ751' 'DU-V'	Spitfire FSM	BAPC.209, ex *Piece of Cake*. 321 Sqn colours.	3-02
❑ 30151*	P-2 Kraguj	ex Fordingbridge, Bournemouth, Yugoslav AF. Fuselage. Arrived 25-2-02.	3-02
❑	Typhoon	cockpit section.	3-02

Elsewhere: Transair's 'gate guardian', Harrier GR.3 XZ995 left for temporary store in Suffolk on 30th October 2001 and it was registered as G-CBGK in preparation for export to the USA. It was replaced by the Wessex ①. The nose of Lightning F.6 XS932 moved to Farnborough, Hants, on 29th June 2001.

❑ G-ARNG	Colt 108	ex locality, White Waltham. CoA 10-12-73.	℗	3-00
❑ G-ASRB	Condor	CoA 1-11-98. Stored.		3-02
❑ G-ATRL	Cessna F.150F	CoA 21-2-98. Dump by 8-01.		2-02
❑ G-BHEH	Cessna 310G	ex Bagby, N1720, N8916Z. CoA 9-12-96. Dump.		2-02

❏ G-BPRP*	Cessna 150E	ex N3569J. CoA 23-5-98. F/n 10-00, dump by 8-01.		2-02
❏ G-BWDE	Navajo P	ex G-HWKN, HB-LIR, D-IAIR, N7304L.		
		CoA 18-12-96. Stored.		2-02
❏ G-CKCK	Enstrom 280FX	ex OO-PVL. CoA 14-5-98. Original pod.		1-00
❏ G-MBTS*	Whing Ding II	Cancelled 6-9-94. Stored in container.		2-02
❏ G-REBL	Hughes 269B	ex N9493F. CoA 9-10-95.	®	1-02
❏ N6819F*	Cessna 150F	dump by 8-01.		2-02
❏ SP-DOF	Iskra	G-BXVZ.	®	2-01
❏ XR517* 'N'	Wessex HC.2	ex Ipswich, Fleetlands, 60, 72, 18. Arr 7-12-01.	①	2-02

Northbrook College: Cessna 310G G-BHEH's rebuild is being conducted in the 'North Hangar', so has moved to the listing above. During January 2001 Queen Airs G-AWKX and G-KEAB were dismantled. G-KEAB along with the famed Baron 55A G-AYKA 'car' moved to Bruntingthorpe, Leics, on 11th September 2001.

❏ G-APNJ	Cessna 310	ex EI-AJY, N3635D. CoA 28-11-74.		1-02
❏ G-OBUS	Archer 181	ex G-BMTT, N3002K. Crashed 18-4-89. Fuselage.		3-00
❏ G-TOBY	Cessna 172B	ex Sandown, G-ARCM, N6952X. Dam 15-10-83.		2-01
❏ WT806*	Hunter GA.11	ex Ipswich, Shawbury, Abingdon, Chivenor,		
		FRADU, CFS, 14. Arrived 3-7-01. Inst.		1-02
❏ XL929	Pembroke C.1	G-BNPU, ex Sandown, Shawbury, 60, Kemble,		
		207, SCCS, TCCS, FCCS, BCCS.		12-01
❏ '2807' '103'	T-6G Texan	G-BHTH, ex N2807G, 49-3072. Crashed 13-3-95.	®	2-02
❏ 51-14526*	T-6G Texan	G-BRWB, ex Duxford, FAF, 51-14526.		
'RC'		*Thumper*. Crashed 5-7-01. Arrived 21-9-01.	®	2-02

TANGMERE south of the A27, east of Chichester
Tangmere Military Aviation Museum: A major new display, dedicated to the genius of R J Mitchell was unveiled on 2nd March 2002, using both Spitfire FSMs. The Swift, while an operational version, stands handsomely for the record breaking of Mike Lithgow. EE459, WB188 and WK281 are on loan from the RAF Museum – RAFM. The Meteor F.8 is a complex composite, including items from VZ530, and includes a rare IFR probe ①. The Gannet cockpit had left by March 2002.
◆ Signposted from the A27. Open daily 10am to 5.30pm from Mar to Oct and 10am to 4.30pm in Feb and Nov. *Closed* December and January. Parties at other times by arrangement. ✉ Tangmere Airfield, Chichester, PO20 6ES ☎ 01243 775223 **fax** 01243 789490 **e-mail** admin@tangmere-museum.org.uk **web** www.tangmere-museum.org.uk

❏ 'K5054'	Spitfire proto	BAPC.214, ex Southampton, Hendon, Thruxton,		
	FSM	Middle Wallop, Thruxton, Andover.		3-02
❏ 'L1679'	Hurricane FSM	BAPC.241, ex Chilbolton, Middle Wallop,		
'JX-G'		Thruxton. 1 Sqn colours. Built by AeroFab.		3-02
❏ 'BL924' 'AZ-G'	Spitfire FSM	BAPC.242, *Valdemaar Atterdag*, 234 Sqn colours.		3-02
❏ EE459	Meteor IV	ex Cosford, St Athan, Abingdon, Hendon,		
	Special	St Athan, Innsworth 7008M, Fulbeck,		
		Cranwell, CFE, FCCS, RAFHSF.	RAFM	3-02
❏ 'WA829' 'A'	Meteor F.8	WA984, ex Southampton, Wimborne,		
		Tarrant Rushton, 211 AFS, 19.	①	3-02
❏ WB188	Hawker P.1067	ex Cosford, St Athan, Colerne, Melksham,		
		Halton 7154M, Hawkers. Hunter prototype.	RAFM	3-02
❏ WK281 'S'	Swift FR.5	ex Hendon, St Athan, Swinderby, Finningley,		
		Colerne 7712M, Northolt, 79. 79 Sqn colours.	RAFM	3-02
❏ XJ580* '131'	Sea Vixen	ex Christchurch, Bournemouth FRL, RAE		
	FAW.2	Farnborough, Llanbedr, 899. Arrived 27-6-00.	®	3-02
❏ XN299 '758'	Whirlwind	ex Southsea, Higher Blagdon, Culdrose, JWE		
	HAR.7	Old Sarum, Fleetlands, 847 'B' Flt, 847, Culdrose,		
		848. 848 Sqn c/s, *Bulwark. The Iron Chicken*.		3-02
❏ 19252	T-33A-1-LO	ex Hailsham, Sculthorpe, French AF.		3-02

W ASHINGTON east of the A24 north of Worthing
By July 2001 a dismantled Meteor T.7 had turned up at a strip in the general area. A surprise find here was the 'pod' of EP.9 Prospector G-ARDG, part of a cache of bits used to create the flyable G-APWZ and 'XM819' at Middle Wallop, Hants.

❏ G-ARDG*	Prospector	ex Durrington, Middle Wallop, Shoreham, Lympne. 'Pod' in poor state. Stored.	8-01
❏ WF877*	Meteor T.7 (mod)	G-BPOA, ex Kemble, North Weald, Higher Blagdon, Tarrant Rushton, Chilbolton, Folland, Gloster, 96, Meteor Flight Wunstorf, 11. Dismantled. F/n 7-01.	8-01

WEST CHILTINGTON on the B2139 south of Horsham
Adrian Brook: G-AGOY will fly in prototype colours when complete. Hawker Trainer G-AIUA moved to King's Lynn, Norfolk, on September 8, 2000. Fellow G-ANWO moved some time ago (correcting *W&R17*, p213) and is *believed* to have gone to the Bristol area for use in the Miles Sparrowjet 'rebirth' project. More details appreciated. Likewise Tiger Moth G-AOBO also moved from this site well prior to early 2000 and is thought to be in Cornwall. Adrian operated Gemini G-AKHP.

❏ G-AGOY	Messenger 3	ex Hatch, Southill, Castletown, EI-AGE, HB-EIP, G-AGOY, U-0247.	®	1-00

WARWICKSHIRE

BAXTERLEY AERODROME south of the A5 near Atherstone
Midland Warplane Museum (MWM): The Oxford, is known to have been fitted with Standard Beam Approach equipment and was DH built. It *may* be AT601 ①.
◆ Visits possible only by prior appointment. ✉ Mark J Evans, 46 Arthur Street, Kenilworth, CV8 2HE **e-mail** mwm@couplandbell.com

❏	Harvard	cockpit section. Stored, off site.		3-02
❏ *	Oxford	ex Canada. Off-site.	® ①	3-02

Others: Along with Tiger Moth G-APGL is an anonymous fuselage frame ①.

❏ G-APGL	Tiger Moth	ex Fairoaks, NM140, LAS, AOPS, 14 RFS, 8 RFS, 8 EFTS, 3 EFTS, 22 EFTS, 3 EFTS, ORTU, Tarrant Rushton SF.	®	3-00
❏	Tiger Moth	ex Cranfield, VAT et al.	①	3-00

BIDFORD AERODROME or Bickmarsh, north-east of Evesham south of Bidford-on-Avon
Avon Soaring Centre:

❏ DKY	Ka7 Rhonadler	BGA.2187. Ex RAFGSA.342. CoA 4-98. Stored.	9-99
❏ DYR	Ka7 Rhonadler	BGA.2489. Ex D-5220. CoA 8-99. Stored.	9-99
❏	L.13 Blanik	BGA.2121. CoA 4-85. Stored.	5-98

COVENTRY AIRPORT or Baginton, at the A45/A423 junction, south of the city
Midland Air Museum (MAM), incorporating the **Sir Frank Whittle Jet Heritage Centre** and **Wings over Coventry** display.
   Notes: See under Keevil, Wilts, for 'another' BGA.804 ①. Prentice VS623 is fitted with the wings from G-AONB (VR244) ②. Meteor NF.14 WS838 is on loan from the RAF Museum ③. The Gannet T.2 is on loan from FAAM ④. The Buccaneer nose section, a Gulf War veteran, is on loan from Robin Phipps ⑤ — see also under Bruntingthorpe, Leics. The Beaufighter nose section is possibly Mk.VI T5298. In which case it was previously 4552M and TFU Defford ⑥. See under Bristol, Glos, for MAM's Beagle 206. See also Croughton, Northants.

The **Shackleton Association**'s trailer-mounted nose 'lodges' care of the museum – SA. They serve to unite air and ground crew and all interested in the 'Shack', producing a house magazine, *The Growler*. (Peter Dunn, *Meadow View*, Parks Lane, Prestwood, Great Missenden, Bucks HP16 0JH.) ¨
◆ Well signed from the A45/A423 junction. Open Apr to Oct Mon to Sat 10am to 5pm, Sun and Bank Hols 10am to 6pm. Nov to Mar daily 10am to 4.30pm. Closed Xmas and Boxing Day. Other times by appointment. Regular special events. ✉ Coventry Airport, Baginton, Coventry CV8 3AZ ☎ / fax 024 76 301033 e-mail midlandairmuseum@aol.com web www.midlandairmuseum.org.uk

❑ G-EBJG		Pixie III	ex Coventry, Stratford. CoA 2-10-36. Remains.	3-02
❑ G-ABOI		Wheeler Slymph	ex Coventry, Old Warden. On loan. Stored.	3-02
❑ G-AEGV		HM.14 'Flea'	ex Coventry, Knowle, Northampton, Sywell.	3-02
❑ G-ALCU		Dove 2	ex airfield, VT-CEH. CoA 16-3-73.	3-02
❑ G-APJJ		Fairey Ultra Light	ex Heaton Chapel, Coventry, Hayes. CoA 1-4-59.	3-02
❑ G-APRL		Argosy 101	ex ABC/Elan, Sagittair, N890U, N602Z, N6507R, G-APRL. *Edna*. CoA 23-3-87.	3-02
❑ G-APWN		Whirlwind Srs 3	ex Cranfield, Redhill, VR-BER, G-APWN, 5N-AGI, G-APWN. CoA 17-5-78. Bristows c/s.	3-02
❑ G-ARYB		HS.125 Srs 1	ex Hatfield. CoA 22-1-68.	3-02
❑ G-MJWH		Vortex 120	hang glider, former microlight.	3-02
❑ —	BGA.804	Cadet TX.1	ex VM589. Stored.	① 3-02
❑ 'A7317'		Pup REP	BAPC. 179, ex Waltham Abbey, North Weald, *Wings*.	3-02
❑ EE531		Meteor F.4	ex Bentham, Coventry , Birmingham, Weston Park, Birmingham, RAE Lasham, 7090M, A&AEE, makers.	3-02
❑ 'JR505'		Typhoon Ib	ex Coventry, Leeds, Gloucester, Kemble. Cockpit and forward fuselage frame. On loan, stored.	5-00
❑ VF301	'RAL-G'	Vampire F.1	ex Stoneleigh, Debden, 7060M, 208 AFS, 595, 226 OCU. 605 Sqn colours.	3-02
❑ VP293	'A'	Shackleton T.4	ex Woodford, Coventry, East Kirkby, Strathallan, RAE, MOTU, 206, 224. Trailer-mounted nose.	SA 3-02
❑ VS623		Prentice T.1	G-AOKZ, ex Shoreham, Redhill, Southend, VS623, CFS, 2 FTS, 22 FTS.	®② 3-02
❑ VT935		BP P. 111A	ex Cranfield, RAE Bedford.	3-02
❑ VZ477		Meteor F.8	ex Kimbolton, 7741M, APS, 245. Nose.	3-02
❑ WF922		Canberra PR.3	ex Cambridge, 39, 69, 58, 82.	3-02
❑ WH646	'EG'	Canberra T.17A	ex Wyton, 360, 45, RNZAF, 45, 10, 50. Nose.	3-02
❑ WS838		Meteor NF.14	ex Cosford, Manchester, Cosford, Shawbury, Colerne, RAE Bedford, RRE, MoS, 64, 238 OCU.	③ 3-02
❑ WV797		Sea Hawk FGA.6	ex Perth, Culdrose A2637, Halton 8155M, Sydenham, 738, 898, 899, Fleetlands, 787.	3-02
❑ XA508	'627'	Gannet T.2	ex Yeovilton, Manadon, A2472, 737. 737 Sqn c/s.	④ 3-02
❑ XA699		Javelin FAW.5	ex Cosford, Locking, 7809M, Shawbury, Kemble, Shawbury, 5, 151. 5 Squadron colours.	3-02
❑ XD626		Vampire T.11	ex Bitteswell, Shawbury, CATCS, CNCS, 5 FTS, RAFC, CFS. Stored.	3-02
❑ XE855		Vampire T.11	ex Upton-by-Chester, Woodford, Chester, 27 MU, 22 MU, 10 MU, AWOCU. Pod, spares.	3-02
❑ XF382	'15'	Hunter F.6A	ex Brawdy, 1 TWU, TWU, 229 OCU, FCS, 65, 63, 92.	3-02
❑ 'XG190'		Hunter F.51	E-425, ex Dunsfold, G-9-446, DanAF Esk.724. 111 Sqn 'Black Arrows' colours by 6-00.	3-02
❑ XJ579		Sea Vixen FAW.2	ex Farnborough, A&AEE, Llanbedr, 899, 766. Nose.	3-02
❑ XK741		Gnat F.1	ex Leamington Spa, Fordhouses, Dunsfold, Hamble, Boscombe Down, Dunsfold. Fuselage.	3-02
❑ XK789		Grasshopper TX.1	ex Warwick, Cosford, Stamford.	3-02
❑ XK907		Whirlwind HAS.7	ex Bubbenhall, Panshanger, Elstree, Luton, ETPS, RRE, Alvis. Cockpit. Stored.	3-02

❏	XL360		Vulcan B.2	ex 44, 101, 35, 617, 230 OCU, Wadd Wing, 230 OCU,		
				Scamp W, 617. *City of Coventry.* 617 Sqn c/s.		3-02
❏	XN685		Sea Vixen FAW.2	ex Chester, Cosford, Cranwell, 8173M,		
				890, 766, 893, HSA Hatfield.		3-02
❏	XR771	'BM'	Lightning F.6	ex Binbrook, 5, 11, 5, 56, 74.		3-02
❏	XX899		Buccaneer S.2B	ex Kidlington, Stock, St Athan, Lossiemouth,		
				208, 12, Gulf Det, 237 OCU, 12, 237 OCU,		
				12, 237 OCU, 16, 15, 12, 208. Nose.	® ⑤	3-02
❏			Beaufighter	ex Birmingham, Coventry. Cockpit.	⑥	3-02
❏	R-756		F-104G	ex Aalborg, Danish AF, 64-17756.	®	3-02
❏	70		Mystère IVA	ex Sculthorpe, Fr AF. *Patrouille de France* colours.		3-02
❏	51-4419		T-33A-1-LO	ex Sculthorpe, French AF.		3-02
❏	17473		T-33A-1-LO	ex Cosford, Sculthorpe, French AF.		3-02
❏	54-2174		F-100D-16-NA	ex Sculthorpe, French AF.		3-02
❏	280020		Fl 282B V-20	ex Coventry, Cranfield, Brize Norton,		
				Travemünde 'CJ+SN'. Frame.		3-02
❏	959*		MiG-21SPS	ex Duxford, Cottbus, LSK. Arrived 25-6-01.		3-02
❏	55-713	'C'	Lightning T.55	ex Warton, ZF598, RSAF 55-713, G-27-72. Saudi c/s.		3-02
❏	29640		SAAB J29F	ex Southend, R Swedish AF.		3-02
❏	24535		HH-43B Huskie	ex Woodbridge, 40 ARRS, Det 2. Stored.		3-02
❏	37414		F-4C-15-MC	ex Woodbridge, New York ANG.		3-02
❏	37699	'CG'	F-4C-21-MC	ex Upper Heyford, Fairford, Illinois ANG, 557 TFS,		
				356 TFS, 480 TFS. 366th TFW c/s, MiG 'kill'.		3-02
❏	60312		F-101B-80-MC	ex Alconbury, Davis-Monthan, Kentucky ANG.		
				60th FIS colours.		3-02
❏	58-2062		U-6A Beaver	ex Mannheim, US Army.		3-02
❏	—	BAPC.9	Humber Mono	ex Birmingham Airport, Yeovilton,		
			REP	Wroughton, Yeovilton, Coventry.		3-02
❏	—	BAPC.32	Tom Thumb	ex Coventry, Bewdley, Coventry, Banbury.		
				Unfinished 1930s homebuild. Stored.		3-02
❏	—	BAPC.126	Turbulent	ex Shoreham, Croydon. Static airframe.		3-02

Air Atlantique Historic Flight: Dakota 6 G-AMPZ (KN442) was sold to Air Services, Berlin, and departed on 28th September 2001. During mid-2001 the **Shackleton Association** (see under Midland Air Museum, above) formed a separate organisation called the **963 Support Group** with the intention of returning WR963 to airworthy condition. A survey has been carried out on the aircraft and AA has pledged engineering support and hangarage when needed. Fund-raising and finding suitably-qualified help are the next major steps! (**e-mail** shack106.chalk@lineone.net) From the 2002 season the Classic Aviation Projects will operate in association with the Historic Flight under the title Canberra Display Team②. (See under Bruntingthorpe, Leics.)
◆ All visits by prior arrangement. Details of the 'Enthusiast Days' and other special events and flights can be had on the **info hotline** ☎ 01203 882629

❏	G-AGTM	Dragon Rapide ✈	ex JY-ACL, OD-ABP, G-AGTM, NF875.		3-02
❏	G-AIDL	Dragon Rapide ✈	ex Biggin Hill, Allied Airways, TX310.		3-02
❏	G-AKIU	Proctor V	ex Nottingham, Bedford, Houghton-on-the-Hill,		
			North Weald, Southend, Edenbridge.		
			CoA 24-1-65.	off site ®	3-00
❏	G-APRS	Twin Pioneer 3	ex Staverton, G-BCWF, XT610, G-APRS,		
		✈	PI-C430 ntu. *Primrose.* 'Raspberry Ripple' c/s.		3-02
❏	G-AYWA	Avro XIX Srs 2	ex Bridge of Wier, Lochwinnoch, Strathallan,		
			Thruxton, OO-VIT, OO-DFA. Spares.	off-site	3-02
❏	G-AZHJ	Twin Pioneer 3	ex Prestwick, Staverton, Prestwick, G-31-16,		
			XP295, Odiham SF, MoA, 1310F, Odiham SF,		
			230. CoA 23-8-90. Spares.	off-site	3-02
❏	G-DHDV	Devon C.2/2 ✈	ex BBMF VP981, Northolt, 207, 21, WCS,		
			Wildenrath CF, AAFCE, MinTech, AAFCE, Paris		
			Air Attaché, Hendon SF, AFWE. Gulf Air c/s.		3-02

AYI		J/1 Autocrat ✈	ex OY-ALU, D-EGYK, OO-ABF.		3-02
259	'M'	Prentice 1✈	G-APJB, ex VR259, 1 ASS, 2 ASS, RAFC. 2 ASS colours.		3-02
226		Anson C.19	ex Duxford, Little Staughton, East Dereham, Colerne 7865M, Shawbury, FTCCF, OCTU Jurby, 187, Hemswell SF, Coningsby CF, CBE. Spares.	off-site	3-02
235*		Anson C.19/2	ex Caernarfon, Higher Blagdon, Andover, Shawbury, SCS, FCCS, CTFU, OCTU, 64 GCS, 2 GCS. Stored. Arrived 8-00.	off-site	3-02
959 N959VP	'L'	Devon C.2	ex Wellesbourne, Biggin Hill, N959VP ntu, G-BWFB, VP959, RAE. Stored.	off-site	3-02
0379'*	'K'	Chipmunk T.10 ✈	G-APLO, ex EI-AHU, WB696, 11 RFS, Ab UAS, 11 RFS. Cam UAS colours.		3-02
413		Anson C.21✈	G-VROE, ex G-BFIR, Duxford, Lee-on-Solent, Enstone, Tees-side, Strathallan, Bournemouth, East Midlands, 7881M, Aldergrove, TCCS, BCCS, 1 ANS. Yellow 'T' bands colours.		3-02
163*		Canberra B.2/6 ✈	G-BVWC, ex DRA Farnborough, DRA Bedford, RAE, Napier, ASM, MoA. B.2 nose format.	②	3-02
711	'833'	Hunter GA.11	ex Culdrose A2645, A2731, Shawbury, FRADU, 14, 54.		3-02
963		Shackleton AEW.2	ex SPT, Waddington, Lossiemouth, 8, 205, 28, 210, 224. Stored.	①	3-02
954		Pembroke C.1	G-BXES, ex N4234C, Tatenhill, White Waltham, 9042M, Northolt, 60, RAFG CS, 2 TAF CS.		3-02
223		Dove 7	G-BWWC, ex Cumbernauld, West Freugh, DGTE, T&EE, RAE. Wings from Dove 5 G-APSO.	®	3-02

Iantic Group / Air Atlantique / Atlantic Aeroengineering / CFS Aeroproducts: The n control-modified Dakotas were withdrawn from use during 2000 and lie dormant. Correcting ', L.188CF Electras LN-FON and 'OL became G-LOFF and G-LOFG respectively in June 2000 not aspire to the US civil register. C-47B G-AMPO moved by road to Lyneham, Wilts, on 22nd ber 2001. C-47B G-AMYJ moved by road to Elvington, N Yorks, on 10th December 2001.

MCA*	C-47B-30-DK	ex KN487, Oakington SF, 46, 525, 44-76634. CoA 10-12-00. Stored.		3-02
MHJ*	C-47B-25-DK	ex SU-AZI, G-AMHJ, ZS-BRW, KG651, 1333 CU, 1383 CU, 24, 109 OTU, 42-108962. CoA 5-12-00. Stored.		3-02
MSV*	C-47B-25-DK	ex F-BSGV ntu, G-AMSV, KN397, Oakington SF, 96, 44-76488. CoA 1-7-01. Stored.		3-02
VDB	Cessna 310L	ex Popham, Perth, N2279F. CoA 8-7-79. Spares.	off-site	3-02
ZLJ*	Trislander	ex Highland, G-OREG, SX-CBN, G-OREG,G-OAVW, G-AZLJ, G-51-319. Arrived 23-12-99CoA 2-2-00. Stored.		3-02
WPG	Robin HR.200	ex Inverness. Crashed 29-10-97. Stored.	off-site	3-02
OFA	L.188CF Electra	ex Atlantic, N359Q, F-OGST, N359AC, TI-LRM, N359AC, HC-AVX, N359AC, VH-ECA. CoA 9-2-00. Spare recovery.		3-02
OFF*	L.188CF Electra	ex Fred Olsen LN-FON, N342HA, N417MA, OB-R-1138, HP-684, N417MA, CF-ZST, N7142C. Stored.		3-02
FRT*	L.188CF Electra	ex Bournemouth, N347HA, N423MA, N23AF, N64405, SE-FGC, N5537. Last flight 3-3-01. CoA 28-10-01. Spares recovery.		3-02
FOI*	L.188CF Electra	ex Fred Olsen, N31231, ZK-TEA, N9724C, ZK-BMP ntu. Last flew 17-12-97. Stored.		3-02

❑ LN-FOL*   L.188CF Electra   G-LOFG, ex Fred Olsen, N669F, N404GN,
                                N6126A. Last flight 15-12-97. Stored.   3-02

Others: The Spitfire is recovering from a landing accident. See under Coventry, West Mids, for its
associated Hurricane project ①. Classic Aviation Projects Canberra operated from Coventry from May
2000. In late 2001 came the announcement that from 2002 it would be operated in association with Air
Atlantique and it can be found under their Historic Flight banner above. The Prentice on the dump was
exchanged for the Tomahawk. The former left by road for Doncaster, S Yorks, on 9th May 2000.
    Departures: Chipmunk 22 WD305 (G-ARGG) was flying again by mid-01; Cherokee G-AVWL
was flying again by 1999; Safir G-SAFR was at Cranfield, Beds, by 6-00.

❑ G-BBXU   Sierra 200   CoA 18-11-93. Wreck.   7-97
❑ G-BDCL   AA-5Traveler   ex EI-CCI, G-BDCL, EI-BGV, G-BDCL, N1373R.
                              CoA 29-11-93. Stored.   3-00
❑ G-BGTS   Cherokee 140F   ex Liverpool, OY-BGD. Crashed 17-6-89. Stored.   12-92
❑ G-BHFL   Cherokee 180   ex N15189. Crashed 1-11-89. Wreck.   12-92
❑ G-BMIU   Enstrom F.28A   ex OO-BAM, F-BVRE ntu. Cr 9-7-86. Cabin, stored.   2-98
❑ G-BPJF*   Tomahawk 112   ex N9312T. Crashed 20-6-98. Dump by 5-00.   3-02
❑ G-NACA   Freelance 180   ex Sandown, Bembridge. Stored.   3-02
❑ G-NDNI   Firecracker   ex Sandown. CoA 11-5-84. Stored.   3-02
❑   Enstrom F.28A   cabin, stored.   2-98
❑ –   Freelance   ex Sandown. Fuselage in rafters.   3-02
❑ –   Freelance   ex Sandown. Fuselage in rafters.   3-02
❑ –   Freelance   ex Sandown. Fuselage in rafters.   3-02
❑ –   Freelance   ex Sandown. Fuselage in rafters.   3-02
❑ MJ627*   Spitfire Tr.IX   G-BMSG, ex Coventry, G-ASOZ Andover, IAAC
                              158, G-15-171, MJ627, 1, 441. 441 Sqn c/s.
                              Damaged 25-4-98.   ⑬ ①   2-01
❑ 408*   Iskra 100   ex Scampton, Duxford, Polish AF. Arrived 27-3-01.   3-02
❑ 70270   F-101B-80-MC   ex MAM, Woodbridge, Davis-Monthan,
                              Texas ANG. Nose. Dump   10-00

KING'S COUGHTON on the A435 north of Alcester
❑ G-BBED   Rallye 220   CoA 13-9-87. Stored.   8-01

LONG MARSTON AERODROME on the B4632, south-west of Stratford-upon-Avon
Jet Aviation Preservation Group (JAPG): Several airframes are on loan, as follows: the Dove and
Meteor T.7 from Gordon Yates; the Shackleton, Canberra and Whirlwind from the local land owner; and
the recently-arrived Supermarine 544 nose from Alan Allen. They are marked ±. Chipmunk T.10
WP784 continues to make excellent progress. It will be a composite rebuild when completed ①. The
single-seat composite Hunter is a complex beast; with an unused F.6 cockpit from Stafford, the centre
section of F.6 XG226, the rear end of a Danish T.7 and the wings from PH-NLH (see under Eaglescott,
Devon). All of this will be completed as an FR.10 (a 'missing' UK Hunter variant) in due course ②. The
Gazelle will ultimately become a complete airframe, JAPG have at least 95% of the helicopter in store ③.
Nimrod R.1 cockpit XW666 moved to Doncaster, S Yorks, by September 2001.
◆ Visitors are welcome at weekends when the JAPG crew are at work on their airframes. ✉ Stewart
    Holder, 62 Avon Street, Evesham, WR11 4LG

❑ G-ANUW   Dove 6   ex Welshpool, North Weald, Stansted,
                              CAFU. CoA 22-7-81.   ±   3-02
❑ WL332   Meteor T.7   ex SAC, Cardiff-Wales, Croston, Moston,
                              FRU, Lossiemouth SF, Ford SF.   ±   3-02
❑ WM367   Meteor NF.13   ex Firbeck, North Weald, Powick,
                              Boscombe Down, AWA, MoA. Nose.   3-02

❑ WP784		Chipmunk T.10	ex Hemel Hempstead, Wycombe AP, Boston, Holbeach, Wellingborough, Reading, Benson, Abingdon, 6 AEF, Leeds UAS, Abn UAS, 8 FTS, Man UAS, QUAS, Air Att Paris, 5 RFS, 17 RFS.	® ①	3-02
❑ WR985	'H'	Shack' MR.3/3	ex SAC, Cosford, 8103M, 201, 120, 206, 203, 206, A&AEE, 206.	±	3-02
❑ WT483	'83'	Canberra T.4	ex SAC, Filton, Samlesbury, 231 OCU, 39, 231 OCU, 16, Laarbruch SF, 68, Laarbruch SF, 69.	±	3-02
❑ WT859*		Supermarine 544	ex Brooklands, Ruislip, Foulness, Culdrose, Fleetlands, Culdrose, Lee-on-Solent A2499, RAE Bedford. Nose. Arrived 9-8-01.	±	3-02
❑ WV382		Hunter GA.11	ex Smethwick, Lee-on-Solent, Shawbury, FRADU, 67.		3-02
❑ XD447	'50'	Vampire T.11	ex SAC, E Kirkby, Tattershall, Woodford, Chester, St Athan, 8 FTS, RAFC, 5 FTS.	®	3-02
❑ XG737		Sea Ven FAW.22	ex Cardiff-Wales, Yeovilton, FRU, Sydenham, 894, 893, 891. Stored.		3-02
❑ 'XJ714'		Hunter 'FR.10'	composite	® ②	3-02
❑ XP346		W'wind HAR.10	ex Tattershall Thorpe, Shawbury, 8793M, Lee-on-Solent, Akrotiri, 84, 22, 225.	±	3-02
❑ XP568		Jet Provost T.4	ex Faygate, Hatfield, Shawbury, RAFC.	®	3-02
❑ XX457	'Z'	Gazelle AH.1	ex Arborfield, 2 Flt, 662, 656, ARWF, GCF.	③	3-02
❑ N-315		Hunter T.7	ex Hucclecote, Batley, Amsterdam, NLS spares, Dutch AF, XM121.		3-02

Others: Whirlwind HAS.7 XL840 moved to Bawtry, S Yorks, in mid-2000.

❑ G-RACA '571'	Sea Prince T.1	ex WM735, Staverton, Kemble, 750, BTU, A&AEE.	9-99

Microlight centre: By June 2001, Tiger Cub G-MMIX had moved to Dumfries, Scotland.

❑ G-MMIR	Mainair Gemini	original 'trike', c/n 051.	6-98

NUNEATON on the A444 north of Coventry
Ted Gautrey: Is thought to continue to restore his Fox Moth.

❑ G-ACCB	Fox Moth	ex Coventry, Redhill, Blackpool, Southport. Ditched 25-9-56.	®	10-95

RUGBY on the A426 east of Coventry
No news on the Auster AOP.9 project here. It is thought to be XR239

❑	Auster AOP.9	ex Popham. Fuselage frame and wings.	®	6-95

STONELEIGH on the B4113 south of Coventry
A strip in the general area is the home to a 'spares ship' Ryan PT-22.

❑	Ryan PT-22	spares for G-BTBH.	1-02

WARWICK on the A429 west of Royal Leamington Spa
Paul Williams: No news on the situation with the gliders.

❑ —		Hutter H.17a	ex Moreton-in-Marsh.	®	1-92
❑ —	BAPC.25	Nyborg TGN.III	ex Moreton-in-Marsh, Stratford. Stored.		1-92

Others: The Fleet continues to make progress in the general area.

❑ G-FLCA	Fleet Canuck	ex Baxterley, Chilbolton, Coventry, Rochester, Blackbushe, CS-ACQ, CF-DQP.	®	3-01

WELLESBOURNE MOUNTFORD AERODROME south of the B4086, east of Stratford
Wellesbourne Wartime Museum: Operated by the **Wellesbourne Aviation Group**, the Museum
charts the history of the airfield centred on the restored underground Battle Headquarters. The Vulcan
nose is owned by Paul Hartley and will be restored to display condition ①.
◆ Open every Sunday 10am to 4pm and Bank Holidays, same times. ✉ Derek Powell, 167
Colebourne Road, Kingsheath, Birmingham, B13 0HB e-mail d.powell@iclway.co.uk

❑		McBroom Argus	hang-glider, built 1974. Stored.	3-02
❑ RA-01378		Yak-52	ex DOSAAF '14'.	3-02
❑ WV679	'O-J'	Provost T.1	ex Dunkeswell, Higher Blagdon, Halton 7615M, 2 FTS.	® 3-02
❑ XA903		Vulcan B.1	ex Sidcup, Cardiff, Farnborough, RB.199 and Olympus test-bed, Blue Steel trials, Avro. Nose.	① 3-02
❑ XJ575		Sea Vixen FAW.2	ex Long Marston, Helston, Culdrose, A2611, 766. Nose.	3-02
❑ XK590	'V'	Vampire T.11	ex Witney, Brize Norton, CATCS, 4 FTS, 7 FTS.	3-02

XM655 Maintenance and Preservation Society: Much tender, loving care continues to be
lavished on XM655 and she is kept 'in steam' when-ever possible. XM655 is owned by John Littler of
Radarmoor, the airfield owners and operators. BAE Systems at Brough and Dunlop Aircraft Tyres have
both been actively involved in keeping Six-Five-Five a-rolling of late.
◆ Occasional ground running days - check via the info-line. Otherwise by prior arrangement. ✉ Derek
Powell, see above. ☎ info-line 07754 532454 web www.xm655.co.uk

❑ XM655	Vulcan B.2	G-VULC, ex N655AV ntu, 44, 101, 50, 12, 35, 9.	3-02

Others: See under Poole, Somerset, for more on the two Bulldogs ①.

❑ G-APPA		Chipmunk 22	ex Carlisle, Glasgow, N5703E, G-APPA, WP917, Glas UAS, 11 RFS, 8 RFS. Stored, dismantled.	6-01
❑ G-BLLV*		Slingsby T.67C	wreck. First noted 8-01	1-02
❑ G-BSYM		Tomahawk II	ex N2507V. Damaged 27-7-94. Dump by 4-01.	9-01
❑ 'N3320'*	'A'	Spitfire FSM	ex Winthorpe. Derelict. First noted 9-01.	1-02
❑ 'WZ868'	'H'	Chipmunk T.10	G-ARMF, ex Twyford, WG322, 63 GCF, Leeds UAS, 22 RFS. Damaged 19-6-96.	® 10-99
❑ XX634*	'T'	Bulldog T.1	ex Shawbury, Lpl UAS, Man UAS, EMUAS, CFS, 3 FTS, CFS, Cam UAS, 2 FTS. F/n 8-01.	① 1-02
❑ XX671*	'D'	Bulldog T.1	ex Shawbury, Birm UAS, 2 FTS. F/n 8-01.	① 1-02

WILTSHIRE

☞ Within the administrative county boundaries of Wiltshire can be found the unitary authority of
Thamesdown (centred upon Swindon).

BOSCOMBE DOWN AIRFIELD south of the A303 at Amesbury
Boscombe Down Museum Project: The first open day held by the project was staged on 1st July
2000 and was a great success. Since then a wide array of airframes and artefacts has been added to the
collection – telling Boscombe's rich tale of aviation history and trials of technology. As well as the
airframes, there are ground support vehicles, flight clothing, ejection seats, an Alpha Jet simulator etc.
    Notes: Many items from the Air Defence Collection (see Salisbury, Wilts) are on loan to the project –
marked ADC. The Auster frame is on loan from David Burke ①. The Lightning nose section is on loan
from Hugh Trevor ②. The MiG-21MF was acquired by Kelvin Petty (see also under Reading, Berks) in
mid-2001and presented to the project in late June ③.

Wiltshire concludes on page 257 after the second photo-spread, stay tuned..

NORFOLK

Jaguar GR.1 XX744
Coltishall, May 2001
Bob Dunn

Friendship 200 G-BHMY
Norwich Airport, August 2000
Roger Richards

Herald 214 G-ATIG
and Herald 210 G-AVEZ
Norwich Airport, August 2000
Phil Whalley

NORFOLK

Ford Transit (!) 'G-DRNT'
Norwich, October 2001
Dave Willis

NORTHAMPTONSHIRE

F-100D Super Sabre '63000'
Croughton, June 2001
Steve Hague

Harvard IIB 42-12417
Harrington, August 2001
David J Burke

NORTHAMPTONSHIRE
Robin HR.100 G-AZKN and
Cessna FRA.150L G-AZLL
Hinton-in-the-Hedges, July 2001
Ken Ellis

NOTTINGHAMSHIRE
Volmer VJ-24W G-MBBZ
Winthorpe, June 2001
Ken Ellis

**NORTHUMBERLAND
AND TYNESIDE**

Phantom FGR.2 XV460
Sunderland, August 2001
David E Thompson

NOTTINGHAMSHIRE

CockpitFest line-up, Winthorpe, June 2
From the rear: Canberras T.4 WJ865,
Bromsgrove; PR.7 WT536, Southampt
PR.9 XH177, resident; T.17 WH863,
resident; B(I)6 WT319, Lavendon;
Jet Provost T.4 XP624, Lavendon;
Canberra T.4 XH584, Doncaster.
Ken Ellis

Javelin FAW.8 XH992
Winthorpe, June 2001
Ken Ellis

Gazelle No.03 XW276
Winthorpe, June 2001
Ken Ellis

OXFORDSHIRE

Spitfire FSM 'EN343'
Benson, June 2001
Steve Hague

Wessex HC.2 XT681
Benson, May 2001
Dave Willis

Hunter GA.11 WV381
Culham, June 2001
Bob Dunn

SHROPSHIRE

Jet Provost T.3 XN549
Shawbury, July 2001
Roger Cook

Whirlwind HAR.10 XP351
Shawbury, April 2000
Alf Jenks

SOMERSET

EH.101 PP3 G-EHIL
Weston-super-Mare, October 2000
Ian Haskell

SOMERSET

Westland WG.30-200 'G-ELEC'
Weston-super-Mare, December 2001
Brian Roffee

MBB Bö105D G-PASB
Weston-super-Mare, October 2000
Ian Haskell

Bell 47H-1 OO-SHW
Weston-super-Mare, November 2001
Tony McCarthy

SOMERSET

Wessex HCC.4 XV733
Weston-super-Mare, November 2001
Tony McCarthy

Whirlwind HCC.12 XR486
Weston-super-Mare, November 2001
Tony McCarthy

Lynx 00-05, Lynx 800 G-LYNX,
Lynx 3 ZE477, Sycamore HR.14 XG54
Weston-super-Mare, May 2001
Tony McCarthy

Firefly TT.1 Z2033
Yeovilton, July 2000
Bob Turner

Bristol Scout REP N5419
Yeovilton, July 2000
Ken Ellis

Skyraider AEW.1 WV106
Yeovilton, April 2001
Ken Ellis

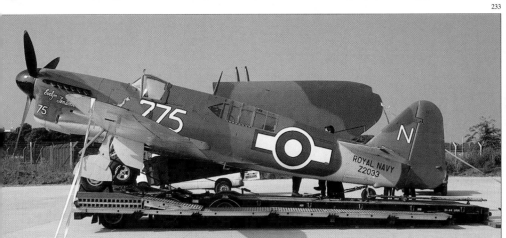

234

SOMERSET

Whirlwind HAS.7 XL853
Yeovilton, July 2000
Bob Turner

Hawker P.1127 XP980
Yeovilton, July 2000
Ken Ellis

P.531 XN334, Jet Provost T.3A XN46
P.1052 VX272, S.510 VV106,
Meteor TT.20 WM292,
Sea Vampire T.22 XA129, T-34C-1 07
Yeovilton, April 2001
Ken Ellis

SOMERSET

Harrier T.4 ZB601 and
Harrier GR.3 XV755
Yeovilton, June 2000
Bob Turner

Ohka 11 15-1585
Yeovilton, April 2001
Ken Ellis

SUFFOLK

Lightning F.1 XG329
Flixton, May 2001
Duncan Parnell

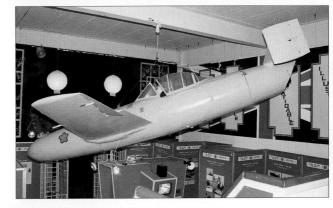

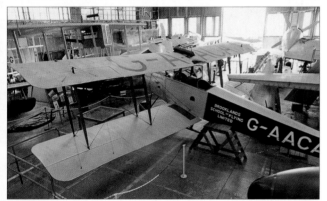

SUFFOLK

F-100D Super Sabre 42196
Flixton, May 2001
Duncan Parnell

SURREY

Avro 504 FSM 'G-AACA'
Brooklands, June 2001
Tony McCarthy

Hawker P.1127 XP984
Brooklands, August 2001
Roger Richards

SURREY

Jaguar GR.1 XX121
Charlwood, September 2000
Tony Wood

Lightning F.53 ZF579
Charlwood, January 2002
Tim R Badham

EAST SUSSEX

Tornado GR.1 ZD710
Robertsbridge, October 2001
David J Burke

WEST SUSSEX

Herald 209 G-CEXP
Gatwick, January 2001
Tim R Badham

Cessna 310G G-BHEH
Shoreham, August 2001
Phil Ansell

Navajo P G-BWDE
Shoreham, August 2001
Phil Ansell

WEST SUSSEX

TS-11 Iskra
Shoreham, August 2001
Phil Ansell

Lee-Richards Annular Biplane
BAPC.20
Shoreham, September 2000
Phil Ansell

Spitfire prototype FSM 'K5054'
Tangmere, July 2001
Tony McCarthy

WARWICKSHIRE

Trislander G-AZLJ
Coventry, July 2001
Stephen Reglar

Avro XIX Srs 2 G-AYWA
Coventry, January 2001
Stephen Reglar

Firecracker G-NDNI
Coventry, November 2000
Paul Singleton

WARWICKSHIRE

L.188CF Electra G-OFRT
Coventry, May 2001
Stephen Reglar

Slingsby Cadet TX.1 BGA.804
Coventry, December 2001
Brian Roffee

Devon C.2 VP959, Anson C.19 TX226
and (wall) Robin HR.200 G-BWRG
Coventry, January 2001
Stephen Reglar

WARWICKSHIRE

MiG-21SPS 959
Coventry, July 2001
Ian Haskell

Slingsby T.67C G-BLLV and
Spitfire FSM 'N3320'
Wellesbourne Mountford, August 200
Alf Jenks

WILTSHIRE

MiG-21MF 7708
Boscombe Down, June 2001
Mark Roberts

243

WILTSHIRE

Harrier T.4 XW269
Boscombe Down, May 2001
David J Burke

Wasp HAS.1 XT437
Boscombe Down, May 2001
David J Burke

Piper Warrior 161 G-BJBY
Old Sarum, December 2001
Es Robinson

WILTSHIRE

Bede BD-5B G-BGLB
Wroughton, May 2001
Dave Willis

Focke-Achgelis Fa330A-1 100509
Wroughton, May 2001
Tim R Badham

EAST YORKSHIRE

Cessna 150E G-ATAT
Hull, February 2002
Andy Wood

EAST YORKSHIRE

Hunter F.6 XF509
Marfleet, August 2001
Andy Wood

Bulldog
Paull, September 2001
Andy Wood

Cessna FRA.150M G-BDEW
Withernsea, February 2002
Andy Wood

SOUTH YORKSHIRE

Apache 160 G-APMY
Doncaster, June 2001
Ken Ellis

HS.125-1B/522 G-BOCB
Doncaster, October 2001
David J Burke

Sedbergh TX.1 WB969
Doncaster, October 2001
David J Burke

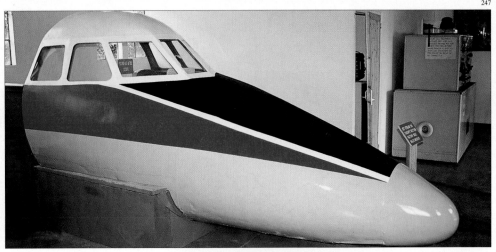

SOUTH YORKSHIRE

Jetstream EMU
Doncaster, August 2001
David J Burke

Bensen B.7 BAPC.275 and
HM.14 'Flea' 'G-AEKR'
Doncaster, June 2001
Ken Ellis

SCOTLAND

Tiger Cub 400 G-MMIX
Dumfries, September 2001
David S Johnstone

SCOTLAND

Hunter F.4 'XF506'
Dumfries, November 2000
Ken Ellis

Canberra T.4 Q497
Dumfries, September 2001
David S Johnstone

Goldwing G-MBPM
East Fortune, July 2001
Ken Ellis

SCOTLAND

Puss Moth VH-UQB
East Fortune, July 2001
Ken Ellis

Spitfire F.21 LA198
East Fortune, July 2000
Ken Ellis

WACO CG-4A
East Fortune, July 2001
Ken Ellis

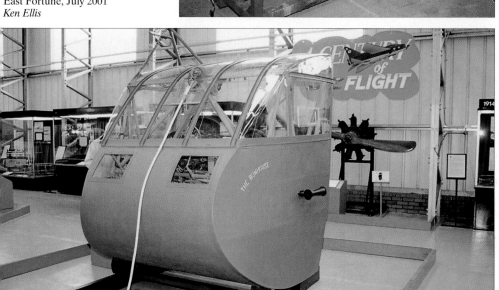

SCOTLAND

Gannet AEW.3 XL497
Prestwick, May 2001
David S Johnstone

Trident 1C G-ARPL
Gilmerton, January 2000
David S Johnstone

ATP c/n 2069
Prestwick, September 2000
David S Johnstone

251

SCOTLAND

Islander G-AXHE
Strathallan, May 2001
David S Johnstone

WALES

Javelin FAW.7 XH837
Caernarfon, May 2001
Ken Ellis

Sea Hawk FB.5 WM961
Caernarfon, May 2001
Ken Ellis

WALES

Dragon Rapide G-AJBJ
Chirk, December 2000
Tim R Badham

Bulldog T.1 XX687
Cardiff Airport, August 2001
Mike Freshney

Watkins CHW BAPC.47
Cardiff, August 2001
Mike Freshney

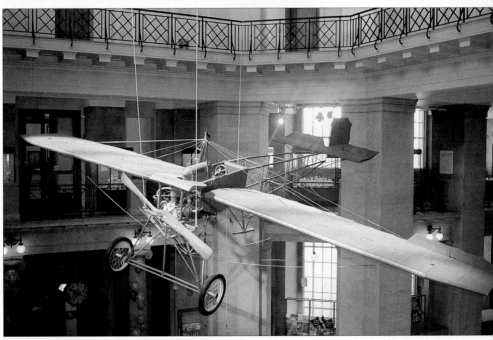

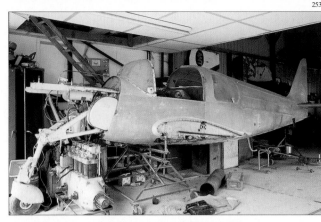

WALES

Norecrin G-BEDB
Chirk, December 2000
Tim R Badham

Gannet AS.4 XA460
Connah's Quay, October 2000
David S Johnstone

Dragon Rapide G-ACZE
Haverfordwest, July 2001
Alf Jenks

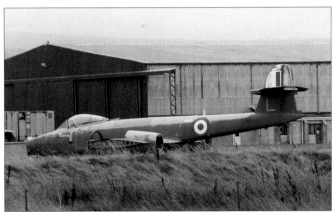

WALES

Canberra TT.18 WH887
Llanbedr, April 2001
Tony McCarthy

Meteor D.16 WH453
Llanbedr, October 2001
Tony McCarthy

VC-10 K.2 ZA143
St Athan, December 2001
Richard Tregear

WALES

Hawk T.1A FRP and VC-10 detritus
St Athan, December 2001
Richard Tregear

Jet Provost T.4 XS177
Valley, August 2001
Tony Wood

Hunter T.8C WV396
Valley, July 2000
Richard Tregear

CHANNEL ISLANDS
Trislander G-BDTN
Guernsey Airport, June 2001
Anthony Mills

IRELAND

HS.748-1/105 EI-BSF
Dublin Airport, April 2001
Lloyd P Robinson

Rallye 100ST EI-BCU and
ST-10 Diplomate EI-BUG
Weston, April 2001
Lloyd P Robinson

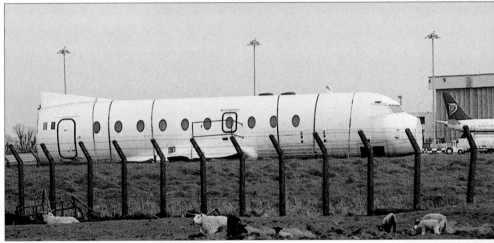

Wiltshire continued from page 224...

Departures: The anonymous red Hunter F.4 cockpit moved to Portishead, Somerset, during September 2000 and during early 2001 the anonymous Gnat nose moved to East Tilbury, Essex.
◆ Presently by prior arrangement *only*. ✉ Museum Project, c/o RAF Unit, Boscombe Down, SP4 0JF.

❑ WH876*		Canberra B.2 (mod)	ex Aberporth, Boscombe Down, A&AEE, 73, 207, 115. Nose. Arrived 22-5-01.	3-02
❑ WT534*		Canberra PR.7	8549M, ex Solihull, Halton, St Athan, 17. Nose. Spares for WH876. First noted 9-01.	3-02
❑ WT648*		Hunter F.1	ex Salisbury, Kexborough, Stock, St Athan 7530M, DFLS. Nose.	ADC 3-02
❑ XF113		Swift F.7	ex Salisbury, Bath, Frome, Farnborough, ETPS, A&AEE, HS. Nose.	ADC 3-02
❑ XE601*		Hunter F.6	ex RAE, ETPS, Hawker. Last flight 15-7-99.	3-02
❑ XF994	'873'	Hunter T.8C	ex Apprentices, Shawbury, Yeovilton, FRADU, 759, 229 OCU, AFDS, 66.	3-02
❑ XG290		Hunter F.6	ex Salisbury, Bournemouth, Bruntingthorpe, Swanton Morley, Bentley Priory, Halton 8711M, Laarbruch SF, A&AEE. Nose.	ADC 3-02
❑ XL564*		Hunter T.7	ex ETPS, HS, 229 OCU, Hawker. Nose. Poor state. Crashed 6-8-98. First noted 5-01.	3-02
❑ XL609*		Hunter T.7	ex Firbeck, Elgin, Lossiemouth 8866M, 12, 216, 237 OCU, 4 FTS, 56. Nose. 12 Sqn c/s.	ADC 3-02
❑ XN726		Lightning F.2A	ex Rayleigh, Foulness, Farnborough, 8545M, Gütersloh, 92, 19. Nose.	② 3-02
❑ XR650	'28'	Jet Provost T.4	ex DERA, Halton 8459M, SoRF, CAW, CATCS, 3 FTS, CAW, 7 FTS.	3-02
❑ XS790		Andover CC.2	ex DERA, Queen's Flight. Nose.	3-02
❑ XT437*	'423'	Wasp HAS.1	ex Lee-on-Solent, *Diomede*, *Arethusa* and *Olna* Flts. First noted 6-01.	3-02
❑ XT597		Phantom FG.1	ex DERA, A&AEE.	3-02
❑ XV401 02	'I'	Phantom FGR.2	ex DERA, Wattisham, 74, 23, 29, 228 OCU, 56, 111, 41.3-	
❑ XX343		Hawk T.1	ex DERA, ETPS. Crashed 8-4-97. Hulk.	3-02
❑ XX919*		BAC 111-402	ex DERA, RAE, D-AFWC ntu, PI-C-1121. Nose.	3-02
❑		Sea Hawk	ex DERA. Nose. *Possibly* WV910.	3-02
❑ A-533	ZD486	FMA Pucará	ex Salisbury, St Mary Bourne, Middle Wallop, Boscombe Down, Abingdon, Finningley, Stanley, Argentine AF. Nose.	ADC 3-02
❑ 7708*		MiG-21MF	ex airfield, Fairford, Slovak AF, Czech AF.	③ 3-02
❑ *		Alpha Jet SIM	—	3-02

Defence Science and Technology Laboratory (DS&TL) Yet still another name change, effective from 1st July 2001. The former Defence Evaluation and Research Agency was reorganised on this date with the establishment of a private company – QinetiQ – and the DS&TL. The company is planned to be floated on the stock market sometime in 2002 and become the 'trading arm' of the organisation. (You pronounce it kinetic, apparently.) DS&TL is the name given to the bits the government does not wish to sell off to the private sector. Just which of the former DERA sites will be QinetiQ or DS&TL or a mix of both is as clear as the company's new name!. On 10th August 2001 the end of a magnificent era came about. ETPS Hunter T.7 XL612 made the last flight of the breed in UK military hands. A decision awaits its fate ①. The 'Chippax' is used by the **1011 Squadron**, ATC ②. BAC 111-402 XX919 was scrapped following spares recovery on 6th July 2000. The nose section moved to the museum project, above. The former Slovak Air Force MiG-21MF was finally disposed of in mid-2001 and moved on loan to the museum project, above. Hunter T.8C XF994 moved to the museum, above, by early 2002.

❑ WP863	Chipmunk T.10 PAX	8360M, ex Bournemouth, Marlborough, Chippenham, Shawbury, CoAT Hamble G-ATJI, RAFC, 664, RAFC.	② 6-01

❑	XF358	'870'	Hunter T.8C	ex Shawbury, Yeovilton, FRADU, 112. Stored.	8-01
❑	XL612*		Hunter T.7	ex ETPS, 8, 1417 Flt, APS Sylt. Last flight 10-8-01.	11-01
❑	XL629		Lightning T.4	ex ETPS, A&AEE. Gate guardian.	7-01
❑	XV784		Harrier GR.3	ex Wittering 8909M, 233 OCU, 4, 1, 4. Dam 2-4-86. Nose.	6-01
❑	XV806	'E'	Harrier GR.3	ex Culdrose, A2607 [3], A2606, Cosford, 4, 3, 233 OCU.	7-98
❑	XW269	'BD'	Harrier T.4	ex Wittering, SAOEU, 233 OCU, 3, 1,	
				233 OCU, 4. BDRT	8-01
❑	XW902*	'H'	Gazelle HT.3	ex Shawbury, 2 FTS, 18, CFS. Arrived 23-11-01.	11-01
❑	XW906	'J'	Gazelle HT.3	ex Shawbury, 2 FTS, CFS. Apprentice school.	8-01
❑	XZ101	'D'	Jaguar GR.1A	9282M, ex St Athan, Coltishall, 41, 2, 6, 2.	1-00
❑	ZA804*	'I'	Gazelle HT.3	ex Shawbury, 2 FTS, CFS. Arrived 29-11-01.	11-01
❑	XZ933*	'T'	Gazelle HT.3	ex Shawbury, 2 FTS, CFS. Arrived by 3-01.	11-01
❑	ZJ651*		Alpha Jet	ex Furstenfeldbruck, Luftwaffe 98+42, 41+42.	
				Arrived 30-3-00.	8-01
❑	ZJ652*		Alpha Jet	ex Furstenfeldbruck, Luftwaffe 41+09. Arr 4-00.	11-01
❑	ZJ653*		Alpha Jet	ex Furstenfeldbruck, Luftwaffe 40+22. Arr 4-00.	11-01
❑	ZJ654*		Alpha Jet	ex Furstenfeldbruck, Luftwaffe 41+02. Arr 30-3-00.	11-01
❑	ZJ655*		Alpha Jet	ex Furstenfeldbruck, Luftwaffe 41+19. Arr 12-99.	11-01
❑	ZJ656*		Alpha Jet	ex Furstenfeldbruck, Luftwaffe 41+40. Arr 24-2-00.	11-01
❑	*		Scout AH.1	Dump. Pod.	6-01
❑	162958*		AV-8B Harrier II	ex St Athan, USMC, VMA-214. Fuselage, tests.	1-02

HORNINGSHAM east of the B3092, west of Warminster
Longleat House: Cameron O-84 G-BAST returned to Lancing, West Sussex.

KEEVIL AERODROME south of the A361, south-west of Devizes
Bannerdown Gliding Club: Kittiwake G-ATXN was flying again by February 2001. Grasshopper TX.1 XA225 arrived on 27th February 2001 but moved to Upavon, Wilts, by December 2001.

❑	G-POOL		ARV Super 2	ex Kemble, G-BNHA. CoA 9-9-90.	2-02
❑	BAA*		T.8 Tutor	BGA.804, ex VM589, XE761. CoA 3-97.	2-02
❑	BJJ*		T.45 Swallow	BGA.1003, ex Lasham. Wreck. Arrived 14-1-01.	2-02
❑	CHM*		Schleicher K.4	BGA.1556, ex Lasham, D-5015. Stored.	2-02
❑	DKV*		Grob Astir CS	BGA.2184. CoA 1-99. Stored.	2-02
❑	EAZ		Schleicher K8B	BGA.2543, ex D-5256, D-KANO, D-5256.	
				Crashed 25-7-97. Wreck, stored in rafters.	2-02
❑	EPR*		Hutter H-17	BGA.2847. Ex PH-269. CoA 6-97. Stored.	2-02
❑	GEQ*		SZD-12A Mucha	BGA.3776. Ex SP-2001, Bury St Edmunds,	
				Tibbenham. Stored. Arrived 12-01.	2-02
❑	WB981*	FFZ	Sedbergh TX.1	BGA.3238. Ex Aston Down. Fuselage. Arrived 9-01.	2-02
❑	WZ793		Grasshopper TX.1	ex Croydon, Basingstoke, Taunton. ®	2-02
❑	XA240		Grasshopper TX.1	ex Yeovilton, Locking, Radley. Stored.	2-02
❑	XA244		Grasshopper TX.1	ex Lasham, Cosford, Walsall. Stored.	2-02
❑	XA295*		Grasshopper TX.1	ex Fareham. Stored. Arrived 12-01.	2-02
❑	XA310*		Cadet TX.3	ex Milfield. Arrived 11-00. ®	2-02

LYNEHAM AIRFIELD west of the A3102, south-west of Wooton Bassett
RAF Lyneham: The Dakota is being prepared for display as a memorial to the RAF Air Dispatch organisation outside 47 Air Despatch Squadron, RLC. The dump is occupied by a large, all-steel 'DC-10' look-alike. During 2000 Trident 2E G-AVFK fuselage had moved on – destination/fate unknown.

❑	G-AMPO*		C-47B-30-DK	ex Coventry, Air Atlantique, LN-RTO, G-AMPO,	
				KN566, Oakington SF, 77, 62, Waterbeach SF,	
				1381 CU, 133 CU, 238, 44-76853. CoA 29-3-97.	
				Arrived 22-9-01.	2-02
❑	XK699		Comet C.2	7971M, ex Henlow, Lyneham, 216. Gate.	2-02

MELKSHAM on the A350 south of Chippenham
Adrian Brimson and **John Phillips**: The pair are seeking original documents for this aircraft.
◆ Viewing by prior permission *only*. ☎ 01225 702485

❑ XL765*	Skeeter AOP.12	ex Northants, Clapham, Leverstock Green, Leamington Spa, Leeds, Rotherham, Wroughton, 17F, 654, 651, SARO. Arrived 22-7-01.	®	2-02

NETHERAVON AIRFIELD on the A345 north of Amesbury
No.7 Regiment, AAC:

❑ XT150	Sioux AH.1	7883M, ex Middle Wallop, comp with 7884M. Gate.	1-02
❑ XV136	Scout AH.1	ex Almondbank, Wroughton. Gate.	1-02

OAKSEY PARK AERODROME south of Cirencester, east of the A429
The Wasp that is/was stored here, has build number WA/B/27 and is almost certainly ex South African.

❑ –	Wasp HAS.1	forward fuselage.	5-99

OLD SARUM AERODROME east of the A345 north of Salisbury
Cessna FRA.150L G-BCVG was up and flying again by autumn 1998 and by mid-2000 Super Cub 135 G-BKJB was in similar fettle. By July 2000 Volmer VJ-24W G-MBBZ had moved to Winthorpe, Notts.

❑ G-ACDI	Tiger Moth	ex Shoreham, BB742, 29 EFTS, 21 EFTS, 13 EFTS, 4 EFTS, 13 EFTS, G-ACDI.	®	10-99
❑ G-BJBY	PA-28 Warrior 161	ex N8415L. Crashed 23-11-97. Wreck.		4-02
❑ G-BKRL	Leopard 001	ex Cranfield. CoA 14-12-91.		7-00
❑ G-BRTK*	PT-13D Kaydet	ex Swanton Morley, N16716, 42-17786. CoA 24-4-93. First noted 3-00.	®	3-00
❑ RA81370*	Yak-18T	damaged. Stored.		8-01
❑ XW130*	'R' Scout AH.1	G-BWJW. ex Thruxton, Fleetlands, 666, 656, 657, 665. CoA 18-11-00. Stored.		8-01

SALISBURY
Air Defence Collection (ADC): Tony Dyer is heavily involved in the Boscombe Down museum project – which see. The cockpit of Hunter F.1 WT648 moved to Boscombe Down, Wilts, by mid-2001. Restoration of the excellent Hurricane project is the main concentration. This will (one day!) be a complete airframe, Tony has 85% so far! A similar project involves a Typhoon, work on which is being undertaken off-site by David D Dyer. By March 2002, the cockpit of Lightning F.6 XS922 had moved on, to an Essex-based collector.
◆ ADC airframes are stored in a variety of locations. Viewing by prior permission only. ✉ Enquiries via Tony Dyer, care of the Boscombe Down Museum Project - see above.

❑ P3554	Hurricane I	ex Swanage, 607, 213, 56, 32. Shot down 5-10-40.	®	3-02
❑	Typhoon	cockpit project.	off-site ®	3-02

SWINDON
Richard Galazka: Restoration of the Harvard is believed to continue.

❑ KF435	Harvard IIB	ex Ottershaw, Wycombe AP, Camberley, Sandhurst, 1 FTS, 2 FTS, 22 SFTS, 20 FTS, 11 (P)AFU.	®	2-96

Others: A Cadet glider is stored, possibly as spares for a motor conversion.

❑ WT899	Cadet TX.3	ex Rush Green, Benington, Syerston, 661 VGS, 643 VGS, Cosford, St Athan.	4-99

TROWBRIDGE on the A361 south-east of Bath
E J Shanley and Sons: The Lynx should still be found in the scrapyard in Green Lane.

❑	Lynx EMU	–	2-02

UPAVON AIRFIELD on the A342 south-east of Devizes
Wyvern Gliding Club:

❑ G-BICT*	Evans VP-1	CoA 20-2-97. Stored.	1-02
❑ D-4019*	Bergfalke II	last flown 1996. Stored.	1-02
❑ XA225*	Grasshopper TX.1	ex Keevil, Petersfield. First noted 12-01.	12-01

WARMINSTER on the A36 east of Frome
Restoration of the Stampe is *assumed* to continue.

❑ G-AYDR	SNCAN SV-4C	ex Raveningham, F-BCLG. CoA 27-3-75.	®	8-93

WINTERBOURNE GUNNER east of the A338 north-east of Salisbury
Defence Science and Technology Laboratory (DS&TL – yet still another name change, effective from 1st July 2001. See under Boscombe Down, Wilts, for still more interesting alphabetic contortions): running was (is?) known as the Defence Nuclear, Biological and Chemical Centre. Wessex HAS.3 XS862 was put up for tender in July 2000 and was removed shortly thereafter.

WROUGHTON AIRFIELD on the A4361 south of Swindon
Science Museum Air Transport Collection and Storage Facility (ScM): With many thanks to Richard Cawsey, we can record a new airframe here. The Hartman Ornithopter was an experimental man-powered device designed and built by Donald Campbell at Hungerford to the order of Emiel Hartman. It was delivered to Cranfield, Beds, for trials on 16th October 1959. It was tested by being towed into the air behind a car, then released to practice flapping while gliding to the ground. It has been with the museum since 1993. Richard describes it as "derigged but appears to be complete and in good condition". (The Donald Campbell involved was the one who went on to found Campbell Gyroplanes of Cricket fame.) Available for disposal since 1994, Pilcher Hawk REP BAPC.57 moved to St Albans, Herts, in late 2001.
◆ Occasional open days and special events. ✉ Science Museum, Wroughton Airfield, Swindon, SN4 9NS ☎ 01793 814466 **web** www.sciencemuseum.org.uk/wroughton

❑ G-AACN	HP Gugnunc	ex Hayes and K1908.	3-02
❑ G-ACIT	DH.84 Dragon	ex Southend, Beagle, ANT Blackpool, BEA,	
		Scottish, Highland. CoA 25-5-74.	3-02
❑ G-AEHM	HM.14 'Flea'	ex Hayes, Whitchurch, Bristol.	3-02
❑ G-ALXT	Dragon Rapide	ex Strathallan, Staverton, 4R-AAI, CY-AAI,	
		G-ALXT, NF865, 5 MU, 18 MU, MCS.	3-02
❑ G-ANAV	Comet 1A	ex South Kensington. CF-CUM. Nose.	3-02
❑ G-APWY	Piaggio P.166	ex Southend, Marconi. CoA 14-3-81.	3-02
❑ G-APYD	Comet 4B	ex Dan-Air, Olympic SX-DAL, G-APYD,	
		BEA. CoA 3-8-79.	3-02
❑ G-ATTN*	Piccard HAB	ex South Kensington, Hayes, South Kensington.	3-02
❑ G-AVZB	Z-37 Cmelak	ex Southend, OK-WKQ. CoA 5-4-84.	3-02
❑ G-AWZM	Trident 3B-101	ex Heathrow, BA, BEA. CoA 13-12-85.	3-02
❑ G-BBGN*	Cameron A-375	ex South Kensington, Hayes, South Kensington.	
		Gondola. *Daffodil II.*	3-02
❑ G-BGLB	Bede BD-5B	ex Booker. CoA 4-8-81.	3-02
❑ G-MMCB	Pathfinder II	microlight.	3-02
❑ G-RBOS	Colt AS-105	hot air airship. CoA 6-3-87.	3-02
❑ EI-AYO	DC-3A-197	ex Shannon, N655GP, N65556, N225JB,	
		N8695SE, N333H, NC16071.	3-02
❑ N18E	Boeing 247	ex Wings and Wheels, Orlando, Sky Tours, NC18E,	
		NC18, NC13340 CAA, United/National A/T.	3-02
❑ N7777G	L-749A-79	G-CONI, ex Dublin, Lanzair, KLM PH-LDT, PH-TET.	3-02
❑ OO-BFH*	Piccard Gas	ex South Kensington, Hayes, South Kensington.	
		Gondola.	3-02
❑ VP975	Devon C.2/2	ex RAE Farnborough, A&AEE, CCCF, 19 GCF, CPE.	3-02

❑ XP505	Gnat T.1	ex South Kensington, RAE Bedford, MinTech, Dunsfold, CFS.	3-02
❑ 100509	Fa 330A-1	ex South Kensington, Farnborough.	3-02
❑ —* BAPC.52	Lilienthal Glider	ex South Kensington, Hayes, South Kensington, Oxford. Original. Stored.	3-02
❑ — BAPC.162	Manflier MPA	major parts.	3-02
❑ — BAPC.172	Chargus Midas	powered hang glider.	3-02
❑ — BAPC.173	Grasshopper	hang glider.	3-02
❑ — BAPC.174	Bensen B.7	gyroglider.	3-02
❑ — BAPC.188	Cobra 88	hang glider.	3-02
❑ —* BAPC.276	Hartman Orni'	ex Cranfield. See above. Here since 1993. Stored.	3-02

YATESBURY north of the A4, east of Calne
Meteor Flight: Considerable progress is being made with WA591. Meteor WF825 is now the property of the flight and another T.7 has been acquired for spares use.
◆ Visits possible by prior arrangement *only*. ✉ Mark Jones, 42 The Ham, Westbury, BA13 4HD e-mail flytst@aol.com

❑ WA591	Meteor T.7	G-BWMF, ex Woodvale, St Athan 7917M, Kemble, CAW, 8 FTS, 5 FTS, CAW, 12 FTS, 215 AFS, 208 AFS, 203 AFS, 226 OCU, CFE.	® 3-02
❑ WF825	'A' Meteor T.7	ex Malmesbury, Monkton Farleigh, Lyneham 8359M, Kemble, CAW, 33, 603. Stored.	3-02
❑ WL360	'G' Meteor T.7	ex Staverton, Hucclecote, Locking 7920M, 229 OCU, 1, Wattisham SF, 211 AFS, 210 AFS, 215 AFS.	3-02
❑ WL405*	Meteor T.7	ex Chalgrove, Farnborough, BCCS, 1 GCF, 231 OCU, Wittering SF, JCU, Hemswell CF. Cockpit/centre section. Arrived 30-10-01.	3-02
❑ WS760	Meteor NF.14	ex Loughborough, Cranfield, Bushey, Duxford, Brampton, Upwood, 7964M, 1 ANS, 64, 237 OCU.	3-02

EAST YORKSHIRE

☛ Within the administrative county boundary of East Yorkshire can be found the unitary authority of the City of Kingston upon Hull.

BEVERLEY
Museum of Army Transport (MoAT): The Beverley continues to dominate the car park. By mid-2001 it was beginning to look on the 'tired' side. It was given a full repaint in unrepresentative, but from a conservation point of view, very welcome, repaint in sand/brown/black 'tactical' colours in October 2001. Sadly, the sand/brown camouflage was applied in wrap-around style to the wings. As well as the many exhibits within the museum, the 'Bev' itself holds others inside itself!
◆ Located in Flemingate, Beverley, and well signed within the town, close to the Minster. Open 10am to 5pm every day, closed over Xmas and New Year. ✉ Flemingate, Beverley, HU17 0NG ☎ 01482 860445 fax 01482 872767 web www.museum/armytransport.co.uk

❑ XB259	Beverley C.1	ex Paull, Luton, RAE, Blackburns, G-AOAI.	3-02

The **Beverley Association** – custodians of a restoration fund for XB259 – serve to unite all those who served in and on 'Bevs' and are working towards the continued well-being and long term restoration of the last intact example. (B R Holt, 46 Aller Brake Road, Newton Abbot, TQ12 4NL.)

BREIGHTON AERODROME in between Bubwith and Breighton, east of Selby
Real Aeroplane Company and **Museum**: As will be seen below, several of the RAC aircraft have gone to the sunnier climes of Florida, perhaps only as a mid-term move. This delightful aerodrome remains a hive of activity with a wide selection of residents and a warm welcome!

Notes: Aircraft owned and operated by 'Taff' Smith or Rob Fleming plus the collection assembled by Nigel Ponsford (NHP) for the up-coming museum and any other aircraft under long-term restoration are listed here. (See also under Wigan, Gtr Man, and Selby, N Yorks, for other elements of Nigel's collection.) The arrival of the Ward Elf in February 2002 completed the 'set' of aircraft built by Mick Ward, joining the 'Flea' and the Gnome ①. Close inspection of the Buchón shows that was previously C4K-154, not the C4K-102 that is given as its 'official' identity. That would make it a 'static' during the *Battle of Britain* film and not G-AWHK. Anyone else care to enter this fray? ②

Departures: Involved in the 'massed' exodus to the USA were: Jungmeister G-BUTX and Nanchang CJ-6A '2028' G-BVVF both by 10-00; and Spitfire PR.XI PL965 (G-MKXI) crated during 8-01, left 7-9-01. Also T-6 52-8543 (G-BUKY) which was not listed in *W&R17*, left for the USA on 20-11-01. Wassmer D.120 G-BMDS, under restoration off-site, was flying by late 2001. Jungmann G-TAFF was resident at Sherburn, by late 2001. Fa 330A-1 100502 is stored at <u>Selby</u>, N Yorks

◆ Signed from Bubwith on the A163. Open 10.30am to 4pm, weekends and Bank hols, Easter to October. Other times by prior arrangement. Different admission rates apply to fly-ins/airshows. ✉ The Aerodrome, Breighton, Selby, YO8 7DH ☎ / fax 01757 228838 web www.realaero.aol.com

❏ G-AEVS	Aeronca 100 ✈	Composite, inc parts from G-AEXD. *Jeeves*.	NHP	3-02
❏ G-AMAW	Luton Minor	ex Batley, Old Warden, Hitchin. CoA 6-8-88.	NHP	3-02
❏ G-AOBG	Somers-K SK.1	ex Benington, Eaton Bray, Cranfield. CoA 6-6-58.	NHP	3-02
❏ G-AXEI	Ward Gnome	ex East Kirkby, Tattershall.	NHP ①	3-02
❏ G-BVGZ*	Fokker Dr I REP	ex Netheravon. Arrived 22-3-02.		3-02
❏ G-BWUE*	HA-1112-M1L Buchón	ex Sandown, Breighton, Duxford, N9938, *Battle of Britain*, G-AWHK, Spanish AF C4K-102. Fuselage arrived 20-11-00, wings 17-11-01.	②	3-02
❏ G-BYPY	Ryan ST3-KR ✈	ex F-AZEV, N18926.		3-02
❏ G-MJLK*	Dragonfly 250	Stored, dismantled.		3-02
❏ G-MMUL*	Ward Elf	ex Newark area. Citroen Ami. Arr 17-2-02.	NHP ①	3-02
❏ G-MWRK*	S-6 Coyote II	Damaged 7-99. Stored.		3-02
❏ 'F50'	HM.14 'Flea'	taxiable. Built by Mick Ward. Citroen Ami.	NHP ①	3-02
❏ U-99	Jungmeister ✈	G-AXMT, ex N133SJ, G-AXMT, HB-MIY, Swiss AF U-99.		3-02
❏ T9738	Magister I ✈	G-AKAT, ex F-AZOR, G-AKAT, T9738, 24 EFTS, 15 EFTS.		3-02
❏ 'BE417' 'AL-X'	Hurricane XII ✈	G-HURR, ex Duxford, Brooklands, RCAF 5589. Night-fighter colours.		3-02
❏ 97+04*	Elster B ✈	G-APVF, ex D-EEQX, 97+04, D-EJUH. CoA 1-7-98.		3-02
❏ '18'-5395'	L-18C Cub ✈	G-CUBJ, ex PH-MBF, PH-NLF, RNethAF R-43, 52-2436.		3-02

Locally: On 22nd August 2000 Auster 5 TJ534 (G-AKSY) moved to Breighton 'proper' ready for flight test. It took to the air again on 17th December and now flies from the aerodrome.

BROUGH AIRFIELD south of the A63 west of Hull
BAE Systems: Like St Athan, Wales, Brough is another venue that has been littered with Hawk Fuselage Replacement Programme (FRP) detritus. This complex new-for-old scheme is largely leaving shells that are best ignored, or the Hawk population will suffer from dual or even *triple* personalities! Essentially, these discarded items have not yet developed sufficient longevity to merit a listing – though the situation is being monitored for the future. The bulk of the hardware are *rear* fuselage sections, which do not come under the defined scope of *W&R* anyway. The likelihood is that all will be swiftly scrapped once the programme is completed. The Blackburn Lincock full-size model was built in 40 days by factory workers for the July 1999 open day ①. Swordfish NF389 will be rebuilt to ASR.III status, complete with under-fuselage radome ②.

Departures: Hawk T.1A XX254 nose to St Athan, Wales, 7-01; anonymous Harrier T.2 nose was scrapped;T-45 Goshawk D.01 rig returned to the USA in 1998.

☐ 'G-EBVO'	Lincock FSM	—	①	3-02
☐ G-AEBJ	Blackburn B-2 ✈	airworthy. Operated by BAe.		3-02
☐ NF389	Swordfish III	ex Yeovilton, Brough, Lee-on-Solent.	® ②	3-02
☐ XV168	Buccaneer S.2B	ex Lossiemouth, 12, 208, 12, FAA. 12 Sqn c/s.		3-02
☐ XX736	Jaguar GR.1	9110M, ex Coltishall, Shawbury, Warton, G-27-327, Indian AF JI013, 6, 226 OCU, JOCU. Fatigue tests.		3-02
☐ ZD353	'H' Harrier GR.5	ex Dunsfold, Brough, Wittering, 233 OCU, 1. Damaged 29-7-91. Undercarriage test rig.		3-02
☐	Jaguar GR.1	nose.		3-02
☐	Hawk	fatigue rig. T.1A life extension test.		3-02
☐	Hawk Mk.203	forward fuselage.		3-02
☐	Harrier GR.5	fatigue rig.		3-02
☐	Eurofighter 2000	fatigue rig, two-seater variant. Nose only.		3-02
☐	Eurofighter 2000	fatigue rig, single-seater cockpit only.		3-02

GRINDALE north-west of Bridlington
British Skysports: The para-trainer Cessna is still in use with the club.

☐ G-BRID	Cessna U.206A	ex N4874F. CoA 20-5-93. Para-trainer.	7-00

HULL
Anderson Antiques: In Wincolmlee, on the banks of the river. Since December 2001 a yellow Cessna has been here and on offer. It was for sale at £1,500 but – so they story goes! – during the January 2002 gales, one wing blew off and ended up floating down the river. The price became £1,000!

☐ [G-ATAT]*	Cessna 150E	ex Shobdon, Billericay, Andrewsfield, Southend, N3041J. CoA 29-7-85. See above.	2-02

Offshore Training Association: At the Malmo Road training school a helicopter fuelling and rescue trainer is in use. It is based on a Daihatsu van (to get the fuelling system realistic), has rotor blades and the 'reggie' 'G-HOTA', but will never get a CoA!

LECONFIELD AIRFIELD on the A164 north of Beverley
Normandy Barracks: Whirlwind HAR.3 XG577 was tendered and scrapped during early 2001.

LINLEY HILL AERODROME or Beverley, west of Leven, off the A165 north-east of Beverley.

☐ G-AYBW	Cessna FA.150K	ex Perth. Crashed 8-10-72. Fuselage.	9-01
☐ G-BAIP	Cessna F.150L	Crashed 30-5-95. Dismantled.	9-01

MARFLEET on the A1033 east of Kingston upon Hull
Humbrol Ltd: The Hunter guards the factory.

☐ XF509	Hunter F.6	ex Chivenor 8708M, Thurleigh, 4FTS, MoA, AFDS, 54.	8-01

OTTRINGHAM on the A1033 east of Hull

☐ G-BRPG	Cessna 120	ex N72703, NC72703. CoA 29.8.94. Stored.	7-99

PAULL on minor road south of Hedon
Fort Paull Armouries: Part of a set-piece depicting a scene from World War Two is a Bulldog cockpit. A plate on the firewall reads 'SAL/BD/0153' – any help?

☐ –*	Bulldog	cockpit, see above.	9-01

PRESTON on the B1239 north of Hedon
The Varsity nose is still kept at the filling station-cum-scrapyard.
❑ WL627   Varsity T.1   ex Hull, Newton 8488M, 6 FTS, 2 ANS, 1 ANS,
                                          BCBS. Nose.   2-02

THWING east of the B1249/B1253 junction, north of Great Driffield
A strip in the area here holds an Auster rebuild project.
❑ G-AHCK*   J/1N Alpha   ex Spilsby, Croft, Skegness. Damaged 14-9-91.   ® 3-02

WITHERNSEA on the A1033 east of Hull
Oblivion: Within the night-club can be found a 'crashed' Cessna.
❑ G-BDEW*   Cessna FRA.150M Crashed 13-8-96.   2-02

NORTH YORKSHIRE

☛ Within the administrative boundary of North Yorkshire is the unitary authority of the City of York.

BAGBY AERODROME on the A19 south-east of Thirsk
Tomahawk G-BGRR was flying again by mid-1999 – correcting *W&R17*. Cessna 152 II G-BRBF was
doing the same by 2001.

CARLTON MOOR on minor road south-east of Carlton-in-Cleveland
Carlton Moor Gliding Club: The glider store has increased.
❑ BAC*   Skylark 3B   BGA.806, ex RNGSA 'CU19', BGA.806. CoA 5-97.   3-00
❑ DUC   Carmam M.100S   BGA.2383, ex F-CCSA. CoA 5-88. Stored.   3-00
❑ EAL   Rhonlerche II   BGA.2530, ex PH-331. CoA 9-91. Stored.   3-00

CARTHORPE west of the A1, south-east of Bedale
Camp Hill Activity Centre: A long forgotten Norecrin is here posed in a 'crash' position on an
island within the estate – corporate kickers and movers are supposed to find a method of rescuing the
crew. Simple, use your WAP to dial 999 and retire to the pub. Team-building? Who needs it!
♦ Access by prior arrangement *only*. ☎ 01845 567788 fax 01845 567065 web www.camphill.co.uk
❑ G-BHXJ*   Norecrin II   ex 'London', F-BEMX. Arrived 1999.   3-02

DISHFORTH AIRFIELD on the A1, west of Ripon
No.9 Regiment, Army Air Corps: SF-28A G-BARZ was flying again by 2000. The existence of
Scout AH.1 XT620 on the dump in any substantial manner beyond late 1995 is very much doubted and
it is best deleted. Scout AH.1 XW616 has moved on by 2000 – scrapped?

ELVINGTON off the A1079 south-east of York
Yorkshire Air Museum (YAM): Acquisition of the Harrier GR.3 was a major 'coup', many
congratulations to those who achieved its arrival and the subsequent acquisition of a Pegasus to complete
it. The Dakota is part of an increasing airborne forces theme. YAM is another museum that is collecting
civilian sporting and general aviation types – a development to be applauded.
    Several of the airframes listed below are on loan to YAM. With the removal of the Venom NF.3, the
Night-Fighter Preservation Team devolved down to the superb Mosquito which has been brought within
the main listing from this edition. The helicopters of the Yorkshire Helicopter Preservation Group are
likewise on loan to YAM, but – as per policy throughout this book over decades (!) – the compiler
wishes to maintain their listing as a separate entity.

Notes: The 'Flea' is on loan from Dave Allan ①. The 'Grain Kitten' REP built by Bill Sneesby, is actually a PV.8 Eastchurch Kitten REP ②. The Spitfire FSM 'guards' the memorial room of the **609 (West Riding) Squadron Association** ③. The Mosquito is on loan from Tony Agar and is a complex composite, using the nose section of HJ711; the rear fuselage of TT.35 RS715 from Elstree; the centre section from Mk XVI PF498 from Leyland; and the outer wings of T.3 VA878 from St Davids ④. The Halifax re-creation is a complex composite: using the centre section from former 58 Squadron Mk II HR792 which came to grief in a take-off accident at Stornoway on 13th January 1945; the wings from Hastings C.1 TG536 from Catterick; myriad Halifax detail parts; Hercules engines courtesy of the French Air Force and ex-Noratlas, plus new-build nose and rear section and many other elements ⑤. The Victor is on loan from André Tempest and team. It regularly taxies. They also have a Victor procedure trainer ⑥. The Lightning is on loan from Peter Chambers ⑦. Buccaneer S.2B XX901 is owned by the **Buccaneer Aircrew Association** (Dave Herriott, 84 Lees Gardens, Maidenhead, SL6 4NT). BAA serves to link all former Buccaneer aircrew ⑧. The original nose of the Hadrian is still to be found at Bacup, Lancs ⑨. The Bf 109G FSM was built by Danny Thornton of Garforth, W Yorks ⑩.

Departures: Venom NF.3 WX788 left for storage locally on 13th February 2002, before settling at Doncaster, S Yorks. Waco CG-4 Hadrian REP '43-241170', previously on the set of *Saving Private Ryan* arrived from Weybourne, Norfolk, and was first noted here in July 2000. During mid-2001 it left the site, reportedly having 'left the country' (Netherlands?).

◆ Signed from the A64 southern York ring, at the A64/A166/A1079 junction. Open 10.30am to 4pm weekdays, 10.30am to 5pm weekends. Late Jun to late Sep 10am to 5pm daily. Winter opening times vary, please check. ✉ YAM, Elvington, York, YO41 4AU ☎ 01904 608595 fax 01904 608246 web www.yorkshireairmuseum.co.uk

❏ 'G-AAAH'	DH.60 Moth FSM	BAPC.270, *Jason*. Unveiled 7-5-00.		3-02
❏ 'G-AFFI'	HM.14 'Flea'	BAPC.76, ex Hemswell, Cleethorpes, Nostell, Rawdon.	①	3-02
❏ G-AJOZ*	Argus II	ex Woodhall Spa, Tattershall, Wigan, Market Drayton, Wigan, Southend, Sywell, FK338, Kemble, ATA 2 FP, 42-32142. Cr 16-8-62. Stored. Arr by 8-00.		3-02
❏ G-AMYJ*	C-47B-30-DK	ex Coventry, Air Atlantique, SU-AZF, G-AMYJ, XF747, G-AMYJ, KN353, 110, 96, 243, 44-76384. CoA 4-4-97. Arrived 10-12-01.	®	3-02
❏ G-AVPN	Herald 213	ex Channel Express, I-TIVB, G-AVPN, D-BIBI, HB-AAK ntu. CoA 14-12-99.		3-02
❏ G-MJRA*	Mainair Tri-Flyer	ex Wetherby. Demon 175 wing.		3-02
❏ G-MVIM	Snowbird IV	ex Wombleton. CoA 28-6-91.		3-02
❏ G-TFRB*	Air Command 532	ex Hartlepool. CoA 6-8-98. Arrived 11-01.		3-02
❏ G-YURO	Europa 001	ex Wombleton. CoA 9-6-95.		3-02
❏ 'F943'	SE.5A REP	G-BKDT, ex Selby, Elvington, Selby.		3-02
❏ 'H1968'	Avro 504K REP	BAPC.42, ex St Athan, Halton.		3-02
❏ [N540]	PV Kitten REP	ex Selby. Stored.	②	3-02
❏ 'P3873''YO-H'	Hurricane I FSM	BAPC.265, 609 Sqn colours. 'Unveiled' 8-10-00.		3-02
❏ 'R6690''PR-A'	Spitfire I FSM	BAPC.254, 1 Sqn RCAF colours.	③	3-02
❏ HJ711 'VI-C'	Mosquito NF.II	ex Huntington. 169 Sqn c/s. *Spirit of Val*.	® ④	3-02
❏ 'LV907'	Halifax II	ex Isle of Lewis. 'NP-F', *Friday 13th*, 158 Sqn c/s.	® ⑤	3-02
❏ RA854*	Cadet TX.1	ex Wigan, TAC, Woodford, RAFGSA, Woodvale, 41 GS. Arrived 6-4-00. Stored.		3-02
❏ 'TJ704' 'JA'	Terrier 2	G-ASCD, ex Holme-on Spalding Moor, Nympsfield, Blackbushe, PH-SFT, G-ASCD, Auster AOP.6 VW993, 651, 663. CoA 26-9-71.	®	3-02
❏ VV901	Anson T.21	ex Bacup, Burtonwood, Cosford, Irton Holme, Leconfield, CFCCU, Dur UAS, 1 RFS.	®	3-02
❏ WH846	Canberra T.4	ex Samlesbury, St Athan, Laarbruch SF, 231 OCU.		3-02
❏ WH903	Canberra B.2	ex 100, 85, MoA, 85, W Raynham TFF, 228 OCU, 102, 617. Nose. Id confirmed.		3-02
❏ 'WK864' 'C'	Meteor F.8	WL168 ex Finningley, 'WH456', St Athan, Swinderby, Finningley, Heywood 7750M, Sylt, 604, 111. 616 Sqn colours.		3-02

❑ WS788	'Z'	Meteor NF.14	ex Leeming 'WS844', Patrington 7967M, 1 ANS, 2 ANS, 152.		3-02
❑ XH278*	'42'	Vampire T.11	ex Felton, Henlow 8595M, Upwood 7866M, 27 MU, RAFC. Arrived 9/10-2-02.	®	3-02
❑ XH767*		Javelin FAW.9	ex Norwich, Monkton Farleigh, Worcester 7955M, Shawbury, 228 OCU, 11, 25. 23 Sqn colours. Arrived 4-2-01.		3-02
❑ XL231		Victor K.2	ex 55, 57, Witt Wing, Victor TF, Witt Wing, 139. *Lusty Lindy*.	⑥	3-02
❑ 'XL571'	'V'	Hunter T.7	XL572 / G-HNTR, ex Brough, Bournemouth, Cosford 8834M, 1 TWU, 2 TWU, TWU, 229 OCU. 92 Sqn, 'Blue Diamonds' colours.		3-02
❑ XN974		Buccaneer S.2	ex BAe Warton, Holme on Spalding Moor, A&AEE.		3-02
❑ XP640	'M'	Jet Provost T.4	ex Halton 8501M, CATCS, 6 FTS, CAW, CFS, 3 FTS. 6 FTS colours.		3-02
❑ XS903	'BA'	Lightning F.6	ex Binbrook, 11, 5-11 pool.	⑦	3-02
❑ XV748*	'3D'	Harrier GR.3	ex Cranfield, Bedford, 233 OCU, 1, 233 OCU, 1. Sectioned fuselage. Arrived 21-10-00.		3-02
❑ XX901		Buccaneer S.2B	ex Kemble, St Athan, Lossiemouth, 208, 12, 237 OCU, 208. *Kathryn - The Flying Mermaid*. Pink c/s.	⑧	3-02
❑	'1'	Jet Provost T.3	ex Linton-on-Ouse. Procedure trainer.		3-02
❑	'2'	Jet Provost T.3	ex Linton-on-Ouse. Procedure trainer.		3-02
❑		Victor	ex Navenby. Procedure trainer.	⑥	3-02
❑ 21417		CT-133 S' Star	ex Sollingen, CAF.		3-02
❑ 538	'3-QH'	Mirage IIIE	ex Chateaudun, 3 *Esc*, FAF.		3-02
❑ N-268		Hunter FGA.78	ex Bournemouth, Qatar AF QA-10, G-9-286, Dutch AF N-268. Dutch colours.		3-02
❑ '237123'		CG-4A Hadrian	BAPC. 157, ex Bacup, Ormskirk.	® ⑨	3-02
❑ —	BAPC.28	Wright Flyer REP	ex Leeds, Eccleston, Cardington, Finningley. off-site, ®		3-02
❑ —	BAPC.41	BE.2c REP	ex St Athan, '6232'. Halton.		3-02
❑ —	BAPC.89	Cayley REP	ex Manchester, Hendon, Lasham. Rolled-out 12-8-99.		3-02
❑ —	BAPC.130	Blackburn 1911 R	ex Stoke, Helston, *Flambards*. Rolled-out 11-6-00.		3-02
❑ —	BAPC.240	Bf 109G FSM	ex Garforth.	⑩	3-02

Yorkshire Helicopter Preservation Group (YHPG): The team continue to work on Whirlwind HAR.10 XP345 to exacting standards. A third Whirlwind has been acquired as a source of spares. As noted above, all of YHPG's airframes are on loan to YAM.

✉ YHPG, Alan Beattie, 18 Marshall Drive, Pickering, YO18 7JT e-mail YHPG@contactbox.co.uk webs www.helicopter-preservation-YHPG.org.uk or www.helicopterpreservation.co.uk for the story of the restoration of WH991. The group produce an excellent newsletter to keep members and 'rotorheads' in general in touch.

❑ WH991		Dragonfly HR.5	ex Storwood, Tattershall Thorpe, Tattershall, Wisbech, Taunton, Fleetlands, Culdrose SF, 705, 700, Eglinton SF, *Centaur* Flt, 705, *Illustrious* Flt.		3-02
❑ XD165*	'B'	Whirlwind HAR.10	ex Wattisham, Netheravon, Halton 8673M, SARTS, 202, 228, 22, 225, 155. Spares. Arr 12-00.	off-site	3-02
❑ XJ398		Whirlwind HAR.10	G-BDBZ, ex Oxford, Luton, XJ398, Culdrose, RAE, ETPS, Weston-super-Mare, DH Engines, A&AEE, XD768 ntu. Ground run 15-4-00.		3-02
❑ XP345		Whirlwind HAR.10	ex Storwood, Tattershall Thorpe, Lee-on-Solent, 8792M, Cyprus, 84 'B' Flt, 1563 Flt, 202, CFS.	®	3-02

GREAT AYTON on the A173 south-east of Middlesbrough
In the general area is a private collection. Viewing is *not* possible.

❑ WM145	Meteor NF.11	ex Rotherham, Finningley, 5, 29, 151, 219. Nose.	2-02
❑ WZ557	Vampire T.11	ex Huntingdon, Acaster Malbis, Woodford, Chester, St Athan, 5 FTS, 16. Black c/s.	2-02

❏ XM169	Lightning F.1A	ex Thirsk, Leuchars 8422M, Leuchars TFF, 23, Binbrook TFF, 111, A&AEE, MoA, EE. Nose.	2-02
❏ XN607	Jet Provost T.3	ex Leeds, 3 FTS. SOC 28-5-76. Nose. All grey c/s.	2-02
❏ XV867	Buccaneer S.2B	ex Leeming, 208, 12, 208, 237 OCU, FAA, 809, 736, 803. Nose.	2-02

HARROGATE on the A61 north of Leeds
A collector here *should* have the nose section of a former Rossington Lightning.

❏ XR726	Lightning F.6	ex Rossington, Binbrook, LTF, 11, LTF, 11, 5. 'TVI726'. Nose.	3-93

KIRKBYMOORSIDE AERODROME on the A170 west of Pickering, south of the town
Slingsby: T-3A 92-0633 had gone by August 2000, reportedly to the USA. During July 2000 a dozen T-67 fuselages were to be found stacked on their noses within the factory, these will probably be utilised in the recent order for Jordan.

❏	T.67 Firefly	c/n 2006, static test airframe.	3-02
❏ ZE686	Viking TX.1	ex BGA.3099. Static test airframe.	3-02

LEEMING AIRFIELD east of the A1, west of Bedale
RAF Leeming: *W&R17* was talking of the possibility of "a change of heart" by the MoD over the axing of more Phantoms. No such luck... FGR.2s XV423 and XV465 were scrapped on 19th July 2001. Yorkshire Air Museum (Elvington, N Yorks) continues to hope that XV499 will come their way... Lightning F.6 XR753 is displayed outside XI Squadron's headquarters – see under Quedgeley, Glos, for its doppelgänger ①.

❏ XA634		Javelin FAW.4	7641M, ex Shawbury, Colerne, Melksham, Gloster. 228 OCU markings.		3-02
❏ XR753	'BP'	Lightning F.6	8969M, ex Binbrook, 11, 5-11 pool, 23, FCTU.	①	3-02
❏ XV499		Phantom FGR.2	ex 74, 92, 228 OCU, 29, 23, 19, 92, 41, 6. Decoy.		3-02
❏ ZD934*	'AD'	Tornado F.2	ex St Athan, 229 OCU. Nose. ABDRT. F/n 11-00.		3-02

LINTON-ON-OUSE AIRFIELD west of the A19, north-west of York
RAF Linton-on-Ouse: 'JP' XM372 was put up for tender during late March 2002.

❏ XM372	'55'	Jet Provost T.3A	8917M, ex Dishforth, 1 FTS, 2 FTS. Crashed 6-12-85. Dump. Poor state.	3-02
❏ XN589	'46'	Jet Provost T.3A	9143M, ex 1 FTS, RAFC. 1 FTS c/s. Gate.	3-02

Memorial Room: Within the base is a superb museum, known as the Memorial Room. It deals with all aspects of Linton's history via a wide array of photographs, archival material and small artefacts.
◆ Visits by prior appointment only. ✉ Station Memorial Room, RAF Linton-on-Ouse, YO30 2AJ. ☏ 01347 848261, ext 7283.

MALTON off the A64 north of Malton at A169 junction
Eden Camp Modern History Theme Museum: Each hut in this former prisoner of war camp has a different theme and the level of presentation is breath-taking. There is much to fascinate the aviation follower, including a Link trainer display, plotting room, items on 617 Squadron, the Comete escape line and much more. All three FSMs were built by TDL Replicas of Lowestoft.
◆ Daily 10am to 5pm, last admission 4pm. (Extended closure Xmas and New Year, call for details.) ✉ Eden Camp, Malton, YO17 6RT. ☏ 01653 697777 fax 01653 698243 e-mail admin@edencamp.co .uk web www.edencamp.co.uk

❏ 'P2793' 'SD-M'	Hurricane FSM	BAPC.236. 501 Sqn colours.	3-02
❏ 'AB550' 'GE-P'	Spitfire FSM	BAPC.230, ex 'AA908'. 349 Sqn colours.	3-02
❏	BAPC.235 Fi 103 (V-1) FSM	—	3-02

NEWBY WISKE north-west of Thirsk, near South Otterington

❏ G-BGFK*	Evans VP-1	Canx 7-4-99. Stored. First noted 11-99.		3-02
❏ E3B-369*	Jungmann	G-BPDM, ex SpanAF. CoA 22-6-96.	®	12-01

RUFFORTH AERODROME south of the A1237, west of York
McLean's Sailplanes: Grunau Baby IIB ASC was exported to Germany several years back. Cadet TX.3 also went to Germany, in 1997. Sedbergh TX.1 WB922 (last noted in June 1998) was at <u>Gallows Hill</u>, Dorset, by April 2001.

❏ G-ATSY*	Super Baladou IV	ex Newcastle. CoA 23-11-91. Arr 11-00. Spares.	3-02
❏ G-BCHX	SF-23A Sperling	ex Netherthorpe, D-EGIZ. Damaged 7-8-82. Frame.	3-02
❏ AUJ	T.21B	BGA.668. Damaged 16-7-85. Stored.	3-02
❏ XA286	Cadet TX.3	ex Eaglescott, Syerston, 615 VGS. Fuselage. Stored.	3-02
❏ XA290	Cadet TX.3	ex Syerston, Dishforth, 661 VGS, 643 VGS. Fuselage.	3-02

Others:

❏ G-LUFT*	Elster C	ex Humberside, North Coates, G-BOPY, D-EDEZ. Spares, stored.	11-00

SELBY on the A19 south of York
Anne Lindsay and **Nigel Ponsford**: See also under Breighton, E Yorks and Wigan, Gtr Man.
◆ Airframes listed held in deep storage or restoration in and around the area and visits are *not* possible.

❏ G-ADPJ	BAC Drone II	ex Breighton, Wigan, Bristol, Benson, Thetford. Damaged 3-4-55. Also parts from G-AEKU.	®	3-02
❏ G-AEFG	HM.14 'Flea'	BAPC.75, ex Breighton, Leeds, Harrogate, Kirkby Overblow, Accrington.	®	3-02
❏ G-APXZ	Knight Twister	ex Breighton, Tumby Woodside, Loughborough, Biggin Hill. Frame.		3-02
❏ G-MBWI	Lafayette 1	ex Leeds, Leigh.		3-02
❏ ALX	Dagling	BGA.491, ex Leeds, Great Hucklow.		3-02
❏ AQY	EoN Primary	BGA.588, ex Breighton, Hemel Hempstead. Stored.		3-02
❏ BVM '150'	Dart 17R	BGA.1269, ex Breighton, Rufforth.		3-02
❏	Hutter H.17a	ex Leeds, Accrington.		3-02
❏	Dickson Primary	ex Leeds, Harrogate.		3-02
❏ XK819	Grasshopper TX.1	ex Breighton, Warmingham, Stoke-on-Trent, Cosford, Malvern, 2 MGSP, Kimbolton.	®	3-02
❏ 100502*	Fa 330A-1	ex Breighton, East Kirkby, Tattershall, Wigan. TAC loan.		3-02
❏ – BAPC.14	Addyman STG	ex Leeds, Harrogate, Wigan.		3-02
❏ – BAPC.16	Addyman UL	ex Leeds, Harrogate, Wigan.		3-02
❏ – BAPC.18	Killick Gyroplane	ex Leeds, Harrogate, Irlam.		3-02
❏ – BAPC.39	Addyman Zephyr	ex Leeds, Harrogate. Substantial parts.		3-02

SHERBURN-IN-ELMET AERODROME on the B1222 east of the town, east of Leeds
Auster J/1 G-AIBY moved to storage in <u>Halifax</u>, W Yorks, by July 2000. Cessna 120 G-BHLW and F.172M G-BAEO were flying by 1999. Cessna F.172M G-YTWO is reported to have been used in the rebuild of fellow G-BAEO and 'consumed'.

❏ G-BNCZ	Rutan LongEz	damaged 12-2-94. Stored.	9-00
❏ G-SACU	Cadet 161	ex N9162X. Crashed 29-6-96.	9-00

SOUTH YORKSHIRE

☞ Within the boundary are the unitary authorities of Barnsley, Doncaster, Rotherham and Sheffield.

ARMTHORPE on the A630 north of Doncaster
No.1053 Squadron Air Cadets: Keep a 'Chippax' in Church Street. 'Parent' is Waddington.

❏ WG419	Chipmunk T.10 PAX	8206M, ex Finningley, MoA, Laarbruch SF, Gütersloh SF, Ahlhorn SF, Oldenburg SF, CFS, Abn UAS, Bir UAS, 15 RFS, 4 BFTS, 6 RFS.	1-96

BAWTRY on the A638 south of Doncaster
No.216 Squadron Air Cadets:

❏ WK584	Chipmunk T.10 PAX	7556M, ex Church Fenton, Linton-on-Ouse, Edzell SF, Ox UAS, Glas UAS, 11 RFS.	2-02

Bawtry Paintball: Located to the north of the town, has a 'chopper' to help the war-gaming area look more like Vietnam, or perhaps Toxteth. SYAM from Doncaster, undertook a strip of useful spares prior to it taking up its new role.

❏ XL840*	Whirlwind HAS.7	ex Long Marston, Norwich, Sibson, Blackpool, Fleetwood, Wroughton, 705, Brawdy SF, Culdrose SF, 705, 820. First noted mid-2000.	2-01

DONCASTER
AeroVenture: Run by the South Yorkshire Aviation Museum. After a tremendous amount of work – and more than a little soul-searching that they were doing the right thing! – SYAM opened up AeroVenture on 24th August 2000 in a very low key manner. On 29th May 2001 they opened up in grand style with Doncaster's Mayoress, guests of honour and a flypast from a 51 Squadron Nimrod from Waddington. Work to develop the site continues and special events are planned.

    Notes: Airframes on loan from Dave Charles are marked. Airframes on loan from Bill Fern are marked BF. Several airframes are owned by AeroVenture curator Naylan Moore via his Classic Aircraft Collection, marked CAC. Naylan is also at work on a Typhoon or Tempest cockpit section acquired from Gloucestershire. HS.125 nose G-BOCB is owned by Mike North ①. Venom NF.3 WX788 is on loan from Steve Hague ②. Cadet TX.3 XN238 will be combined with an anonymous fuselage, '1397' acquired from Bidford, Glos and is *likely* to be BGA.972. This exhibit is also on loan from Bill Fern ③. Sioux AH.1 XT242 is a composite, with parts of XW179 included. It is on lona from The Aeroplane Collection④. Lightning F.6 XS897 is owned by a consortium of six museum members ⑤. Identity of this Venom is *possibly* FB.1 WK393 was sold as scrap 28th February 1958 or WK394 struck off charge 20th August 1957, both 'originating' from Silloth ⑥. The appearance of the Valetta nose is a surprise. It was picked up at the RAF Museum's clear-out of surplus material at Cardington prior to the latter's move to Wyton, Cambs. Presumably it came from Henlow before that and is said to have been with an ATC unit before joining the museum's stock. During strip-down it revealed a CFS badge ⑦.

    Departures: 'Salmson' FSM 'C850' moved to King's Lynn, Norfolk; Bill Fern's Hunter F.1 nose WT684 (first noted here February 2000) moved on to Lavendon, Bucks, by mid-2001; Peter Clayphon's Hunter T.7 cockpit XL609 moved to Boscombe Down, Wilts, by 10-01; Sycamore HR.14 XG506 was scrapped in mid-2001, with useful parts helping several others of the type.

◆ At the Doncaster Lakeside. Access off the A638 beyond 'The Dome' or follow signs off the M18/ A6182 for 'Yorkshire Outlet'. Open Thu, Fri, Sat, Sun, 10am to 5pm. ✉ Sandy Lane, Doncaster, DN4 5EP ☎ 01302 761616.

❏ 'K-158'	Whippet REP	BAPC.207, ex Sunderland, Stoke-on-Trent.	DC	3-02
❏ G-ALYB*	Auster 5	ex Firbeck, Bristol, White Waltham, RT520, 85 GCS, 84 GCS. CoA 26-5-63. Frame.	®	3-02
❏ G-AOKO*	Prentice 1	ex Coventry, Southend, VS621, CFS, 2 FTS, 22 FTS. CoA 23-10-72. Stored. Arrived 9-5-00.		3-02
❏ G-APMY*	Apache 160	ex Firbeck, Connah's Quay, Halfpenny Green, EI-AJT. CoA 1-11-81.		3-02

☐ G-ARGI		Auster 6A	ex Newark-on-Trent, Chirk, Heathfield, VF530, 661. CoA 4-7-76. Frame, stored.		3-02
☐ G-ARHX		Dove 8	ex Sunderland, Booker, Southgate, Leavesden. CoA 8-9-78.	DC	3-02
☐ G-AVAA		Cessna F.150G	ex Firbeck, Shobdon, Bournemouth. CoA 5-7-96. Fuselage.		2-00
☐ G-BOCB*		HS.125-1B/522	ex Cardiff, Hatfield, G-OMCA, G-DJMJ, G-AWUF, 5N-ALY, G-AWUF, HZ-BIN. CoA 16-10-90. Cockpit. First noted 10-01.	①	3-02
☐ G-DELB		Robinson R.22B	ex Firbeck, Sherburn, Retford, N26461. Crashed 27-12-94. Stored.		3-02
☐ G-MJKP*		Hiway Skystrike	first noted 10-01.		3-02
☐ WA662*		Meteor T.7	ex Firbeck, Willington, Chalgrove, Llanbedr, Farnborough, FCCS, 3, Wildenrath SF, Gütersloh SF, 3.	®	3-02
☐ WB560		Chipmunk T.10 PAX	ex Firbeck, Fownhope, St Athan, Ox UAS, 242 OCU, 2 SoTT, South Cerney SF, ITS, 7 AEF, Nott UAS, 4 AEF.	CAC	3-02
☐ WB733*		Chipmunk T.10	ex Firbeck, Sevenoaks, Shawbury SF, Hamble CoAT, Marham SF, 4 SoTT 'hack', Lyneham SF, Upavon SF, HUAS, 11 RFS.		3-02
☐ [WB969]*		Sedbergh TX.1	ex Wroot. Arrived 10-01.		3-02
☐ [WE987]*		Prefect TX.1	BGA.2517, ex Wroot. Arrived 12-01.		3-02
☐ WJ903*		Varsity T.1	ex Firbeck, Dumfries, Glasgow Airport, 6 FTS, AE&AEOS, 1 ANS, 2 ANS, 3 ANS. Nose.		3-02
☐ WK626*		Chipmunk T.10	ex Firbeck, Salisbury, Welling, White Waltham, Bicester, 8213M, Odiham SF, Ox UAS, South Cerney SF, 1 FTS, Bicester SF, Odiham SF, FTCCS, Lon UAS, Cam UAS, Colerne SF, Leeds UAS, Nott UAS, 16 FRS, 18 RFS. Fuselage.	BF	3-02
☐ WL131*		Meteor F.8	ex Firbeck, Guernsey 7751M, APS Sylt, 601, 111. Nose.	BF	3-02
☐ WN890*		Hunter F.2	ex Firbeck, Robertsbridge, Stamford, Hedge End, Boscombe Down, A&AEE, AWA. Nose.	CAC	3-02
☐ WP255		Vampire NF.10	ex Haverigg, Firbeck, Ecclesfield, Bingley, Church Fenton, 27 MU, CNCS, 1 ANS, CNCS, 23. Pod.	CAC	3-02
☐ WX788*		Venom NF.3	ex Elvington, Kenilworth, Long Marston, Cardiff-Wales, Bledlow Ridge, Connah's Quay, DH. Arrived 2-02. Stored, dismantled.	②	3-02
☐ [WZ822]*		G'hopper TX.1	ex Firbeck, Robertsbridge, Halton, London. Stored.	BF	3-02
☐ XD377*	'A'	Vampire T.11	ex Firbeck, Barton, Elvington, Cosford, Birmingham, Shawbury 8203M, Hawarden, 66. Pod, stored.	BF	3-02
☐ XE317*	'S-N'	Sycamore HR.14	ex Firbeck, Winthorpe, Portsmouth, CFS, 275, G-AMWO ntu.	®	3-02
☐ XE935*	'30'	Vampire T.11	ex Firbeck, Sibson, Hitchin, Woodford, Chester, St Athan, 8 FTS.		3-02
☐ XG297*		Hunter FGA.9	ex Firbeck, Newton-le-Willows, Bacup, Macclesfield, Bitteswell, HSA, 20, 28, 20, 4. Nose.	off-site BF	3-02
☐ XH584*		Canberra T.4	ex Firbeck, Sunderland, Marham, 231 OCU. Nose. First noted 10-00.		3-02
☐ XK421		Auster AOP.9	ex Firbeck, Thurcroft, Firbeck, Hedge End, Fownhope, Long Marston, Innsworth, Bristol, Caldicote, 8365M, St Athan, Detmold, Middle Wallop. Frame, stored.	CAC	3-02
☐ XM350*	'89'	Jet Provost T.3A	ex Firbeck, Church Fenton 9036M, 7 FTS, 1 FTS, RAFC, A&AEE.		3-02
☐ [XM411]*	'X'	Jet Provost T.3	ex Firbeck, Otterburn, Halton 8434M, St Athan, Shawbury, Kemble, CFS. Nose section.		3-02

☐ XM561*	Skeeter AOP.12	ex Firbeck, East Kirkby, Tattershall, Moston, Middle Wallop, Arborfield 7980M, Wroughton, HQ 1 Wing, HQ 2 Wing, 651.		3-02
☐ XN238	Cadet TX.3	ex Firbeck, Robertsbridge, St Athan, 622 VGS. Forward fuselage.	BF ③	3-02
☐ XN386	'435' Whirlwind HAR.9	ex Lancaster, Blackpool, Heysham, Wroughton, Yeovilton, A2713, Fleetlands, *Endurance* Flt, 846, 814.		3-02
☐ XN511*	Jet Provost T.3	ex Firbeck, Robertsbridge, 'XM426', Lutterworth, Liversedge, Kemble, CFS, 1 FTS, CFS. Nose.	BF	3-02
☐ XP190*	Scout AH.1	ex Firbeck, Wroughton, Arborfield.		3-02
☐ XP902*	Scout AH.1	ex Firbeck, Otterburn, Edinburgh, Dishforth, Netheravon, Wroughton, Garrison Air Sqn, 3 CBAS. Cockpit.		3-02
☐ XR754*	Lightning F.6	ex Firbeck, Walpole, King's Lynn, Stock, Honington, Binbrook 8972M, 11, 5-11, 23, 5, A&AEE. Nose.	BF	3-02
☐ XT242*	'12' Sioux AH.1	ex Firbeck, Hooton Park, Warmingham, Long Marston, Wimborne, Middle Wallop, Blue Eagles. Composite, parts from XW179. Arr 4-6-00.	④	3-02
☐ XS481*	Wessex HU.5	ex Firbeck, Dishforth, Wroughton, Yeovilton, Culdrose, Yeovilton, 771, 707.		3-02
☐ XS897*	Lightning F.6	ex Firbeck, Rossington, Binbrook, 5, 11, 5, 11, 56, 74. Stored.	⑤	3-02
☐ XW666*	Nimrod R.1	ex Long Marston, Warton, Woodford, Kinloss, 51. Crashed 16-5-95. Cockpit. Arrived by 9-01.		3-02
☐ E-424*	Hunter F.51	ex Firbeck, East Kirkby, Tattershall, Cosford, Dunsfold, G-9-445, Aalborg, RDanAF, Esk.724.		3-02
☐ ET-273*	Hunter T.53	ex Firbeck, Chelford, Macclesfield, Leavesden, Elstree, Hatfield, DanAF Esk.724, RNethAF N-302. Nose.		3-02
☐ —	Vampire FB.5	ex Firbeck, Malmesbury, 229 OCU. Pod, stored.		3-02
☐	Venom FB.1	ex Firbeck, Dumfries, Silloth. Pod, single-seat.	BF ⑥	3-02
☐ *	Valetta	ex Cardington, Henlow (?), ATC unit (?). Nose.	⑦	3-02
☐ —	C-10A EMU	ex Sunderland, Wycombe Air Park, Bushey, West Ruislip, Stanmore, St Albans, Radlett. Nose.		3-02

Museum and Art Gallery: The 'Flea' and the Bensen are displayed on the second floor.
◆ Open Mon-Sat 10am to 5pm and Sun 2pm to 5pm. ⌧ Chequer Road, Doncaster, DN1 2AE ☎ 01302
734293 **fax** 01302 735409 **e-mail** museum@doncaster.gov.uk **web** www.doncaster.gov.uk

☐ 'G-AEKR'	HM.14 'Flea'	BAPC.121, ex Breighton, Firbeck, Nostell Priory, Crowle, Finningley.	3-02
☐ *	Bensen B.7	BAPC.275, built by S J R Wood, Warmsworth. Flew in the early 1960s. Volkswagen 1600.	3-02

FIRBECK west of the A60 north of Worksop
South Yorkshire Aviation Museum (SYAM): By August 2000 the site was clear. Departures: all to Doncaster, S Yorks, unless noted: Auster G-ALYB, Apache 160 G-APMY, Meteor T.7 WA662, Chipmunk T.10 WB733; Varsity T.1 nose WJ903; Chipmunk T.10 fuselage WK626; Meteor F.8 nose WL131; Hunter F.2 nose WN890; Grasshopper TX.1 WZ822; Vampire T.11 pod XD377; Sycamore HR.14 XE317; Vampire T.11 XE935; Hunter FGA.9 XG297 nose; Canberra T.4 nose XH584 by 10-00; Jet Provost T.3 XM350, Jet Provost T.3 nose XM411; Jet Provost T.3 nose XM474 to Levenshulme, Gtr Man, by 7-00; Skeeter AOP.12 XM561; Jet Provost T.3 nose XN511; Scout AH.1 XP190; Scout AH.1 cockpit XP902; Lightning F.6 nose XR754; Sioux AH.1 XT242 4-6-00; Wessex HU.5 XS481; Lightning F.6 XS897; Hunter F.51 E-424; Hunter T.53 nose ET-273; the anonymous Venom FB.1 pod. The cockpit of Cessna F.150H G-AWCL is unaccounted for.

NETHERTHORPE AERODROME north of the A619, west of Worksop
Cessna F.152 II G-BHNA was active again by March 2001.

SHEFFIELD
Brimpex Metal Treatments: Work continues on the Campbell-Bensen and the 'Flea'. The former was involved in blade-tip propulsion experiments. The hunt is on for another gyroplane to restore.
◆ Visits by prior arrangement *only*. ✉ 5 Devonshire Close, Dore, Sheffield, S17 3NX ☎ 0114 2366484 **fax** 0114 2620184 **e-mail** brimpex@demon.co.uk

❑	BAPC.13	HM.14 'Flea'	ex Kirk Langley, Wigan, Peel Green, Styal, Urmston, Berrington, Tenbury Wells, Knutsford.	® 3-02
❑		C-Bensen B.7	—	® 3-02

WEST YORKSHIRE

☛ Within the administrative county boundary of 'West Yorkshire' can be found the unitary authorities of Bradford, Calderdale, Kirklees, Leeds and Wakefield.

BATLEY on the A652 north of Dewsbury
Northern Aeroplane Workshops (NAW): Are making good progress with their Sopwith Camel, which will fly with the Shuttleworth Collection in due course. The workshop and fuselage within are on display at the **Skopos Motor Museum**.
◆ At the Alexander Mills in Alexander Road, signed. Open daily 10am to 5pm. Visits to see work in progress are on a prior permission *only* basis. ✉ Skopos Motor Museum, Alexander Mills, Alexander Road, Batley, WF17 6JA. ☎ 01924 444423 NAW c/o C Page, 20 Lombard Street, Rawdon, near Leeds, LS19 6BW **e-mail** c-spage@ukgateway.net

❑	[G-BZSC]	Camel F1 REP	fuselage, project under construction.	3-02

BIRD'S EDGE on the A629 north-west of Penistone

❑	G-BKIR	SAN D.117	ex F-BIOC. CoA 28-8-92.	® 11-95

HALIFAX
An Auster is in a garage store in the city.

❑	G-AIBY*	J/1 Autocrat	ex Sherburn, 'Halifax'. CoA 13-4-81. Stored.	7-00

HUDDERSFIELD AERODROME or Crosland Moor, south of the A670 west of the city
By late 2001, DR.1050 G-AWEN had moved to Spalding, Lincs. CEA DR.1051M G-BTIW is believed to have moved to the Isle of Man, circa 1997.

❑	G-AYKK	SAN D.117	ex F-BHGM. CoA 22-5-85.	® 5-99
❑	G-BLYY	Archer II	ex OO-PAY, N9792K. Wreck, open store.	9-99
❑	C-GDQD*	Thurston Teal	G-TEAL. Damaged 3-93. Fuselage.	5-00

LEEDS
A private owner *should* still keep a Bensen gyroglider in the area.

❑	–	BAPC.200	Bensen B.7	ex Cheltenham, Long Marston, Stoke.	11-93

LEEDS-BRADFORD AIRPORT or Yeadon, on the A658 north-east of Bradford
It has been a long, long time since we have recorded anything new on the *W&R* scene here. In October 2000 a Shorts 360 fuselage arrived for the fire crews. The last time they had anything real to 'play' with was 1985 when Varsity T.1 WL678 gave up the ghost. The Avian is to be found off-site.

❑	G-ATND	Cessna F.150F	crashed 9-12-72. Engine test-rig.	3-02
❑	G-AWES	Cessna 150H	ex Blackpool, Glenrothes, N22933. Dam 2-10-81.	® 3-02
❑	G-ODUB*	Bandeirante	ex PH-FVC, G-BNIX, N8536J. Spares.	® 3-02

❏ EI-BPD* Short 360-100 ex Southend, Aer Arran, Gill, G-RMCT, Aer Lingus
EI-BPD, G-BLPU, G-14-3656. Damaged 4-2-01.
Arrived 12-10-01. Fire crews. 3-02

Locally: The Avian is under restoration, but 'off-site'.
❏ G-ACGT Avian IIIA ex Linthwaite, EI-AAB. CoA 21-7-39. ® 1-01

SIDDAL on the A646 south of Halifax
John S Shackleton Ltd: A visit to the Cinder Hill site in August 2000 found that it had been cleared,
perhaps as long ago as 1992 and that all aircraft remains had been melted down at about the same time.
This will have included the former Warton SAR Flight Whirlwind HAS.7 XG597.

WAKEFIELD
The cockpit of Harvard III EZ259 (G-BMJW) is *thought* to have been exported, perhaps to Holland.

PART TWO
CHANNEL ISLANDS

ALDERNEY AIRPORT
The overall yellow Aztec continues to provide the fire crews with practice.
❏ G-ASHV Aztec 250B ex Guernsey, N5281Y ntu. CoA 22-7-85. Dump. 12-99

GUERNSEY
The island provides a home for three interesting *W&R* airframes. The Mooney and the EAA Biplane at
Sausmarez Park ① and the Noralpha within St Peter Port ②.
❏ G-ASTH Mooney M.20 ex France, N6906U. Crashed 16-11-66. Stored. ① 4-90
❏ G-ATEP EAA Biplane CoA 18-6-73. ① 1-00
❏ G-ATHN Noralpha ex F-BFUZ, French mil No.84. CoA 27-6-75. Stored.② 1-00

GUERNSEY AIRPORT
❏ G-BAZJ Herald 209 ex Air UK, Alia 4X-AHR, G-8-1. Fire crews. 10-01
❏ G-BBYO Trislander ex ZS-KMH, G-BBYO, G-BBWR. CoA 1-5-92.
Fuselage. 10-01
❏ G-BDTN* Trislander ex S7-AAN, VQ-SAN, G-BDTN. CoA 10-6-98.
Stored, dismantled. First noted 6-01. 6-01
❏ N32625* Seneca 200 dump by 1-00. 10-01
❏ N97121 Bandeirante ex City-Line, PT-SDK. Withdrawn by 4-97. 10-01
❏ XM409 Jet Provost T.3 ex Firbeck, Moreton-in-Marsh, Halton 8082M,
Shawbury, 2 FTS. Nose. 10-01
❏ XS888 '521' Wessex HAS.1 ex Lee-o-S, Wroughton, Fleetlands. Dump. 10-01

JERSEY AIRPORT
The fire service compound located north of the Runway 09 threshold, has a steel airliner mock-up for
'burning' exercises as well as the three 'real' airframes.
❏ G-AOJD Viscount 802 ex BA, BEA. CoA 13-6-77. Fire. 7-00
❏ G-BBXJ Herald 203 ex BIA, I-TIVI. Crashed 24-12-74. Fuselage. Fire. 7-00
❏ G-BMTP Tomahawk 112 ex N2392B. Damaged 1-9-92. Spares. 11-95
❏ XP573 '19' Jet Provost T.4 ex Halton '8236M', Kemble, Shawbury, R-R,
1 FTS, CFS. Really 8336M. Fire crews. 9-00

PART TWO
SCOTLAND

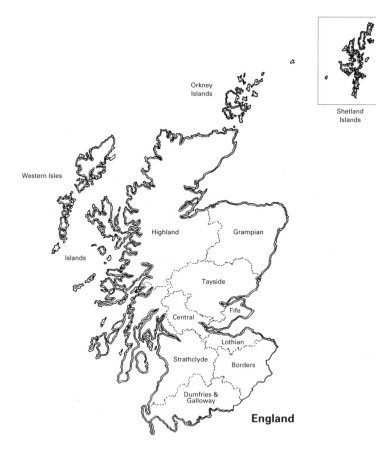

The 'regions' of Scotland work on a wholly 'single tier' unitary authority structure.
The regions are as follows:

Borders	–
Central	Clackmannan, Falkirk and Stirling.
Dumfries & Galloway	–
Fife	–
Grampian	Aberdeenshire, City of Aberdeen, Moray.
Highland	–
Islands	Argyll & Bute, Orkney, Shetland, Western Isles.
Lothian	City of Edinburgh, East Lothian, Falkirk, Midlothian, West Lothian.
Strathclyde	City of Glasgow, East Ayrshire, East Dumbartonshire, East Renfrewshire, Inverclyde, North Ayrshire (including the Isle of Arran), Renfrewshire, South Ayrshire, South Lanarkshire, West Dumbartonshire.
Tayside	Angus, Perth & Kinross.

ABERDEEN
HQ Aberdeen Wing, Air Cadets / 2489 Squadron Air Cadets: Within the TAVR Gordon Barracks, Bridge of Don, took delivery of the former Buchan Phantom on 25th October 2001. It had been in store at Lossiemouth in the intervening period. They will undertake a restoration programme.

❑ XV581*   Phantom FG.1   ex Lossiemouth, Buchan 9070M, Wattisham, 43, 111, 43. Nose. Arrived <u>25-10-01</u>.   10-01

Others: An ARV may still be in the area.

❑ G-BNHC   ARV Super 2   Crashed 4-8-96.   ® 12-96

ABERDEEN AIRPORT or Dyce, off the A96 north-west of Aberdeen
The fuselage of Gulfstream I G-BNCE moved to <u>Dundee</u>, Scotland on 8th August 2000. The fire dump is occupied by a wholly 'synthetic' Sikorsky S-61 look-alike and an equally 'ersatz' Boeing 737-ish fuselage – the former for rescue/egress training, the latter for burning.

❑ G-TIGH   Super Puma   ex Bristow, F-WXFL. *City of Edinburgh.*   Crashed 14-3-92. Fuselage, rescue training.   3-02

ABOYNE AERODROME south of the A93 west of Banchory
The unfinished Jodel D.11 project G-BDMM had gone by January 2001.

❑ G-AVYK   Terrier 3   ex Auster AOP.6 WJ357, 651, 657, 1903 Flt. CoA 28-8-93.   off-site ®   1-01
❑ G-BAHP   Volmer Sportsman   CoA 18-10-93. Stored.   1-01
❑ G-BHVV   J3C-65 Cub   ex F-BGXF, 42-38384. CoA 3-7-85.   6-01

ARBROATH
Anson C.19 TX183 (G-BSMF) was moved, via Wellesbourne Mountford, Warks, during May 2001 to Dubai for the Gulf Air museum.

BANCHORY on the A93 west of Aberdeen
The house (and the Vulcan?) was up for sale in April 2001.

❑ XH563   ·Vulcan B.2MRR   ex Rotherham, Scampton 8744M, 27, 230 OCU, MoA, 230 OCU, Wadd W, 230 OCU, 12, 83. Nose.   1-01

Others: Both Airedales are under restoration in the general area.

❑ G-ARXD   Airedale   ex Netherley. CoA 13-6-86.   ®   2-02
❑ G-ASAI   Airedale   ex Dundee, Islay. CoA 20-5-77.   ®   2-02

BENBECULA AIRPORT Western Isles
RAF Enclave: Phantom FGR.2 XV467 was scrapped in April 2000.

BLAIRGOWRIE on the A923 north-west of Dundee
❑ G-AZZG   Cessna 188-230   ex Lairg, Inverness, Southend, OY-AHT, N8029V. CoA 1-5-81. Stored.   5-97

BORGUE on the B727 west of Kirkcudbright
Brighouse Bay Caravan Park: Displayed inside the camp is the former Carlisle Meteor.

❑ WS792   'K'   Meteor NF.14   ex Carlisle, Cosford 7965M, 5 MU, 1 ANS, 2 ANS.   6-00

BRIDGE OF WEIR on the A761 north-west of Paisley
Neil Geddes: Tiger Moth G-AREH moved to <u>Glenrothes</u>, Scotland.

❑ –   Grasshopper TX.1 ex Strathallan, Aberdeen. Stored.   1-00

CHARTERHALL south of Edinburgh, off the A697 near Greenlaw
A long-damaged Turbulent is stored on the former airfield.

☐ G-APOL	Turbulent	Damaged 24-7-93. Stored.	8-99

CRUDEN BAY on the A975 south of Peterhead
Hobson Home for Distressed Aeroplanes: Malcolm's three 'in-patients' are thought to remain.

☐ G-AVKM	Condor	ex Edderton. Damaged 3-3-82.	2-00
☐ G-AXBU	FR.172F	ex Bearsden, Kirknewton, Inverkeithing. Cr 13-10-74.	2-00
☐ G-BCIL	AA-1B Trainer	ex Auchnagatt, N6168A. Crashed 14-6-86.	2-00

CUMBERNAULD AERODROME north of the A80, north of Cumbernauld
The saga of Cessna F.172N CS-AQW continues. It was registered as G-BZKB and air tested on 10th
August 2000. Beaver AL.1 'XP822' (XP806) left on 20th November 2000 bound for Canada.
Trislander G-BCCU (CoA 26-1-99) was in store by at mid-1999, but was flying again by April 2001.

☐ G-AISC	Tipsy B	ex Henstridge, Yeovil. CoA 23-5-79. Fuselage.	2-02
☐ G-BEVR*	Trislander	ex JY-JQE, G-BEVR, XA-THE[2], G-BEVR.	
		CoA 6-7-82.	® 2-02
☐ G-BNIP	Silvaire 8A	ex N77820, NC77820. CoA 10-2-93. Stored.	2-02
☐ G-BWUC	PA-18-135	N719CS, ex SX-ASM, EI-1818, I-EIYB,	
		MM54-2369, 54-2369. Stored, dismantled.	2-02

CUPAR on the A91 west of St Andrews
An enthusiast keeps a Victor nose in the area. SAN D.150 G-BFEB was flying again by mid-2001.

☐ G-ARTJ	Bensen B.8M	ex East Fortune, Cupar, Currie, Cupar.	6-95
☐ XA917	Victor B.1	ex Crowland, Barnham, Marham 7827M,	
		Wyton, A&AEE, HP. Cockpit.	8-95

CURRIE on the A70 south-west of Edinburgh
A private collector has a 'Chippax' here.

☐ WB670*	Chipmunk T.10	8361M, ex Southend, MoS, 5 FTS, LAS,	
	PAX	12 RFS, 5 RFS. Rear of WG303.	9-99

DUMFRIES off the A701 north-east of Dumfries on the former airfield
Dumfries and Galloway Aviation Museum (DGAM): Run by the Dumfries and Galloway
Aviation Group, the restored watch tower that forms the centrepiece of the museum contains a huge array
of artefacts, all well presented. The tower and grounds continue to be refined. The Trident fuselage is
now open to the public and includes an extensive interior display and 30 seat lecture hall.
   Notes: Chipmunk T.10 WD386 was fitted with the rear end of WD377. By November 2001 this
project was being worked on off-site on behalf of the museum ①. Canberra T.4 nose WJ880 is used as a
travelling display ②. Vampire XD547 has the wings of XD425 ③.
◆ Open Sat and Sun 10am to 5pm Easter to Oct. Also, Wed Jun to Aug, 6pm to 9pm. Follow signs for
   Enterprise Park from the A701. Other times by arrangement. ✉ David Reid, 11 Ninian Court,
   Lochside, Dumfries, DG2 9PS. ☎ 01387 251623 **e-mail** david-reid-50@hotmail.com **web**
   http://members.xoom.com/ dgamuseum/

☐ G-AHAT	J/1N Alpha	ex Firbeck, Exeter, Taunton, Old Sarum,	
		HB-EOK ntu. Crashed 31-8-74. Frame.	3-02
☐ G-AWZJ	Trident 3B-101	ex Prestwick ,Heathrow, BA, BEA.	
		CoA 12-9-85. Forward fuselage.	3-02
☐ G-MMIX*	Tiger Cub 440	ex Long Marston. First noted 6-01.	3-02
☐ P7540	Spitfire IIa	ex Loch Doon, 312, 266, 609, 66. Cr 6-7-41.	® 3-02
☐ WA576	Sycamore 3	ex East Fortune, Strathallan, Halton 7900M,	
		RAE, A&AEE, G-ALSS ntu.	3-02

❑ WD386	'O'	Chipmunk T.10	ex Firbeck, Cranfield, Tenby, St Athan, 1 FTS, Ox UAS, 22 RFS , 2 BFTS. SOC 29-7-70.	①	3-02
❑ WJ880		Canberra T.4	ex Firbeck, North Weald, Halton 8491M, 7, 85, 100, 56, Laarbruch SF, RAE, 16, Laarbruch SF, Gütersloh SF, 104. Nose.	②	3-02
❑ WL375		Meteor T.7(mod)	ex West Freugh, RAE. RAE Bedford colours.		3-02
❑ XD547	'Z'	Vampire T.11	ex Aberfoyle, Strathallan, Milngavie, Glasgow, CATCS, 8 FTS, 1 RS, 263.	③	3-02
❑ 'XF506'	'A'	Hunter F.4	WT746, ex Saighton, Halton 7770M, St Athan, AFDS. 'Black Arrows', 111 Sqn colour scheme.		3-02
❑ FT-36		T-33A-1-LO	ex Sculthorpe, Belgian AF, USAF 55-3047. *Little Miss Laura.*		3-02
❑ 318	'8-NY'	Mystère IVA	ex Sculthorpe, French Air Force.		3-02
❑ Q497*		Canberra T.4	ex Warton, Samlesbury, frustrated Indian AF B.52, Bracebridge Heath, Samlesbury, Kemble, WE191, 231 OCU, 237 OCU, 231 OCU, 245. Fuse. Arr by 8-01.		3-02
❑ 42163	'005'	F-100D-11-NA	ex Sculthorpe, FAF. USAF colours, *Shillelagh.*		3-02
❑ 68-0060		F-111E	ex 20 TFW. Escape pod. Crashed 5-11-75.		3-02
❑	'ZT-E'	Spitfire FSM	ex Dundonald, Prestwick. Damaged 11-96.	off-site	3-02

DUNDEE AIRPORT also known as Riverside, on the A85 to the south of the city
Tipsy Belfair G-APOD left by road on 10th October 2001, destination unconfirmed.

❑ G-BNCE*	Gulfstream I	ex Aberdeen, Aberdeen Airways, N436M, N436, N436M, N43M, N709G. CoA 9-4-92. Arrived 8-8-00. Dump.		3-01

DUNDONALD south of the A759, north-east of Troon
Dundonald Aviation Centre: Within Fraser's Garden Centre, the collection – established by John Hunter – has expanded considerably in terms of artefacts with a display building opened during June 1997. The centre has an active 'digs' policy with much to see within the display hall, including a series of sea salvaged engines. Whirlwind HAR.10 XP359 is due to be reduced to spares ①. With yet *another* Buccaneer nose section 'inbound', Vampire T.11 XD602 moved on in July 2001, heading for South Shields, N&T. This 'Bucc' is to be used for spares recovery ②.
♦ Open weekends 9am to 5pm. Other times by prior arrangement. ✉ Fraser's Garden Centre, The Crossroads, Dundonald, KA2 9BT ☎ 01563 850215 or 01294 212296 e-mail jpflightwear@aol.com

❑ WJ721	Canberra TT.18	ex Bacup, Samlesbury, 7, 50, 40. Nose.		3-02
❑ XP359	Whirlwind HAR.10	ex Stafford 8447M, Abingdon, Wroughton, 103, 110, 225.	①	3-02
❑ XT280	Buccaneer S.2B	ex Birtley, East Fortune, Lossiemouth, 12, 208, 12, 16, 237 OCU. Nose. 12 Sqn colours.		3-02
❑ XV161*	Buccaneer S.2B	ex Birtley, East Fortune, Lossiemouth 9117M, 12, 208, 12. Nose. Arrived 9-7-01.	②	3-02
❑ XX888	Buccaneer S.2B	ex Ottershaw, Shawbury, St Athan, 16, 15. Nose. Sand colours.		3-02

EAST FORTUNE AERODROME north of the A1, west of East Linton
National Museums of Scotland – Museum of Flight (MoF): Spitfire F.21 LA198 is being restored for eventual display in the Kelvingrove Museum and Art Gallery in Glasgow, Scotland. This is with a full-time staff of four led by Barry Ratcliffe with a completion date of September 2002. Restoration of the Beaufighter has started.
Working in support of all aspects of the museum is the **Aviation Preservation Society of Scotland** (APSS): The society have started construction of a flyable Sopwith 1 1/2 Strutter reproduction, but it is too early to give it s 'formal' listing. Other current work centres on the Bolingbroke and Anson

restorations, several engine rebuilds and a radio and radar exhibition. (✉ c/o Museum of Flight, see above. e-mail Jim Mattocks at j-f@jmattocks.freeserve.co.uk)

Notes: The Kay Gyroplane from Glasgow, Scotland, is on loan ①. The APSS Brantly is a composite, using parts from G-ASLO and G-AXSR ②. The Hiway Skytrike noted in *W&R17* (p273) is actually a Highway Super Scorpion and was donated by the PFA East of Scotland Strut. It never flew in Scotland. Its identity is now confirmed ③. Fergus McCann donated the Eurowing Goldwing. Built as a kit by Eurowing at their East Kilbride facility, assembled by a Scottish syndicate and operated in Scotland for 20 years, it is a highly appropriate item ④. Previously listed as Typhoon BAPC.244 this machine is now known to be a Mainair Tri-Flyer 250 with a Solar Wings Typhoon wing. Its identity is as given ⑤. Slingsby Gull I BED is *possibly* the former VW912 ⑥. The Buccaneer cockpit is thought to be XK533. However, another possibility is XK533 ⑦. The Catto CP-16 microlight 'trike' was donated by Robin Henderson in 1983, it never aspired to a G-Mxxx allocation ⑧.

◆ Open daily (except Xmas and New Year) 10.30am to 5pm. Weekdays only Oct to Mar when only two of the exhibition hangars will be open – Jets and Spaceflight Hangar open by prior permission only. Parties by appointment. Guided tours of the storage hangar are possible, enquire prior to arrival. A series of regular events, including an airshow, are staged – SAE for details. There is also a brand new gift shop and a cafe with food of great renown. ✉ East Fortune Airfield, East Lothian, Scotland, EH39 5LF ☎ 01620 880308 fax 01620 880355 e-mail museum_of_flight@sol.co.uk web www.nms.ac.uk/flight

❏ G-ACVA	Kay Gyroplane	ex Glasgow, Strathallan, Perth, Glasgow, Perth.		①	3-02
❏ G-ACYK	Spartan Cruiser	ex Hill of Stake, Largs. Cr 14-1-38. Fuselage, stored			3-02
❏ G-AFJU	Miles Monarch	ex York, Strathallan, Lasham, Staverton, X9306, G-AFJU. CoA 18-5-64.		APSS	3-02
❏ G-AGBN	GAL Cygnet II	ex Strathallan, Biggin Hill, ES915, MCCS, 52 OTU, 51 OTU, 23, G-AGBN. CoA 28-11-80.			3-02
❏ G-AHKY	Miles M.18-2	ex Perth, Strathallan, Blackbushe, HM545, U-0224, U-8. CoA 20-9-89.			3-02
❏ G-ANOV	Dove 6	ex CAFU Stansted, G-5-16. CoA 31-5-75.			3-02
❏ G-AOEL	Tiger Moth	ex Strathallan, Dunstable, N9510, 7 FTS, 2 GU, 11 RFS, 1 RFS, 7 RFS, 7 EFTS. CoA 18-7-72.			3-02
❏ G-ARCX	Meteor Mk 14	ex Ferranti, WM261. CoA 20-2-69.			3-02
❏ G-ASUG	Beech E.18S	ex Loganair, N575C, N555CB, N24R. CoA 23-7-75.			3-02
❏ G-ATFG	Brantly B.2B	ex Newport Pagnell. CoA 25-3-85.		APSS ②	3-02
❏ G-ATOY	Comanche 260B	ex Elstree, N8893P. Crashed 6-3-79. *Mythtoo*, Sheila Scott's aircraft. Fuselage.			3-02
❏ G-AXEH	Bulldog Srs 1	ex Prestwick, Shoreham. Prototype. CoA 15-1-77.			3-02
❏ G-BBVF	Twin Pioneer 2	ex Shobdon, XM961/7978M, SRCU, Odiham SF, 230, 21. Damaged 11-3-82.			3-02
❏ G-BDFU	Dragonfly MPA	ex Blackpool Airport, Warton, Prestwick. Stored.			2-00
❏ G-BDIX	Comet 4C	ex Lasham, Dan-Air, XR399, 216. CoA 11-10-81.			3-02
❏ G-JSSD	Jetstream 3100	ex Prestwick, N510F, N510E, N12227, G-AXJZ. CoA 9-10-90.			3-02
❏ G-MBJX	Super Scorpion	ex Halton. Acquired 1998. Canx 13-6-90.		③	3-02
❏ G-MBPM	EW-21 Goldwing	CoA 21-8-98.		④	3-02
❏ G-MMLI	Typhoon	BAPC.244. ex Glasgow. Canx 7-9-94. Stored		⑤	3-02
❏ BED	Gull I	BGA.902, ex Newbattle, 'G-ALPHA'.		⑥	3-02
❏ BJV	T.21A	BGA.1014, ex Feshiebridge, SE-SHK.			3-02
❏ W-2	Weir W-2	BAPC.85, ex Glasgow, East Fortune, Hayes, Knockholt, Hanworth, Cathcart. On loan.			3-02
❏	Jetstream 1 (Super 31 EMU)	ex Hatfield, East Midlands, N14234, N102SC, N200SC ntu, N1BE, G-BBBV, G-8-12. Fuselage.			3-02
❏ VH-SNB	Dragon I	ex Strathallan, VH-ASK, RAAF A34-13.			3-02
❏ VH-UQB	Puss Moth	ex Strathallan, Bankstown, G-ABDW.			3-02
❏ LA198 'RAI-G'	Spitfire F.21	ex Cardington, St Athan, Leuchars, Locking, Worcester, 7118M, 3 CAACU, 602, 1.		®	3-02
❏ TE462	Spitfire XVI	ex Ouston 7243M, 101 FRS, Finningley SF.			3-02

❑	'TJ398'	Auster AOP.5	BAPC.70, ex Inverkeithing, Perth. Stored.	APSS	3-02
❑	TS291	T.8 Tutor	BCB / BGA.852, ex Portmoak, TS291.		3-02
❑	VM360	Anson C.19	G-APHV, ex Strathallan, Kemps, BKS, TRE, A&AEE. Stored.	by APSS ®	3-02
❑	VX185	Canberra B.5	ex Wroughton, South Kensington, 7631M, EE. Nose.		3-02
❑	WB584	Chipmunk T.10 PAX	7706M, ex Manston, Kilmarnock, Edinburgh, Shawbury, Debden CF, 11 GCF, Tangmere SF, Glas UAS, 8 FTS, Bri UAS, 12 RFS, 22 RFS. 'Hands-on'.		3-02
❑	WF259	'171' Sea Hawk F.2	A2483, ex Lossiemouth SF, 736.		3-02
❑	WV493	'29' Provost T.1	G-BDYG, ex Strathallan, Halton 7696M, 6 FTS. CoA 28-11-80. Stored.		3-02
❑	WW145	'680' Sea Ven FAW.22	ex Lossiemouth, 750, 891.		3-02
❑	XA109	Sea Vampire T.22	ex Lossiemouth, 831, JOAC.		3-02
❑	XA228*	G'hopper TX.1	ex Glenalmond School. Arrived 6-00. Stored.	APSS	3-02
❑	XG594	'517' Whirlwind HAS.7	ex Strathallan, Wroughton, 71, A&AEE, 705, 846, 737, 701, RAE Bedford, 700. FAAM loan.		3-02
❑	XL762	Skeeter AOP.12	ex Middle Wallop, Halton 8017M, 2 RTR, 9 Flt, 652, 22 Flt, 654, 651. Stored.		3-02
❑	XM597	Vulcan B.2	ex Waddington, 50, 35, 101, 9, 50, 35, Wadd W, 12.		3-02
❑	XN776	'C' Lightning F.2A	ex Leuchars, 92, 19.		3-02
❑	XT288	Buccaneer S.2B	ex Lossie' 9134M, A&AEE, 208, 12, RN. Stored		3-02
❑	XV277	Harrier GR.1	ex Ipswich, Yeovilton A2602 [2], A2600 [2], Filton, HSA.		3-02
❑	*	Beaufighter II	ex Hendon, Duxford, Hendon, Cranfield. Nose. Arrived 11-12-00.		3-02
❑		Buccaneer S.1 CIM	ex Lossiemouth.	⑦	3-02
❑	9940	Bolingbroke IVT	ex Strathallan, RCAF 5 B&GS.	by APSS ®	3-02
❑	3677	MiG-15bis SB	ex Cáslav, Ostravian Air Regt, Czech AF. c/n 613677.		3-02
❑	309	MiG-15UTI	ex Polish AF. c/n 3309. Cockpit section.		3-02
❑	BF-10*	Beaufighter TF.10	ex Swartkop, South Africa, Alverca, Lisbon, Port AF, RD220. Arrived 12-12-00.	®	3-02
❑	591	Rhonlerche II	ex D-0359.		3-02
❑		'FI+S' MS.505 Criquet	G-BIRW, ex Duxford, OO-FIS, F-BDQS. CoA3-6-83. Luftwaffe colours. Stored.		3-02
❑	191659	'15' Me 163B-1a	ex Cambridge, Cranfield, Brize Norton, II/JG400.		3-02
❑	155848	'WT' F-4S-MC	ex Yeovilton, VMFA-232, USMC. 'WT'.		3-02
❑		CG-4A	ex Aberlady. Nose section. The Bunhouse.		3-02
❑	—	BAPC.49 Pilcher Hawk	ex Edinburgh. First flown at Eynsham 1896, crashed at Stanford Hall, Leics, 30-9-1899.		3-02
❑	—	BAPC.160 Chargus 18/50 hg	ex Tranent. (Acquired 1975.)		3-02
❑	—	BAPC.195 Moonraker 77 hg	ex Edinburgh. Birdman-built, circa 1977.		3-02
❑	—	BAPC.196 Sigma II Metre hg	ex Penicuik. Southdown Sailwings-built c 1980.		3-02
❑	—	BAPC.197 Cirrus III hg	ex Edinburgh. Scotkites-built 1977.		3-02
❑	—	BAPC.245 Electra Floater hg	ex Edinburgh. Built 1979. Stored		3-02
❑	—	BAPC.246 Hiway Cloudbase	ex Edinburgh. Built 1978, acquired 1995.		3-02
❑	—	BAPC.247 Albatros ASG.21	ex Edinburgh. Built 1977, acquired 1995.		3-02
❑	—	BAPC.262 Catto CP-16	ex Gifford. Acquired 1983. No wings.	® ⑧	3-02

Microlight Centre: Motor Cadet III G-BODG was sold in the USA during mid-2001.

❑	G-BEYN	Evans VP-1	Stored.	5-97
❑	G-BSNO	Denney Kitfox	crashed 9-7-97. Wreck, stored.	8-98

EDINBURGH
Ferranti: The factory in the South Gyle Estate is still guarded by a dramatically-posed Lightning.

❑	ZF584	Lightning F.53	ex Turnhouse, Warton, RSAF 53-682, G-27-52. Gate.	5-01

EDINBURGH AIRPORT or Turnhouse, on the A8 east of Edinburgh
❏ G-BFFE	Cessna F.152 II	CoA 19-4-98. Stored.	2-00
❏ G-MALK	Cessna F.172N	ex PH-SVF, PH-AXF. Crashed 23-7-97. Dump.	3-02
❏ 'L1070'	Spitfire FSM	BAPC.227. 'XT-A', 603 Sqn colours. Displayed.	3-02

ELGIN on the A941 south of Lossiemouth and north of Elgin
Buccaneer Service Station: Ian Aitkenhead keeps the 'Brick' in excellent condition on the forecourt.
❏ XW530	Buccaneer S.2B	ex Lossiemouth, 208, 12, 208, 216, 16, 15, 16.	6-01

ERROL south of the A90, east of Perth
The Vampire and Gannet are kept by a private collector locally. The Gannet is a composite, including bits from XA463, XG889 ①.
❏ 'XE897'	Vampire T.11	XD403, ex Leuchars, Errol, Strathallan, Woodford, Chester, 4 FTS, 1 FTS, 7 FTS, 8 FTS, 5 FTS, 4 FTS.	9-01
❏ XG882	'771' Gannet T.5	ex Lossiemouth 8754M, 845.	① 9-01

FALGUNZEON on the A711 south-west of Dumfries
Dumfries and Galloway Gliding Club: The T.45 is an amalgam of BGA.1041 and BGA.1032 ①.
❏ BRQ	EoN 460 Srs 1C	BGA.1177. Ex G-ARFU. CoA 8-96. Stored.	7-97
❏ DCG	Schleicher Ka 2B	BGA.2004. Ex D-7064. Stored.	7-97
❏ DGT	Schleicher Ka 2B	BGA.2110. Ex D-5469. Stored.	7-97
❏ DHP	T.45 Swallow	BGA.2130. CoA 10.89.	® ① 5-95

FORDOUN AERODROME on the A90 north-east of Brechin
❏ G-AWSS	Condor	CoA 19-10-94. Stored.	3-98

FORRES on the A96 west of Elgin
Christies Garden Centre: The Buccaneer nose is here, with other parts kept inside.
❏ XX892	Buccaneer S.2B	ex Lossiemouth, 208, 237 OCU, 16. Nose.	12-01

FYVIE on the B947 west of Peterhead
Mark Reeder: Mark is undertaking the construction of a full-size reproduction of a DH Hornet for the De Havilland Heritage Museum (see under London Colney, Herts). This will use as many original parts as possible and will include the tail section from Sea Hornet NF.21 VW957 '415' found at St David's, Dyfed, many a long year ago and displayed at DHHM. (See also under Chelmsford, Essex.)

GILMERTON on the A772 south-east of Edinburgh
Bernard Hunters: The nose of Trident 1C G-ARPL moved to <u>Glasgow</u>, Scotland, by May 2001.

GIRVAN on the A77 north of Stranraer
The Flix: A 'fun pub' in Bridge Street has a Tiger Cub 'flying' from the ceiling.
❏ G-MJUH	Tiger Cub 440	CoA 5-8-92.	4-98

GLASGOW
Museum of Transport: The Pilcher REP was built by 2175 Squadron Air Cadets, Glasgow ①, and awaits restoration. Spitfire F.21 LA198 at East Fortune, Scotland, is due to come here circa 2006.
◆ Mon to Thu and Sat 10am to 5pm. Fri and Sun 11am to 5pm. Nearest underground is Kelvin Hall.
  ✉ Kelvin Hall, 1 Bunhouse Road, Glasgow, G3 8DP ☎ 0141 2872720 **fax** 0141 2872692
❏	BAPC.48 Pilcher Hawk REP	Stored.	① 3-02

No.2175 Squadron Air Cadets: Base a 'travelling' Bulldog at their Hillingdon HQ.

❑	'XX530'*	'F' Bulldog T.1	XX637, ex Cranwell, St Athan 9197M, North UAS, 2 FTS.	12-01

Others : Two are stored locally.

❑	G-AWJF	Nipper T.66	ex airport and local area. CoA 7-6-88. off-site ® 12-01
❑	G-AZHT	Airtourer T3	ex airport and local area. Crashed 29-4-88. 6-95

GLASGOW AIRPORT or Abbotsinch, north of the M8 west of Renfrew
Trident G-ARPP is in Glasgow Airport house colours and used for towing and air-bridge positioning training. A very black, steel airliner shell is used by the fire crews and was joined by the nose of a sister in mid-2000, for 'hot' fire training.

❑	G-ARPL*	Trident 1C	ex Gilmerton, Edinburgh, BA, BEA. CoA 13-8-84.
			Nose. Fire crews. First noted 5-01.	3-02
❑	G-ARPP	Trident 1C	ex Heathrow, BA, BEA. CoA 16-2-86.	3-02

GLENROTHES on the A92 north of Kircaldy
A Tiger Moth has arrived for continued restoration.

❑	G-AREH*	Tiger Moth	ex Bridge of Weir, Lochwinnoch, Kilkerran, G-APYV ntu, 6746M, DE241, 22 RFS, 22 EFTS. CoA 19-4-66. ® 8-01

GREENOCK west of Glasgow on the A8
James Watt College: The college acquired a Bulldog via the auction of 25th October 2001.

❑	XX690*	'A' Bulldog T.1	ex Shawbury, Lpl UAS, 3 FTS, CFS, York UAS, RNEFTS, EL UAS, RNEFTS, 2 FTS	1-02

INSCH AERODROME west of the B992 at Auchleve

❑	G-AISS*	L-4H Cub	ex D-ECAV, SL-AAA, 44-79781. CoA 25-6-97. Stored.	1-01
❑	G-BALK	SNCAN SV-4C	ex Aboyne, 'Cheshire', Liverpool, Littleborough, F-BBAN, French mil No.387. Spares.	1-01

INVERNESS
Highland Aircraft Preservation Society: HAPS aims to establish a museum in the area.
✉ James Campbell, HAPS, 50 Newton Park, Kirkhill, Inverness, IV5 7QB ☎ 01403 831459 **e-mail** james@ haps.freeserve.co.uk

❑	WT660*	Hunter F.1	ex Cullen, New Byth, Carlisle, 229 OCU, DFLS. Arrived 4-10-99. Stored.	2-00

INVERNESS AIRPORT or Dalcross, off the A96 north-east of Inverness
The Buccaneer – on loan from Ken Charlton – is stored on behalf of the Fresson Trust ①.

❑	G-BTVG*	Cessna 140	ex N2114N, NC2114N. CoA 15-4-99. Stored.	12-01
❑	XK532	'632' Buccaneer S.1	ex Lossiemouth 8867M, Manadon, A2581, Lossiemouth, 736. Stored.	① 12-01

KILKERRAN AERODROME east of the B741, north-east of Girvan
Chrislea Super Ace G-AKVF (not listed under this heading in *W&R17*) and Cessna F.150H G-AWOT both moved to Andover, Hants, on 16th March 2000.

❑	G-ATAV	Condor	CoA 6-8-94. Stored.	8-99
❑	G-BIZT	Bensen B.8M	CoA 12-8-88. Stored.	8-99

KILMARNOCK north-east of Ayr
No.327 Squadron Air Cadets: In Aird Avenue, off Dundonald Road.

❏ WJ872	Canberra T.4	8429M, ex Halton, Wyton SF, 360, 13, Akrotiri SF, 231 OCU.	1-98
❏	Hunter CIM	—	1-98

KINLOSS AIRFIELD on the B9011 north of Forres
RAF Kinloss: Luscombe 8A G-AGMI was flying by July 2000. Instructional Nimrod MR.2 XV253 (9118M) made a rare appearance on the airfield in September 2001. This was prior to it hitching a lift on an Antonov An-124 on 21st October 2001 to join the MRA.4 line at Woodford, Cheshire.

LEUCHARS AIRFIELD on the A919, north-west of St Andrews
RAF Leuchars: Phantoms XT864 and XT867 were put up for tender in mid-2001 ①.

❏ XR713	'C'	Lightning F.3	8935M, ex LTF, 5, 11, 5, LTF, 11, LTF, 5, 111, Wattisham TFF, 111. Displayed, officially ABDR.		9-01
❏ XT864	'BJ'	Phantom FG.1	8998M, ex 111, 892, 767. Gate.	①	9-01
❏ XT867	'BH'	Phantom FG.1	9064M, ex 111, 892, 767, 700P. ABDR.	①	9-00
❏ XV577	'AM'	Phantom FG.1	9065M, ex 43. ABDR.		9-00
❏ XV582	'M'	Phantom FG.1	9066M, ex WLT, 43. *Black Mike*. All black c/s.		9-01
❏ XV586	'AJ'	Phantom FG.1	9067M, ex 43, 893.		9-01
❏ ZD906*		Tornado F.2	ex St Athan, 229 OCU. Nose. ABDRT. F/n 11-00.		9-01

LOCH EARN on the A85 west of Crieff
Cessna FR.172F G-DRAM was flying again by mid-2001.

❏ G-DHCB	Beaver 1	ex G-BTDL, XP779. CoA 16-9-97. Stored.	5-01

LONGSIDE on the A950 west of Peterhead
Malcolm Dunn: Is *thought* still to have the Cessna.

❏ 'G-ASOK'	Cessna F.172F	D-ECDU, ex Cruden Bay, Coventry, Denham, Chirk.	12-93

LONGSIDE AERODROME on the A950 west of Peterhead
Bond Helicopters: During 2000 Bö 105B XA-NAN went to Eurocopter for sale to Sweden. For former Swedish Bö 105CBS pod Fv 09413 is thought to have been scrapped.

LOSSIEMOUTH AIRFIELD south of the B4090, west of Lossiemouth
RAF Lossiemouth: Buccaneer S.2B XV863 was taken off the gate on 9th November 2001 and replaced by Tornado GR.1 ZA475. Buccaneer B.2B XX885 left by road on 19th June 2000 for the combined road/sea trip to Scampton, Lincs.

❏ XV863	'S' Buccaneer S.2B	9145M, ex 9115M, 9139M, 16, 237 OCU, 208, 237 OCU, 208, 809. Pink c/s. Off gate 9-11-01.	12-01
❏ ZA475*	'FH' Tornado GR.1B	ex 12, 16. Gate, put in place 19-12-01.	12-01
❏ ZD900*	Tornado F.2	ex St Athan, Warton, A&AEE. Nose. Armament training aid.	3-01

MAYBOLE on the A77 south of Ayr

❏ OO-NAT	MS.880B Rallye	ex G-BAOK. Fuselage.	8-99

MINTLAW on the A950 west of Peterhead

❏ G-MBFZ*	Goldwing	CoA 5-9-00. Stored.	1-01
❏ G-MJUF*	Tiger Cub 440	Canx 27-4-90. Stored.	1-01

MONTROSE on the A92 north of Arbroath

Montrose Air Station Museum (MASM): Within the museum site can be found arguably the oldest buildings designed for military flying extant in the UK - opened in 1913.

Notes: Vampire T.11 XE874 is fitted with the booms of XD528 (the rest of it is at Firbeck, S Yorks). The booms of XE874 are *also* present, just to confuse things! Sea Hawk XE340 is on loan from the Fleet Air Arm Museum, Yeovilton, Somerset ①. Vampire XE874 and the Sycamore are on loan from a private collector ②.

◆ At Waldron Road, north end of Montrose. Open Sun 12noon to 5pm and at other times by prior arrangement. Occasional special events, send SAE for details. ✉ Waldron Road, Broomfield, Montrose, DD10 9BB ☎ 01674 673107 ☎/fax 01674 674210 e-mail 106212.152@compuserve.com web http://airspeed/freeservers/com

❑ XD542	'N'	Vampire T.11	7604M, ex Edzell, Cranwell, 'XD429', Colerne, Melksham, FWS, CGS. Camo.	3-02
❑ XE340	'131'	Sea Hawk FGA.6	ex Strathallan, Wroughton, Staverton, Brawdy, 801, 898, 897, 800.	① 3-02
❑ XE874	'61'	Vampire T.11	ex New Byth, Valley 8582M, Woodford, Chester, Shawbury, 1 FTS, 4 FTS, 8 FTS, 4 FTS, 1 FTS, 4 FTS, 7 FTS.	② 3-02
❑ XJ380		Sycamore HR.14	ex New Byth, Drighlington, Finningley 8628M, Catterick, CFS, MoA, HS, 275.	② 3-02
❑ XJ723		W'wind HAR.10	ex OPITB, Wroughton, 202, 228, 155.	3-02

Neil Butler: Work continues on the Prentice. (See also Fordoun, Scotland.)

❑ VS356	Prentice T.1	G-AOLU, ex Stonehaven, Perth, Strathallan, Biggin Hill, EI-ASP, G-AOLU, VS356, CFS, 2 FTS. CoA 8-5-76.	® 3-02

Oil Petroleum Training Industry Board: Took delivery of a WG.30 during July 2001. OPTIB was last featured in *W&R16* when they disposed of their MBB Bö 105 pod G-BATC.

❑ N116WG*	WG.30-160	ex Weston-super-Mare, Yeovil, PanAm. Arr 27-7-01.	7-01

ORPHIR near Kirkwall, Orkney Islands

❑ G-ASRP	SAN DR.1050	ex F-BITI. Ditched 17-3-86. Stored.	10-94

PATHHEAD on the A68 south-east of Edinburgh

❑ G-BOHN	Tomahawk 112 II	ex Edinburgh, Cardiff-Wales, N23593. Crashed 13-8-93. Cockpit, plaything.	1-97

PERTH AIRPORT or Scone, on the A94 north-east of Perth

Perth College: Using some of the former AST buildings and four of its airframes, airframe and aero engine skills are still taught at Perth.

❑ G-ASVO*	Herald 214	ex Shoreham, Alton, Bournemouth, Channel Express, PP-SDG, G-ASVO, G-8-3. Damaged 8-4-97. Cockpit. Arrived 10-00.	3-02
❑ G-AYGB	Cessna 310Q	ex N7611Q. CoA 23-10-87.	3-02
❑ G-BCIE*	Warrior 151	ex N9588N. Dumped by 3-02	3-02
❑ G-BEWP	Cessna F.150M	crashed 4-10-83.	3-02
❑ G-BTIN*	Cessna 150C	ex N7805Z. Damaged 12-98. First noted 4-99.	3-02
❑ XL875	Whirlwind HAR.9	ex Wroughton, Lee SAR Flt, CU SAR Flt, 847, 848, 815.	3-02
❑ XT140	Sioux AH.1	ex Middle Wallop.	3-02

Others: Two Cessna hulks have gone: FRA.150L G-BBCF (last noted 8-98); F.152 G-BHWS (12-95).

❑ G-AOFJ	Auster 5	CoA 20-9-79.	® 2-00
❑ G-APXU	Tri-Pacer 150	ex Rochester, Bredhurst, N1723A. CoA 20-2-85.	® 2-00

PORTMOAK AERODROME west of Glenrothes

The hulk of a K-8 should still be found in the rafters. Another K-8 is stored in a shed.

☐ DFQ	Schleicher K-8B	BGA.2083, ex D-5077. Stored.	7-92
☐ EFP	Schleicher K-8B	BGA.2653, ex D-8859. Stored.	3-95

PRESTWICK AIRPORT east of the A79 north of Ayr

BAE Systems: It is believed that the BAE complex here no longer contains any of the Bulldog and Jetstream airframes previously listed. There were as follows, with the 'last noted' dates in brackets: Jetstream 1 N7RJ nose (2-92); Jetstream 41EFT fatigue rig (1-98); Jetstream 41 static rig (1-98); Jetstream 200 fuselage (12-95); Bulldog static test 1-98; Jetstream 32 fuselage c/n 988 (12-95).

HMS *Gannet:* With the disbanding of 819 Squadron on 31st October 2001, the Sea King SAR Detachment here became Gannet SAR Flight – a detachment of 771 Squadron. The Gannet 'guardian' moved during July to a new location within the enclave, pending a decision on its future.

☐ XL497	'041' Gannet AEW.3	ex Lossiemouth, 849.	3-02

Others: During August and September 2000 the following AS.202 Bravos were sold in Finland: G-BNTE, G-BNTH becoming OH-NTH, G-BNTK becoming OH-NTK, G-BNTL - OH-NTL, G-BNTN - OH-NTN and G-BNTO - OH-NTO. G-BNTJ followed in October 2000.

☐ N250TB*	Aztec 250D	ex G-VHFA, G-BZFE, G-AZFE, EI-BPA, G-AZFE, N13962. Stored. First noted 5-01.	3-02
☐	c/n 2068 ATP/J61	fuselage. Fire crews.	3-02
☐	c/n 2069 ATP/J61	fuselage. Fire crews. Rear section burnt by 1-99.	3-02

SKELMORLIE on the A78 north of Largs

☐ G-ATDB	Noralpha	ex Prestwick, F-OTAN-6, Fr mil 186. CoA 22-11-78.	8-93

STONEHAVEN on the A90 north of Montrose

Pete Morris: Is working on the restoration of a Terrier 2 with another for spares.

☐ G-ASAX	Terrier 2	ex Auster AOP.6 TW533, 652, LAS, AOPS, 663. CoA 1-9-96.	®	1-00
☐ G-ASBU	Terrier 2	ex Netherley, Auster T.7 WE570, LAS, CFS, 2 FTS, CFS. Crashed 12-8-80.		1-00

STRATHALLAN AERODROME west of the B8062, north of Auchterarder

☐ G-AXHE	BN-2A Islander	ex Cumbernauld, Carlisle, Cark, 4X-AYV. Cr 5-2-94.	5-01
☐ R1914	Magister I	G-AHUJ, ex Aboyne, Balado, Kemble, 137, 604, Middle Wallop SF, 604. CoA 9-7-98. Stored.	12-01

STRATHAVEN AERODROME on the A71 south-east of East Kilbride

The Grasshopper is a composite with the one at Carlisle, Cumbria, *qv*. Cyclone AX3 G-MYHG was flying again by mid-2001.

☐ G-MJUO	Quicksilver	Canx 1-95. Stored.	8-00
☐ —	Skycraft Scout	fuselage. Stored, unflown. Possibly G-MJDM.	8-00
☐ —*	Skycraft Scout	fuselage. Stored, unflown.	8-00
☐ DCL	'104' L-13 Blanik	BGA.2009. Ex Enstone. CoA 8-92. Stored.	8-00
☐ DMJ	Schleicher K-8B	BGA.2221. Ex PH-290. Stored.	8-00
☐ WZ824	Grasshopper TX.1	ex Ringmer, Dishforth, St Bees.	8-00

STRATHDON on the A97 north of Ballater

☐ N15750	Beech D.18S	ex Corgarff, 'CF-RLD', Lasham, G-ATUM, D-IANA, N20S. Cockpit section.	2-97

SUMBURGH AIRPORT Shetland Islands, on the A970 south of Lerwick
The Potez 840 should continue to serve the firemen. S-61N G-BXSN was restored and flown out to Aberdeen on 3rd May 2000.

☐ F-BMCY	Potez 840	wheels-up landing 29-3-81. Fire dump.	2-01

TAIN north of Inverness

☐ G-ATWS*	Luton Minor	CoA 26-3-69.	® 7-01

THORNHILL AERODROME on the A873 north-west of Stirling
The para-trainer *may* still be here.

☐ G-ATES	Cherokee Six 260	ex Glenrothes, Ipswich. Crashed 8-2-81. Para-trainer.	8-99

WEST FREUGH AIRFIELD on the A715 south-east of Stranraer
Defence Science and Technology Laboratory (DS&TL – yet still another name change, effective from 1st July 2001. See under Boscombe Down, Wilts, for still more interesting alphabetic contortions.)

☐ XN817	Argosy C.1	ex A&AEE, MinTech, MoA. Dump.	9-01
☐ XT852	Phantom FGR.2	ex BAe Scampton, A&AEE, HSA, A&AEE, HSA, A&AEE, McDD. Dump.	9-01

YARROW on the A708 west of Selkirk

☐ G-ANOK	SAAB Safir	ex Strathallan, East Fortune, SE-CAH ntu. CoA 5-2-73. Stored.	10-01

PART THREE

WALES

The 'regions' of Wales work on a wholly 'single tier' unitary authority structure.
The regions are as follows:

Clwyd   Denbighshire, Flintshire, Wrexham.
Dyfed   Carmarthenshire, Ceredigion, Pembrokeshire.
Gwent   Monmouthshire, Newport, Torfaen.
Gwynedd   Anglesey, Conwy, Gwynedd.
Powys   –
Mid Glamorgan   Blanau Gwent, Bridgend, Caerphilly, Merthyr Tydfil,
                    Rhondda, Cynon and Taff.
South Glamorgan   Cardiff, Vale of Glamorgan.
West Glamorgan   Neath Port Talbot, Swansea.

ABERGAVENNY, 'Gwent', on the A40 west of Monmouth
❑ N9191   Tiger Moth   G-ALND, ex Shobdon, Shipdham, N9191, 5 SoTT,
                                        19 EFTS, Duxford CF, 6 CPF. Crashed 8-3-81.   ®   3-96

ABERPORTH AIRFIELD, 'Dyfed', north of the A487, east of Cardigan
Defence Science and Technology Laboratory (DS&TL – yet still another name change, effective from 1st July 2001. See under Boscombe Down, Wilts, for still more interesting alphabetic contortions): The Hunter is kept at the range control station on behalf of **1429 Squadron Air Cadets**. It is 'parented' by St Athan. *W&R17* (p281) 'wrote off' Canberra WH876 on the dump here. The nose was sectioned off and moved to Boscombe Down, Wilts, on 2nd May 2001. The remainder was scrapped.
❑ WT680   'J' Hunter F.1   7533M, ex Weeton, DFLS, West Raynham SF.   10-98

AMMANFORD, 'Dyfed', on the A483 north of Swansea
No.2475 Squadron Air Cadets: Should still keep a Canberra nose.
❑ WH739   Canberra B.2   ex St Athan, 100, 85, 45, 75 RNZAF,   Upwood SF, 50, 101. Nose.   10-98

BRAWDY, 'Dyfed', north of the A487 east of St David's
No.14 Signals Regiment: Cawdor Barracks. The Hunter was offered for tender during 2001 and is due to move to the East Midlands.
❑ XE624   'G' Hunter FGA.9   8875M, ex 1 TWU, 2 TWU, TWU, 229 OCU,   West Raynham SF, 1. Gate.   4-01

BRIDGEND, 'Mid Glamorgan', on the A473 west of Cardiff
De Havilland Aviation Ltd: Maintain a workshop here. See under Swansea, Wales, and Bournemouth, Dorset, for their flying operation and *another* 'WL505'! ①
♦ The workshop is *not* available for inspection.
❑ WL505   Vampire FB.9   G-FBIX, ex Bruntingthorpe, Cranfield, St Athan,   Ely, 19, RAFC, 73.   ①   1-01
❑ XE956   Vampire T.11   G-OBLN, ex St Albans, Hatfield, CATCS, 1 FTS,   8 FTS, 3 CAACU, APS, 67.   ®   1-01
❑ XE985   Vampire T.11   ex London Colney, Woodford, Chester, St Athan,   5 FTS.   2-00
❑   Vampire FB.6   ex Switzerland. Pod, unflown.   2-00
❑   Vampire FB.6   ex Switzerland. Pod, unflown.   2-00

CAERNARFON AERODROME, 'Gwynedd' (or Caernarfon airparc, or Llandwrog)
                                   north of the A487, SW of Caernarfon
Caernarfon Air Museum: (Note name change.) The museum tells the story of aviation in general and aviation in North Wales in particular. The mountain rescue exhibit is a graphic story of wartime crashes — Allied and Luftwaffe. The Weedhopper may be G-MJSM — comments? ① Away from the public gaze for some time, Anson C.19/2 TX235 moved to Coventry, Warks.
♦ Open March 1 to end of October, 10am to 5pm. ✉ Caernarfon airparc, Dinas Dinlle, Caernarfon, LL54 5TP ☎ 08707 541500 **fax** 08707 541510 **e-mail** info@caeairparc.com www caeairparc.com

❑ G-ALFT   Dove 6   ex Higher Blagdon, Stansted, CAFU. CoA 13-6-73.   3-02
❑ G-AMLZ   Prince 6E   ex Coventry, VR-TBN ntu, G-AMLZ. CoA 18-6-71.   3-02
❑ G-AWUK   Cessna F.150H   ex Shobdon, Stansted, Oaksey Park, Bristol,   Biggin Hill. Crashed 4-9-71. Cockpit. Stored.   3-02
❑ G-MBEP   Eagle 215B   first noted 1-97. On loan from R W Lavender.   3-02
❑   Weedhopper   loaned from Ray Bancroft, Prestatyn.   ①   3-02
❑ WM961   'J' Sea Hawk FB.5   ex Higher Blagdon, Culdrose A2517, FRU, 802, 811.   3-02
❑ WN499   'Y' Dragonfly HR.3   ex Higher Blagdon, Blackbushe, Culdrose SF. Plaything.   3-02

❏ WT694		Hunter F.1	ex Newton, Debden 7510M, 229 OCU, DFLS, 54.	3-02
❏ WV781		Sycamore HR.12	ex Finningley, Odiham, Digby 7839M, HDU,	
			CFS, ASWDU, G-ALTD ntu. Forward fuselage.	3-02
❏ XA282		Cadet TX.3	ex Syerston, 635 VGS.	3-02
❏ XH837		Javelin FAW.7	ex Northolt, Ruislip 8032M, 33. Forward fuselage.	3-02
❏ XJ726	'F'	W'wind HAR.10	ex Sibson, Wroughton, 2 FTS, CFS, ME SAR Flt, 22.	3-02
❏ XK623	'56'	Vampire T.11	ex Bournemouth 'G-VAMP', Moston,	
			Woodford, Chester, St Athan, 5 FTS.	3-02
❏ XL618	'05'	Hunter T.7	ex Cottesmore 8892M, Shawbury, Kemble,	
			1 TWU, 229 OCU, Jever SF, Gütersloh SF.	3-02
❏	BAPC.201	HM.14 'Flea'	ex Talysarn. Fuselage, rudder, wing spars. Modded u/c.	3-02
❏		Tiger Moth	ex Shobdon, Fownhope. Frame in 'workshp' scene.	3-02
❏		Varsity T.1 EMU	ex Higher Blagdon.	3-02

CARDIFF, 'South Glamorgan'
National Museum and Gallery: (Note correct name.) Keeps Wales' most significant aviation artefact, the Watkins CHW. Between August 2001 and February 2002, the museum hosted an exhibition supported by US engine manufacturer General Electric, entitled 'Flight'. Included in the exhibition were two airframes from the IWM, Duxford – Cadet TX.3 XN239 and Hurricane FSM 'R4115'.
◆ Tuesday to Sunday and Bank Holidays 10am to 5pm. ✉ Cathays Park, Cardiff, CF1̲0̲ 3NP ☎ 029 20 397951 **fax** 029 20 373219

❏	BAPC.47	Watkins CHW	ex St Athan, Cardiff.	8-01

Welsh Industrial and Maritime Museum: The Wessex is to be found at N̲a̲n̲t̲g̲a̲r̲w̲, Wales.

CARDIFF AIRPORT, 'South Glamorgan', (or Rhoose), on the A4226 west of Barry
Airport: A number of BA Boeing 747-236s were placed into store here during 2001, and pre 11th September. It is too early to judge if they will become long-termers. The fire crews here have a three-engined bright red (but going black!) synthetic fire trainer to play with as well as the real airframes. By late 2000, Pembroke C.1 WV753 was reduced to a gutted shell and can be deleted.

❏ G-AVGH	Cherokee 140	CoA 5-12-91. Fuselage. Fire crews.	2-01
❏	Jetstream 41 EMU	ex WAM, Hatfield, Prestwick. Based on Srs 200	
		G-ATXJ. CoA 8-2-71. Fire crews.	2-02

Barry Technical College: Within the industrial and business park on the airport perimeter. To make room for the Bulldogs HS.125-1B/522 G-BOCB was scrapped during January 2001. Local stalwart Dave Thomas saved the cockpit section and by October 2001 it had found its way to D̲o̲n̲c̲a̲s̲t̲e̲r̲, S Yorks.

❏ G-BDAX		Aztec 250C	ex 5B-CAO, N6399Y. CoA 12-11-93.	11-01
❏ XX672*	'E'	Bulldog T.1	ex Shawbury, Birm UAS. Arrived 12-7-01.	11-01
❏ XX687*	'F'	Bulldog T.1	ex Shawbury, EM UAS, Lpl UAS. Arrived 18-7-01.	11-01

CHESTER AIRPORT (or Hawarden or Broughton), 'Clwyd', on the B5129 west of Chester
BAE Systems:

❏		HS.748	ex Hatfield. Forward fuselage. Dump.	11-97
❏	c/n 2075	ATP	ex Chadderton. Fuselage.	4-98
❏ 'WE275'		Venom FB.50	G-VIDI, ex Dunsfold, Cranfield, Swiss AF J-1601.	
			45 Sqn c/s. Damaged 7-7-96. Fire dump.	5-97

Hawarden Air Services: By 2000 Bulldog 120 G-BHXA was flying.

❏ G-ASXH	Bensen B.8M	CoA 22-8-73.		3-96
❏ G-BHXB*	Bulldog 120	ex Botswana DF OD2, G-BHXB. CoA 23-4-98̲. Stored.		2-99
❏ G-BYED*	Jet Provost T.5A	ex N166A, XW302, 6 FTS, 3 FTS, RAFC, 1 FTS.		
		Force-landed 12-2-01. Arrived 7-01.	®	8-01
❏ G-FLYY*	Strikemaster	ex Humberside, RSaudiAF 1112, G-27-31.		
	Mk.80	First noted 8-01.	®	8-01

❏ G-OJCM	Rotorway Exec 90	crashed 25-9-95. Wreck.	8-96
❏ G-UPCC	Robinson R-22	ex G-MUSS. Crashed 5-6-94.	8-96
❏ CCCP-07268	An-2 *Colt*	YL-LEV, Latvia, USSR.	4-98
❏ CCCP-17939	An-2 *Colt*	YL-LFC, Latvia, USSR.	4-98
❏ CCCP-19733	An-2 *Colt*	YL-LEZ, Latvia, USSR.	10-00
❏ CCCP-20320	Mi-2 *Hoplite*	YL-LHN, Latvia, USSR.	2-00
❏ CCCP-20619	Mi-2 *Hoplite*	YL-LHO, Latvia, USSR.	2-00
❏ CCCP-40748	An-2 *Colt*	YL-LFA, Latvia, USSR.	4-98
❏ CCCP-40749	An-2 *Colt*	YL-LFD, Latvia, USSR.	4-98
❏ CCCP-40784	An-2 *Colt*	YL-LEY, Latvia, USSR.	4-98
❏ CCCP-40785	An-2 *Colt*	YL-LFB, Latvia, USSR.	4-98
❏ CCCP-54949	An-2 *Colt*	YL-LEX, Latvia, USSR.	4-98
❏ CCCP-56471	An-2 *Colt*	YL-LEW, Latvia, USSR.	4-98
❏ c/n S45/T42	Tucano T.1	ex Waverton, Belfast City. Bomb damaged 1990. ®	2-99
❏ '03' r	Mi-24 *Hind-D*	ex Latvia, USSR. (3532461715415).	10-00
❏ '04' r	MiG-23ML	ex Latvia, USSR. (024003607).	1-00
❏ '05' b	Yak-50	YL-CBH, ex Latvia. (832507).	11-97
❏ '05' r	Yak-50	YL-YAK, ex Strathallan, CIS. (832507?)	11-95
❏ '06' r	Mi-24 *Hind-D*	ex Latvia, USSR. (3532464505029).	10-00
❏ '09' g	Yak-52	YL-CBI, ex Wrexham, Chester, Latvia. (811202).	11-96
❏ '20' b	Yak-52	YL-CBJ, ex Strathallan, CIS. (790404).	11-97
❏ '23' r	MiG-27 *Flogger*	ex Latvia, USSR. (83712515040).	10-00
❏ '35' r	Su-17M-3 *Fitter*	ex Latvia, USSR. ('25102')	2-00
❏ '50' r	MiG-23MF	ex Latvia, USSR. (023003508).	2-00
❏ '54' r	Su-17B *Fitter*	ex Latvia, USSR. (69004/5).	10-00
❏ '56' r	Yak-52	ex Strathallan, CIS. (811504 or 811502)	11-97
❏ '71' r	MiG-27K *Flogger*	ex Latvia, USSR. (61912507006)	10-00
❏ —	Mi-24V *Hind*	ex Latvia, USSR. (3532424810853).	2-00

No.2247 Squadron Air Cadets: 'Parented' by Sealand, in Manor Lane to the east of the airfield.

❏ XE852	'H' Vampire T.11	ex Woodford, Chester, Shawbury, 1 FTS, 4 FTS. ®	8-01

CHIRK, 'Clwyd', on the A5 north of Oswestry

❏ G-AJBJ	Dragon Rapide	ex Coventry, Blackpool, NF894, 18 MU, HQ TCCF. CoA 14-9-61.	10-01
❏ 'G-AJCL'	Dragon Rapide	G-AIUL, ex Southend, British Westpoint, NR749, Kemble, 2 RS. CoA 29-9-67. Stored.	10-01
❏ G-AKOE	Dragon Rapide	ex Booker, X7484, PTS. CoA 25-2-82. Stored.	10-01
❏ G-ATFV	Bell 47J-2A	ex 9J-ACX, G-ATFV, It AF MM80417. CoA 8-8-92.	10-99
❏ G-BAYL	Norecrin VI	ex Ivychurch, Solihull, Bodmin, F-BEQV. Fuselage.	10-01
❏ G-BEDB	Norecrin	ex Liverpool, Chirk, F-BEOB. CoA 11-6-80.	10-01

CONNAH'S QUAY, 'Clwyd', on the A548 west of Chester
North East Wales Institute, Dee-side College: See also under Wrexham, Wales.

❏ G-AZMX	Cherokee 140	ex Chester Airport, Halfpenny Green, SE-FLL, LN-LMK. CoA 9-1-82.	3-02
❏ XA460	'768' Gannet AS.4	ex Brawdy, 849.	3-02
❏ XR658	Jet Provost T.4	ex Bournemouth, Wroughton, Abingdon 8192M, RAFEF, 6 FTS, CAW, 7 FTS.	3-02

COWBRIDGE, 'South Glamorgan', on the A48 west of Cardiff
The Whirlwind still battles it out at the paintball wargames park.

❏ XG592	Whirlwind HAS.7	ex Cardiff, Wroughton, 705, 846, 705, 700, C(A), HS, Westland.	1-02

HAVERFORDWEST AERODROME, 'Dyfed', or Withybush, on the A40, N of Haverfordwest
DH.2 REP '5964' (G-BFVH) flew again on 12th July 2000.

❑ G-ACZE*	Dragon Rapide	ex Dorchester, G-AJGS, G-ACZE, Z7266, 3 FP, 6 AONS, G-ACZE. CoA 11-8-95. F/n 3-00.	®	3-00
❑ G-AHAP	J/1 Autocrat (m)	ex St Just. CoA 20-2-91.	®	3-00
❑ G-ASAN*	Terrier 2	ex Auster T.7 VX928, 661, HCEU, 661. CoA 28-6-96. First noted 4-01.	®	4-01
❑ G-ASEG	Terrier 1	ex AOP.6 VF548, 653, 10 IRF, APSF. Damaged 2-97.		4-01
❑ G-BPGK	Aeronca 7AC	ex Llanelli, N4409E. Crashed 7-5-91.	®	10-99
❑ G-BTWU	Tri-Pacer 135	ex N3320B.	®	10-99

KENFIG HILL, 'Mid Glamorgan', north of the B4281 east of Pyle
No.2117 Squadron Air Cadets: Off Main Street, and behind Pwll-y-Garth Street. The Hunter,
'parented' by St Athan, is hard to find! When found, it is overall grey and unmarked.

❑ WT569	Hunter F.1	ex St Athan 7491M, A&AEE, Hawkers trials.	2-02

LLANBEDR, 'Gwynedd', on the A496 south of Harlech
Former **Maes Artro Village**: The nose of the Hunter is on loan from local 2445 Squadron Air Cadets.

❑ 'MAV467' 'RO'	Spitfire V FSM	BAPC.202, ex *Piece of Cake*.	3-02
❑ VS562	Anson T.21	ex Portsmouth, Llanbedr 8012M, A&AEE, AST Hamble, CS(A).	10-01
❑ WN957	Hunter F.5	ex TEE Llanbedr, Stafford, North Weald, 7407M, RAE. Nose.	10-01
❑ XJ409	Whirlwind HAR.10	ex Grangetown, Cardiff-Wales, Wroughton, Warton SAR Flt, 1310F, 228, 155, XD779 ntu.	3-02
❑ A92-664	Jindivik 3	ex DRA, RAE. Composite.	10-01

LLANBEDR AIRFIELD, 'Gwynedd', west of Llanbedr and the A496 on the road to Shell Island
Defence Science and Technology Laboratory (DS&TL – yet still another name change, effective
from 1st July 2001. See under Boscombe Down, Wilts, for still more interesting alphabetic contortions.)
The Meteor may be moving locally before too long.

❑ WH453	'L' Meteor D.16	ex 5 CAACU, 72, 222. Stored.	3-02
❑ WH887	'847' Canberra TT.18	ex St Athan, FRADU, Upwood SF, 21, 542, 1323 Flt. Dump.	3-02
❑ XV435	'R' Phantom FGR.2	ex 92, 228 OCU, 92, 228 OCU, 23, 228 OCU, 14.	3-02
❑ 'A92-LLAN1'	Jindivik 3	A92-480, gate guard.	3-02

LLANTRISANT, 'Mid Glamorgan', on the A4119 north-west of Cardiff
Mr and Mrs J Little's Bulldog T.1 XX669 moved to Andover, Hants, by March 2001. Dave Thomas'
Lightning F.53 ZF582 moved to Reading, Berks, on 12th August 2000.

LLANWRTYD WELLS 'Powys', on the A483 west of Builth Wells

❑ XM358	Jet Provost T.3A	ex Twyford, North Scarle, Colsterworth, Halton 8987M, 1 FTS, 3 FTS, 1 FTS, CFS, RAFC, CFS, 7 FTS, 2 FTS.	2-00

MILFORD HAVEN, 'Dyfed', on the A4076 south of Haverfordwest
No.1284 Squadron Air Cadets: Keep their 'JP' nose at their HQ. It carries a plate marked
PAC/W/10164, which *should* make it T.3 XN503.

❑	Jet Provost	ex Salisbury, Firbeck, Coventry, Bicester, Kemble. Nose.	4-95

MOLD, 'Clywd', on the A494 west of Chester.
Derek Griffiths: Derek keeps his Canberra nose in this general area. (It was previously listed under Sealand, Wales.) Derek founded the **International Cockpit Club** after *CockpitFest 2001* at Newark, Notts. The club serves to unit and inform anyone who owns, would like to own, or just likes the idea of cockpit collecting. To visit the Canberra, and/or, to join the ICC, apply to:
✉ 21 Bryn-Y-Foel, Rhosemor, near Mold, CH7 6PW **e-mail** derekg-griffiths@btinternet.com

❏ WH984	Canberra B.15	ex Bruntingthorpe, Hinckley, Bruntingthorpe, Cosford 8101M, HS, 9, Binbrook SF, 9. Nose.	4-98

NANTGARW on the A470 north-west of Cardiff
Wales Museums Service: A restoration and large object store here holds a Wessex.

❏ XM300*	Wessex HAS.1	ex Cardiff, Cardiff-Wales, Farnborough, RAE, Westlands. SAR colours. Stored.	2-02

NEWPORT, 'Gwent'
No.210 Squadron Air Cadets:

❏ WD293	Chipmunk T.10 PAX	7645M. ex Caerleon, Cwmbran, QuB UAS, StA UAS, G&S UAS, StA UAS, Chatham Flt, SMR, 1 BFTS.	10-98

PENDINE RANGES, 'Dyfed', on the A4066 east of Tenby
Proof and Experimental Establishment: (The PEE has almost certainly been renamed, in line with all the other changes!) The two F-4J(UK)s that went to Foulness, Essex, as noted in *W&R17* have been identified as ZE350 and ZE352. That leaves ZE363 to pin down. It is believed that there has been a clear-out here and all of the airframes listed in *W&R17* have gone: Canberra T.4 WH844; Hunter F.6A XG158; Wessex HAS.1 XM926; Lightning F.3 XP708; Lightning F.6 XS895; Buccaneer S.2A XT274; Buccaneer S.2 XV340; F-4J(UK)s ZE355 and ZE362. This leaves one 'newcomer':

❏ XV373*	SH-3D	ex Foulness, A&AEE, RAE. Arrived 26-2-<u>97</u>.	2-02

PETERSTONE, 'Gwent', on the B4239 north-east of Cardiff

❏ N5834N	Commander 114	force-landed 23-10-98. Hulk.	2-02

ROSEMARKET, 'Dyfed', north-east of Milford Haven
The Cub remains in external store, on a local golf course! The others are stored elsewhere.

❏ G-AYCN	J3C-65 Cub	ex F-BCPO. CoA 27-1-89. Stored.	8-95
❏ G-BBKR	Scheibe SF-24A	ex D-KECA. CoA 30-3-79. Stored..	5-95
❏ G-BHPM	PA-18-95 S' Cub	ex F-BOUR, ALAT, 51-15501. Stored.	5-95
❏ G-BJNY	Aeronca 11CC	ex CN-TYZ, F-OAEE. CoA 9-8-90. Stored.	1-95

RUTHIN 'Clwyd', on the A494 south-west of Mold
Phantom Preservation Group: See also under Nantwich, Cheshire.
◆ Visits by prior arrangement only. ✉ Mark A Jones, 4 Bro Clywedog, Rhewl, Ruthin, LL15 1BA. e-mail mark3045@freeuk.com

❏ —	Phantom FGR.2	Nose section. Stored.	2-02

ST ATHAN AIRFIELD, 'South Glamorgan', on the B4265 west of Barry
RAF St Athan: The gondola of the airship K88 made the move to <u>Newbury,</u> Berks. During the summer of 2000, the **University of Wales Air Squadron** acquired a Flying Flea - complete with Scott A2S engine – locally. They plan to restore it to display condition.

❏ 'XV498'	Phantom FGR.2	XV500 / 9113M, ex 56, 29, 23, 56, 111, 43, 54. 92 Sqn colours. Displayed.	11-01
❏ —*	HM.14 Flea	ex 'local'.	® 12-00

RAF Exhibition Production and Transportation Team (EPTT): *W&R17* (286) got this somewhat around its neck, so delete all references to M&RU! Operated under contract by Hunting Contract Services, the airframes are based on a former airfield site in the East Midlands. EPTT is 'parented' these days by the Directorate of Recruitment and Selection at Cranwell, Lincs. That being the case, the EPTT 'fleet' is now listed under that Lincolnshire location!

Defence Aviation Repair Agency (DARA): The end of the **BAC VC-10** is within sight and scrappings are well underway. The replacement airframe has yet to be determined.

The Tornado GR.4 programme is nearly complete and there is work underway up-grading some of the GR.1s, but others – as can be seen below – are now entering deep store and spares reclaim. First **Tornado GR.1** to be retired and readied for spares reclaim was ZA319. It was first flown at Warton, Lancs, on 10th July 1979 and entered service with 'Thomas The Tank Engine' (TTTE!) at Cottesmore, Leics, on 17th November 1981. It transferred to 15(R) Squadron at Lossiemouth, Scotland, on 3rd November 1999. When delivered to St Athan, by Flt Lts Bruce Chapple and Bill Corser, it had 'clocked' 3,926:25 total time. It seems like only yesterday that Tornados were arriving at Cottesmore to start the whole ball rolling...

Several *W&Rs* have mused over the **Tornado F.2** centre fuselages for the 'damaged' F.3s scheme. There is now a scheme whereby the 'F.2' centre fuselages held here (actually from the 'duff' F.3s) will go to DASA in Germany for refurbishment and further use in the F.3 programme! Forward and rear fuselages of F.2s started to appear in the scrapping compound by the turn of the century and it would appear that F.2s will soon be a thing of the past.

Like Brough, East Yorks, St Athan is another venue that has been littered with **Hawk Fuselage Replacement Programme** (FRP) detritus. This complex new-for-old scheme is largely leaving shells that are best ignored, or the Hawk population will suffer from dual or even *triple* personalities! Essentially, these discarded items have not yet developed sufficient longevity to merit a listing – though the situation is being monitored. The bulk of the hardware are *rear* fuselage sections, which do not come under the defined scope of *W&R* anyway.

During the middle of March 2002, it was announced that the **Sea Harrier FA.2** fleet was to be wound down, perhaps as early as 2004. With the 'SHAR' being a first-generation Harrier 'with attitude' the cross-over of logistics to the GR.7 has been deemed not cost effective. This would leave the fleet without a dedicated fighter, although there were noises coming from MoD that the GR.9 upgrade would involve enhanced self-protection. By the time *W&R19* appears the fleet could well *all* be listed!

Departures: Canberra PR.7 forward fuselage WT538 departed 1-01, believed scrapped; **Harrier GR.7** ZD462 to Cosford, Shropshire 22-10-01; **Hawk T.1A** XX304, forward fuselage repaired for possible use in FRP, to Shawbury, Shropshire, 25-9-01 (remainder of the fuselage to Barry Tech, Cardiff; **Jaguar GR.1** XX979 arrived by 10-01, to Coltishall, Norfolk, 19-2-02; XZ375 arrived by 10-01, to Coltishall, Norfolk 19-2-02; Tornado GR.1s ZA460 arrived 27-11-99, to the dump by 1-02, scrapped and removed 2-02; ZA471 arrived 17-11-00 as ZA460; ZA590 dumped out by 11-01, then as ZA460; **Tornado F.2s** ZD900 nose to Lossiemouth, Scotland, remainder scrapped 2-01; ZD904 scrapped 2-01; ZD906 nose to Leuchars, Scotland, by 11-00, remainder scrapped 2-01; hybrid ZD934 nose to Leeming, N Yorks, by 11-00, remainder scrapped 2-01; ZD935 left for Shawbury, Shrop, 22-3-00; ZD936 cockpit to Bedford, Beds, by 11-00, centre fuselage to EADS Germany mid-2001 for further assessment to see if it could be repaired; ZD937 to the dump by 11-00, scrapped 2-01; ZD938 nose to Shawbury, Shropshire, 1-3-00; ZD939 forward fuselage to Cosford, Shrop, 18-2-02; ZD941 scrapped 2-01; **Tornado F.3** ZE210 nose scrapped 2-01; **VC-10 K.2s** ZA140 arrived 3-5-00 and scrapped by 3-01; ZA141 scrapped by 9-00; ZA143 scrapping started 8-00 and it had gone by 10-01; ZA144 arrived by 12-00, scrapped by 6-01 although its cockpit may have survived; **AV-8B Harrier II** fuselages 162958 arrived 10-00, moved to Boscombe Down, Wilts, by 1-02; 162730 arrived 10-4-01 but moved to Wyton, Cambs, 13-2-02.

❏ WJ717	'841'	Canberra TT.18	9052M, ex 4 SoTT, FRADU, 61, 15. Stored.	11-01
❏ XS180	'21'	Jet Provost T.4	'8238M' [Really 8338M], ex Lyneham, St Athan, Halton, Kemble, CAW, 6 FTS. Rescue exercises.	11-01
❏ XT773		Wessex HU.5	9123M, ex Abingdon, Wroughton. ABDRT	11-01
❏ XV103*		VC-10 C.1K	ex 10. Arrived 11-12-00. Scrapping by 11-01.	11-01
❏ XX254*		Hawk T.1A	ex Brough, Chivenor, 7 FTS, 1 TWU, 2 TWU. Front fuselage. First noted 7-01. Stored.	7-01
❏ XX326*		Hawk T.1A	ex Brough, 19, 92, 2 TWU. Front fuselage. F/n 7-01.	7-01
❏ XX722	'EF'	Jaguar GR.1	9252M, ex Shawbury, Warton, Shawbury, 6, 54, JOCU. Stored. Fuselage, poor state. ABDRT	1-02

❑ XX839	'GW'	Jaguar T.2B	ex 9256M, 54, 41, 16, 226 OCU. Stored. Arr 2-95.	11-01
❑ XX847		Jaguar T.2	ex Coltishall, 6, 41, 226 OCU, 31, 20, 14,	
			226 OCU, 17, 14, 2, 226 OCU, 6, 226 OCU.	1-02
❑ XX977	'DL'	Jaguar GR.1	9132M, ex Abingdon, Shawbury, 31. ABDRT	11-01
❑ XZ322	'N'	Gazelle AH.1	9283M, ex Shawbury, 670, ARWS, 6 Flt. ABDRT	11-01
❑ XZ630		Tornado GR.1	8986M, ex Brüggen, BAe Warton, A&AEE. ABDRT	11-01
❑ XZ938*	'45'	Gazelle HT.2	ex Shawbury, 705. ABDRT. Arrived 27-2-02.	2-02
❑ XZ941*	'B'	Gazelle HT.2	ex Shawbury, 2 FTS, Odiham hack, CFS. Arr 10-10-01.	10-01
❑ XZ991	'3A'	Harrier GR.3	9162M, ex 233 OCU, 4, 1417F, 233 OCU, 1,	
			R-R, 1, 3, 1.	11-01
❑ XZ993	'M'	Harrier GR.3	9240M, ex Laarbruch, St Athan, 4, 1, 1453F, 3.	11-01
❑ ZA142	'C'	VC-10 K.2	ex 101, A40-VI, G-ARVI. Arrived 27-3-01. Scrapping.	2-02
❑ ZA319*	'TAV'	Tornado GR.1	ex 15, TTTE. Arrived 3-9-01. Stored.	11-01
❑ ZA320*	'TAW'	Tornado GR.1	ex 15, TTTE. Arrived 5-9-01. Stored.	1-02
❑ ZA321*	'TAB'	Tornado GR.1	ex 15, TTTE. Arrived 5-9-01. Stored.	11-01
❑ ZA325*	'TAX'	Tornado GR.1	ex 15, TTTE. Arrived 8-10-01. Stored.	11-01
❑ ZA352*	'TAU'	Tornado GR.1	ex 15, TTTE. Arrived 19-11-01. Dump by 2-02.	2-02
❑ ZA399*	'AJC'	Tornado GR.1	ex 617, 20, TWCU. Arrived 28-11-01. Stored.	1-02
❑ ZA455*	'F'	Tornado GR.1	ex 15, 12, 31, 15, 9, 15. Arrived 10-9-01. Stored.	11-01
❑ ZA490*	'FJ'	Tornado GR.1	ex 12. Arrived 2-3-02.	3-02
❑ ZD350	'A'	Harrier GR.5	9189M, ex Wittering, 1. Crashed 7-8-92. Nose.	11-01
❑ ZD580	'002'	Sea Harrier F/A.2	ex Yeovilton, 800. Collision 16-9-96. Stored.	10-01
❑ ZD901	'AA'	Tornado F.2	ex 229 OCU. F.2-F.3 exchange.	2-02
❑ ZD903	'AB'	Tornado F.2	ex 229 OCU. Nose. Armament training aid.	8-01
❑ ZD905		Tornado F.2	ex 229 OCU. F.2-F.3 exchange. Stored.	10-01
❑ ZD932	'AM'	Tornado F.2	ex 229 OCU. F.2-F.3 exchange. ABDR.	1-02
❑ ZD933	'AO'	Tornado F.2	ex 229 OCU. F.2-F.3 exchange.	11-01
❑ ZD940		Tornado F.2	ex 229 OCU. F.2-F.3 exchange.	11-01
❑ ZE163*		Tornado F.3	ex 56. Damaged. Arrived 22-5-97. Under repair.	2-02
❑ ZE253*	'AC'	Tornado F.3	ex 56. Arrived 27-11-01. Stored.	11-01
❑ ZE290*	'AG'	Tornado F.3	ex 56. Arrived 11-9-01. Spares reclaim.	11-01
❑ ZE296*	'AD'	Tornado F.3	ex 56, 43, 56. Arrived 11-9-01. Spares reclaim.	11-01
❑ ZE339*		Tornado F.3	ex 56, 5, 56, 25, 5. Arrived 4-9-00. Spares reclaim.	11-01
❑ ZG994*		Islander AL.1	ex Bembridge, 1 Flt AAC. Cr 30-6-99. Fuse. F/n 5-01.	11-01

No.4 School of Technical Training / Civilian Technical Training School: Not part of DARA, the school is part of HQ Personnel and Training Command (Training Group Defence Agency). Gazelle AH.1 XZ322 was listed under this heading in *W&R17*, it is more properly listed under DARA, above. Gnat T.1 XP502 moved to Ipswich, Suffolk, on 3rd May 2000.

❑ XM419	'102'	Jet Provost T.3A	8990M, ex 7 FTS, 3 FTS, CFS, RAFC, CFS,	
			3 FTS, RAFC, 6 FTS, RAFC, 2 FTS.	9-01
❑ XN551	'100'	Jet Provost T.3A	8984M, ex 7 FTS, RAFC, 1 FTS, 3 FTS, 6 FTS, RAFC.	9-01
❑ XW404	'77'	Jet Provost T.5A	9049M, ex 1 FTS.	9-01
❑ XW409	'123'	Jet Provost T.5A	9047M, ex 7 FTS, 1 FTS.	9-01
❑ XX626*	'W'	Bulldog T.1	9290M, ex Wales UAS, CFS. Arrived 11-00.	9-01
❑ (XX635)	'S'	Bulldog T.1	8767M, ex Ems UAS.	9-01
❑ XX686*	'4'	Bulldog T.1	9291M, ex CFS, 3 FTS, Gla UAS, Ox UAS,	
			Gla UAS, Lpl UAS, 2 FTS. Arrived 11-00.	9-01
❑ XX710*	'5'	Bulldog T.1	ex Newton, Man UAS, Yorks UAS. Cr 21-7-97.	
			Wreck. Arrived 20-3-01.	3-01
❑ XX763	'24'	Jaguar GR.1	9009M, ex Shawbury, 226 OCU.	9-01
❑ XX764	'13'	Jaguar GR.1	9010M, ex Shawbury, 226 OCU, 14.	9-01

SEALAND, 'Clwyd', on the A550 south-west of Ellesmere Port
Defence Aviation Repair Agency (DARA): Approach road changes at the facility forced the move of the Hunter from the gate for the early part of 2001. It returned to 'duty' by July 2001. The RAF

element 'parents' a series of ATC airframes (eg Birkdale, Hawarden, Royton). The nose of Canberra B.15 WH984 is more properly listed under <u>Mold</u>, Wales.

❑ 'WT720'	'B' Hunter F.51	8565M, ex Cranwell 'XF979', Brawdy, Dunsfold, G-9-436, Esk.724, Dan AF E-408. 74 Sqn c/s, Gate.		8-01
❑ XS735	'R' Dominie T.1	ex Cranwell, 55, 6 FTS, RAFC, CAW. GIA.		3-98

Ian Starnes: Ian's two airframes are more properly listed under <u>Chester</u>, Cheshire.

SWANSEA AIRPORT, 'West Glamorgan', (or Fairwood Common), on the A4118 west of Swansea
De Havilland Aviation Ltd (DHA) / **Vintage Jet Flying Group**: On 29th May 2000 pilot Sepp Pauli took Sea Vixen D.3 XP924 (G-CVIX) into the air again and off on a ferry flight to its new base at Bournemouth. With this started the operation of the aircraft on the airshow circuit and a sight that many people thought would never be seen again.

As explained in *W&R17* DHA moved their operating base to Bournemouth, Dorset, during 2001. Some maintenance is still carried out here, as is some conversion flying training. Essentially, readers should refer under Bournemouth for full details of the DHA operation. The engineering workshop and store are at Bridgend, Wales. At Bridgend can be found the *real* WL505 just to confuse things! ① The Sea Vampire T.22 is being restored for Martin Cobb by DHA ②.

Departures for <u>Bournemouth</u>: Vampire T.11 XE920 (G-VMPR) 2-4-01; Sea Vixen D.3 XP924 (G-CVIX) 29-5-00; Vampire T.55 U-1234 (G-DHAV) by 3-01.

❑ 'WL505'	Vampire FB.6	G-MKVI, ex 'VZ304', Bruntingthorpe, Cranfield, Swiss AF J-1167. 614 Squadron colours. Stored.	①	2-00
❑ WZ507	'74' Vampire T.11	G-VTII, ex Bruntingthorpe, Cranfield, Carlisle, CATCS, 3/4 CAACU, 5 FTS, 8 FTS, 229 OCU.		2-00
❑ N6-766	Sea Vampire T.22	G-SPDR, ex VH-RAN ntu, RAN, XG766.	® ②	2-00

Others:

❑ G-MJAZ	Vector 610	CoA 23-9-93. Stored.		5-98
❑ D-5084	Schleicher K.8b	BGA.2688. Stored.		5-98
❑ 'FT323'	Harvard II	EX884, ex 'Exeter', Cranfield, Bushey, East Ham, Port AF 1513, SAAF 7426, EX884, 41-33857.	®	3-97

TALBOT GREEN, 'Mid Glamorgan', on the A473 west of Cardiff
No.2077 Squadron Air Cadets: The Canberra (*thought* to be WH701) was scrapped by June 2001.

VALLEY AIRFIELD, 'Gwynedd', south of the A5, south-east of Holyhead
RAF Valley: The Hawk Composite Servicing School have a Hawk nose for instruction. A 'synthetic' Hawk fire training aid serves on the dump. Jet Provost T.4 XS177 left by road in February 2002.

❑ WV396	'91' Hunter T.8C	9249M, ex Yeovilton, FRADU, 229 OCU, 20. Red/white c/s. Gate		8-01
❑ XT772	Wessex HU.5	8805M, ex Wroughton, 781. SARTU inst.		11-01
❑ XX300	Hawk T.1	8827M, ex Chivenor, 2 TWU, 1 TWU. Crashed 2-10-82. Nose.		4-98

WELSHPOOL, 'Powys', on the A483 west of Shrewsbury
Military Aircraft Cockpit Collection (MACC): Run by Sue and Roy Jerman. The Whirlwind HAR.10 cockpit is on loan from Dave Higgins ①. The Harrier GR.1 nose is a 'spare' from the huge store at Stafford, marked '4 Spare Ser 41H-769733', which falls within the 'XW' range ②. Hunter IF-68 was acquired by HSA in December 1962 and was converted into a T.69 for the Iraqi Air Force, hence its nose became 'spare' ③.

With the possibility of a move, the collection has been trimmed down: Sea Hawk F.1 nose WF145, Scimitar F.1 XD235 (which arrived from Southampton on 20-2-99) and Vampire T.11s XD599 and XE864 all moved to <u>Ingatestone</u>, Essex, during mid-01. Vampire T.11 pod XE921 (which arrived from Stoke-on-Trent by 7-01) moved to <u>Yarmouth</u>, Isle of Wight. Jet Provost T.3 XN492 cockpit moved to

Haydock, Merseyside. The anonymous Phantom nose went to a collector in East Sussex. The 'JP' procedure trainer moved to Kendall, Lancs.
◆ *Private* collection, visits possible by prior arrangement *only*.

❏ WH775		Canberra PR.7	ex Bruntingthorpe, Cosford 8868M/8128M, 100, 13, 31, 17, 31, 13, 82, makers.	3-02
❏ WK102		Canberra T.17	ex Bruntingthorpe, Cosford 8780M, 360, 45, RNZAF, 207.	3-02
❏ WP515	'CD'	Canberra B.2	ex Bridgend, Cardiff-Wales, St Athan, 100, 85, CAW, RAFC, 231 OCU, 109, 12.	3-02
❏ XJ758		Whirlwind HAR.10	ex Oswestry, Shrewsbury, Shawbury 8464M, CFS, 230, CFS, 217, 1360F, 22.	① 3-02
❏ XM652		Vulcan B.2	ex Burntwood, Sheffield, Waddington, 50, 35, 44, 9. Nose.	3-02
❏ XN650	'456'	Sea Vixen FAW.2	ex Bruntingthorpe, Cardiff, A2639/A2620/A2612, Culdrose, RAE, 892. Nose.	3-02
❏ XS923	'BE'	Lightning F.6	ex Bruntingthorpe, Cranfield, Binbrook, 11, LTF, 5-11 pool.	3-02
❏ XT277		Buccaneer S.2A	ex Bruntingthorpe, Cosford 8853M, Shawbury, 237 OCU, 12.	3-02
❏ XW541*		Buccaneer S.2B	ex Ingatestone, Stock, Foulness, Honington, 8858M, St Athan, 12, 16, 15.	3-02
❏ ZD710*		Tornado GR.1	ex Robertsbridge, Stock, St Athan, 14. Cr 14-9-89. Cockpit.	3-02
❏		Harrier GR.1	ex Market Drayton, Stafford, Abingdon, Hamble.	② 3-02
❏ IF-68		Hunter FGA.9	ex Firbeck, Kexborough, Macclesfield, Bitteswell, Dunsfold, G-9-83, Belgian AF IF-68.	③ 3-02

WELSHPOOL AERODROME, 'Powys', or Trehelig, south of the town
at the A493/A490 junction

❏ G-ALWS	Tiger Moth	ex Bromsgrove, Rothesay, Strathallan, Perth, N9328, Upwood SF, 6 FTS, 15 EFTS, 17 EFTS, 15 EFTS, 19 EFTS, Duxford SF, Farnborough SF.	® 10-01
❏ G-BKCY	Tomahawk 112	ex OO-XKU. CoA 7-11-94. Fuselage.	7-98
❏ G-BPER	Tomahawk 112	ex N91465. Fuselage.	10-01
❏ G-BXMN*	Tiger Moth	ex N82RD, N8353, ZS-IGJ, CR-AGL, Port AF, NL772. Crashed 25-5-99. First noted 8-00.	8-00
❏ T8191	Tiger Moth	G-BWMK, ex Lee-on-Solent, FAAHF, Yeovilton SF, Culdrose SF, Yeovilton SF, BRNC, Lossiemouth SF, Arbroath SF, Culdrose SF, Bramcote, Gosport, 3 FF, 22 EFTS, 4 FIS, 3 EFTS.	® 10-01

WREXHAM, 'Clwyd'
North East Wales Institute: Located next to the football ground, see under Connah's Quay for another NEWI site. The HS.125 is used as a procedures trainer. NEWI at Connah's Quay still holds the wing box, tail and parts of the mid-fuselage for structures teaching.

❏ G-ARYA	HS.125-1	ex Connah's Quay, Hawarden, Connah's Quay, Chester, Hatfield. Nose.	1-00
❏ XP585	'24' Jet Provost T.4	8407M, ex Halton, St Athan, RAFC, 6 FTS, RAFC.	1-98

YSTRAD MYNACH, 'Mid Glamorgan' on the A472 south of Merthyr Tydfil
A private owner has taken delivery of a 'JP'.

❏ XP638*	'A' Jet Provost T.4	9034M, ex Waddington, Halton, Shawbury, CATCS, CAW, 6 FTS. Arrived 7-2-02.	2-02

PART FIVE
IRELAND

Northern Ireland
Antrim
Armagh
Down
Fermanagh
Londonderry
Tyrone

Ireland
Carlow
Cavan
Clare

Cork
Donegal
Dublin
Galway
Kerry
Kildare
Kilkenny
Laois
Leitrim
Limerick
Longford
Louth

Mayo
Meath
West Meath
Offaly
Roscommon
Sligo
Tipperary
Waterford
Wexford
Wicklow

NORTHERN IRELAND

BALLYMONEY on the A26 south-east of Coleraine, Antrim

❑ G-BPJH	Super Cub 95	ex MM52-2380, I-EICA, MM52-2380, 52-2380.	
		Damaged 1-9-92.	® 4-96

BANN FOOT north-west of Craigavon, Armagh

❑ G-PFAL	FRED II	CoA 27-7-88.	1-00
❑ EI-AUT	F.1A Aircoupe	ex Cork, G-ARXS, D-EBSA, N3037G. CoA 30-7-76.	1-00

BELFAST, Down
Campbell College: The Vampire 'pod' has returned here.

❑ XD525*	Vampire T.11	ex Holywood, Belfast, Aldergrove 7882M,	
		1 FTS, 4 FTS, 5 FTS, 7 FTS. Pod.	3-02

Flight Experience Workshop (FEW): No response or updates on this organisation.

❑ WT486	Canberra T.4	ex Aldergrove 8102M, Wildenrath, 14, 17, 88,	
		Wildenrath SF. Nose.	3-98
❑ XM414	Jet Provost T.3A	ex Binbrook, Colsterworth, Halton 8996M, 7 FTS,	
		RAFC, 1 FTS, RAFC, 2 FTS.	3-98
❑		Sunderland V FSM forward fuselage, wooden.	3-98

No.817 Squadron Air Cadets: (Note correct squadron number.)

❑ VP957	Devon C.2/2	8822M, ex Bishop's Court, Belfast Airport, Northolt,	
		207, 21, WCS, SCS, NCS, SCS, WCS, SCS,	
		Andover SF, 38 GCF, AAFCE, 2 TAF CS, BAFO	
		CS. Forward fuselage.	10-00

BELFAST AIRPORT or Aldergrove, on the A26 west of the city (Antrim)
By March 2002 the hulks of Warrior G-BFWK and Aztec 250V G-ESKU had both gone. The former reduced to components, the latter possibly to Biggin Hill, Gtr Lon.

❑ G-AVFE	Trident 2E	ex BA, BEA. CoA 6-5-85. Fire crews.	9-01
❑ G-BBSC*	Sierra 200	CoA 3-6-99. Stored.	3-02
❑ G-BCBX	Cessna F.150L	ex F-BUEO. CoA 19-2-95. Stored.	3-02
❑ G-BNMK	Dornier Do 27A-1	ex OE-DGO, 56+04, BD+397, BA+399. Stored.	3-02
❑ G-KNAP*	Warrior II	ex G-BIUX, N9507N. Crashed 13-7-99.	® 3-02
❑ XT456	'XZ' Wessex HU.5	ex 8941M ABDR, Wroughton, 847, 846, 845. Dump.	9-01

RAF Aldergrove: The nose sections are used by RAF Careers, both are trailer-mounted and do 'the rounds'. Grounded after suffering a twisted fuselage, XR529 may have a new life ahead of it... ①

❑ XE643	Hunter FGA.9	8586M, ex Abingdon, 208, 56, 63, 66, 92. Nose.	10-00
❑ XR529*	'E' Wessex HC.2	ex 72, SARTU, 2 FTS, 18, 78, 72.	® ① 3-02
❑ XR700	Jet Provost T.4	8589M, ex Abingdon, Shawbury, CATCS, 3 FTS,	
		1 FTS. Nose.	10-00

BELFAST CITY AIRPORT or Sydenham, off the A2, east of the city centre (Antrim)
Bombardier: Turn to page 320 of *W&R16* for a reference on Tucano demonstrator G-BTUC. The deal for it to move to the 'mainland' for possible restoration to flying condition fell through - much to the advantage of Ulster Aviation Heritage, who took delivery of it at <u>Langford Lodge</u>, in January 2001.

CASTLEROCK
By October 2001 F.337F had arrived to provide spares for FA.337G RA-4147 (previously G-BOYR).

❑ EI-AVC*	F.337F	ex Abbeyshrule, N4757. Spares, hulk.	10-01

FIVEMILETOWN on the A4 east of Enniskillen, Tyrone
Blessingbourne Carriage Museum: The museum has a Scout on permanent loan. While it might at first seem out of place in the collection, the sound of Scouts hovering overhead was a part of the background noise of the Province for many years...
◆ Open by prior appointment *only*. ✉ Blessingbourne, Fivemiletown, Co Tyrone, BT75 0QS
❑ XW795   Scout AH.1   ex Middle Wallop, Almondbank, Wroughton,
659, 655, 669.   3-02

HOLYWOOD on the A2 east of Belfast, Down
Ulster Folk and Transport Museum: The 'original' Ferguson REP, the Short SC.1 and the Sherpa cockpit are in a 'hands-on' gallery known as 'The Flight Experience', staged in association with Bombardier Aerospace ①. Other than the three mentioned above, all other airframes are in store and not available for inspection. See under New Ross, Ireland, for a possible insight into Gemini G-AKEL ②. The registration G-ARTZ has been used twice, both times on Rex McCandless' products, see under St Merryn, Corn, for the second use ③.
◆ Open daily, closed three days at Xmas. Telephone for details of opening times. ✉ Cultra Manor, Holywood, BT18 0EU ☎ 028 9042 8428 fax 028 9042 8728 web www.nidex.com/uftm

❑ G-AJOC	Messenger 2A	ex East Fortune, Strathallan, Dunottar. CoA 18-5-72. Stored.		3-02
❑ G-AKEL	Gemini 1A	ex Kilbrittain Castle. CoA 29-4-72. Stored.	②	3-02
❑ G-AKGE	Gemini 3C	ex Kilbrittain Castle, EI-ALM, G-AKGE. CoA 7-6-74. Stored.		3-02
❑ G-AKLW	Sealand	ex Bradley Air Museum, Connecticut, Jeddah, RSaudiAF, SU-AHY, G-AKLW. Stored.		3-02
❑ G-AOUR	Tiger Moth	ex Belfast, NL898, 15 EFTS. Cr 6-6-65. Stored.		3-02
❑ G-ARTZ(1)	McCandless M-2	ex Killough. Stored.	③	3-02
❑ G-ATXX	McCandless M-4	ex Killough. wfu 9-9-70. Stored.		3-02
❑ G-BKMW	Short Sherpa	ex Belfast City, CoA 14-9-90. Cockpit section.	①	3-02
❑ — ALA	Nimbus I	BGA.470, ex Bishop's Stortford, Duxford. Stored.		3-02
❑ VH-UUP	Scion I	ex East Fortune, Strathallan, G-ACUX, VH-UUP, G-ACUX. Stored.		3-02
❑ XG905	Short SC.1	ex Shorts, Sydenham, Thurleigh, RAE.	①	3-02
❑ IAHC.6	Ferguson Mono	REP, ex Dublin.	①	3-02
❑ IAHC.9	Ferguson Mono	REP, ex Belfast Airport, Holywood. Stored.		3-02

Kinegar Camp: The 'pod' of Vampire T.11 XD525 returned to <u>Belfast</u>, Northern Ireland.

LANGFORD LODGE AIRFIELD on the shores of Lough Neagh, west of Belfast, Antrim
Ulster Aviation Heritage: Run by the Ulster Aviation Society, a large building near the entrance to the airfield serves as a visitor centre and 'introduction' to the hangar. As well as the display hangar, the control tower of rare design has been restored. Special events are held, including fly-ins. All of this has been made possible thanks to Langford Lodge Engineering, who operate on the site. The Eurowing Goldwing is a very relevant exhibit, having made its first flight from Langford Lodge. With the disbanding of 72 Squadron in March 2002, UAS have their eyes on a Wessex HC.2.
◆ Open Saturdays 1pm to 6pm, Feb to Nov, and at other times by prior appointment. ✉ 33 Old Mill Meadows, Dundonald, BT16 1WQ ☎ on-site (and info-line) 028 9445 4444 web www.ulsteraviationsociety.co.uk

❑ G-BDBS	Shorts 330	ex Belfast City, Shorts, G-14-3001. CoA 2-9-92.		3-02
❑ G-BTUC*	Tucano	ex Belfast City, Shorts, G-14-007, PP-ZTC. CoA 20-8-91. Arrived 1-01.		3-02
❑ G-MJWS*	Goldwing	donated by Jeff Salter.		3-02
❑ EI-BAG	Cessna 172A	ex Upper Ballinderry, Portadown, Enniskillen, Abbeyshrule, G-ARAV, N9771T. CoA 26-6-79.	®	3-02
❑ EI-BUO	Sea Hawker	ex Newtownards. Damaged 9-91.		3-02

☐	JV482		Wildcat V	ex Newtownards, Castlereagh, Lough Beg, 882. Crashed 24-12-44.	®	3-02
☐	WN108	'033'	Sea Hawk FB.3	ex Newtownards, Belfast City, Shorts Apps, Sydenham AHU, Bournemouth, FRU, 806, 895, 897, 800.		3-02
☐	WZ549	'F'	Vampire T.11	ex Newtownards, Coningsby, Tattershall, Coningsby 8118M, CATCS, 1 FTS, 8 FTS, FTU, C(A).		3-02
☐	XV361		Buccaneer S.2B	ex Lossiemouth, 208, 15, 208, 12, 15, 809, 800.		3-02
☐	—	BAPC.263	Chargus Cyclone	ex Ballyclare. Built 1979. Last flight 4-4-88.		3-02
☐	—	BAPC.266	Rogallo h-glider	donated by Charles Linford. Last flown 1978.		3-02
☐	*		Tucano EMU	ex Belfast City, Shorts. Test rig.		3-02

LONDONDERRY

| ☐ | G-ARAP | 7EC Traveler | ex Eglinton. Crashed 22-9-81. | ® | 12-92 |
| ☐ | G-BRFI | 7DC Champion | ex Ballymoney, N1058E, NC1058E. Dam 1990. | ® | 4-96 |

LONDONDERRY AIRPORT or Eglinton, north-east of the town
The 'JP' undertook a forced-landing on the nearby mud flats following difficulties ①.

| ☐ | G-BYED* | Jet Provost T.5A | ex N166A, XW302, 6 FTS, 3 FTS, RAFC, 1 FTS. Crashed 12-2-01. | ① | 3-02 |

LOUGH FOYLE Londonderry
Just off shore can be seen the hulk of Corsair II JT693:R, ex 1837 Squadron.

MOV ENIS AERODROME near Garvagh, Londonderry

☐	G-AWJA	Cessna 182L	ex N1658C. Crashed 12-9-84. Fuselage.	6-97
☐	G-BIEW	Cessna U.206G	ex OO-DMA, N7344C. Crashed 31-12-88. Fuselage.	6-97
☐	G-EESE	Cessna U.206G	ex N6332U ntu. Crashed 29-8-89. Forward fuselage.	6-97

NEW TOW NARDS AERODROME south of the town, between the A20 and A21, Down

| ☐ | G-ARCT | PA-18-95 | ex EI-AVE, G-ARCT. Damaged 29-3-87. | ® | 7-99 |
| ☐ | N80B* | Pitts S-2A | stored. Crashed 11-7-99. First noted mid-1997. | | 12-99 |

UPPER BALLINDERRY on the A26 west of Belfast, near Crumlin, Antrim
During September 2000, the chicken farm in which the Whitney Straight has been stored for many a long year was put up for sale. The 'Straight was offered as part of the deal or as a separate purchase ①. **Andrew Allen** acquired a Rallye Club during 2001 for eventual restoration to flying condition ②.

| ☐ | G-AERV | Whitney Straight | ex Newtownards, EM999, Kemble, Abingdon SF, Halton SF, G-AERV. CoA 9-4-66. Stored. | ① | 9-00 |
| ☐ | EI-BGB* | Rallye Club | ex Abbeyshrule, G-AZKB. CoA 18-5-91. | ② | 3-02 |

IRELAND

ABBEYSHRULE AERODROME Westmeagh, north-west of Mullignar
The long-resident trio of Airedales (EI-AYL, -BAL and -BBK) made the trip to the UK in March, arriving at Spanhoe Lodge, Northants, on 15th March 2001. Rallye Club EI-BGB moved to Upper Ballinderry, Northern Ireland, during 2001. Cessna F.337F EI-AVC slipped the *W&R* 'net', having been a long term part of the scenery here. By December 1999 it had been broken for spares, with a wing going to 337B G-RORO and the rear engine to F.337F G-AZKO. It is reported as having gone to a

scrapyard south-west of Dublin. Its usefulness was not over, however. By October 2001, it was to be found at <u>Castlerock</u>, Northern Ireland, helping another 'push-me-pull-you'.

❏ EI-ANN	Tiger Moth	ex Dublin, Kilcock, G-ANEE, T5418, 63 GCF, 24 EFTS, 19 EFTS, 12 EFTS. Crashed 18-10-64. Spares for EI-AOP.	11-93
❏ EI-AOP	Tiger Moth	ex Dublin, G-AIBN, T7967, 18 EFTS, 1667 CU, 1 GCF, 16 PFTS. Crashed 5-5-74.	® 11-93
❏ EI-ARW	SAN DR.1050	ex F-BJJH. Crashed 28-7-86. Wreck.	8-98
❏ EI-ATK	Cherokee 140	ex G-AVUP. Crashed 14-2-87. Wreck.	8-98
❏ EI-AUJ	Rallye Club	ex Birr, G-AXHF, F-BNGV. Wreck.	6-97
❏ EI-AUP	Rallye Club	ex Coonagh, G-AVVK. Crashed 1-9-83. Wreck.	5-99
❏ EI-AWE	Cessna F.150L	Fuselage, stored.	5-99
❏ EI-AYS	PA-22 Colt 108	ex G-ARKT. Stored.	5-99
❏ EI-AYT	Rallye Minerva	ex G-AXIU. Crashed 12-11-89. Stored.	5-96
❏ EI-BCW	Rallye Club	ex G-AYKE.	6-97
❏ EI-BFI	Rallye 100ST	ex F-BXDK. Crashed 14-12-85. Spares.	5-00
❏ EI-BGD	Rallye Club	ex F-BUJI, D-EKHD ntu.	8-98
❏ EI-BGS	Rallye 180GT	ex F-BXTY. Crashed 20-7-90. Spares.	5-96
❏ EI-BGU	Rallye Club	ex F-BONM.	8-98
❏ EI-BHB	Rallye 125	ex F-BUCH. Stored, dismantled.	5-99
❏ EI-BIC	Cessna F.172N	ex OO-HNZ ntu. Crashed 13-4-95.	6-00
❏ EI-BIM	Rallye Club	ex F-BKYJ.	6-97
❏ EI-BJJ	Aeronca Sedan	ex G-BHXP ntu, EI-BJJ, N1214H.	6-97
❏ EI-BKU	Rallye C'dore	ex F-BRLG. Wreck.	5-99
❏ EI-BMV	AA-5 Traveler	ex G-BAEJ. Crashed 21-3-93.	8-98
❏ EI-BNR	AA-5 Traveler	ex N9992Q, CS-AHM. Crashed 21-2-88.	5-00
❏ EI-BOP	Rallye C'dore	ex Coonagh, G-BKGS, F-BSXS. Crashed 29-3-86.	5-99
❏ EI-BPJ	Cessna 182A	ex G-BAGA, N4849D. *The Hooker*. Wreck.	5-00
❏ EI-BUJ	Rallye C'dore	ex G-FOAM, G-AVPL.	6-97
❏ EI-CAA	Cessna FR.172J	ex G-BHTW, 5Y-ATO. Damaged 12-93. Wreck.	5-00
❏ G-BSUH	Cessna 140	ex N89088, NC89088. Damaged 6-93.	5-00
❏ G-SKYH	Cessna 172N	ex A6-GRM, N76034. Crashed 21-7-91. Stored.	6-00

BALLYJAMESDUFF on the R194 south of Cavan, Cavan
N Reilly: No news on either the Plus D or the Cadet.

❏ EI-ANA	Taylorcraft Plus D	ex G-AHCG, LB347, 657, 655.	® 4-92
❏ XE808	Cadet TX.1	ex Syerston, 617 VGS, 645 VGS. Stored.	4-92

CARLOW on the N9 south-west of Dublin, County Carlow
Carlow Institute of Technology: By August 2001 the college had gained an instructional airframe.

❏ 220*	CM-170-1	ex Casement, IAC. Arrived by 8-01. Inst.	8-01

CASEMENT AIRFIELD or Baldonnel, west of Dublin, County Dublin
Irish Air Corps (IAC): CM-170 Magister 220 had moved to <u>Carlow</u>, Ireland, in August 2001 and 216 to <u>Cork</u>, Ireland, at little later. In exchange for Dove 6 G-ASNG (for the planned museum) Cessna FR.172H 207 moved to <u>Waterford</u>, Ireland, by June 2001.

Listed here because it is seems the best place (!), Cessna FR.172H 209 suffered an accident on 10th November 1993. Since then it is believed to have been at Finner Camp, Co Donegal. By April 2001 it had turned up at the Engineer Stores yard in The Curragh, Dublin. It is thought that it is to be converted into a para-trainer for the Army Parachute Association, but its eventual location is not known, Gormanston no longer being a possibility.

❏ 34	Magister	ex Dublin, Casement, N5392.	1-02
❏ 141	Anson XIX	ex Dublin, Casement.	1-02

❏	164		Chipmunk T.20	stored.	1-02
❏	183		Provost T.51	ex Dublin, Casement.	1-02
❏	198		Vampire T.11	ex 'gate', XE977, 8 FTS. Unflown by IAAC.	1-02
❏	199*		Chipmunk T.20	ex Gormanston. Dismantled. First noted 9-01.	3-02
❏	202		Alouette III	ditched 20-10-95. Stored.	4-97
❏	215		CM-170-1	stored.	1-02
❏	217		CM-170-1	stored.	9-01
❏	218		CM-170-1	stored.	1-02
❏	219		CM-170-1	stored.	9-01
❏	221	'3-KE'	CM-170-2	ex French Air Force No.79. Inst. Dismantled.	1-02
❏	233		SF-260MC	ex I-SYAS. Fuselage. Stored.	2-95
❏	'98'		Cessna 172B	ex Southend, G-ARLU, N8002X. Damaged 30-10-77.Avionics rig.	1-02
❏	G-ASNG*		Dove 6	ex Waterford, Cork, (EI-BJW), Coventry, HB-LFF, G-ASNG, HB-LFF, G-ASNG, PH-IOM.	1-02
❏			Alouette III	instructional, non-flying, rig. c/no 1012	1-02

CELBRIDGE on the R403 west of Dublin, Kildare
The Proctor is due to move to Dromod, Ireland, in due course. (Refer to New Ross, Ireland.)

❏	G-AHWO	Proctor V	ex Whitehall, Dublin, (EI-ALY). Cr 5-5-59. Stored.	3-02

CHURCHTOWN south of Dublin city centre, Dublin
Nutgrove Shopping Centre: A Grob Astir 'thermals' over the bargains.

❏	EI-124	G.102 Astir CS	displayed since 1993.	5-99

CORK
Technical College: Took delivery of a former IAAC CM-170 by September 2001.

❏	216*	CM-170-1	ex Casement.	9-01

DELGANY east of the N11, south of Dublin, Wicklow.
Mick Donohoe: Is thought to be at work on restoring the 'Flea'.

❏	IAHC 3	HM.14 'Flea'	ex Carbury.	® 4-96

DROMOD on the N4 north of Longford, Leitrim
Cavan and Leitrim Railway: South East Aviation Enthusiasts Group were busy moving their collection of aircraft from New Ross, Ireland, to this site during March and April 2002. Following negotiations with the railway operators, the aircraft will add further to the appeal of the site which already has vintage vehicles of all kinds and even a submarine as well as the locos and rolling stock! A display building will be built, with the hope that all the airframes will go under cover for the first time. See under New Ross for details of the airframes.

DUBLIN
Institute of Technology: In Bolton Street, still has its instructional airframe.

❏	EI-BHM	Cessna F.337E	ex Farranfore, Weston, OO-PDC, OO-PDG. CoA 9-7-82.	9-01

Former **Irish Aviation Museum** (IAM):

❏	EI-AOH	Viscount 808	ex Dublin Airport, Aer Lingus. Nose section.	10-97
❏	G-ANPC	Tiger Moth	ex Edinburgh (?), Strathallan, Portmoak, R4950, 2 GS, Kirton-in-Lindsey SF, Hemswell SF, Oakington SF, 28 EFTS, 25 PEFTS, 17 EFTS, Benson SF. Crashed 2-1-67.	4-96

Area: On 2nd December 1998 a cargo was unloaded from Antonov An-12BP RA-11768 at Shannon Airport. This was no less a creature than former Finnish Air Force Brewster Buffalo BW-372 salvaged from a lake near the Finnish border with the CIS. Stored in this area since, it was offered for sale in November 2000 by a company from Richmond, British Columbia, Canada.

❑ BW-372*	Buffalo	ex Finnish Air Force. Shot down 25-6-42. Arrived 12-98. Stored.	11-00

DUBLIN AIRPORT or Collinstown, on the R122, north of the City, Dublin

❑ EI-ABI	DH.84 Dragon ✈	ex EI-AFK, G-AECZ, AV982, EE, 7 AACU, 110 Wing, G-AECZ. *Iolar*. Aer Lingus 'Historic Flight'.	7-01
❑ EI-BEM	Short 360-100	ex ALT, East Midlands, G-BLGC, G-14-3642. *St Senan*. Crashed 31-1-86. Cabin trainer.	9-93
❑ EI-BSF	HS.748-1/105	ex Ryanair, EC-DTP, G-BEKD, LV-HHF, LV-PUM. *Spirit of Tipperary*. CoA 21-5-87. Cabin trainer.	4-01

FOYNES on the N69 west of Limerick, Limerick
Foynes Flying-Boat Museum: Located in the original transatlantic flying-boat terminal on the River Shannon, the museum recalls the era of the great 'boats 1937-1945. Among other items at this nascent museum are the engines and other remains from BOAC Sunderland III G-AGES, which came to grief off Kerry on July 28, 1943. The museum is also a shrine to Irish Coffee, invented here by chef Joe Sheridan and first served up to revive passengers in 1942!
◆ Open March 31 to October 31, 10am to 6pm – last visit 5pm ✉ Flying-Boat Museum, Foynes, Limerick, Ireland. ☎ / Fax 00 353 69 65416 e-mail famm@eircom.net web www.webforge.net

GALWAY
Eyre Square Centre: Ireland's oldest extant registered glider is displayed here.

❑ VM657	IGA.6 T.8 Tutor	ex County Wicklow.	4-99

GALWAY AIRPORT on the N64 east of the city

❑ G-AFNG	Moth Minor	ex AW112 EAAS, Wyton SF, Binbrook SF, G-AFNG. CoA 21-10-98.	6-99

GORMANSTON AIRFIELD on the N1 north of Dublin, Meath
IAAC: The airfield was "phased down" in IAAC terms on 24th April 2001 and flying transferred to Casement. The airfield will be sold off for redevelopment. Chipmunk 168 is/was the only component of the IAAC's unofficial 'historic flight'. Chipmunk T.20 199 moved to <u>Casement</u>, Ireland.

❑ 168	Chipmunk T.20 ✈	airworthy.	6-98
❑ 191	Vampire T.55	ex Dublin, Casement.	6-98

GOWRAN GRANGE near Dublin, Kildare
Dublin Gliding Club:

❑ EI-102	Kite 2	ex IGA.102, IAC.102. Stored.		5-99
❑ EI-128	Schleicher Ka 6CR —		®	5-99
❑ WZ762	Grasshopper TX.1	EI-135, ex Cosford, Rugby. (Wings of WZ756.)		8-01

NEW CASTLE north of the N7 near Rathcoole, Dublin
By mid-2000 Avro Cadet EI-ALU had moved to <u>Bristol</u>, Glos.

NEW ROSS, Wexford, on the N25 north-east of Waterford
South East Aviation Enthusiasts Group (SEAEG): *W&R17* (p298) noted that "The search for a museum site continues". As we close for press, the hard-working team were busy moving the entire

collection to <u>Dromod</u>, Ireland. For this edition, the listing of aircraft can remain here, but refer to Dromod to see what it has to offer.

Notes: Phil Bedford's collection of aircraft are marked ¶. Phil is restoring T.8 Tutor CBZ to its original 1944 condition as a long-span Cadet TX.2. CBZ was converted into a motor glider with an enclosed cockpit and will use the cockpit of RA881 in the rebuild ①. The gliders are all under restoration to fly, but will be based here when out on 'ops'. The identity of Gemini G-ALCS is in doubt. Markings indicate it *may* be from G-AKEL (see Holywood, Northern Ireland) ②. See under Celbridge, Ireland, for Proctor G-AHWO which will also make the move.

◆ Visits by prior appointment *only*. ✉ Phil Bedford, 10 Walled Gardens, Castletown, Celbridge, Kildare, Ireland. **e-mail** pbedford@tcd.ie

❏ EI-BDM	Aztec 250D	ex Waterford, Kildimo, G-AXIV, N6826Y.			3-02
❏ G-ALCS	Gemini 3C	ex Waterford, Kilbritain. Cockpit.		②	3-02
❏ G-AOGA	Aries 1	ex Casement, Dublin, Kilbrittain Castle,			
		EI-ANB, G-AOGA. Damaged 8-8-69.			3-02
❏ G-AOIE	Douglas DC-7C	'EI-AWA', ex Waterford, Shannon, PH-SAX,			
		G-AOIE Caledonian, BOAC. Fuselage.		¶	3-02
❏ NC285RS	Navion	ex Naas, Abbeyshrule. Cr 11-6-79. *My Way*. Fuse.			3-02
❏ VP-BDF	Boeing 707-321	ex Waterford, Dublin, N435MA, G-14-372,			
		G-AYAG, N759PA. *Spirit of 73*. Nose.			3-02
❏ EI-139	T.31B	ex Gowran Grange, BGA.3485, G-BOKG,			
		XE789. Last flew 8-8-96. CoA 2-8-97.		¶	3-02
❏ CBK	Grunau Baby III	BGA.1410, ex Naas, Breighton, Stoke-on-Trent,			
		Firbeck, RAFGSA.378, D-4676.		¶	3-02
❏ CBZ	T.8 Tutor	BGA.1424, ex Naas, Gowran Grange,			
		Jurby, RAFGSA.214, RA877.	¶ ® ①		3-02
❏ 173	Chipmunk T.20	ex Waterford, Gormanston, IAAC.			3-02
❏ '176'	Dove 6	VP-YKF, ex Waterford, Cork, 3D-AAI,			
		VQ-ZJC, G-AMDD.			3-02
❏ 184	Provost T.51	ex Waterford, Casement, IAAC.			3-02
❏ 187	Vampire T.55	ex Waterford, Casement, IAAC.			3-02
❏ 192	Vampire T.55	ex Waterford, Casement, IAAC.			3-02
❏ RA881	Cadet TX.1	ex Breighton, Halfpenny Green (?). Cockpit.		①	3-02
❏	IAHC.1 HM.14 'Flea'	ex Waterford, Dublin, Coonagh.			3-02
❏	Hector	frame		of-site	3-02

POWERSCOURT Wicklow
❏ EI-AUS	J/5F Aiglet Tnr	ex G-AMRL. CoA 2-12-75. Stored.	4-95

RATHCOOLE Cork
❏ G-AXVV	L-4H-PI	ex F-BBQB, 43-29572. CoA 16-6-73. Stored.	6-98

SHANNON AIRPORT on the N19, south of Ennis, Clare
During July 2000, Boeing 707-323G N709PC was scrapped.

SLIGO Sligo
Gerry O'Hara: Gerry's homegrown aircraft are *believed* to be still stored here.
❏ —	IAHC.7 Sligo Concept	single seat low wing monoplane. Unflown, stored.	8-91
❏ —	IAHC.8 O'Hara Gyro	on Bensen lines. Unflown. Stored.	8-91

TRIM on the R154 north-west of Dublin, Meath
❏ EI-ASU	Terrier 2	ex Rathcoole, G-ASRG, Auster T.7 WE599,		
		LAS, HCCS.	®	6-95

WATERFORD AIRPORT south-east of Waterford, Waterford

❑ EI-BFE	Cessna F.150G	ex G-AVGM. Dismantled.	4-99
❑ EI-BKK	JT.1 Monoplane	ex G-AYYC. Dismantled.	4-99
❑ 207*	Cessna FR.172H	ex Casement, IAAC. Fire crews. First noted 6-01.	6-01

WESTON AERODROME near Leixlip, Kildare

❑ EI-ALP	Avro Cadet	ex Castlebridge, G-ADIE. CoA 6-4-78. Stored.	6-01
❑ EI-BBG	Rallye 100ST	CoA 1-12-83. Fuselage, stored.	1-02
❑ EI-BCU*	Rallye 100ST	Derelict by 8-01.	1-02
❑ EI-BEA	Rallye 100ST	CoA 10-5-86. Fuselage, stored.	1-02
❑ EI-BFP	Rallye 100ST	ex F-GARR. CoA 1-10-87. Stored.	6-01
❑ EI-BKN*	Rallye 100ST	ex F-GBCK. CoA 5-98. Stored.	1-02
❑ EI-BUG*	ST-10 Diplomate	ex G-STIO, OH-SAB. CoA 8-98. Stored.	6-01
❑ EI-BVK*	Tomahawk 112	ex OO-FLG, OO-HLG, N9705N. CoA 5-98. Stored.	1-02
❑ EI-CGG*	Aircoupe 415C	ex N2522H, NC2522H. CoA 10-00. Stored.	1-02

PART SIX
RAF OVERSEAS

This is an ever-dwindling listing of all British military aircraft in the *W&R* categories on Crown territory or property. Please note that this section does *not* appear in any index.

CYPRUS
AKROTIRI AIRFIELD
RAF Akrotiri: The Lightning was given a thorough make-over during September and October 2001.

❑ XD184	W'wind HAR.10	8787M, ex 84 'A' Flt, 1563F, 228, 155. SAR c/s. Gate	4-00
❑ XR504*	Wessex HC.2	ex 84, 22, SARTS, 18, 1 FTU. Spares.	12-00
❑ XS929	'L' Lightning F.6	ex Binbrook, 11, LTF, 11, 56, 11. 56 Sqn c/s. Gate	10-01
❑ XT479	´ Wessex HU.5	ex Wyton, 84, A&AEE, 847, 707. Derelict.	12-00
❑ XV470	'BD' Phantom FGR.2	9156M, ex 56, 228 OCU, 19, 228 OCU, 92,	
		56, 92, 56, 17, 14, 2.	4-00

FALKLAND ISLANDS
MOUNT PLEASANT AIRPORT
RAF Enclave: The Phantom stands guard over the Tornados.

❑ XV409	'H' Phantom FGR.2	9160M, ex 1435 Flt, 29, 228 OCU, 56, 111, 56,	
		111. *Hope*. Displayed.	7-01

GERMANY
BRUGGEN AIRFIELD
RAF Brüggen: The end of an era, over the weekend of 15th/16th June, 2001 the base paid its official farewell to the RAF. The Army took it over, becoming Javelin Barracks, but their tenure will be relatively short. Jaguar GR.1 composite 'XX822' started the journey to <u>Coltishall</u>, Norfolk, on 10th August 2001. Last noted in November 1999, ABDRT Harrier GR.3 XZ998 moved to the museum at Hermeskiel by May 2000.

APPENDIX A
AUCTIONS

29th November 2000 – Phillips: London

Another sale for the Ministry of Defence's Disposal Sales Agency. As will be seen by some of the 'last flown' dates on the Bulldogs and the gliders, the new policy of 'hot sales' has started. The gliders were all offered with their trailers with Lot 13 being an 'empty' trailer which notched up £1,900. 'Ownership' of the Hunters (they were US MDAP financed) had been resolved, allowing the Hunters to finally be disposed of. Additionally, six Avon turbojets and six Avco Lycoming IO-360-A1B6 pistons were sold from Stafford, Staffs.

Column one gives the type in lot order; column two identity; column three the 'last flown' date as given in the catalogue; column four the highest bid – not necessarily reflecting a sale, and not including the buyer's premium of VAT if applicable; column five the location (with a reference to the main text if applicable) and column six a 'forwarding reference'.

Bulldog T.1	XX541	31-3-00	£9,000	Shawbury, Shropshire	N9179C
Bulldog T.1	XX658	10-4-00	£8,800	Shawbury, Shropshire	G-BZPS
Bulldog T.1	XX663	8-6-00	£11,000	Shawbury, Shropshire	F-AZLK
Bulldog T.1	XX529	10-4-00	£10,500	Shawbury, Shropshire	G-BZOJ, then N178BD
Bulldog T.1	XX620	31-8-00	£11,000	Shawbury, Shropshire	N621BD
Bulldog T.1	XX522	10-4-00	£13,000	Shawbury, Shropshire	G-DAWG
Valiant TX.1	ZD657	3-6-00	£8,000	Newton, Notts	
Valiant TX.1	ZD658	1-5-00	£9,000	Newton, Notts	
Valiant TX.1	ZD659	11-6-00	£8,000	Newton, Notts	
Valiant TX.1	ZD660	17-6-00	£9,000	Newton, Notts	
Kestrel TX.1	ZD974	4-9-98	£25,000	Newton, Notts	
Kestrel TX.1	ZD975	12-9-99	–	Newton, Notts	withdrawn
Gazelle HT.3	XZ932	29-9-97	£62,000	See Shawbury, Shropshire	–
Gazelle HT.2	XW868	21-5-97	£62,000	See Shawbury, Shropshire	–
Gazelle HT.2	XW907	7-7-97	£62,000	See Shawbury, Shropshire	–
Gazelle HT.2	XW894	21-5-97	£80,000	See Shawbury, Shropshire	–
Hunter GA.11	XF368	25-4-95	£10,200	See Shawbury, Shropshire	–
Hunter GA.11	WV256	24-4-95	£10,200	See Shawbury, Shropshire	–
Hunter GA.11	XF300	12-6-95	£12,000	See Shawbury, Shropshire	–
Hunter T.8B	XF995	11-4-94	£15,000	See Cranwell, Lincs	–
Hunter T.8B	XF967	5-4-93	£24,000	See Cranwell, Lincs	–
Hunter T.8B	WV322	5-5-91	£28,000	See Cranwell, Lincs	–

24th May 2001 – Phillips: London

What turned out to be the first of two sales for the Ministry of Defence's Disposal Sales Agency. Still more Bulldogs, Gazelles, Wessex and 14 Lycoming IO-360s engines featured. Sadly, although the catalogue was good on airframe hours and fatigue index for the Bulldogs, it was somewhat wanting on 'last flown' dates! (As will be seen by the realised prices of some of the Bulldogs, these were high hour and Fl airframes. Bulldog XX689 was in black and yellow colours.

Column one gives the type in lot order; column two identity; column three the 'last flown' date as given in the catalogue; column four the highest bid – not necessarily reflecting a sale, and not including the buyer's premium of VAT if applicable; column five the location (with a reference to the main text if applicable) and column six a 'forwarding reference'.

Bulldog T.1	XX615	-00	£7,800	Shawbury, Shropshire	F-AZKI
Bulldog T.1	XX659	-00	£7,000	Shawbury, Shropshire	UK owner
Bulldog T.1	XX555	-00	£8,200	Shawbury, Shropshire	F-AZKJ
Bulldog T.1	XX666	-00	£7,200	Shawbury, Shropshire	USA
Bulldog T.1	XX617	-00	£10,200	Shawbury, Shropshire	N25GA
Bulldog T.1	XX640	-00	£8,200	Shawbury, Shropshire	N640RH
Bulldog T.1	XX627	-00	£9,000	Shawbury, Shropshire	N321BD
Bulldog T.1	XX661	-00	£13,000	Shawbury, Shropshire	N661BD
Bulldog T.1	XX689	-00	£11,500	Shawbury, Shropshire	USA
Bulldog T.1	XX614	-00	£12,000	Shawbury, Shropshire	G-CBAM
Bulldog T.1	XX560	-00	£12,000	Shawbury, Shropshire	N560XX
Bulldog T.1	XX697	-00	£12,000	Shawbury, Shropshire	N697BD
Bulldog T.1	XX629	-00	£9,000	Shawbury, Shropshire	G-BZXZ
Bulldog T.1	XX556	-00	£12,000	Shawbury, Shropshire	N556WH
Bulldog T.1	XX612	-00	£12,000	Shawbury, Shropshire	G-BZXC
Bulldog T.1	XX521	-00	£7,200	Shawbury, Shropshire	G-CBEH
Bulldog T.1	XX516	-00	£12,000	Shawbury, Shropshire	N516BG
Bulldog T.1	XX701	-00	£12,500	Shawbury, Shropshire	N701AB
Bulldog T.1	XX543	-00	£9,800	Shawbury, Shropshire	G-CBAB
Bulldog T.1	XX524	-00	£11,500	Shawbury, Shropshire	G-DDOG

Bulldog T.1	XX631	-00	£10,500	Shawbury, Shropshire	G-BZXS
Bulldog T.1	XX546	23-3-00	£12,000	Shawbury, Shropshire	G-CBCO
Bulldog T.1	XX624	9-9-00	£13,000	Shawbury, Shropshire	G-KDOG
Bulldog T.1	XX515	-00	£15,500	Shawbury, Shropshire	G-CBBC
Gazelle AH.1	XW903	15-12-97	£35,000	See Shawbury, Shropshire	—
Gazelle AH.1	XZ329	30-1-98	£48,000	See Shawbury, Shropshire	—
Gazelle AH.1	XW885	4-2-98	£36,000	See Shawbury, Shropshire	—
Gazelle AH.1	XW911	11-12-97	£35,000	See Shawbury, Shropshire	—
Gazelle AH.1	XZ317	30-1-98	£42,000	See Shawbury, Shropshire	—
Gazelle HT.3	XX382	26-9-97	£32,000	See Shawbury, Shropshire	—
Gazelle HT.3	XW862	26-9-97	£42,000	See Shawbury, Shropshire	—
Gazelle HT.3	XW858	23-7-97	£58,000	See Shawbury, Shropshire	—
Gazelle HT.3	XW898	28-1-97	£60,000	See Shawbury, Shropshire	—
Gazelle HT.3	ZA803	24-6-97	£56,000	See Shawbury, Shropshire	—
Wessex HC.2	XT606	1-6-97	£25,000	See Shawbury, Shropshire	—
Wessex HC.2	XS677	1-6-97	£25,000	See Shawbury, Shropshire	—

25th October 2001 – Phillips: London

Another in the series of Ministry of Defence Disposal Sales Agency sales. Highlight of the sale was what was billed as "the remaining Bulldogs" – the entire disposal of the fleet having taking very little time. Also under offer were 11 AVCO Lycoming IO-360 engines, eight of which were zero-time.

Column one gives the type in lot order; column two identity; column three the 'last flown' date as given in the catalogue; column four the highest bid – not necessarily reflecting a sale, and not including the buyer's premium of VAT if applicable; column five the location (with a reference to the main text if applicable) and column six a 'forwarding reference'.

Bulldog T.1	XX690	6-9-00	£12,000	Shawbury, Shropshire	to Greenock, Scotland
Bulldog T.1	XX670	20-4-01	£12,000	Shawbury, Shropshire	USA
Bulldog T.1	XX628	30-5-01	£13,200	Shawbury, Shropshire	G-CBFU
Bulldog T.1	XX706	23-5-01	£12,000	Shawbury, Shropshire	N3043A
Bulldog T.1	XX562	23-5-01	£14,000	Shawbury, Shropshire	USA
Bulldog T.1	XX526	21-3-01	£15,000	Shawbury, Shropshire	USA
Bulldog T.1	XX549	30-5-01	£14,500	Shawbury, Shropshire	G-CBID
Bulldog T.1	XX518	14-3-01	£17,500	Shawbury, Shropshire	G-UDOG
Bulldog T.1	XX552	22-3-01	£16,500	Shawbury, Shropshire	N415BD
Bulldog T.1	XX708	30-5-01	£22,000	Shawbury, Shropshire	N708BD
Wessex HCC.4	XV733	13-3-98	£50,000	See Shawbury, Shropshire	—

APPENDIX B
EXPORTS

Within the text, all known exports are of course listed, but not highlighted as such. The table here should help to tie all of this activity together. Column 4 gives the location under which it was to be found within *W&R* and Column 5 the destination, new identity etc.

G-AMTK	Tiger Moth	Berkhamsted, Herts	Italy -00
G-APKY	Hiller UH-12B	Northampton, Northants	USA 1-02
G-BIWY	WG.30-100	Weston-super-Mare, Som	Italy 11-00
G-BNTE	AS.202 Bravo	Prestwick, Scotland	Finland 8-00
G-BNTH	AS.202 Bravo	Prestwick, Scotland	Finland 8-00, as OH-NTH
G-BNTK	AS.202 Bravo	Prestwick, Scotland	Finland 8-00, as OH-NTK
G-BNTL	AS.202 Bravo	Prestwick, Scotland	Finland 8-00, as OH-NTL
G-BNTN	AS.202 Bravo	Prestwick, Scotland	Finland 8-00, as OH-NTN
G-BNTO	AS.202 Bravo	Prestwick, Scotland	Finland 8-00, as OH-NTO
G-BODG	Motor Cadet III	East Fortune, Scotland	USA -00
G-BPLG	MS.317	Uckfield, E Sussex	France -00
G-BTKI	T-6G-NF Texan	Bredon, H&W	USA 5-00
G-BUTX	Jungmeister	Breighton, E Yorks	USA 10-00
G-BWRG	M.1D Sokol ✈	Sandown, Isle of Wight	Germany 17-5-00
G-BWUD	Lavochkin La-9	Duxford, Cambs	New Zealand 8-00
G-SWIS	Vampire FB.6	Bournemouth, Dorset	New Zealand (?) -01
G-DYAK	LET Yak C-11	Little Gransden, Cambs	Germany 6-00

ASC	Grunau Baby IIB	Rufforth, N Yorks	Germany circa 1996
N79863	F6F-5K Hellcat	North Weald, Essex	USA 12-7-01
XA-NAN	Bö 105B	Longside, Scotland	Sweden -00
AE977	G-TWTD	Sea Hurricane X ✈	Audley End, Essex	USA 1-02 as N33TF
ML417	G-BJSG	Spitfire IX ✈	Duxford, Cambs	USA -01 as N2TF
PL344	G-IXCC	Spitfire IX ✈	Wycombe Air Park, Bucks	USA 5-01 as N644TB
PL965	G-MKXI	Spitfire PR.XI ✈	Breighton, E Yorks	USA 7-9-01
TX183	G-BSMF	Anson C.19	Arbroath, Scotland	Dubai 5-01
VZ467	G-METE	Meteor F.8 ✈	Cranfield, Beds	Australia 5-01
WP845		Chipmunk T.10 PAX	Bruntingthorpe, Leics	Canada -00
WT898		Cadet TX.3	Rufforth, N Yorks	Germany -97
XE796		Cadet TX.3	North Weald, Essex	Netherlands circa 1998
XF368	G-BZRH	Hunter GA.11 ✈	Exeter, Devon	South Africa 17-6-01
XF967	G-BZRI	Hunter T.8B ✈	Exeter, Devon	South Africa 17-6-01
XK149		Hunter F.6A	Bruntingthorpe, Leics	USA 10-4-00
XL601		Hunter T.7	Exeter, Devon	Belgium 1-99
XL613	G-BVMB	Hunter T.7A ✈	Exeter, Devon	South Africa 17-6-01
XM471		Jet Provost T.3A	Cosford, Shropshire	USA 7-99 as N471XN
XN470	G-BXBJ	Jet Provost T.3A	Binbrook, Lincs	Dubai late 1999
XN769		Lightning F.2 nose	Sidcup, Gtr London	Malta late 2000
'XP822'	XP806	Beaver AL.1	Cumbernauld, Scotland	Canada 22-11-00
XR569		Gnat T.1	Bruntingthorpe, Leics	USA 16-12-00
XS677		Wessex HC.2	Shawbury, Shropshire	New Zealand 16-8-01asZK-HBE
XT606		Wessex HC.2	Shawbury, Shropshire	New Zealand 20-8-01
XW911		Gazelle AH.1	Shawbury, Shropshire	USA 5-01 as N911XW
XX391		Gazelle HT.2	Shawbury, Shropshire	New Zealand 7-01 as ZK-HTB
XX441		Gazelle HT.2	Shawbury, Shropshire	New Zealand 7-01 as ZK-HBH
XX446		Gazelle HT.2	Shawbury, Shropshire	New Zealand 7-01 as ZK-HTF
XZ317		Gazelle AH.1	Shawbury, Shropshire	Swaziland -01 as 3D-HGZ
XZ995	G-CBGK	Harrier GR.3	Shoreham, W Sussex	USA 12-01
ZF581		Lightning F.53	Portsmouth, Hants	Netherlands by 11-01
ZF595		Lightning T.55 nose	Bruntingthorpe, Leics	USA 20-5-01
1366		Chipmunk T.20	Bedford, Beds	USA 8-00
'2028'	G-BVVF	Nanchang CJ-6A	Breighton, E Yorks	USA 10-00
'290'	F-AZJD	Dewoitine D.26	Duxford, Cambs	France 8-01
1342	G-BYDS	Bf 109E	Audley End, Essex	USA -00
41	G-LYNE	P-51D-20-NA	Tees-side, D&C	USA -01
6247	G-OMIG	SBLim-2A	Duxford, Cambs	Brazil 20-11-00
09008	G-BZMN	SBLim-2	Ipswich, Suffolk	USA 6-01
—		P-39Q-BE	Sandown, Isle of Wight	USA 1-6-00
41-13570		P-40E-CU	Sandown, Isle of Wight	USA 29-9-00

Appendix C
LOST and FOUND!

This section seeks to get readers scratching around to solve some of the many 'unfinished' stories within the pages of
W&R. Listed below are aircraft that have been shunted into the LOST! column from the pages of this edition. The ultimate
aim is to 'find' these, and this mostly takes the form of a confirmed scrapping, or similar. A few airframes are sufficiently
resilient to make a 'come back'. Note that, as with all of the book, the criterion for an aircraft entering LOST! or FOUND! is
a physical input and not an assumption or interpretation of registration changes etc. Over to YOU!

Lost!
G-AHHU Auster J/1N Alpha, last in Southampton, Hants, area (12-91); **G-AIGF** Auster J/1N Alpha, last in
Southampton, Hants, area (12-96); **G-AWFH** Cessna F.150H, last at Winsford, Cheshire (12-930; **G-BATM** Cherokee
Six last at Plaistow, West Sussex (1-93); **G-BCAC** Rallye Minerva last at Trafford Park, Gtr Man (5-92); **G-BFPE**
Cherokee 140C last at Framlingham, Suffolk (4-92); **G-BFZA** Alpavia RF-3 last at Bedford, Beds (3-90); **N11824**
Cessna 150M last at Framlingham, Suffolk (3-94); **ZH762** Skyship 600 gondola, offered for tender at Cardington, Beds,
1-98 (3-98); **42-93510** C-47A nose (6W-SAE) last at Kew, Gtr Lon (8-94).

Found!
G-ALAX Dragon Rapide still at Andover, Hants; **G-BPLG** MS.317 last in Fenland, Cambs - see Uckfield, E Sussex.

Appendix D
ABBREVIATIONS

Without the use of abbreviations for the 'potted' histories of the aircraft listed in *W&R*, the book would perhaps be twice the size. Readers should face few problems, especially if they have previous editions to refer to. There follows a decode of abbreviations to help readers wend their way through the individual histories. Footnotes have been added to go into greater depth with some entries. To save repetition, abbreviations that are clearly combinations of others are not listed in full, eg MEAFCS, breaks into MEAF and CS, ie Middle East Air Force Communications Squadron.

A&AEE	Aeroplane and Armament Experimental Establishment. From the late 1980s became the Aircraft and Armament Evaluation Establishment. Now QinetiQ!	ATDU	Air Torpedo Development Unit	
		ATE	Army Training Estate	
		ATF	Airframe Technology Flight	
		Att	Air Attache	
AAC	Army Air Corps	AuxAF	Auxiliary Air Force	
AACU	Anti-Aircraft Co-operation Unit	aw/cn	A Waiting CollectioN	Note 2
AAFCE	Allied Air Forces Central Europe	AWFCS	All Weather Fighter Combat School	
AAIU	Air Accident Investigation Unit	AWOCU	All Weather Operational Conversion Unit	
ABDR	Aircraft Battle Damage Repair	AWRE	Atomic Weapons Research Establishment,	
ACC	Allied Control Commission	BA	British Airways	
ACSEA	Allied Command, South East Asia Note 1	BAAT	British Airways Airtours	
ACU	Andover Conversion Unit	BAC	Bristol Aero Collection	
ADS	Air Director School	BAC	British Aircraft Corporation	
AE&AEOS	Air Engineers and Air Electronic Operators School	BAe	British Aerospace	
		BAF	British Air Ferries	
AEF	Air Experience Flight	BAFO	British Air Forces of Occupation	
AES	Air Engineers School	BAH	British Airways Helicopters	
AES	Air Engineering School	BAM	Booker Aircraft Museum	
AETW	Air Engineering Training Wing	BANS	Basic Air Navigation School	
AFDS	Air Fighting Development Squadron,	BAOR	British Army of the Rhine	
AFDU	Air Fighting Development Unit	BAPC	British Aviation Preservation Council	
AFEE	Airborne Forces Experimental Establishment	BATUS	British Army Training Unit, Suffield (Can)	
AFN	Air Forces North	BBMF	Battle of Britain Memorial Flight	
AFNE	Air Forces Near East	BBML	British Balloon Museum and Library	
AFS	Advanced Flying School	BC	Bomber Command.	
AFTS	Advanced Flying Training School	BCAL	British Caledonian Airlines	
AFU	Advanced Flying Unit	BCBS	Bomber Command Bombing School,	
AFWF	Advanced Fixed Wing Flight	BDRF	Battle Damage Repair Flight	
AIU	Accident Investigation Unit	BDTF	Bomber Defence Training Flight	
ALAT	Aviation Legere de l'Armee de Terre	BDU	Bomber Development Unit	
AMARC	Aerospace Maintenance& Regeneration Center, Arizona, USA	BEA	British European Airways	
		BEAH	British European Helicopters	
AMIF	Aircraft Maintainance Instruction Flight.	BEAS	British Executive Air Services	
AMS	Air Movements School	BFTS	Basic Flying Training School	
ANG	Air National Guard	BFWF	Basic Fixed Wing Flight	
ANS	Air Navigation School	B&GS	Bombing & Gunnery School (RCAF)	
AONS	Air Observer and Navigator School	BG	Bomb Group	
AOTS	Aircrew Officers Training School	BIH	British Independent Helicopters	
APS	Aircraft Preservation Society	BLEU	Blind Landing Experimental Unit	
APS	Armament Practice Station	BMA	British Midland Airways now bmi	
arr	arrived, denotes airframe arrived at location by surface transport.	BOAC	British Overseas Airways Corporation	
		BPPU	Bristol Plane Preservation Unit	
AR&TF	Aircraft Recovery and Transportation Flight, St Athan – tri-service 'mover' of fixed-wing airframes. (See MASU)	BRNC	Britannia Royal Naval College	
		BSE	Bristol Siddeley Engines	
		B&TTF	Bombing & Target Towing Flight	
ARWF	Advanced Rotary Wing Flight,	BTF	Beaver Training Flight	
AS	Aggressor Squadron	BTU	Bombing Trials Unit	
AS&RU	Aircraft Salvage and Repair Unit	BUA	British United Airlines	
ASF	Aircraft Servicing Flight	BW	Bomb Wing	
ASS	Air Signals School	C(A)	Controller (Aircraft) see also CS(A) Note 3	
AST	Air Service Training	CAA	Civil Aviation Authority	
ASWDU	Air-Sea Warfare Development Unit	CAACU	Civilian Anti-Aircraft Co-operation Unit	
ATA	Air Transport Auxiliary	CAF	Canadian Armed Forces.	
ATAIU	Allied Technical Air Intelligence Unit	CAFU	Civil Aviation Flying Unit	
ATC	Air Training Corps (Air Cadets)	Cam Flt	Camouflage Flight,	

CATCS	Central Air Traffic Control School		see DERA
CAW	College of Air Warfare	DU	Development Unit, as suffix
CBE	Central Bombing Establishment,	EAAS	East Anglian Aviation Society
CC	Coastal Command.	EASAMS	European avionics consortium
CCAS	Civilian Craft Apprentices School,	ECTT	Escadre de Chasse Tous Temp
CCF	Combined Cadet Force	EE	English Electric
CF	Communications Flight as suffix with other	EFTS	Elementary Flying Training School
	unit, or for an airfield.	EOD	Explosive Ordnance Disposal
CFCCU	Civilian Fighter Control and Co-op Unit	EP&TU	Exhibition, Production and Transport Unit
CFE	Central Fighter Establishment see CFE-	ERFTS	Elementary & Reserve Flying Trng School
	EAF.	ERS	Empire Radio School
CFE-EAF	Central Fighter Establishment - Enemy	Esc	Escadre, French squadron
	Aircraft Flight	ETPS	Empire Test Pilots School
CFS	Central Flying School	ETS	Engineering Training School
C&TTS	Communications and Target Towing Sn	ETU	Experimental Trials Unit
CGS	Central Gliding School	EWAD	Electronic Warfare and Avionics Detachment
CGS	Central Gunnery School	EWE&TU	Electronic Warfare Experimental and
CIFAS	Centre d'Instruction des Forces Aeriennes		Training Unit
	· Strategiques	F	Flight, suffix to number
CIT	Cranfield Institure of Technology	FAA	Fleet Air Arm.
CNCS	Central Navigation and Control School	FAA	Fuerza Aerea Argentina
CoA	Certificate (or Permit) of Airworthiness.	FAAHAF	Fleet Air Arm Historic Aircraft Flight
Cott	Cottesmore, in relation to V-Bomber wings.	FAAM	Fleet Air Arm Museum
CPF	Coastal Patrol Flight	FAF	French Air Force.
cr	crashed, or other form of accident.	FAH	Fuerza Aerea Hondurena.
CR	Crash Rescue, training airframe.	FC	Fighter Command.
CRD	Controller, Research and Development	FC&RS	Fighter Control and Reporting School
C&RS	Control and Reporting School	FCS	Fighter Control School
CS	Communications Squadron, as a suffix with	FEAF	Far East Air Forces Note 1
	other units, or for an airfield.	FECS	Far East Communications Flight
CS(A)	Controller, Supplies (Air), see also CA	FF	Ferry Flight,
	Note 3	FF&SS	Fire Fighting and Safety School
CSDE	Central Servicing Development Es.	FGF	Flying Grading Flight
CSE	Central Signals Establishment	FLS	Fighter Leader School
CSF	Canberra Servicing Flight	FOAC	Flag Officer, Aircraft Carriers
CTE	Central Training Establishment	FOCAS	Friends of Cardington Airship Station
CTTS	Civilian Technical Training School	FOFT	Flag Officer, Flying Training
C&TTS	Communications & Target Towing Squadron	FONA	Flag Officer, Naval Aviation
CU	Communications Unit, as suffix	FONAC	Flag Officer, Naval Air Command
CU	Conversion Unit, as suffix	FP	Ferry Pool
DARA	Defence Aviation Repair Agency, Fleetlands,	FPP	Ferry Pilots Pool
	St Athan, Sealand.	FRADU	Fleet Requirements and Direction Unit
dbr	damaged beyond repair, to distinguish an	FRL	Flight Refuelling Ltd
	aircraft that was written off but did not crash	FRS	Flying Refresher School
deH	de Havilland	FRU	Fleet Requirements Unit
del	delivered, an airframe that arrived by air.	FSM	Full Scale Model
DERA	Defence Evaluation and Research Agency —	FSS	Ferry Support Squadron
	replaced DRA and DTEO.	FSS	Flying Selection Squadron
Det	Detachment, flight or other unit detached	FTC	Flying Training Command
	from main base.	FTS	Flying Training School
DFLS	Day Fighter Leader School	FTU	Ferry Training Unit
DLO	Defence Logistics Organisation	FU	Ferry Unit
DOSAAF	Dobrovol'noe Obshchestvo Sodeiestviya	FWS	Fighter Weapons School
	Armii, Aviatsii i Flotu – Voluntery Society	GAM	Groupe Aérien Mixte
	for the Support of the Army, Aviation and	GCF	Group Communications Flight
	Fleet - Soviet reservist society	GE	Groupement Ecol
DPA	Defence Procurement Agency replaced	GIA	Ground Instructional Aircraft
	MoD(PE)	GS	Glider School
DRA	Defence Research Agency – see DERA	GSU	Group Support Unit
DSA	Disposal Sales Agency	GTS	Glider Training School
DSDA	Defence Storage and Distribution Agency tri-	GU	Glider Unit
	service unit with the following sites:	GWDS	Guided Weapons Development Squadron
	Ashchurch, Aston Down, Bicester (not the	HAB	Hot air balloon
	airfield), Donnington, Llangenneach,	HAM	Historic Aircraft Museum, Southend
	Stafford, West Moors	HC	Home Command
DTEO	Defence Test and Evaluation Organisation –	HCEU	Home Command Examining Unit

HCF	Hornet Conversion Flight	ntu	Not taken up, registration applied for, but
HDU	Helicopter Development Unit		not worn, or paperwork not concluded
HGSU	Heavy Glider Servicing Unit	(O)AFU	(Observers) Advanced Flying Unit
HMTS	Harrier Maintenance Training School	OCTU	Officer Cadet Training Unit
HQ	Headquarters	OCU	Operational Conversion Unit
HS	Handling Squadron	OTU	Operational Training Unit
HSA	Hawker Siddeley Aviation	(P)AFU	(Pilot) Advanced Flying Unit
HTF	Helicopter Training Flight	pax	Passenger, as used in Chipmunkpax trainer
IAAC	Irish Army Air Corps	PCSS	Protectorate Comms and Support Squadron
IAF	Indian Air Force	PEE	Proof & Experimental Establishment
IAM	Institute of Aviation Medicine	PFA	Popular Flying Association
IGN	Institut Geographique National	PFS	Primary Flying School
IHM	International Helicopter Museum	PFTS	Primary Flying Training School
ITF or 'S	Instrument Training Flight / Squadron	PP	Pilots' Pool
IWM	Imperial War Museum	PPS	Personal Plane Services
JASS	Joint Anti-Submarine School	PRDU	Photo Reconnaissance Development Unit
JATE	Joint Air Transport Establishment - see	PRU	Photographic Reconnaissance Unit
	JATEU	PTC	Personnel and Training Command
JATEU	Joint Air Transport Evaluation Unit –	PTF	Phantom Training Flight
	replaced JATE	PTS	Primary Training School
JCU	Javelin Conversion Unit	QF	Queen's Flight
JEHU	Joint Experimental Helicopter Unit	RAAF	Royal Australian Air Force
JMU	Joint Maritime Unit	RAE	Royal Aircraft / Aerospace Establishment
JOCU	Jaguar Operational Conversion Unit	RAeS	Royal Aeronautical Society
JTU	Joint Trials Unit (Nimrod AEW)	RAF	Royal Air Force
JWE	Joint Warfare Establishment	RAFA	Royal Air Force Association
LAS	Light Aircraft School	RAFC	Royal Air Force College
LC	Logistics Command	RAFEF	Royal Air Force Exhibition Flight
LCS & 'U	Lightning Conversion Squadron / Unit	RAFG	Royal Air Force Germany
LTF	Lightning Training Flight	RAFGSA	Royal Air Force Gliding & Soaring Assoc
LWRE	Long Range Weapons Research Est	RAFHSF	Royal Air Force High Speed Flight
MAM	Midland Air Museum	RAFM	Royal Air Force Museum
MASL	Military Aircraft Spares Ltd	RAN	Royal Australian Navy.
MASU	Mobile Aircraft Support Unit – DARA	RC	Reserve Command
	Fleetlands, tri-service 'mover' of	RCAF	Royal Canadian Air Force
	helicopters.See AR&TF.	RCN	Royal Canadian Navy
MBA	Museum of Berkshire Aviation	RCS	Rotary Conversion Squadron
MC	Maintenance Command	Regt	Regiment
MCS	Metropolitan Communications Squadron	RFS	Reserve Flying School
MEAF	Middle East Air Force Note 1	RHK	Royal Hong Kong
MECS	Middle East Communications Squadron	RMAF	Royal Malaysian Air Force
MGSP	Mobile Glider Servicing Party	RNAY	Royal Naval Aircraft Yard
MinTech	Ministry of Technology, see also MoA,	RNEC	Royal Naval Engineering College
	MoS Note 3	RNGSA	Royal Navy Gliding and Soaring Association
MoA	Ministry of Aviation, see MinTech, MoS	RNHF	Royal Navy Historic Flight
	Note 3	RNoAF	Royal Norwegian Air Force
MoD	Ministry of Defence	RNZAF	Royal New Zealand Air Force
MoD(PE)	Ministry of Defence (Procurement	ROC	Royal Observer Corps
	Executive) – see DPA	RPRE	Rocket Propulsion Research Establishment
MoS	Ministry of Supply, see MinTech, MoA	RRE	Royal Radar Establishment
	Note 3	RRF	Radar Reconnaissance Flight
MoTaT	Museum of Transport & Technology, NZ	RRHT	Rolls-Royce Heritage Trust
MOTU	Maritime Operational Training Unit	RS	Radio School
MPA	Man-powered aircraft	RSRE	Radar and Signals Research Establishment
MU	Maintenance Unit Note 4	RSS & 'U	Repair & Servicing Section / Unit
NAAS	Navigator and Airman Aircrew School	RTR	Royal Tank Regiment
NACDS	Naval Air Command Driving School	RWE	Radio Warfare Establishment
NASA	National Aeronautical and Space Admin	SAAF	South African Air Force
NASU	Naval Aircraft Servicing Unit	SAC	School of Army Co-operation
NBC	Nuclear, Bacteriological and Chemical	SAF	School of Aerial Fighting
NCS	Northern Communications Squadron	SAH	School of Aircraft Handling
nea	Non effective airframe Note 2	SAR	Search and Rescue
NECS	North Eastern Communications Squadron	SAREW	Search and Rescue Engineering Wing
NIBF	Northern Ireland Beaver Flight	SARTS	Search and Rescue Training Squadron
NSF	Northern Sector Flight	SC	Signals Command
		Scamp	Scampton, to distinguish a V-Bomber wing.

SCBS	Strike Command Bombing School			Aggressor Squadron
SCS	Southern Communications Squadron		TFW	Tactical Fighter Wing
SEAE	School of Electrical and Aeronautical		TGDA	Training Group Defence Agency
	Engineering		Thum Flt	Temperature and HUMidity Flight
SF	Station Flight, usually with an airfield name		TMS	Tornado Maintenanc eSchool
SFDO	School of Flight Deck Operations		TMTS	Trade Management Training School
SFTS	Service Flying Training School		toc	Taken on charge	Note 2
ShF	Ship's Flight		TRE	Telecommunications Research Establishment
SHQ	Station HQ		TS	Training Squadron
SLAW	School of Land/Air Warfare		TTC	Technical Training Command
SMR	School of Maritime Reconnaissance		TTU	Torpedo Training Unit
soc	Struck off charge	Note 2	TWU	Tactical Weapons Unit
SoRF	School of Refresher Training		UAS	University Air Squadron	Note 6
SoTT	School of Technical Training	Note 5	UNFICYP	United Nations Forces In Cyprus
SRCU	Short Range Conversion Unit		USAAC	United States Army Air Corps
SRW	Strategic Reconnaissance Wing		USAAF	United States Army Air Force
SS	Signals Squadron		USAF	United States Air Force
SS	Support Squadron		USMC	United States Marine Corps
SU	Support Unit		USN	United States Navy
SVAS	Shuttleworth Veteran Aeroplane Society		VAFA	Vintage Aircraft Flying Association
TAC	The Aeroplane Collection		VAT	Vintage Aircraft Team
TAF	Tactical Air Force		VGS	Volunteer Gliding School
TAW	Tactical Airlift Wing		Wadd	Waddington, denoting a V-Bomber wing
TC	Transport Command		WAP	Wycombe Air Park
TEE	Trials and Experimental Establishment		WCS	Western Communications Squadron
TEU	Tactical Exercise Unit		wfu	Withdrawn from use
TF	Training Flight		Witt	Wittering, denoting a V-bomber wing.
TFF	Target Facilities Flight		WLT	Weapons Loading Trainer
TFS	Tactical Fighter Squadron		WSF	Western Sector Flight
TFTAS	Tactical Fighter Training			

Notes

1 RAF 'Holding Units': For administrative purposes, the history cards of some RAF aircraft become fairly vague when transferred to either Middle East or Far East theatres of operations. Accordingly, the following abbreviations denote the 'operator' for the segment of an aircraft's life in that theatre, even though it may have been used by several front-line units : ACSEA, FEAF, MEAF.

2 History Card 'milestones': There are several RAF aircraft history card 'milestones' referred to in the main text. Essentially an aircraft starts off as A Waiting Collection (Aw/cn) - a signal from the manufacturer that the aircraft is ready for issue to service; it is then taken on charge (toc) and becomes a part of the RAF; after service life, it may eventually to be declared a non-effective airframe (nea) and down-graded to instructional or fire-training use; the final act is for it to be struck off a charge (soc), either being written-off in an accident, scrapped, sold to another user etc etc.

3 Government 'owning' bodies: Technical 'owner' of UK military machines is the C(A) or CS(A) and at times these are noted within the aircraft history cards instead of a unit, although it may well be a pointer to the aircraft being operated at that time of its life by a test or trials unit. In similar manner, MinTech, MoA or MoS can appear, frequently meaning operation by the RAE, or DRA.

4 Maintenance Unit (MU): Mentioned in the text: 4 Stanmore Park (detachment); 5 Kemble; 6 Brize Norton, 7 Quedgeley; 8 Little Rissington; 9 Cosford; 10 Hullavington; 12 Kirkbride; 14 Carlisle; 15 Wroughton; 16 Stafford; 19 St Athan (also 32); 20 Aston Down; 22 Silloth; 23 Aldergrove; 27 Shawbury; 29 High Ercall; 32 St Athan (also 19); 39 Colerne; 44 Edzell; 46 Lossiemouth; 47 Sealand; 48 Hawarden; 54 Cambridge; 57 Wig Bay; 60 Leconfield; 71 Bicester.

5 School of Technical Training (SoTT): The following are mentioned in the main text: 1 Halton; 2 Cosford; 4 St Athan; 8 Weeton; 9 Newton; 10 Kirkham; 12 Melksham.

6 University Air Squadron (UAS): Prefixed with a university name: Abn Aberdeen, Dundee & St Andrews; Bir Birmingham; Bri Bristol; Cam Cambridge; Dur Durham; Edn Edinburgh; Elo East Lowlands; Ems East Midlands; G&S Glasgow & Strathclyde; Lee Leeds; Liv Liverpool; Lon London; Man Manchester & Salford; Nor Northumbrian; Not Nottingham; Oxf Oxford; QUB Queens University Belfast; Stn Southampton; Wal Wales; Yor Yorkshire.

Note that some types have been 'bundled' into 'families' for ease of reference: BALLOONS, HANG-GLIDERS (modern examples, Pilchers etc are listed separately), ORNITHOPTERS (flapping wing devices).

A.109 (Agusta) 39, 147
A-10 see Thunderbolt II
A-20 see Havoc
AA-1, AA-5 Traveler etc – see Yankee 50
Active (Arrow) 14
AD – see Skyraider
Adam RA-14 136
Addyman STG etc - glider 157, 268
Aeronca types
 62, 148, 262, 290, 291,299, 300
AFEE 10/42 'Rotajeep' 75
Air Command 503 80, 265
Airacobra (Bell P-39) 30
Airbus A300 50, 63
Aircoupe (Alon etc, also Ercoupe)
 88, 165, 204, 214, 297, 304
Airedale (Beagle)
 34, 146, 169, 173, 275
Airguard (Chrislea) 200
AIRSHIPS (all types) 18, 153, 182, 260
Airtourer (AESL etc) 67, 281
Akro (Stephens) 185
Albacore (Fairey) 194
Albatros – see L 39
Alcyon (MS.733) 58
Aldritt Monoplane 212
Alpha Jet (Dassault/Dornier) 257, 258
Alouette II and III (Sud) 75, 76, 301
Ambassador (Airspeed) 27
American Eagle 207
Amiot AAC.1 - see Ju 52
ANEC types 14, 160
Andover (HS, inc HS.748) 32, 47, 68,
 69, 94, 181, 183, 257, 288, 302
Anson (Avro, inc Avro XIX) 24, 36,
 64, 150, 157, 160, 171, 175, 180,
 200, 220, 221, 265, 279, 290, 300
Antoinette 153
Antonov An-2 Colt 36, 160, 289
Apache (Piper PA-23 - see Aztec) 34, 62
Archaeopteryx (Granger) 174
Archer - see Cherokee
Argosy (AWA) 132, 176, 181, 219, 285
Aries - see Gemini
ARV Super 2 77, 258, 275
Ashton (Avro) 157
AS.355 Twin Squirrel (Aérospatiale) 48
ASW-20 (glider) 61
ATP (BAe, or J61)
 94, 155, 156, 157, 284, 288
Attacker (Supermarine) 194
Audax (Hawker) 212
Auster, (all marks, inc Husky, Taylorcraft,
 Terrier)10, 25, 27, 34, 36, 41, 44, 45, 47,
 48, 54, 55, 56, 67, 74, 75, 76, 79, 82, 85,
 91, 93, 131, 133, 134, 138, 144, 145,
 154, 162, 169, 170, 173, 175, 176, 180,
 189, 221, 223, 264, 265, 269, 270, 272,
 275, 276, 278, 283, 284, 290, 300, 303
Avenger (Grumman TBM) 26, 194

Avian (Avro) 156, 273
Avro 504 14, 28, 78, 79, 149, 153, 156,
 204, 206, 265
Avro 707 156, 180, 303
Avro XIX - see Anson
Aztec (Piper PA-23/PA-27, also Apache,
 Geronimo) 10, 11, 33, 56, 85, 91, 94,
 144, 146, 147, 154, 159, 178, 188, 199,
 207, 212, 269, 273, 284, 288, 303
B-17 - see Flying Fortress
B-24 - see Liberator
B-25 - see Mitchell
B-26 - see Invader
B-29 - see Superfortress
B-52 - see Stratofortress
Babe (Bristol) 65
Baby (Sopwith) 194
BAC 111
 27, 48, 49, 60, 69, 89, 179, 206, 257
BAC 221 (see also Fairey FD-2) 194
BAe 146 and RJ 69
BALLOONS (all types) 17, 18, 24, 70,
 88, 153, 211, 214, 215, 260
Balliol (BP, inc Sea Balliol) 161, 171, 180
Bandeirante (Embraer) 69, 272, 273
Baron (Beech) 29, 130
Barracuda (Fairey) 194
Battle (Fairey) 149
BE.2 (RAF) 90, 149, 153, 204, 266
Beagle 206 62, 65
Bearcat (Grumman) 30
Beaufighter (Bristol) 12, 30, 150, 220, 279
Beaufort (Bristol) 150
Beaver (DHC) 28, 75, 76, 220, 282
Bede BD-5 Micro 41, 83, 260
Beech 17 'Staggerwing' 57, 58
Beech 18 (all models)
 29, 56, 129, 278, 284
Belfast (Short) 60, 181
Bell 47 - see Sioux
Bell 212 - see Iroquois
Belvedere HC.1 (Bristol)
 150, 156, 191, 192
Bensen gyroplanes 47, 156, 172, 192, 195,
 198, 201, 261, 271, 272, 276, 281, 288
Bergfalke (glider) 85, 260
Beta (Rollason) 17
Beverley (Blackburn) 27, 176, 261
Bf 109 – see Messerschmitt
Bird Dog - see Cessna singles
Blackburn B-2 34, 61, 263
Blackburn Monoplanes 14, 266
Blake Bluetit 58
Blenheim - see Bolingbroke
Blériot (all models, see also Humber Mono
 and JAP-Harding Mono
 14, 22, 181, 182, 206
BN-1 (Britten Norman) 78
Boeing 247 260
Boeing 707 / 720 60, 92, 130, 132, 179

Boeing 727 60
Boeing 737 50
Boeing 747 92
Bolingbroke (Bristol, 'Blenheim')
 28, 150, 279
Bölkow Bö 102 191
Bölkow Bö 105 – see MBB
Bölkow Bö 208 Junior 52, 80
Bonanza (Beech) 60
Boulton Paul P.111A 219
Boxkite (Bristol) 14, 62
Brantly B.2 / 305 16, 191, 192, 278
Brigand (Bristol) 65
Bristol 173 65
Britannia (Bristol) 13, 27, 65, 66, 179
Brochet MB.50 Pipistrelle 185
Brochet MB.84, MB.100 135, 136
Broussard (Max Holste) 32
Brown Helicopter 172
Buccaneer (Blackburn) 25, 38, 49, 55, 61,
 64, 66, 71, 89, 92, 129, 132, 137, 144,
 148, 151, 163, 167, 176, 181, 185, 194,
 195, 200, 202, 208, 220, 263, 266, 267,
 277, 279, 280, 281, 295, 299
Buchón – see Messerschmitt Me (Bf)
Bücker – Bü 131 - see Jungmann, Bü 133 -
 see Jungmeister
Bulldog (Bristol) 149
Bulldog (SAL) 20, 28, 44, 92, 187, 214,
 224, 263, 278, 281, 288, 293
C-47 - see Dakota / Skytrain
C-119 Boxcar (Fairchild) 56
C-130 – see Hercules
Cadet (Avro) 62, 304
Cadet (Slingsby - glider) 25, 45, 62, 78,
 91, 151, 160, 161, 174, 175, 219, 258,
 259, 265, 268, 271, 288, 300, 303
Camel (Sopwith)
 22, 153, 179, 194, 206, 272
Canberra (EE etc, inc Short SC-9)
 11, 21, 23, 24, 33, 35, 36, 39, 41, 43, 49,
 50, 54, 55, 60, 61, 63, 64, 70, 79, 80, 81,
 88, 92, 95, 96, 130, 131, 132, 135, 139,
 141, 150, 151, 154, 159, 160, 161, 163,
 171, 172, 175, 176, 179, 180, 181, 184,
 185, 201, 205, 207, 212, 221, 223, 257,
 265, 277, 279, 282, 287, 290, 291, 292,
 295, 297
Carmam M.100S - glider 264
Carvair (ATL.98) 202
CASA 1-131 - see Jungmann
CASA 2-111 - see Heinkel He 111
CASA 352L - see Ju 52
Cassutt Racer 169
Catalina (Consolidated PBY) 57, 74, 181
Caudron G.III 149
Cayley Glider 266

CEA – see Jodel, Robin
Cessna single-engined, high wing, types
  10, 11, 16, 19, 23, 33, 34, 37, 40, 41, 44,
  50, 54, 59, 60, 61, 62, 67, 69, 76, 77, 81,
  82, 85, 87, 90, 91, 94, 95, 139, 141, 143,
  145, 146, 147, 148, 153, 155, 162, 168,
  169, 172, 174, 177, 178, 179, 188, 199,
  200, 204, 210, 212, 216, 217, 263, 264,
  270, 272, 276, 280, 281, 282, 283, 287,
  298, 299, 300, 301, 304
Cessna twin-engined types
  23, 67, 94, 155, 216, 217, 283
Cessna 188 Agwagon   275
Cessna 336, 337 (the CLT twins)
                            166, 297, 301
CF-100 Canuck (Avro Canada)   25
Cheetah - see Traveler
Cherokee (Piper, all types, inc Archer
  Arrow, Cadet, Lance, Six, Warrior etc)
  22, 32, 34, 45, 51, 52, 59, 60, 61, 67, 77,
  82, 94, 138, 146, 147, 155, 165, 178,
  189, 207, 210, 217, 222, 259, 268, 272,
  283, 284, 288, 289, 297, 300
Chilton DW.1, DW.2   16, 79, 159
Chinook (Boeing CH-47) 71, 77, 137, 205
Chipmunk (DHC)   10, 15, 20, 21, 28,
  31, 32, 42, 54, 75, 78, 80, 84, 88, 91, 94,
  96, 133, 137, 148, 150, 155, 158, 160,
  171, 175, 177, 180, 196, 198, 206, 211,
  221, 222, 224, 257, 269, 270, 276, 277,
  279, 291, 301, 302, 303
Chrislea Skyjeep   144
Cierva C.24 / C.30A (Rota)
                        25, 84, 149, 153, 190
Cirrus glider (Schemp-Hirth)   153
Civilian Coupe   147
Clarke TWK glider   151
Cloudster (Rearwin)   79
Cmelak (LET Z-37)   260
Cobra (Bell AH-1)   178
Cody Biplane   153
Colditz Cock - glider   139
Colt - see TriPacer
Comanche (Piper)   34, 77, 278
Comet (DH.88)   14, 44, 82, 84
Comet (DH.104 - see also Nimrod)
  27, 62, 84, 96, 129, 138, 171, 179, 213,
  214, 258, 260, 278
Commander singles (112, 114 etc)
                            188, 291
Concorde (BAC/SNIAS)
                        27, 38, 62, 63, 65, 193
Condor (Druine/Rollason)
                178, 216, 276, 280, 281
Constellation (Lockheed)   260
Cornell (Fairchild PT-19/PT-23 etc)
                            182, 185
Corsair (Vought etc)   29, 30, 32, 194
Cosmic Wind (Le Vier)   168
Cougar (Campbell)   191
Coyote (Rans)   262
Criquet (MS - see Fieseler Fi 156)
Cub (Piper, inc Super Cub)   17, 29, 67,
  133, 135, 136, 148, 166, 188, 203, 262,
  275, 276, 281, 291, 297, 299, 303
Currie Wot   45
Cygnet (GAL)   278

Cygnet (Hawker)   14, 182
Dagling (RFD - glider)   11, 268
Dakota (Douglas C-47, DC-3 etc)
  12, 26, 56, 68, 71, 87, 137, 153, 180,
  201, 221, 259, 260, 265
Dart (Slingsby)   268
Defiant (BP)   150, 160
Demoiselle (Santos Dumont)   198, 207
Demon (Hawker)   12
Denney Kitfox   279
Deperdussin   14
Desford Trainer (Reid & Sigrist)   131
Desoutter   14
DH.9, DH.9A   12, 149
DH.51   14
DH.71   78
DG-202 (Glaser-Dirks - glider)   61
Dickson Primary   268
Dinah (Mitsubishi Ki 46)   181
Dingbat (Wakinson)   159
Djinn (Sud)   192
Dolphin (Sopwith)   182
Dominie - see Dragon Rapide and HS.125
Doppelraab - glider   177
Dornier Do 27   297
Douglas DC-7   303
Dove, Devon and Sea Devon (DH)
  27, 63, 64, 66, 67, 84, 175, 180, 188,
  209, 219, 220, 221, 222, 260, 269, 278,
  287, 297, 301, 303
Dove (Sopwith)   14
Dragon - microlight   136, 262
Dragon (DH)   70, 78, 260, 278, 302
Dragon Rapide (DH and Dominie)
  17, 32, 48, 69, 84, 156, 158, 182, 220,
  260, 289, 290
Dragonfly (Viking)   211
Dragonfly (Westland, all marks)   88, 94,
  171, 179, 191, 192, 194, 195, 266, 287
Draken (SAAB)   26, 140, 176
Drone (BAC, Kronfeld)   172, 206, 268
Drover (DHA)   74
EAA Biplane   273
Eagle microlight   287
Eagle (McDD F-15)   27, 203
Eagle (Slingsby - glider)   168
EAP (BAe)   133
Easy Riser - microlight   156
Edwards Helicopter   81
EH-101 (EHI Merlin)   38, 73, 151
Eider Duck   85
Ekin Airbuggy   156
EKW C-3605   33, 49
Electra (Lockheed L.188)   50, 221, 222
Elf (Parnall)   14
Elster (Putzer)   204, 262, 268
Emeraude (Piel etc, inc Linnet)
                        67, 169, 211
Enstrom helicopters
  56, 69, 169, 214, 217, 222
EoN gliders   61, 156, 177, 200, 268, 280
Ercoupe – Aircoupe
Eton (Slingsby - glider)   156
Eurofighter Typhoon   263
Europa (Shaw)   265
Evans VP-1, VP-2
  12, 52, 77, 165, 260, 268, 279

F4U/FG-1 - see Corsair
F6F - see Hellcat
F7F - see Tigercat
F8F - see Bearcat
F.27 Friendship (Fokker, inc FH.227)
                        47, 164, 200
F-4 - see Phantom II
F-5 - see Tiger II
F-15 - see Eagle
F-100 - see Super Sabre
F-101 - see Voodoo
F-104 - see Starfighter
F-105 - see Thunderchief
F-111 (General Dynamics)   26, 203, 277
Fa 330 (Focke Achgelis)
                25, 90, 181, 196, 261, 268
Fairchild 24 (and Argus)   166, 180, 265
Fairey IIIF   195
Fairey FD-2 (see also BAC 221)   180
Fairey ULH   65, 219
Falcon (Slingsby T.1 - glider)   43
Falcon Major (Miles)   14
Falke (Slingsby T.61, Scheibe)   199
Farman F.141   182
Fauvel AV.36 glider   20
FE.2 (RAF)   198
Felixstowe F.5   201
Fennec - see Trojan
Ferguson Monoplane   298
Fiat CR-42   151
Fieldmaster/Firemaster (NAC)   87
Fieseler Fi 103 (V-1) 26, 88, 89, 90, 151,
  153, 154, 167, 181, 267
Fieseler Fi 156 Storch (inc MS 500 etc
  Criquet)   25, 29, 181, 198, 279
Firecracker (NDN)   222
Firefly (Fairey)   158, 171, 194, 196
Firefly -microlight   169
Firefly (Slingsby T.67)   224, 267
Fl 282 (Flettner)   220
'Flea' – see Mignet HM.14
Fleet Canuck   224
Flycatcher (Fairey)   194
'Flying Flea' – see Mignet HM.14
Flying Fortress (Boeing B-17) 26, 29, 151
Fokker D.VII   151
Fokker D.VIII   39, 201
Fokker Dr.I   57, 89, 195, 262
Fokker E.III   22, 153
Fokker S.11 Instructor   82
Fournier RF-3, -4, -5 etc
                147, 155, 174, 199
Fox Moth (DH)   223
FRED (Clutton)   175, 297
Freelance (NAC)   222
Frelon (Sud)   191
Fuji FA.200   35, 77
Fulmar (Fairey)   194
Fury (Hawker, biplane) 14, 188, 206, 212
Fw 189 (Focke-Wulf)   86
Fw 190 (Focke-Wulf)   151, 154, 163
Gadfly HDW.1   191
Gamecock (Gloster)   64
Ganagobie (Avions Lobet)   52
Gannet (Fairey) 17, 19, 25, 38, 45, 79, 88,
  143, 176, 194, 195, 207, 208, 219, 284,
  289

Gazelle (Westland/SNIAS)
  15, 16, 60, 70, 71, 73, 75, 76, 92, 137,
  171, 176, 187, 197, 207, 223, 258, 292
Gemini (Miles - inc Aries)
  12, 62, 216, 298, 303
Geronimo - see Apache
Gladiator (Gloster)   15, 30, 64, 149, 150
Globe GC-1 Swift   134, 199
Gloster E.28/39   153
GM.1 Wicko (Foster-Wickner)   79
Gnat (Folland etc) 11, 23, 49, 54, 55, 66,
  71, 74, 78, 83, 141, 143, 176, 178, 181,
  183, 219, 261
Goevier glider   160
Goldwing - microlight   282, 298
Grain Kitten (PV)   265
Grasshopper (Servotec etc)   191
Grasshopper (Slingsby - glider)
  15, 33, 41, 49, 51, 61, 67, 75, 78, 92,
  133, 141, 150, 152, 164, 166, 167, 169,
  171, 192, 202, 204, 210, 219, 258, 260,
  268, 270, 275, 279, 302
Great Lakes (Oldfield)   94
Griffiths GH.4 gyroplane   44
Grob G-109   94
Grob gliders   258, 301
Grunau Baby (DFS - glider)   11, 89, 303
Gugnunc (HP)   260
Gulfstream (Grumman)   277
Gull (Slingsby - glider)   206, 278
Gunbus (Vickers)   149
Hadrian - see WACO CG-4
Hafner R-II   192
Halifax (HP)   65, 150, 154, 265
Hamilcar (GAL)   50, 75
Hampden (HP)   139, 182
HANG-GLIDERS (all types) 19, 22, 64,
  78, 88, 93, 156, 157, 172, 176, 195, 206,
  219, 224, 261, 279, 299
Hanriot HD.1   151
Hart (Hawker)   149, 180
Harrier (HSA, inc Kestrel, P.1127, Sea
  Harrier and AV-8A) 25, 34, 35, 38, 40,
  63, 64, 65, 71, 83, 88, 92, 95, 130, 131,
  132, 134, 137, 138, 147, 151, 152, 153,
  155, 159, 167, 174, 177, 178, 182, 183,
  187, 194, 195, 197, 198, 206, 213, 258,
  263, 266, 279, 293, 295
Harvard (NA T-6, SNJ etc) 26, 29, 30, 31,
  32, 48, 57, 79, 89, 129, 140, 150, 165,
  168, 175, 184, 194, 217, 218, 259, 294
Hastings (HP)   25, 175, 180
Havoc (Douglas A-20)   133
Hawk (BAe, inc T-45 Goshawk)   50, 96,
  138, 187, 213, 257, 263, 292, 294
Hawk Trainer - see Magister
Hawker P.1067 - see Hunter
Hawker P.1121   181
Hawker P.1127 – see Harrier
He 111 (Heinkel, inc CASA 2-111)
  26, 56, 151
He 162 (Heinkel)   151, 154
Heath Parasol   209
Hector (Hawker)   303
Hellcat (Grumman)   30, 194
Herald (HP)
  19, 27, 48, 164, 214, 265, 273, 283

Hercules (Lockheed C-130 / L.100)   24
Hermes (HP)   27
Heron (DH)   64, 84, 148, 175
Hiller UH-12, HT.1 etc   33, 195
Hind (Hawker)   14, 182, 191
Hispano Buchón
  - see Messerschmitt Bf 109
Hiway microlights133, 156, 176, 270, 278
Hobbycopter (Adams Wilson)   47, 210
Hollman HA-2 Sportster   16
Horizon (Gardan)   60
Hornet Moth (DH)   14, 84
Horsa (Airspeed)   68, 75, 76, 84
Hotspur (GAL)   68, 75
Hoverfly (Sikorsky)   150
HP.115 (Handley Page)   190, 194
HS.125 (HS, inc Dominie)
  10, 13, 50, 60, 79, 84, 92, 147, 153, 183,
  219, 270, 294, 295
HS.748 - see Andover
Hudson (Lockheed)   151
Hughes 269/369/500, OH-6 etc
  192, 210, 217
Humber Mono (see also Blériot)   220
Humming Bird (DH)   12, 14
Huntair Pathfinder - microlight   260
Hunter (Hawker, inc P.1067) 11, 12, 20,
  22, 24, 25, 32, 34, 36, 39, 45, 46, 48, 49,
  50, 53, 55, 64, 66, 67, 68, 70, 74, 81, 89,
  129, 132, 134, 143, 144, 148, 150, 156,
  164, 171, 175, 177, 178, 181, 185, 189,
  190, 194, 200, 201, 204, 206, 207, 208,
  209, 210, 211, 212, 213, 217, 219, 221,
  224, 257, 258, 262, 266, 270, 271, 277,
  281, 282, 287, 288, 290, 294, 295, 297
Hunting H.126   181
Hurricane (Hawker, inc Sea Hurricane)
  14, 24, 28, 30, 36, 57, 64, 86, 88, 89, 91,
  136, 137, 146, 147, 150, 153, 159, 161,
  172, 180, 204, 206, 217, 259, 262, 265,
  267
Huskie (Kaman HH-43)   220
Husky - see Auster
Hutter H.17 - glider   223, 258, 268
Hyabusa – see Nakajima Ki-43
Ilyushin Il-2   140
Iroquois (Bell UH-1, inc Bell 212)
  26, 48, 75, 76, 192, 196, 210
IS.28, IS.28 (ICA - motorglider) 141, 202
Iskra (TS-11)   129, 217, 222
Islander (BN-2, PBN et al, inc Trislander)
  39, 64, 86, 94, 152, 216, 221, 273, 276,
  284
Invader (Douglas B-26)   92, 163
Isaacs Fury   48, 211
Jackaroo (Thruxton, see also Tiger Moth)
Jaguar (SEPECAT) 71, 129, 137, 138, 161,
  181, 184, 187, 208, 213, 258, 263, 292,
  293
JAP-Harding Monoplane (see also Blériot)
  153
Javelin (Gloster) 25, 64, 147, 176, 180,
  201, 219, 266, 267, 288
Jenny JN4 (Curtiss)   204
Jet Gyrodyne (Fairey)   19
Jet Provost (Hunting - inc Strikemaster)10,
  11, 20, 21, 23, 26, 28, 29, 36, 42, 43, 45,

  48, 54, 58, 66, 67, 77, 78, 80, 88, 95, 96,
  130, 131, 134,137, 138, 140, 141, 144,
  147, 151, 155, 156, 157, 158, 161, 162,
  166, 167, 171, 176, 178, 181, 183, 184,
  187, 195, 197, 198, 202, 203, 207, 210,
  212, 213, 223, 257, 266, 267, 270, 271,
  273, 288, 289, 290, 292, 293, 295, 297,
  299
JetRanger (Bell and others, also Kiowa)
  95, 178
JetStar (Lockheed)   79
Jetstream (BAe, née HP) 10, 40, 82, 137,
  157, 159, 179, 199, 271, 278, 288
Jindivik (GAF)   65, 290
Jodel types (CEA, SAN, Wassmer, all vari-
  ants)   67, 82, 91, 144, 178, 203, 211,
  212, 272, 283, 300
Ju 52 (Junkers, inc Amiot AAC.1,
  CASA 352L)   25, 179
Ju 87 (Junkers)   151
Ju 88 (Junkers)   151
Jungmann (Bücker Bü 131 and
  CASA 1-131)   32, 33, 37, 151, 268
Jungmeister (Bücker Bü 133)
  30, 37, 57, 262
Ka-26 'Hoodlum' (Kamov)   191
Kay Gyroplane   277
Kaydet - see Stearman
Kensinger KF   161
Kestrel - see Harrier
Kestrel (Slingsby - glider)   61
Ki 100 (Kawasaki)   181
Killick man powered gyro   268
King Air (Beech)   60
Kite (Slingsby T.6 - glider)   11, 21, 302
Kittiwake (Arkle etc)   179
Kittyhawk (Curtiss P-40, inc Warhawk)
  30, 32, 57, 182
Klemm monoplanes   16, 90
Knight Twister (Payne)   268
Kraguj (SOKO)   216
KZ-VIII (SAI)   185
L 39 Albatros (Aero)   32
Lafayette microlight   268
Ladybird (Manuel - microlight)   206
Lake La-4   82
Lancaster (Avro) 25, 57, 73, 137, 139, 150,
  154, 208
Lance (see Cherokee)
Lansen (SAAB)   11
Lavochkin La-11   30
Lee-Richards Annular Biplane   216
Leopard (CMC)   259
Leopard Moth (DH)   32, 85
LET 410   129
Levi Go-Plane   86
Liberator (Consolidated B-24)   26, 180
Lightning (EE - inc P.1)11, 18, 21, 22, 25,
  37, 39, 40, 42, 52, 59, 64, 68, 70, 90, 95,
  96, 130, 132, 135, 138, 140, 141, 145,
  146, 148, 151, 156, 161, 164, 166, 167,
  171, 172, 176, 180, 181, 197, 201, 204,
  205, 208, 209, 212, 220, 257, 258, 266,
  267, 271, 279, 282, 295
Lilienthal glider   153, 261
Lincock (Blackburn)   263
Lincoln (Avro)   143, 180

Linnet - see Emeraude
Lockheed 10 153
Lone Ranger (AES) 171
L-Spatz glider 145
Luton Major 87, 171
Luton Minor (inc OH-7 Coupe)
  20, 56, 87, 144, 155, 157, 171, 262, 284
LVG C.VI 15
Lynx (Westland) 15, 16, 38, 71, 76, 176,
  191, 192, 193, 197, 205, 259
Lysander (Westland) 14, 24, 150
MB.339AA (Aermacchi) 43
Magister (Miles - inc Hawk Trainer) 14,
  16, 19, 24, 75, 162, 182, 262, 284, 300
Magister (Potez ÇM-170) 300, 301
Mainair microlights77, 156, 224, 265, 278
Malibu (Piper) 50
MAN-POWERED AIRCRAFT
  (all types) 78, 212, 261, 278
Martin Monoplane 83
Martinet (Miles) 19
Martlet - see Wildcat, see Southern
MBB (Bölkow) Bö 105 39, 171, 191, 192
McCandless M-2 / M-4 40, 298
Me (Bf) 109 (Messerschmitt, inc Ha 1 112
  Buchón) 17, 25, 54, 89, 151, 262, 266
Me (Bf) 110 (Messerschmitt) 151
Me 163 Komet (Messerschmitt)
  15, 25, 153, 181, 279
Me 262 (Messerschmitt) 181
Me 410 (Messerschmitt) 181
Mentor (Beech T-34, inc Turbo) 196
Merchantman - see Vanguard
Mercury Dart 33
Messenger (Miles)
  14, 55, 62, 66, 216, 218, 298
Meteor (Gloster / AWA, all marks)
  25, 41, 48, 53, 58, 64, 65, 67, 68, 74, 80,
  91, 143, 150, 157, 164, 167, 171, 175,
  177, 180, 195, 201, 205, 207, 211, 212,
  217, 218, 219, 222, 261, 265, 266, 270,
  275, 277, 278, 290
Mew Gull (Percival) 14
ME.1 (Manning-Flanders) 22
MiG-15 Fagot / Midget
  (inc S-102, Lim etc) 25, 182, 195, 279
MiG-17 Fresco (SBLim-5 etc) 49
MiG-19 Farmer 177
MiG-21 Fishbed / Mongol
  22, 26, 49, 54, 220, 257
MiG-23, MiG-27 Flogger 71, 289
MiG-29 Fulcrum 167
Mignet HM.14 (Pou du Ciel or 'Flea'
  inc later types) 12, 14, 23, 42, 78, 81,
  82, 141, 147, 156, 171, 176, 179, 201,
  206, 212, 216, 219, 260, 262, 265, 268,
  271, 272, 288, 291, 301, 303
Mil Mi-1 (SM-1) 192
Mil Mi-2 Hoplite 191
Mil Mi-4 Hound 192
Mil Mi-24 Hind 26, 71, 192, 289
Miles M.18 278
Minicab (Gardan etc) 86, 135
Mini Coupe (Chris Tena) 77
Mirage III (Dassault) 266
Missel Thrush – see ANEC
Mitchell (NAA B-25) 26, 30, 56, 143, 151

Mitsubishi A6M Zeke 26, 32
ML Utility 75
Mohawk (Miles) 12
Monarch (Miles) 160, 278
Monospar ST-12 (GAL) 65
Mooney M.20 23, 37, 165, 175, 273
Morane BB 198
Morava L-200 147
Mosquito (DH) 25, 30, 150, 180, 265
Mosquito (Turner - gyroplane) 40, 84
Moth (DH.60, all types)
  14, 24, 51, 153, 179, 214, 265
Moth Minor (DH) 51, 84, 302
Motor Cadet (glider conversions) 11
MS 'N' (Morane Saulnier) 22
MS.230, -315, -317 'Parasols' 140
MS.500 etc Criquet -
  see Fieseler Fi 156 Storch
Murray Helicopter 192
Musketeer (Beech, inc Sierra, Sundowner)
  22, 222, 297
Mustang (NAA P-51) 26, 29, 30, 32, 53,
  57, 58, 151, 154, 159
MW.2B Excalibur (Whittaker) 38
Mystère IVA (Dassault) 25, 42, 43, 52, 90,
  129, 141, 164, 171, 176, 201, 220, 277
Nakajima Ki-43 Hyabusa 30
Navajo (Piper) 50, 60, 82, 94, 146, 217
Navion (Ryan) 303
Neptune (Lockheed SP-2) 182
Nimbus (Short – glider) 298
Nimrod (Hawker) 30, 212
Nimrod (HS - see also Comet)
  40, 41, 96, 198, 209
Nipper (Tipsy etc) 33, 52, 162, 172, 281
Noralpha (Nord) 57, 95, 273, 284
Nord 1002 Pinguoin 28, 57, 145
Nord 3202 162
Norecrin (Nord) 264, 289
Northrop F-5 Tiger / Freedom Fighter
  23, 177
Nyborg TGN.III 223
O.A.7 Optica (Edgeley) 58
OH-7 Coupe - see Luton Minor
O'Hara Autogyro 303
Ohka 11 (Yokosuka MXY-7)
  88, 156, 182, 195
ORNITHOPTERS (all types)
  15, 22, 141, 142, 156, 261
OV-10 Bronco (Rockwell) 28
Oxford (Airspeed) 24, 150, 218
P.1 - see Lightning
P.6 (BP) 160
P.1052 (Hawker) 195
P.1127 - see Harrier
P-39 - see Airacobra
P-40 - see Kittyhawk
P-47 - see Thunderbolt
P-51 - see Mustang
Pacer, Vagabond etc (Piper) 77, 211
Paris (MS.760) 57
Pawnee (Piper) 17, 81, 145, 162
PBY – see Catalina
Pegasus (Ultrasports - microlight)
  80, 95, 193
Pembroke (Percival)
  28, 180, 208, 217, 221

Penn-Smith Gyroplane 13
Percival Q6 168
Phantom II (McDonnell F-4)
  20, 23, 26, 32, 36, 37, 42, 55, 61, 86, 88,
  92, 134, 137, 145, 151, 161, 163, 170,
  172, 181, 182, 194, 203, 220, 257, 267,
  275, 279, 282, 285, 290, 291
Piaggio P.166 260
Pilatus P.2 22, 29
Pilatus P.3 91
Pilcher Hawk 85, 279, 281
Pioneer (SAL) 181
Pitts S-1, S-2 15, 94, 148, 153, 185, 299
Pixie (Parnall) 219
Potez 840 284
Pou du Ciel (see Mignet HM.14)
Prefect TX.1 (Slingsby - glider) 180, 270
Prince - see Sea Prince
Prentice (Percival)
  15, 74, 146, 175, 219, 221, 269, 283
Proctor (Percival)
  25, 139, 146, 198, 204, 220, 301
Prospector (Edgar Percival) 75, 218
Provost (Percival)
  11, 15, 19, 129, 141, 143, 175, 180, 189,
  198, 201, 208, 224, 279, 301, 303
PT-13, PT-17 - see Stearman
Pterodactyl (Westland-Hill) 153
Pucará (FMA) 25, 171, 181, 201, 257
Puma (Aerospatiale/Westland,
  inc Super Puma) 71, 187, 275
Pup (Beagle) 44, 64, 69, 77, 91
Pup (Sopwith) 14, 75, 150, 194, 219
Puss Moth (DH) 278
Queen Air (Beech) 33, 62, 63, 130, 146
Queen Bee - see Tiger Moth
Quickie (QAC) 22, 199
Quicksilver (Eipper - microlight 144, 284
Rainbow Eagle microlight 33
Rally (Rotec - microlight) 142
Rallye (MS, SOCATA etc) 11, 47, 61, 67,
  82, 87, 94, 141, 144, 147, 156, 175, 188,
  189, 222, 282, 299, 300, 304
Rand KR-2 147
Rattler Strike - microlight 175
RE.8 (RAF) 24
Retriever (Piasecki HUP-3) 192
Rhonadler glider 61, 218
Rhonlerche glider 61, 264, 279
Robin types (inc CEA, eg DR.400)
  11, 17, 94, 147, 168, 188, 207, 221
Robinson R-22 16, 69, 149, 152, 169, 191,
  207, 210, 270, 289
Roe Biplane 207
Roe Triplane 14, 153, 156
Rolls-Royce Thrust Measuring Rig 153
Rotachute III 75
Rotodyne (Fairey) 191
Rotorway, Exec and Scorpion 156, 289
Rutan Vari-Eze and LongEz22, 52, 64, 268
Ryan PT-21, PT-22 etc 182, 223, 262
SAAB J29 Tunnen 220
Sabre (NAA F-86) 26, 29, 150, 172
Safir (SAAB) 19, 176, 285
Sandringham - see Sunderland
SARO P.531 (see also Scout, Wasp)
  76, 194, 195

SARO SRA.1 78
SARO SR.53 181
Scheibe motorgliders 176, 291
Schleicher gliders
137, 214, 258, 280, 284, 294, 302
Schweizer TG-3A 26
Scimitar (V-Supermarine)
55, 62, 78, 164, 194
Scion (Short) 210, 298
Scout (Bristol) 160, 194
Scout (Westland, see also SARO P.531
and Wasp) 11, 15, 70, 75, 76, 79, 131,
162, 177, 178, 191, 192, 202, 203, 205,
258, 259, 271, 298
Scud glider 206
SE.5A (RAF etc, inc scale versions)
14, 70, 90, 95, 149, 153, 206, 265
Seafire - see Spitfire
Seagull - see Walrus
Sealand (Short) 298
Sea Fury (Hawker) 30, 54, 163, 194, 196
Sea Hawk (Hawker)25, 37, 38, 55, 71, 74,
80, 129, 175, 194, 196, 208, 219, 257,
279, 283, 287, 299
Sea Harrier (Lavery) 298
Sea King (Westland/Sikorsky inc Sikorsky
S-61L/N) 38, 40, 72, 73, 291
Sea Prince (Percival, inc Prince)
38, 41, 48, 74, 195, 201, 207, 223, 287
Sea Venom - see Venom
Sea Vixen (DH) 21, 25, 49, 78, 80, 84, 130,
176, 194, 195, 196, 201, 205, 206, 208,
209, 212, 217, 219, 220, 224, 295
Sedbergh (Slingsby - glider)
51, 174, 182, 258, 270
Seneca (Piper) 52, 60, 67, 85, 207, 273
SF-260 (SIAI-Marchetti) 301
SH-3 - see Sea King
Shackleton (Avro)
25, 38, 40, 156, 167, 175, 207, 219, 223
Sheriff (Britten) 132
Sherpa (Short SB.4) 93
Short 184 194
Short S.27 196
Short SB.5 180
Short SC.1 154, 298
Short 330, 360 and Sherpa
51, 52, 69, 74, 171, 273, 298, 302
SIAI-Marchetti SF.260 297
Sikorsky S-55 - see Whirlwind
Sikorsky S-61 - see Sea King
Silvaire (Luscombe) 41, 70, 145, 276
Sioux (Westland-Bell and all marks, inc
Bell 47) 75, 76, 88, 171, 176, 191, 192,
195, 205, 211, 259, 271, 283, 289
SIPA 90 series 52, 77
Skeeter (SARO, all marks)
47, 50, 55, 75, 76, 78, 153, 176, 181,
191, 202, 205, 259, 271, 279
Skua (Blackburn) 194
Skycraft Scout - microlight 284
Skylark (Slingsby) 264
Skyraider (Douglas) 30, 195
Sligo Concept 303
SM-2 (WSK) 192
Snowbird (Noel) 265

Somers-Kendal SK.1 262
Sopwith 11/2 Strutter 95, 149
Southampton (Supermarine) 150
Southern Martlet 14
SPAD XIII 26
Spartan Cruiser 278
Sperling (SF-23) 268
Spitfire (V-Supermarine and others, also
Seafire) 11, 14, 20, 21, 22, 25, 28, 30,
31, 32, 40, 45, 46, 53, 54, 57, 63, 78, 86,
89, 89, 90, 91, 93, 95, 131, 132, 133,
136, 137, 139, 146, 147, 148, 149, 150,
152, 153, 154, 156, 159, 163, 164, 172,
177, 180, 182, 188, 194, 197, 199, 200,
203, 216, 217, 222, 224, 265, 267, 277,
278, 280
Sportsman (Volmer VJ-22) 275
Sprint (FLS) 58
SR-71 (Lockheed, Blackbird) 26
ST-10 Diplomate (SOCATA) 304
Stampe SV-4 (all marks) 12, 18, 22, 30, 47,
51, 70, 155, 169, 185, 260, 281
Starfighter (Lockheed etc, F-104)
74, 140, 220
Stearman (Boeing PT-13, PT-17,
N2S, Kaydet etc)
26, 31, 51, 57, 67, 68, 165, 166, 259
Stinson 108 etc 87, 189
Stranraer (Supermarine) 151
Stratofortress (Boeing B-52) 26
Strikemaster - see Jet Provost
Striker (Flexiform - microlight) 200
Student (Miles) 19
Sukhoi Su-7, Su-22 Fitter43, 144, 212, 289
Sunderland (Short, inc Sandringham)
25, 78, 150, 297
Sundowner - see Musketeer
Super Guppy (Aerospacelines) 129
Superfortress (Boeing B-29) 26
Supermarine S.6 78, 153
Supermarine 510 195
Supermarine 544 224
Super Baladou (Wassmer) 268
Super Cub - see Cub
Super Cruiser (Piper) 79
Super Sabre (NAA F-100) 26, 90, 167,
172, 176, 201, 203, 220, 277
Surrey AL.1 45
Swallow (BA and Klemm) 45, 56, 210
Swallow (Slingsby T.45 - glider)
196, 258, 280
Swift (Comper) 14, 39, 185
Swift (V-Supermarine)
78, 81, 171, 175, 177, 217, 257
Swordfish (Fairey) 25, 182, 194, 196, 263
Sycamore (Bristol)
40, 62, 65, 75, 93, 156, 171, 175, 190,
191, 201, 270, 276, 283, 288
SZD gliders - Blanik, Mucha)
11, 218, 258, 284
T.21 (Slingsby - glider)
11, 142, 189, 268, 278
T.31 (Slingsby - glider) 157, 199, 303
T-33A (Lockheed, inc Canadair-built)
26, 28, 42, 58, 140, 164, 172, 176, 201,
217, 220, 266, 277

Tabloid (Sopwith) 149
Tampico (SOCATA) 207
Taylor Monoplane / Titch 211, 304
Taylorcraft types - see Auster
Team Minimax - microlight 95
Tempest (Hawker) 22, 140, 150, 163, 182
Terrier - see Auster
Texan - see Harvard
Thunderbolt (Republic P-47) 26, 30, 180
Thunderbolt II (Fairchild A-10) 23, 26
Thunderchief (Republic F-105) 26, 167
Thunderstreak (Republic F-84) 172, 182
Thurston Teal 272
Tigercat (Grumman) 30
Tiger Cub (MBA - microlight)
142, 155, 165, 276, 281, 282
Tiger Moth (DH, inc Queen Bee
- see also Jackaroo) 14, 16, 18, 22, 28,
32, 33, 51, 53, 55, 66, 76, 78, 79, 81, 84,
87, 147, 148, 150, 169, 175, 189, 195,
197, 199, 212, 218, 159, 278, 281, 287,
288, 295, 298, 300, 301
Tipsy B, Belfair, Junior 87, 276
Tom Thumb (Crossley) 220
Tomahawk (Piper) 22, 33, 42, 45, 52, 69,
70, 85, 144, 164, 165, 174, 199, 214,
222, 224, 273, 283, 295, 304
Tomtit (Hawker) 14
Tornado (Panavia)
10, 25, 96, 137, 138, 151, 163, 184, 185,
187, 267, 282, 293, 295
Tourbillon (Chasle YC-12) 33
Trainer/Traveler - see Yankee
Travel Air CW-12Q/2000 22, 146
Trident (HS) 27, 52, 60, 83, 84, 152, 156,
179, 188, 210, 213, 260, 276, 281, 297
Tri-Pacer (Piper, plus all PA-22 types)
139, 167, 178, 189, 207, 216, 283, 290,
300
Triplane – see Roe
Triplane (Sopwith) 14, 150, 194
Trislander - see Islander
TriStar (Lockheed) 21, 24, 60
Tri-Traveler/Traveler (Champion) 82
Trojan (NAA T-28, and Sud Fennec)
32, 201
TSR-2 (BAC) 25, 181, 207
Tucano (Embraer/Short)
220, 289, 298, 299
Turbulent (Druine etc)
45, 91, 155, 161, 276
Tutor (Avro) 14
Tutor (Slingsby T.8 - glider) 36, 67, 138,
160, 257, 278, 302, 303
Twin Comanche (Piper)
10, 50, 82, 165, 210
Twin Pioneer (SAL) 41, 181, 220, 278
Typhoon (Hawker)
25, 64, 90, 150, 188, 216, 219, 259
U-2 (Lockheed) 26
UH-1 - see Iroquois
V-1 - see Fieseler Fi 103
Valetta (Vickers - see also Viking)
180, 201
Valiant (Vickers) 59, 92, 129, 150, 206
Valiant (Vultee BT-15) 185

Vampire (DH all marks, inc Sea Vampire) 12, 25, 32, 36, 41, 42, 44, 45, 49, 55, 59, 64, 70, 78, 79, 80, 83, 84, 87, 88, 90, 132, 138, 140, 141, 143, 155, 167, 170, 171, 172, 175, 180, 182, 185, 194, 195, 198, 201, 207, 219, 224, 266, 270, 271, 277, 279, 283, 287, 288, 294, 297, 299, 301, 302, 303

Vanguard (Vickers, Merchantman) 132, 206

Varga Kachina 60

Varsity (Vickers) 25, 132, 175, 180, 189, 206, 213, 264, 288

VC-10 (Vickers, inc Super VC-10) 27, 177, 292, 293

Vector (Aerodyne - microlight) 294

Venom (DH, also Sea Venom) 11, 25, 48, 49, 58, 64, 78, 84, 95, 157, 171, 175, 182, 194, 199, 206, 208, 223, 270, 271, 279, 288

Ventura (Lockheed) 182

Vertigo (Cranfield) 192

Victor (HP) 25, 59, 92, 129, 130, 151, 163, 181, 205, 208, 266, 276

Viking (Grob - glider) 177, 267

Viking (Vickers - biplane 'boat) 206

Viking (Vickers - see also Valetta) 206

Vimy (Vickers) 153, 206

Viscount (Vickers) 12, 27, 52, 59, 67, 179, 206, 207, 273, 301

Voisin biplane 206

Volmer VJ-24 - microlight 156, 175

Voodoo (McDonnell F-101) 220, 222

Vulcan (Avro) 25, 41, 49, 59, 64, 94, 129, 132, 145, 150, 157, 164, 171, 176, 181, 205, 210, 220, 224, 275, 279, 295

Waco CG-4A Hadrian/Haig 76, 266, 279

Waco UPF-7 64

Wallace (Westland) 12, 149

Wallbro Monoplane 200

Wallis WA-116 etc 152, 165

Walrus (Supermarine, inc Seagull) 151, 162, 194

Ward Elf, Gnome 262

Warrior - see Cherokee

Wasp (Westland, see also P.531 and Scout) 11, 25, 39, 45, 71, 72, 76, 158, 162, 191, 195, 196, 203, 257, 259

Wassmer - see Jodel

Watkins CHW 288

Watkinson CG-4A Series IV 192

Wanderlust (Broburn - glider) 19

Weedhopper - microlight 93, 287

Weir W-2 278

Weihe (DFS - glider) 137

Wellington (Vickers) 150, 206

Wessex (Westland, all marks) 25, 37, 38, 39, 40, 61, 67, 68, 71, 72, 73, 74, 77, 81, 92, 94, 134, 136, 151, 158, 161, 176, 177, 187, 188, 189, 191, 192, 194, 195, 198, 203, 209, 213, 271, 273, 291, 292, 294, 297

Westland WG.30 147, 164, 191, 192, 283

Westland WG.33 192

Westland 606 - see Lynx

Wheeler Slymph 219

Whing Ding (Hovey - microlight) 93, 217

Whippet (Austin) 269

Whirlwind (Westland WS-55 and Sikorsky S-55, all marks) 25, 37, 38, 41, 42, 52, 59, 77, 81, 92, 95, 132, 134, 145, 164, 171, 176, 181, 187, 189, 190, 191, 192, 194, 195, 201, 208, 213, 217, 219, 223, 266, 269, 271, 277, 279, 283, 288, 289, 290, 295

Whitney Straight (Miles) 160, 299

Widgeon (Westland) 168, 169, 171, 191

Wight Quadruplane 78

Wildcat (Grumman, inc Martlet) 30, 57, 194, 299

Wilga (PZL) 148

Willow Wren glider 206

Woodhams Sprite 88

Wren (EE) 14

Wright Flyer 266

Wyvern (Westland) 194

Yakovlev Yak-1, Yak-3 etc 30, 32, 204

Yakovlev Yak-11 (C-11) 22

Yakovlev Yak-18, Yak-50 etc) 30, 31, 33, 57, 224, 259, 289

Yale (NAA NA-64) 28

Yankee (AA-1, AA-5, inc Trainer, Traveler) 50, 82, 144, 149, 158, 222, 276, 300

York (Avro) 27, 180

Zlin monoplanes 147, 148

Zurowski ZP.1 helicopter 176

We hope that you enjoyed this book . . .

Midland Publishing titles are edited and designed by an experienced and enthusiastic trans-Atlantic team of specialists.

Further titles are in preparation but we welcome ideas from authors or readers for books they would like to see published.

In addition, our associate company, Midland Counties Publications, offers an exceptionally wide range of aviation, spaceflight, astronomy, military, naval and transport books and videos for sale by mail-order around the world.

For a copy of the appropriate catalogue, or to order further copies of this book, please write, telephone, fax or e-mail:

Midland Counties Publications
4 Watling Drive,
Hinckley, Leics, LE10 3EY, England
Tel: (+44) 01455 233 747
Fax: (+44) 01455 233 737
E-mail: midlandbooks@compuserve.com
www.midlandcountiessuperstore.com

Midland Counties
BOOKS & VIDEOS

An indispensible companion volume . . .

EUROPEAN WRECKS & RELICS
2nd edition

Otger van der Kooij

When the first edition of European Wrecks & Relics was published in 1989 it was eagerly snapped up by enthusiasts. Now, with inputs from a huge network of sources, the second edition takes the story of Europe's amazing variety of museum, retired and derelict aircraft into the 1990s.

As with the previous edition, and its UK-based partner, Wrecks & Relics, this book does not just chronicle what is currently to be found, but all known activity since the first edition appeared. With the astonishing developments in Europe that saw the dissolving of the so-called 'Iron Curtain', European Wrecks & Relics charts the 'peace dividend' with details of the disposal of hundreds of military aircraft across the Continent.

Coverage has been extended in this issue to include the Czech Republic, Hungary, Poland and Slovakia. Photographic content is lavish and in full colour. The page count in this second edition is up by a third.

Hardback
210 x 148 mm, 480 pages
207 colour photographs
1 85780 085 0   **£24.95**

2nd Edition
**EUROPEAN
WRECKS & RELICS**
Otger van der Kooij

Aberdeen	275	Benson	177	Brooklands	205	Christchurch	51	Dublin	301

Aberdeen 275
Aberdeen Airport 275
Abergavenny 287
Aberporth 287
Abbeyshrule 299
Aboyne 275
Adlington 93
Alconbury 23
Alderney 273
Aldershot 68
Altcar 158
Alton 68
Ammanford 287
Andover 69
Andrewsfield 52
Arborfield 15
Arbroath 275
Armthorpe 269
Ashford 87
Ashington 213
Astley 179
Aston Down 61
Audley End 53
Axbridge 188
Aylesbury 20
Bacup 93
Bagby 264
Balderton 172
Ballyjamesduff 300
Ballymoney 297
Bamburgh 169
Banbury 177
Banchory 275
Bann Foot 297
Barkham 16
Barkston Heath 135
Barnstaple 45
Barrow-in-Furness 41
Barton 154
Basingstoke 69
Bassingbourn 23
Bath 188
Batley 272
Bawtry 269
Baxterley 218
Beccles 199
Beck Row 200
Bedford 10
Bedford Airfield 10
Beeston 172
Belfast 297
Belfast Airport 297
Belfast City Airport 297
Bembridge 86
Benbecula 275

Benson 177
Bentley Priory 146
Berkhamstead 82
Berkswell 159
Beverley 261
Bexhill 210
Bicester 177
Bidford 218
Biggin Hill 146
Binbrook 135
Binbrook Airfield 135
Binfield 16
Bird's Edge 272
Birkdale 158
Birkenhead 158
Birlingham 80
Birmingham 159
Birmingham Airport 159
Birtley 169
Blackbushe 69
Blackpool 93
Blairgowrie 275
Bletchley Park 20
Bodmin 37
Bodney Camp 161
Borgue 275
Boscombe Down 224
Bosham 213
Boston 135
Boston Aerodrome 136
Boulmer 170
Bourn 23
Bournemouth 47
Bournemouth Airport 48
Bovington 50
Braintree 53
Bramley 70
Brampton 23
Brawdy 287
Bredhurst 87
Bredon 80
Breighton 262
Brenchley 87
Brenzett 87
Bridge of Weir 275
Bridgend 287
Bridgnorth 179
Brierley Hill 159
Brighton 211
Bristol 61
Bristol Airport 188
Brize Norton 176
Bromsgrove 80

Brooklands 205
Brough 262
Bruntingthorpe 96
Brunton 170
Burbage 130
Burslem 197
Burton-upon-Trent 197
Bury St Edmunds 200
Caernarfon 287
Callington 37
Cam 62
Camberley 207
Cambridge 23
Cambridge Airport 24
Cannock 197
Canterbury 88
Capernwray 94
Cardiff 288
Cardiff Airport 288
Cardington 10
Cark 41
Carlisle 41
Carlisle Airport 41
Carlow 300
Carlton Moor 264
Carthorpe 264
Casement 300
Castlerock 297
Caterham 207
Catford 147
Celbridge 301
Chadderton 155
Chalgrove 177
Charlwood 207
Charnock Richard 94
Charterhall 276
Chatham 88
Chattenden 88
Chelford 35
Chelmsford 53
Cheltenham 62
Cheshunt 82
Chessington 147
Chester 35
Chester Airport 288
Chesterfield 43
Chetwynd 179
Chilbolton 70
Chipping 94
Chipping Camden 62
Chipping Ongar 53
Chirk 289
Chislet 88
Chorley 94

Christchurch 51
Churchtown 301
Clacton-on-Sea 53
Clacton Aerodrome 54
Clapham 10
Clavering 54
Cleethorpes 136
Clevedon 189
Clothall Common 82
Coalville 131
Cockerham 95
Colchester 54
Colehill 51
Colmworth 10
Colsterworth 136
Coltishall 161
Comberton 24
Compton Abbas 51
Connah's Quay 289
Coningsby 136
Corby 167
Cork 301
Cosford 179
Cottesmore 131
Coventry 159
Coventry Airport 218
Cowbridge 289
Cowes 86
Cranfield 10
Cranwell 137
Crawley 213
Croft 138
Croughton 167
Crowland 138
Croydon 148
Cruden Bay 276
Culdrose 37
Culham 177
Cumbernauld 276
Cupar 276
Currie 276
Deanland 211
Defford 80
Delgany 301
Deopham Green 161
Derby 43
Derby Aerodrome 44
Digby 139
Diseworth 132
Dishforth 264
Doncaster 269
Donington 132
Dorchester 51
Dover 89
Dromod 301

Dublin 301
Dublin Airport 302
Dulwich 148
Dumfries 276
Dundee Airport 277
Dundonald 277
Dunkeswell 45
Dunsfold 208
Dunstable 11
Duxford 24
Eaglescott 45
Earls Colne 54
East Dereham 162
East Fortune 277
East Grinstead 213
East Kirkby 139
East Midlands Airport 132
East Tilbury 54
East Winch 162
East Wretham 162
Eastwood 55
Eaton Bray 11
Eccleshall 197
Eccleston 95
Edinburgh 279
Edinburgh Airport 280
Egham 208
Eggington 44
Elgin 280
Elstree 82
Elvington 264
Ely 32
Enstone 178
Errol 280
Eshott 170
Eversden 33
Evesham 81
Exeter 45
Exeter Airport 46
Fairoaks 208
Falgunzeon 280
Farley 70
Farnborough 70
Farnborough Airfield 70
Farnham 208
Farnsfield 172
Faversham 89
Faygate 213
Felixstowe 200
Felthorpe 162
Felton 170
Fenland 139
Filton 63

Firbeck 271	Hatch 12	Keevil 258	Llanbedr Airfield 290	Nantgarw 291
Fivemiletown 298	Hatfield 82	Kemble 65	Llantrisant 290	Nantwich 37
Fleet 71	Hatfield Airfield 82	Kendal 95	Llanwrtyd Wells 290	Narborough 163
Fleetlands 71	Haverfordwest 290	Kenfig Hill 290	Loch Earn 282	Nayland 204
Flixton 200	Haverigg 42	Kenley 152	London 152	Neatishead 163
Ford 213	Hawkinge 89	Kesgrave 203	London Airport 152	Netheravon 259
Fordingbridge 71	Haxey 140	Kew 152	London Colney 83	New Castle 302
Fordoun 280	Haydock 158	Kewstoke 189	Londonderry 299	New Ross 302
Forres 280	Hayward's Heath 214	Kidlington 178	Londonderry Airport 299	New Waltham 142
Foulness Island 55	Hedge End 74	Kilkerran 281		Newark-on-Trent 173
Fownhope . 81	Hednesford 197	Kilmarnock 282	Longside 282	Newbury 17
Foynes 302	Helston 38	Kingsbridge 47	Longton 198	Newby Wiske 268
Framlingham 201	Hemel Hempstead 83	Kingscliffe 168	Long Marston 222	Newcastle Airport 170
Fyfield 55	Hemswell 140	Kings Langley 83	Lossiemouth 282	Newcastle upon Tyne 170
Fyvie 280	Hendon 148	King's Lynn 162	Loughborough 133	
Gainsborough 140	Henley-on-Thames 178	Kington 81	Lough Foyle 299	Newhaven 210
Gallows Hill 51		Kinloss 282	Louth 141	Newmarket 204
Galway 302	Henlow 12	Kirdford 214	Lower Stondon 12	Newport 86
Galway Airport 302	Henstridge 189	Kirkbymoorside 267	Ludham 162	Newport, Wales 291
Gamlingay 33	Hereford 81	Kirton-in-Lindsey 141	Ludlow 185	Newport Pagnell 21
Gatwick 213	Heswall 158	Laindon 56	Luton 13	Newton 173
Gilmerton 280	Hibaldstow 141	Lakenheath 203	Luton Airport 13	Newton-le-Willows 158
Girvan 280	Hinckley 132	Lambourn 17	Lydd 91	
Glasgow 280	High Halden 90	Lancing 214	Lyneham 258	Newtownards 299
Glasgow Airport 281	High Wycombe 20	Land's End 39	Macclesfield 36	Northampton 168
Glatton 33	Hinton-in-the-Hedges 168	Land's End Aerodrome 39	Madeley 185	Northolt 152
Glenrothes 281	Hitchin 83	Langar 172	Madley 81	North Coates 142
Glentham 140	Hixon 198	Langford Lodge 298	Malpas 36	North Luffenham 134
Gloucestershire Airport 63	Hockley Heath 159	Langport 189	Malton 267	North Moreton 178
Godalming 209	Hollington 210	Lasham 74	Malvern Wells 81	North Weald 56
Goodwood 214	Holywood 298	Lashenden 90	Manchester 155	Norton Fitzwarren 189
Goole 140	Honington 202	Lavendon 21	Manchester Airport 156	
Gormanston 302	Hook 74	Leavesden 83	Mansfield 172	Norwich 163
Gosport 72	Hooton Park 36	Leconfield 263	Manston 91	Norwich Airport 164
Gowran Grange 302	Horham 202	Lee-on-Solent 74	March 34	Nottingham 173
Grainthorpe 140	Horley 209	Leeds 272	Marfleet 263	Nuneaton 223
Gransden Lodge 33	Horningsham 258	Leeds-Bradford Airport 272	Margate 92	Nuthampstead 85
Gravesend 89	Houghton 33	Leeming 267	Marham 163	Nympsfield 67
Great Ayton 266	Hucknall 172	Leicester 133	Market Drayton 185	Oakham 134
Great Dunmow 55	Huddersfield 272	Leicester Aerodrome 133	Marksbury 189	Oakhill 189
Great Waltham 55	Hull 263	Lelant 39	Martham 163	Oaksey Park 259
Great Yarmouth 162	Humberside Airport 141	Leuchars 282	Maybole 282	Odiham 76
Greenford 148	Hungerford 16	Levensulme 155	Melton Mowbray 133	Okehampton 47
Greenock 281	Husbands Bosworth 133	Lewes 210	Melksham 259	Old Sarum 259
Grindale 263	Ingatstone 55	Lichfield 198	Membury 17	Old Warden 13
Guernsey 273	Innsworth 64	Lingfield 209	Mendlesham 203	Orphir 283
Guernsey Airport 273	Insch 281	Linley Hill 263	Metheringham 142	Ottringham 263
Guildford 209	Iver Heath 20	Linton-on-Ouse 267	Mickleover 44	Oxford 178
Hailsham 210	Inverness 281	Liskeard 39	Middle Wallop 75	Paddock Wood 92
Halesworth 202	Inverness Airport 281	Littlehampton 216	Milford Haven 290	Panshanger 85
Halfpenny Green 197	Ipswich 202	Little Gransden 33	Mintlaw 282	Pathhead 283
Halifax 272	Isle of Man Airport 85	Litle Snoring 162	Mold 291	Paull 263
Halstead 55	Ivybridge 47	Little Staughton 33	Molesworth 34	Pendine 291
Halton 20	Ivychurch 90	Liverpool 158	Monewden 203	Perth 283
Hamble 74	Jersey Airport 273	Liverpool Airport 158	Montrose 283	Peterborough Business 34
Hanwell 148	Jurby 85	Llanbedr 290	Moreton-in-Marsh 67	
Harrington 167			Moston 156	Peterborough Sport 34
Harrogate 267			Movenis 299	
Haslemere 209			Mytchett 209	

Petersfield	77	St Mawgan	40	Southend-on-Sea	60	Thornton-Cleveleys		West Walton
Peterstone	291	St Merryn	40	South Woodham			96	Highway	166
Plymouth City		Salford	157	Ferrers	60	Thruxton	79	Weston	304
Airport	47	Salisbury	259	Spadeadam	42	Thurrock	61	Weston-on-Trent	199
Poole, Dorset	51	Samlesbury	95	Spalding	144	Thwing	264	Weston-super-Mare
Poole, Somerset	189	Sandown	86	Spanhoe Lodge	169	Tibenham	166		190
Popham	77	Sandown Aerodrome		Spilsby	144	Tilstock	188	Weston Zoyland	193
Portishead	190		86	Stafford	198	Titchfield	79	Weybourne	167
Portmoak	284	Sandtoft	142	Stalbridge	51	Toton	174	Weybridge	210
Portsmouth	77	Sandy	15	Stamford	144	Tremar	40	White Waltham	19
Powerscourt	303	Scampton	143	Stanford	134	Trim	303	Whittlesey	34
Preston, E Yorks	264	Sealand	293	Stanley	52	Trowbridge	259	Wigan	157
Preston, Lancs	95	Sedlescombe	212	Stansted	60	Tunstead	166	Wigston	135
Prestwick	284	Seething	165	Stapleford Tawney	60	Twyford	21	Windermere	43
Predannack	39	Seighford	198	Stock	60	Uckfield	212	Winsford	37
Pulborough	216	Selby	268	Stockport	157	Upavon	260	Winterbourne Gnr
Quedgeley	68	Sevenoaks	93	Stoke-on-Trent	198	Upper Ballinderry			260
Radcliffe	156	Shanklin	87	Stone	199		299	Winthernsea	264
Radcliffe on Trent		Shannon	303	Stonehaven	284	Upper Hill	81	Winthorpe	174
	174	Shardlow	44	Stoneleigh	223	Uxbridge	154	Witney	178
Ramsbottom	95	Shawbury	185	Stondon	61	Valley	294	Wittering	35
Rathcoole	303	Shawbury Airfield		Stoney Cove	134	Waddington	145	Woburn Sands	21
Rattlesden	204		185	Stowmarket	204	Wainfleet	145	Woking	210
Rayleigh	58	Shawell	134	Strathallan	284	Wakefield	273	Wolverhampton	160
Reading	18	Sheffield	272	Strathaven	284	Wallington Green	154	Wolverhampton
Redhill	209	Sherburn-in-Elmet		Strathdon	284	Walpole	204	Business	199
Redhill Aerodrome			268	Stretton, Cheshire	37	Walpole St Andrew		Woodford	157
	210	Shipdham	165	Sturgate	145		166	Woodhall Spa	145
Reigate	210	Shobdon	81	Sudbury	204	Walton on Thames		Woodhurst	35
Rendcomb	68	Shoreham, Kent	93	Sumburgh	285		210	Woodley	19
Retford	174	Shoreham, West		Sunbury-on-Thames		Wannock	212	Woodvale	159
Rettendon	59	Sussex	216		210	Warminster	260	Woolwich	154
Reymerston	165	Shrivenham	178	Sunderland	170	Warton	96	Worcester	81
Ridgewell	59	Sidcup	152	Sutton	154	Warwick	223	Wrexham	295
Ripley	44	Siddal	273	Sutton Bridge	145	Washington	218	Wroughton	260
Robertsbridge	211	Skegness	144	Sutton Coldfield	160	Waterbeach	34	Wycombe Air Park
Rochester	92	Skelmorlie	284	Swansea	294	Waterford	304		21
Romsey	77	Sleaford	144	Swanton Morley	165	Watford	85	Wymondham	167
Rosemarket	291	Sleap	188	Swindon	259	Wattisham	205	Wyton	35
Rothwell	169	Sligo	303	Syerston	174	Watton	166	Yarcombe	47
Royton	156	Smeeth	93	Tain	284	Wellesbourne		Yarmouth	87
Rufforth	268	Solihull	160	Talbot Green	294	Mountford	224	Yarrow	284
Rugby	223	Somersham	34	Tangmere	217	Wellingborough	169	Yateley	80
Rugeley	198	Sopley	77	Tatenhill	199	Wells	190	Yatesbury	261
Rush Green	85	South Kensington	152	Tattershall Thorpe		Welshpool	294	Yearby	52
Ruthin	291	South Lambeth	153		145	Welshpool		Yeovil	193
St Albans	85	South Scarle	174	Tees-side Airport	52	Aerodrome	295	Yeovilton	193
St Athan	291	South Shields	170	Terrington St		West Chiltington	218	Ystrad Mynach	295
St Austell	40	Southampton	78	Clement	166	West Freugh	284	
St Ives	34	Southampton Airport		Thatcham	19	West Hanningfield	61	
St Leonards-on-Sea			79	Thornhill	284	West Horndon	61	In *these* shoes?
	212	Southend Airport	59	Thorpe Abbotts	166	West Thurrock	61	I don't think so!